14- 120- 605

QUANTITY
FOOD
PURCHASING

QUANTITY FOOD PURCHASING

LENDAL H. KOTSCHEVAR

*Professor, School of Hotel, Restaurant
and Institution Management
Michigan State University, East Lansing, Michigan*

New York • London, John Wiley & Sons, Inc.

Preface

This book is written for those who are purchasing or will be purchasing food in quantity. Emphasis has been placed on the selection and specification requirements for the major foods purchased by food services. An attempt has been made to present purchase criteria as concisely as possible because of the wide variety of foods that must be covered.

It should be recognized that the types of foods being offered to institutions are changing rapidly. Technological advances promise to revolutionize the methods of quantity food production and the types of foods used. Grades and standards for these new products are, for the most part, lacking. Yet those who must purchase these foods will find much helpful criteria in this book, for an attempt has been made to remain basic regardless of the type of food purchased.

While this book stresses quantity food buying from the standpoint of the quantity food service buyer, salesmen, distributors, wholesalers and others who sell to food services will find much of value to assist them in meeting better the needs of their customers.

Seeley Lake, Montana
July, 1961

LENDAL H. KOTSCHEVAR

v

Contents

1 The Market and the Buyer

Quantity food buying for a food service is a highly complex and specialized task. The buyer must thoroughly know the market in which he deals, how it functions, and how it is regulated. The marketing of foods from their growing to their use is his concern. Adequate purchase cannot be made without knowing methods of processing, storage, transportation and other handling of the foods he uses. The buyer must know the type and quantity of food required to suit the production need. Decisions in this area are sometimes challenging. He must know a great deal about food production and service. The procedures and skills leading to successful purchase must be learned; these will differ for each type of food purchased.

A buyer does not deal solely with inanimate items such as food. He will come in contact with many different individuals under highly competitive conditions. Personality and character traits suitable to operation in the field of buying are required. A high code of ethics, a sense of fair play, open-mindedness, honesty, perserverance and patience are necessary, as well as skills and technical knowledge.

The field of purchasing is a highly dynamic one, and the buyer must never cease to study and learn if he is to retain competency. It is the alert, knowing buyer who best searches the market and selects foods that maintain high standards in his operation.

THE MARKET

The market is a dynamic entity upon which our economy is built. It serves to move commodities from the producer to the consumer. Today's market is a highly complex structure compared with that of simple

1

societies. Wide choice is offered. Rules and regulations must be observed. Market movement is built on a highly intricate financial and business process. Men spend their lives studying and learning how our markets function. Although it is not possible for a food buyer to become an expert in all phases of marketing, he should know enough to be able to function adequately in it.

What Is Marketing?

Marketing is not only the search, selection and purchase of commodities but it is also any activity in which time and place utility is created in a commodity. Possession or ownership may be a factor in marketing.

Marketing activities may be conducted over a wide area during a long period of time. The buyer seldom sees all the activities and individuals involved. The growing or production of a commodity and its harvest, processing, manufacture, storage, transportation and distribution create time and place utility.

What Is a Market?

A market is distinguished, not by its physical features, but by the action that occurs there. A market is a place where a transfer of ownership takes place. There are formalized markets where buyers and sellers or their agents meet. These may be such markets as the Chicago Grain Exchange or the New York fruit and vegetable auctions, but a market may also be over the telephone, in an exchange of telegrams, on the side of a road, in an office or on a street corner. The important essential is that a transfer of ownership must take place.

Few food buyers today go to market. Purchases are made by telephone, with salesmen or acceptance of written bid. The degree of formality may vary. Buyers and sellers negotiate and agree on terms. In many instances the final transfer does not take place until the goods have been inspected and accepted upon delivery at the food service.

The procedures that have grown up, making possible the transfer of ownership, are extensive. They involve financing, storing, grading, inspecting and many other factors that must be understood or agreed upon by the buyer and seller in changing ownership.

Types of Markets

Markets for food buyers may be classified: (1) by the type of food marketed, (2) by the marketing agent and channels through which the commodities move and (3) by the place of the market in the marketing structure.

1. Buyers will select different markets for purchasing different com-

modities. Few will buy all requirements from only one. Specialization
of markets occurs at the institutional level, and fresh vegetables and
fruits, meats, poultry and groceries will come from different markets
equipped to handle the specific commodity.

2. Buyers may have a choice of markets. They may buy direct; perhaps from local sources. They may buy from wholesale jobbers who
purchase, in turn, from brokers or wholesalers. Sometimes buyers may
purchase direct from a manufacturer's salesmen.

3. Markets may be known as primary, secondary or local. Primary
markets are centralized areas that act as main depots into which com-
modites are moved. Chicago is the primary market in this country for
cereals and one of the large primary markets for fruits and vegetables.
Boston is a primary market for fish.

Primary markets arise because good transportation is available to
bring plentiful supplies of the raw product into these markets for distribution to consumers. Processors, manufacturers and others concentrate in or near this primary market, and the goods are changed to
forms required for sale. Distribution then occurs.

Prices quoted on the primary market influence the pricing on all
markets. Buyers learn to watch primary markets to learn in advance
what they may expect to happen on their own local markets.

Secondary markets function as receivers of goods from primary markets. They distribute to local markets. Population growth and shifts,
increased volume and changing procedures are causing a decline in the
importance on the primary market, with the secondary market taking
over many of the primary market functions as well as its own. Chicago,
once the primary market for meat products, is fast becoming less important as the secondary markets of Kansas City, Omaha, St. Paul and
others take over its functions. This change is reducing marketing costs
by lessening handling and transportation. It also reduces the number of
marketing agents through whom the commodities must pass on their
way to consumers.

Direct marketing is also reducing the importance of the primary
market and even the secondary market. No longer do cattle feeders go
to the Chicago market to purchase feeding stock; agents now purchase
their requirements on the range and ship direct to feeders. The volume
of products moved through our supermarket systems directly from the
producer has revolutionized many marketing techniques in moving
commodities to retail outlets.

Several food services with great volume are filling some of their requirements by direct purchase. Stouffer's buys animals on the Chicago
market and processes them for shipment to its restaurants. Some large

restaurants and hotels have hired a buying firm to purchase for them. By consolidating their buying they have been able to circumvent some marketing agents. Smaller organizations have formed buying groups or co-operatives that attempt to do the same.

Marketing Functions

To bring about a transfer of ownership, certain marketing activities must occur. These are usually classified as: (1) exchange, (2) information, (3) physical supply and (4) general business functions. An understanding of the manner in which these are performed will enable the buyer to deal more effectively in the market.

1. Exchange functions are concerned with the buying, selling, merchandising, price setting and other factors required in transferring ownership. Sellers must seek buyers. Offerings must be evaluated and compared. Negotiations are frequently required to establish price, quality and service rendered. Specification of what is required is necessary. Inspecting and receiving are a part of the exchange function. The exchange function ceases when title of ownership changes.

Industrial purchasers, such as food services, must define their needs much more precisely than other types of buyers. Specifications are used for this definition. They must also keep in mind that "merchandise well purchased is well sold" and that "the profit in selling is made in the buying." Good merchandising begins in buying. Merchandising is the presentation of a commodity in such a manner as to create interest and thereby a sale. Price setting is an important factor in the exchange function.

2. The information function covers those activities that bring market information to buyers and sellers. What, when, how much, what quality, what price, trends and other factors are of interest to those engaged in marketing activities. This information may be obtained from a number of sources.

Market reports appear in almost every newspaper. These are summaries of the day's happenings on market exchanges over the country. Much marketing information may be obtained from governmental sources. A free daily market report covering marketing events is available from the United States Department of Agriculture (USDA). This report covers commodities on the market, prices paid, railroad car movements, quantities sold, market conditions and other marketing information. The prices quoted in this report are those paid to original receivers in large lots and do not cover smaller sales. Buyers should learn to know the terms used in these market reports. Trade associations, vendors' catalogs, professional journals and other publications give valued marketing information. Salesmen are an excellent source of information too, for they are usually aware of market conditions and trends.

The establishment and promulgation of grades are important information activities. Grading is the sorting of products into groups according to established standards. Without grades our markets could function only with difficulty. Personal inspection may not be required when grades are used in buying and selling, and agreement on transfer of ownership may be reached much more quickly. Processors are able to standardize their products through grading and move them onto the market. Financing is aided, for grades establish values. Trade acceptances, loans, purchase contracts and other instruments of finance have more security when based on grades. Legal problems are frequently reduced when grading factors are established. Market confidence is built upon grades, and few individuals concerned with marketing would be willing to see grading eliminated. Grade standards for foods may be usually obtained from government sources. There are also many grade standards developed by the trade.

Advertising is an important source of information to buyers. Advertisements may take a number of forms. They may be purchased space in newspapers, magazines or other publications. They may appear in brochures or pamphlets. Consumer services, salesmen, radio and even labeling are used to advertise.

If advertising gives information of value to a buyer and leads him to make a rational, wise purchase, it is of economic good. If advertising, however, seeks to lead buyers into unrational or unwise purchases, it is to be condemned.

Buyers should be aware that "trade puffing" or highly praising a product is characteristic of those wishing to sell and that this is not considered an illegitimate trade practice. Rational criteria will expose puffing. Wild extravagant claims or attempts to gain sales through misleading or false statements, misinformation or a failure to give proper information constitute, however, bad or illegal practices.

Trade associations may encourage good labeling. The National Canners Association has published a dictionary of recommended descriptive terms to be used in labeling canned goods and describing accurately the qualities of the products in the can.

Good descriptive labeling may be considered helpful advertising by enumerating essential quality factors of a product. There should be no attempt to rank as good, better or best. Descriptive labeling uses single words or phrases of known definition to indicate maturity, color, uniformity, texture, consistency and the presence or absence of minor de-

FIG. 1-1. Good descriptive labeling and federal grades together on a label are helpful guides for the buyer in selecting the quality he wants. Courtesy United States Department of Agriculture.

fects resulting from different degrees of care in preparation. The label also gives the quantities in terms of cupfuls, number of servings, number of pieces, or some other common factor other than weight, to indicate quantity in the container.

Brands are a form of advertising used to identify a product with a particular producer or distributor. Some general brands are used to identify a group of products within a quality range. A brand identifies products and their quality in the consumer's mind and brings about repeat sales.

Many buyers agree that brand buying has advantages. Branded products tend to be higher in quality than unbranded products. A manufacturer or distributor has his reputation to uphold when he puts his brand on a product. There are many brands that assure a buyer of a standard consistent quality each time the product is purchased. This encourages buyers to buy by brand. Brands, however, are only what the manufacturer or distributor wishes to make them. They are unlike grades in this respect. A brand may be advertised as "of highest quality" and not have to conform to any standard except what the owner of the brand may feel is highest quality. Brands may vary in quality in different markets. This frequently is true of branded meats. Branded products are usually higher in price and vary less in price than unbranded products. Identical products may be labeled with different brands and sell as different qualities and at different prices. Nevertheless, it is sometimes desirable to purchase by brand. Buyers who learn the dependability of a brand in quality are wise to seek it on the market because it may be the best product for the best price. Many buyers purchase by brand, descriptive label and by grade. Combining all three frequently gives high efficiency in buying.

3. Physical supply functions usually revolve around transportation and storage. Improved shipping techniques and refrigeration have broadened market offerings. Rapid rail, truck or air-freight transport brings foods to market that otherwise could not be shipped because of their high perishability. This factor, plus improved packaging, improved handling and improved storage facilities, has reduced loss and improved quality.

Storage is an important physical supply function in marketing food-stuffs. Without it, the orderly flow would be disrupted and high losses would occur." Many staple foods are produced in a relatively short season but must be held for continuous supply to the market over the entire year." Canned goods processed and stored in the growing season gradually move out onto the market during the remainder of the year. Lowered prices just before warehouses are again to be filled with new stock indicate attempts to clear warehouses for the new stock. Bonded storage is used for security and financing. Improved storage facilities for highly perishable foods have been developed, and not only are temperature and humidity controlled but the quantity of oxygen, bacteria and other factors in the air are also controlled to give longer storage life.

More and more foods are being held in frozen storage as food services turn to frozen foods rather than fresh for their supplies. Much cold-storage food is used. Cold-storage foods are those held 30 days or more

FIG. 1–2. This brand tag gives good buying information. Inspection for wholesomeness and grade stamps, class of chicken and area of production give the buyer valuable information. In addition, the buyer sees the packer's top brand label. Some descriptive material is also given.

at temperatures of 30 to 45° F. Some states limit the time foods can remain in cold storage. A common limit is 12 months. Labeling or identification of cold-storage foods is sometimes required. If foods are once removed from cold storage, most states prohibit their return. Cold storage retains high quality and may improve certain foods, such as meats, flour, cheese, winter apples or pears.

4. General business functions generally revolve around finance. Commodities are usually transferred on the basis of money used as a medium of exchange. This may involve exchange of foreign currency. If so, the exchange value of the two currencies will be part of the transaction. Credit, interest, insurance, taxes and a host of other items come under finance.

Proper financing may reduce costs. Buyers should know that inventories in excess of requirements cost money through waste, theft, carrying charges, space occupation, interest, depreciation and other factors. Food inventories should be turned over at least 36 times per year in dollar value. Inventory size may vary, however, according to whether an operation is close to sources of supply, the buying policy of the operation, the requirements for operation and the savings to be obtained in quantity purchases. Purchasing goods on the first of the month and paying for them on the tenth of the next month make it possible for the buyer to use the seller's money for 40 days. This is a cost to the seller and must be a factor in the price charged. Buyers should realize that sellers cannot make good price arrangements if an organization is slow in paying bills.

Producers, Consumers and Middlemen

Producers are those who create form and substance in a commodity. They may be a canner, a meat packer or a miller. There are others, also, who are considered producers. A cook who takes foods and makes a meal is a producer. Similarly, the farmer, the fisherman or the cattle raiser are producers. A produce house that purchases spinach in bulk, stems, washes and packages it is functioning as a producer.

Consumers may be of two types: industrial and ultimate. Industrial consumers are those who use commodities in manufacturing or purchase items for resale. Food services are industrial consumers. Ultimate consumers are those who purchase for their own or for household use. The type of market and the market procedures used for buying differ for industrial and ultimate consumers. The problem of resale and the necessity of making a profit bring about different motivation in buying. Precise standards become important when mass quantities of food are moved through the market. Industrial buyers should know, however,

FIG. 1–3.   Fruit buyers at an auction.   This type of middleman is used to move large quantities of highly perishable commodities through marketing channels at low cost. Frequently these buyers represent or act for others.   Courtesy USDA.

much about the ultimate consumer, for the goods that he produces (and he is a producer as well as a consumer) must meet the needs, finally, of this ultimate consumer market.

Between the producer and the consumer many individuals function in creating time and place utility for commodities.   The individuals do not change form or substance.   They are called middlemen and make a distinct contribution in moving goods through the market.   Because of this service and, in some instances, because of the risk they take, they add a charge to the price of the commodity.   The amount may depend upon whether the middleman takes ownership or not, and on the services rendered.   Wholesalers, jobbers, retailers, truck hucksters and others take ownership and store the commodity.   Some may break it down into smaller lots and assemble other goods with it for delivery.   Financing is a part of their cost.   Middlemen who do not take ownership, such as auctioneers, brokers, commission men or those who take goods on consignment, do not incur some of these costs.   Their charge is less. Average markups of some middlemen may be 5% or less; others may take 10 to 15%.   Wholesalers may average 25% and retailers, 35%.

Buyers should learn the functions performed by middlemen and their costs of operation. Usually the fewer middlemen through which a commodity must pass, the less the charge. Frequently buyers fail to appreciate the costs and contribution made by middlemen in moving commodities through the market. When buyers become familiar with marketing costs and the services rendered by middlemen, they will know better when prices are fair and when they are excessive.

Marketing Criticism

Much criticism of the market has occurred because the percentage of the consumer dollar going to the farmer has dropped consistently while the percentage taken by processors and other marketing agents has increased. The following table indicates the farmer's share in some commodities:

Commodity	Farmer's Share in Cents per Dollar Paid at Retail Level	
	Range	Mean
Unprocessed crops, such as beans, fruits, vegetables	18 to 46¢	35¢
Processed crops, such as flour, cereals, canned goods	19 to 71¢	49¢
Eggs		69¢
Poultry		60¢

The prices of commodities are apt to fluctuate more at the producer or farm level, next at the wholesale level and least at the retail level. The reason is probably that marketing margins are much less flexible than commodity prices. In a period of rising prices middlemen take less of the consumer's dollar and, in a period of falling prices, take more. As we move toward the purchase of more and more convenience foods, processors will tend to take more and more of the restaurant dollar spent for food.

Market Regulation

As our marketing structure has grown in complexity and extent, a need has arisen for measures that would give order to marketing activities and protect marketing agents as well as public interest. Many regulatory codes have been voluntarily adopted by markets or by trade associations. In situations where conflicts arise among producers, middlemen, consumers or others, or where it is necessary to safeguard and protect public interest and health, federal, state and local laws have been passed to give the necessary control. These laws have strengthened the market structure rather than hurt it.

Today the number of laws pertaining to food are many, and a brief summary of federal laws must be limited to mentioning only the most important ones and their major provisions.   Much information can be gained by referring to government publications, books and other materials indicated in the references of this book.   Certain inadequacies or omissions here in this short discussion that follows will be corrected later under discussions of specific food groups.

There are ten main laws or jurisdictional bodies that are important in regulating the food market.

1. The Pure Food, Drug and Cosmetic Act of 1938 regulates many practices in handling food in interstate commerce.   Labels on any packaged food must:

   a. bear the common name or names of the food item;
   b. contain the name and address of the manufacturer, packer or distributor;
   c. list the net contents either by count, fluid or avoirdupois measure;
   d. be sufficiently prominent to be easily comprehended and must contain no foreign language that might circumvent label requirements;
   e. bear the specific name and not collective name of ingredients if the product is not a commonly known food except that the group words *spice, flavoring, coloring* and so forth may be used instead of the exact spice, flavoring, coloring and so forth;
   f. bear in order of greatest proportion to least the names of ingredients if the food is not a common food; thus, it would be illegal to list ingredients for corned beef hash as corned beef, potatoes and onions if potatoes were in greater quantity than corned beef;
   g. bear exact definition of dietary properties if claims are made of dietary values;
   h. bear the term "artificial" if artificial coloring or flavoring is used or "chemical preservative" if a chemical preservative is used.

Bulk or open-container foods are exempt from the labeling provisions.

Sanitary preparation, processing and packaging of food are required, and no product of a "diseased animal, contaminated, filthy, putrid, decomposed or otherwise unfit food" can be used.   Damage or inferiority in a food cannot be concealed, and no substandard food can be added to increase the bulk or weight or to create the illusion of greater value than the food has.   No substance considered a valuable part of the food may be omitted, and one food cannot be sold under the name of another. Inspectors may enter any establishment at reasonable times if the product is being manufactured for interstate commerce.

Later amendments regulated the use of additives in food.   Many colorings, preservatives and other substances considered harmful or suspected of harmful properties were prohibited.   A manufacturer or processor must bear the burden of proof that a compound is not injurious to health. Formerly, the government had to prove the product harmful.

The act is administered by the Food and Drug Administration in the Department of Health, Education and Welfare.

2. The Federal Meat Inspection Act was passed in 1906. It provided for inspection by the Bureau of Animal Industry in the USDA of all establishments from which meat is shipped in interstate commerce:

  a. to detect and destroy diseased and unfit meat,
  b. to require that preparation and handling of meat be in a clean and sanitary manner,
  c. to require the application of marks of inspection on meat products,
  d. to prevent the use of harmful substances in meat foods,
  e. to prevent false and deceptive labeling.

3. The Agricultural Marketing Act provided for inspection and grading of fresh and processed foods other than meat. Under the provisions of this act the USDA established a number of inspection divisions.[1] A grain inspection division functions chiefly as an inspection agency for raw cereals. The dairy inspection division has responsibility for dairy products, including margarine. Fresh fruits and vegetables are under another division, while the processed fruits and vegetables division has responsibility for the inspection of canned, frozen, dried and other processed fruits and vegetables. Poultry, eggs and meat come under another division. Lists of inspection agencies may be obtained by writing the Agricultural Marketing Service (AMS), USDA. For the most part, inspection agencies are located at shipping points, destination markets and other areas where the various commodities are apt to be moving through marketing channels.

Under provisions of this law, federal inspectors examine commodities and certify their quality. The standard for grading used may be federal or the buyer's own. When a federal standard is used, a buyer may request a certificate of quality. This states the grade and other trade factors important in marketing the product.

When the buyer's own standard is used, the inspection is called an "acceptance" inspection. The inspector accepts the product on the basis not of federal standards but on those of the buyer. Frequently government standards are too broad for use by the institution having been established to cover all conditions on the market. Food services frequently desire a more precise statement of quality and will usually

[1] See SRA-AMS, USDA, revised January 4, 1957, for an explanation of inspection procedures.

F. P. I. 20

ORIGINAL

UNITED STATES DEPARTMENT OF AGRICULTURE

VIRGINIA DEPARTMENT OF AGRICULTURE AND IMMIGRATION

INSPECTION CERTIFICATE

N⁰ 4377

This certificate is issued in compliance with the regulations of the Secretary of Agriculture governing the inspection of various products pursuant to the Act making appropriations for the United States Department of Agriculture, the Acts of Virginia Assembly, and is admissible as prima facie evidence in all courts of the United States and of Virginia. This certificate does not excuse failure to comply with any of the regulatory laws enforced by the United States Department of Agriculture, or by the Virginia Department of Agriculture and Immigration.

Inspection point **Winchester, Va.**   *Billing point* **Winchester, Va.**   *Date* **Oct. 4, 1945**

Applicant **Winchester Packing Co.**   *Address* **Winchester, Va.**

Shipper **Same**   *Address* **Same**

I, the undersigned, on the date above specified made personal inspection of samples of the lot of products herein described, and do hereby certify that the quality and/or condition, at the said time and on said date, pertaining to such products, as shown by said samples, were as stated below:

Car initial and number **FGEX 5 1 8 1 3**   *Kind of car* **Refrigerator**

Inspection begun **1:30 P. M. Oct. 4, 1945**   *Inspection completed* **6:15 P. M. Oct. 4, 1945**
                     (Hour, date)   (Hour, date)

Car equipment and condition at completion of inspection:

Products: **York Imperial APPLES – in tub type bushel baskets labeled "W Brand, Winchester Packing Co., Winchester, Va." and stamped "U. S. No. 1, 2¼ inches up, York." Loader's count 516 baskets.**

Loading: **Through load, end to end offset, 3x3 rows, 4 layers.**

Pack: **Tight. Ring faced. Paper pads under lids. Good amount of oiled paper distributed uniformly through baskets.**

Size: **Generally 2¼ to 3, mostly 2¼ to 2½ inches in diameter.**

Quality and condition: **Mostly well formed, some fairly well formed, clean, 15% to full red, mostly 25% to 50% good red color. Grade defects within tolerance. Generally hard. No decay.**

Grade: **As marked, U. S. No. 1, 2¼ inches up.**

Fee **$5.16**
Expenses
Total **5.16**

L. F. Laney

Inspector.

U. S. GOVERNMENT PRINTING OFFICE 8—7194 A   PLEASE REFER TO THIS CERTIFICATE BY NUMBER

FIG. 1–4. Buyers may request with purchases inspection certificates as shown here. Courtesy USDA.

have their own specifications which are more narrow than government specifications. If the product meets the buyer's specifications, the inspector stamps the invoice, the packages, the tapes and the seals to verify this fact, completing the process of acceptance inspection.

FIG. 1–5. A federal acceptance seal indicating a product meets a buyer's quality
standards. This stamp is used in acceptance
type inspection. Courtesy USDA.

The purveyor pays for the cost of all inspections, except those requested by the buyer when he sends in isolated samples or if he makes a
claim that foods do not meet specifications and, then, upon federal
examination, they do so.

When a standard is first published it is called tentative. When it is
seen that the standard meets requirements of the trade, it then becomes
official. A standard may remain tentative for many years until experience proves it meets trade needs.

The respective inspection divisions establish the standards of quality
for the foods they inspect. Industry and other interested parties are
consulted, and frequently the standards reflect many trade practices
already in effect.

In 1956 the provisions of the Agricultural Marketing Act were extended to cover fish and shellfish. The Fish and Wildlife Bureau in the
Department of Interior was given the responsibility for formulating
regulations governing inspection of marine foods. It is also establishing
quality standards.

Different inspections are offered to ascertain grade. These vary with
the different inspection divisions. The processed fruit and vegetable
division offers four types of inspection. (*a*) Processed foods may be sent
into laboratories for inspection. The results only certify grade of the
sample and not that of the lot from which it came. (*b*) Certification of
grade of a lot is possible when inspectors withdraw warehouse samples.
(*c*) When a federal inspector is in the plant at all times while foods are
processed, the inspection is called "continuous" inspection. Preparation, sanitation, plant management and other factors are observed in
addition to inspecting the raw and processed commodities. If standards
are met, certificates for quality are issued or, if desired, management

may use the federal shield certifying grade.   (*d*) If a federal inspector is not in the plant at all times but only intermittently, products processed while the inspector is in the plant may be certified as to grade.

The code number on a certificate may be used on bills of lading, invoices and other papers to identify the lot.   The use of the federal grade shield with a grade designated in it indicates that a product meets federal standards and no certificate is required.   The use of the shield is voluntary.   Buyers may request certificates of inspection and require purveyors to furnish them.

Meats and some other processed foods are inspected under continuous inspection, and the federal grade shield may be used.   Many other divisions of the USDA certify quality by inspecting samples drawn from lots, as in (*b*) above.

The federal courts have interpreted that if a label on a food in inter-

FIG. 1–6.   A USDA inspector checks quality and wholesomeness of tangerines before they are processed into canned tangerine juice.   The plant has contracted with the USDA for continuous inspection.   Products produced under this type of inspection may bear the federal grade shield.   Courtesy USDA.

state commerce uses any terms indicating grade, the food must come up to that standard. If it does not, the food is considered misbranded. Thus, if the word "Choice" appears on the label of canned fruit, the fruit should be of that quality or better if it goes through interstate commerce.

Inspectors will be concerned with three standards in their inspection of processed foods. These are quality, identity and fill.

Standards for quality attempt to classify products within defined grade limits. Minimum standards for such factors as tenderness, color and freedom of defects are established for the various grades. If the foods do not meet these quality standards, they must be labeled "Below Standard in Quality" followed by a statement explaining why. Sometimes this below standard food is acceptable for certain quantity food production uses. It may be excessively broken or contain excessive peel or have some other defect that lowers it in standard but it still may have good utility in food production. Being below standard in quality does not mean the food is unwholesome. Scores or percentage points are sometimes used to evaluate each factor. These are totaled and the total score indicates the grade of the product. Standards of quality may be changed to meet permanent trends or changes in the market, but they are not changed each year to meet temporary fluctuations on the market.

Standards of identity define what a food is.[2] Names such as chili sauce, fruit cocktail and succotash cannot be used unless the food item is a specific mixture. The name of a common food cannot be used to indicate another food. True Roquefort cheese must come from Roquefort, France, and a similar cheese made in this country must be labeled "American" bleu or "domestic" bleu. Similarly, words such as "evaporated," "canned," "peach" and "mutton" indicate a specific product, and a product is misbranded if the standard of identity is not maintained. Standards of identity, by stating exactly what a product is, prevent misrepresentation. Thus, a mixture composed of water, pectin, acid, sugar, artificial coloring, strawberry flavoring and grass seed cannot be marketed as strawberry jam. It actually was allowed at one time. A few canned foods must meet certain drained weight standards because identity of the product is concerned with that factor. Cured meats may not be over their original weight after curing. The Food and Drug Administration has the responsibility for the formulation and promulgation of standards of identity.

Standards of fill require that containers be properly filled with food. Slack or deceptive filling is prohibited. The standards vary for different

[2]Identities for foods are published in SRA No. 2, Food and Drug Administration, Department of Health, Education and Welfare, Washington, D.C.

foods and different types of packaging. If a container does not meet a standard of fill, it must be labeled "Below Standard of Fill." ∦

\The use of a federal grade on a label of a food meeting that grade is entirely voluntary. Standards of identity and fill are not, and all commodities in interstate commerce must comply with the provisions under these two standards. Seizure and destruction of the offending products is possible if the food is unwholesome, misbranded or does not meet standards of identity or standards of fill. Prosecution may occur, and courts can order offenders to go out of business, pay fines, go to jail or combine any of the three penalties.

In 1957, 13,443,000 lb of unfit or contaminated foods were seized. This amounts to 129 tons per week.

4. The Perishable Agricultural Commodities Act regulates fresh fruit and vegetable trade practices in interstate and foreign commerce by licensing dealers and establishing fair-trade practices. Inspection of fruits and vegetables is frequently required. Administration of the act is by the USDA.

5. The Tea Inspection Act regulates the import of tea and establishes standards for purity, quality and fitness for human consumption. This law is administered by the Food and Drug Administration.

6. The original framers of the Constitution considered the control of weights and measures so important that they provided for it in that treatise. The Bureau of Standards in the Department of Commerce has the responsibility for controlling weights and measures. Many state and local laws are modeled on regulations emanating from this bureau. For the most part, the history of this bureau has been more that of an advisory body than a regulatory one.

Three important laws have been passed by the federal government to control weights and measures specifically for food. (a) A law was passed establishing the standard size of a barrel at 7056 cu in. or 105 dry qt or 9 qt more than 3 bu. This barrel will hold two 98-lb sacks of flour. The barrel for cranberries, as an exception, was fixed at 5826 cu in. or space sufficient to hold approximately 100 lb of cranberries. (b) A standard container act established the dimensions for 2, 4 and 12 qt capacity climax baskets and the standard berry and till boxes at ½ pt, 1 pt, 1 qt and multiples of 1 qt dry measure. No other size boxes of these types are permitted on the market. (c) A later act fixed the legal capacity of hampers and stave baskets at ⅛, ¼, ½, ⅝, ¾, 1, 1¼, 1½ and 2 bu. Splint baskets were limited to 4, 8, 12, 16, 24 and 32 qt capacities dry measure. The use of false bottoms and other deceptive practices was prohibited. The first and last of these three acts were made applicable to practices within states as well as interstate commerce.

7. A United States Warehouse Act provides that agricultural and processed food products moving in interstate commerce can be certified for storage. Inspection and grading based on federal standards are required for certification.

8. The Federal Trade Commission Act of 1915 deals with advertising that might be injurious to an actual or potential competitor in trade. Other trade practices also came under the provisions of the act. In 1938 the Wheeler-Lea Amendment provided penalties for misbranding, mislabeling or misrepresenting a food item as to source, origin, composition, or giving false or misleading information, or passing off a food for another's, or presenting any disparaging information or misrepresentation regarding a competitor. Extravagant and false claims in advertising were brought under more strict control than under the original act of 1915. Another amendment repealed certain features of the anti-trust laws so milk and other foodstuffs could be controlled by boards or other groups without violating the law. This provision has enabled states to set up regulatory bodies to control the marketing of milk, fruits, vegetables and other foods.

9. The Bureau of Public Health in the Department of Health, Education and Welfare has much responsibility for protecting public health. This would be natural, for there are many sanitary problems encountered in food production, marketing and consumption. Because of pollution of mussel, clam and oyster beds, which resulted in outbreaks of typhoid and diptheria, the bureau was given jurisdiction over the certification of growing areas for these products. They also supervise shellfish preparation and shipment.

The milk ordinance of the bureau acts as a standard for most state and local ordinances governing the production, processing and marketing of milk. Names, identities, grades and labeling of dairy products are all covered by this ordinance. Broad powers of the bureau, required for public interest in the prevention of disease, enable it to exert considerable influence in the preparation and marketing of food.

10. The Bureau of Internal Revenue in the Treasury Department has regulatory powers over some foods, either through administrative practices or by law. Through inspection, weight certification and other means, they are able to control certain features in the import and export of foodstuffs. Through control of duties collected on alcoholic beverages, regulatory powers are exercised. The Federal Alcohol Administration regulates taxes, unfair competition, mislabeling and misadvertising of alcoholic beverages. Many laws previously cited also apply to alcoholic beverages. Sanitary practices, mislabeling and misbranding are provided for these products under the Pure Food, Drug and Cosmetic Act

or other laws. Adulteration provisions in standards of identity would prevent the use of rectified alcohol, which, with colorings and flavorings, may be claimed to be equal to other alcoholic products. Standards of identity also prevent the appropriation of names that are misleading or used to imply that one beverage is another.

THE BUYER

A quantity food buyer must weigh many factors in buying. He must get the right kind and right amount of food at the right time at the right price. Buying must be co-ordinated with food production, quality, quantity and cost control, and functions of merchandising and selling.

Buyers need to know a great deal about preparing, cooking and serving food so that they can make proper selections. Preparation times, the manner in which foods move through production and the factors that affect waste in preparation and cooking should be known to make good purchase decisions.

Food should be selected for its intended use. It is a waste to purchase a higher quality than required for the production need. Buying whole nuts to chop is a waste. Why pay a premium price for the red color in apples—color is a significant factor in grade—when the apples are to be peeled? Why use sliced bacon for a salad dressing for wilted greens when bacon ends may be purchased for much less, diced and fried, and they suit the purpose just as well? Good, ripe, canned tomatoes that are broken are preferable to whole canned tomatoes for making sauces and soups. Buyers who say they purchase only the best quality should end their statement with, "for the use intended." Frequently factors having little to do with the utility of a product in food production are rated high in grading and these increase the cost of the product. Other factors important in quantity cookery are not important in establishing grade. Buyers should know that "You can't make a silk purse out of a sow's ear," and that cheap products frequently result in cheap foods but in quantity buying quality is dictated by production need and not by factors always reflected in price. The food service buyer must always remember he is an industrial buyer.

Buyers should follow market conditions. Quantities and prices follow seasonal variations. Pork has two lows each year. Fresh cabbage from the southern states usually appears early on our northern markets. If corn is cheap, farmers may hold it back from the market and feed livestock with it. Cattle may not go to slaughter but may be brought up by these feeders. Prices may rise but later, when these cattle come to market as fed-stock, prices may drop because of a market glut. Sudden changes in growing conditions, such as frost, drought or excessive demand, are quickly reflected on the market. Usually commodities are best in quality and lowest in price at the peak of their season. Awareness of the social, political and economic trends, and the effects of research and science, will enable buyers to better evaluate market events.

The greater probability of price change, the greater the need to follow the market closely. Some foods are fairly stable in price, and once the crop is harvested and the foods processed, there will be little variation in price until the following year. Perishable products vary in price. Canned goods, flour, sugar and fresh items, such as apples, Irish potatoes and winter cabbage, that store well vary from 3 to 9% in price. Medium variability, 10 to 15%, exists in such items as sweet potatoes, globe onions, garlic and winter squash. High variability, 16 to 25%, is found in lettuce, cantaloupe, peaches, spring and summer cabbage and so forth. If the market is well organized and a steady flow of the perishable products comes onto the market, prices will tend to be more stable. This stability is seen in bananas, which, while highly perishable, are fairly steady in price. Improved market procedures and better storage and shipping are tending more and more to stabilize prices of perishable commodities.

It has been said that the menu starts with buying and buying starts with the menu. Buyers should advise those responsible for preparing menus of market conditions, the quality, quantity and cost of foods on the market. Buyers should be alert to call attention to favorable buys or to menu items high in cost. Menus, however, that are dictated by motives arising out of favorable buys frequently fail. Menus should give consideration to market conditions but should not be dictated by them.

Low prices do not necessarily mean low plate cost. Frequently bargains are *not* bargains. Loss in preparation may make cheap items high priced. It may be difficult to justify paying a higher price for center-cut pork chops, but a cutting test on a wholesale pork loin may indicate it is less expensive to do so. Labor costs should be known and evaluated. Many operators fail to realize the loss incurred in preparing many items for cooking. Wastes may sometimes be high. Good buyers are alert to obtain data on yields and labor required to prepare items so that they may better evaluate the processed market offerings. The cost of an item as purchased (AP) should not be the significant cost in buying. It is the cost of the edible portion (EP) or as served (AS) that counts.

Quality and value recognition are prime requisites in a good buyer. Knowledge of factors making up quality or grade and the recognition of these factors can be obtained only by study and observation. Unless a buyer knows what quality *is* and can recognize it, he is unable to make adequate price comparisons. Frequently buyers are unable to inspect goods, and under such conditions it is necessary to precisely define what is desired and then later inspect to see that there has been performance. Grades and other standards of quality have been introduced in the trade for this purpose. Buyers should learn to use these in establishing product specifications.

The accurate estimation of quantities required is frequently difficult and yet buyers are called upon to supply the exact quantity required. Excessive quantities mean waste and loss while an insufficiency can cause frustration, turmoil and scratchy tempers. Buyers are better able to predict quantities required for purchase if they have a system that will give them: (1) a knowledge of total portions and portion size required, (2) accurate estimate of preparation, cooking and portioning losses, (3) portion control and (4) inventory control.

Buying Ethics

Buying requires a high standard of ethics. A buyer has considerable power in giving orders that have value and prestige. Sellers, in some cases, will not hesitate to obtain these orders by illegitimate means. Although a rigid, cold atmosphere in the buyer's office or an unbending formality is not conducive to effective negotiation and a free exchange of buying information, a buyer should be careful not to compromise his freedom of action by his action or contacts. The point at which compromise occurs must be decided by the buyer. Acceptance of invitations to meals, social functions or other favors from sellers may be undesirable. At other times there may be occasions where a buyer may accept and feel no obligation is incurred. Buyers and sellers working closely together will develop bonds of mutal respect and friendship. This cordiality and warmth are requisites for the development of good, effective purchasing atmosphere. The important consideration is that the buyer should in no way limit his freedom of purchasing action. Every buyer should establish his own code of ethics. The following might be used as a model.

1. Be courteous at all times.

2. Establish regular hours for salesmen to call and adhere rigidly to the established schedule. See out-of-town salesmen at once, if convenient. See all, but devote only the time required to conclude the necessary purchasing business.

3. Be fair. Remember that there must be give and take in all buying and selling situations.

4. Keep a sense of humor.

5. Compare price, quality and service and purchase on the basis of these and other rational factors.

6. In dealing with competitors, do not play one against the other. Do not disclose other competitors' prices and do not pass on information about competitors.

7. Use your delegated responsibility and your company's money as your own.

8. Do not discuss business affairs out of the office.

9. Set a high degree of conduct and let others benefit by your example.

10. Never compromise your freedom of action as a buyer.

The underlying reasons why buyers purchase what they do and from whom they do have been found indicative of their buying efficiency. Motives for buying are classed as *rational* and *emotional*. Industrial buyers should purchase on the basis of rational motives only.

Rational motives might be such factors as purchasing on the basis of dependability of a product or vendor, economy in use, wholesomeness, cost, quality or service rendered by the vendor. Some emotional motives might be the desire for distinctiveness, emulation, pride, social achievement, expression of artistic taste, desire to attract attention and the pleasing personality of a salesman who calls.

Procedures for Buying

Buying procedures must be varied to meet individual food service needs. Before any procedures are decided, the administrative and financial policies of the operation should be ascertained. Buying methods established should receive approval of top administration officials before being put into effect. Buying is a management function, and the establishment of policies and procedures, qualities and quantities required, should be the responsibility of management.

Buying procedures that are established should reflect:

a. the type of institution,

b. nearness to supply,

c. adequacy of storage facilities,

d. taxes, insurance and other costs incurred in financing purchases,

e. general market and economic conditions, such as availability, seasonality, price trends, supply and financial resources of the institution,

f. shelf life of the food,

g. the production need,

h. inspection services required for certification of grade and wholesomeness.

Buying procedures will differ for each type of product. The more staple products are purchased by formal methods. Highly perishable items, such as fresh fruits and vegetables, are oftentimes ordered by informal methods. Items infrequently purchased or purchased in small quantities may be ordered by informal procedures. Buying procedures may be classified as (1) open market or informal and (2) bid or formal.

1. For open type or informal buying, contact between vendor and buyer is made by salesmen, telephone or other means. A distinguishing feature is that negotiations are largely oral. Type of product, amount, quality, quantity and other essentials required to inform the vendor of the exact conditions for purchase are given in this conversation. Buyers frequently work with a set of specifications at hand when they discuss requirements. After price quotations and other essential information are received and the seller's reliability and service weighed with the price given, the buyer will make a purchase decision. It is not always recommended that price be used as the sole determinant in making this decision. An experienced buyer will know that some vendors deliver a higher quality item than others, and a higher price can be paid. Other vendors may give more reliable service and for that reason may be favored. Buyers should also realize that orders must be of sufficient size to pay for delivery and handling, and, where only a small price differential exists, orders should be lumped together to make it economical for a vendor to deliver the order.

Comparative prices should usually be obtained from two or more sellers, but sometimes conditions are such that only one seller will be contacted. At times vendors may supply food items automatically, based on previous agreement, such as a dairy, a bakery or a coffee company that keeps up an established inventory in the facility by daily delivery. In such instances management should check frequently to ascertain that quantities and qualities marked on delivery slips have been received.

Price comparison or *call sheet* buying is frequently used in informal buying, especially where a number of sellers are in close proximity to the institution. This sheet may also be called a *quotation and order* sheet. Call sheets should be set up so that the commodities required, the amount, and the specification information can be listed in the left-hand columns. The column for listing specification information is frequently omitted from some sheets, but experience has shown that fewer mistakes are made and a better meeting of minds occurs between seller and buyer if this information is there for reference. Other columns are provided to the right for listing prices quoted by respective vendors. The name of each vendor is written at the top of these columns, and, as price quotations are received, the price is written down in the column for that vendor. When all prices are obtained, the prices are reviewed, and, as purchase decisions are made, the price quoted by the seller from whom the commodity is desired will be circled. A clerk or secretary can then inform these sellers of items to be delivered. The sheet is then sent to the receiving area where quantity and quality are checked upon delivery. Some operations may not give quantities to the receiving area preferring not to have this listed so receivers must check quantity and mark it on

STEWARD'S MARKET QUOTATION LIST													
ON HAND	ARTICLE	WANTED	QUOTATIONS			ON HAND	ARTICLE	WANTED	QUOTATIONS				ON HAND
	BEEF						Pig's knuckles, fresh						
	Corned beef						Pig's knuckles, corned						
	Corned beef brisket						Pig, suckling						
	Corned beef rump						Pork, fresh loin						
	Corned beef hash						Pork, larding						
	Beef chipped						Pork, spare ribs						
	Beef breads						Pork, salt strip						
	Butts						Pork, tenderloin						
	Chuck						Sausages, country						
	Fillets						Sausages, frankfurter						
	Hip short						Sausages, meat						
	Hip full						Shoulders, fresh						
	Kidneys						Shoulders, smoked						
	Livers						Shoulders, corned						
	Loin, short						Tongues						
	Strip						Tongues, beef smoked						
	Shell strip						Tongues, fresh						
	Ribs beef						Tongues, lambs						
	Shins						Tripe						
	Suet, beef												
	Tails, ox						**POULTRY**						
	VEAL						Chickens						
	Breast						Chickens, roast						
	Brains						Chickens, broilers						
	Feet						Chickens, broilers						
	Fore quarters						Chickens, supreme						
	Hind quarters						Cocks						
	Head						Capons						
	Kidneys						Ducks						
	Legs						Ducklings						
	Liver						Fowl						
	Loins						Geese						
	Racks						Goslings						
	Saddles						Guinea hens						
	Shoulder						Guinea squabs						
	Sweet breads												

FIG. 1–7. Two examples of call sheets used by food services. These examples omit specification details frequently helpful in establishing buying requirements. An addi-

the sheet at delivery. The accounting office checks invoice prices against those listed on this call sheet.

Another type of informal purchasing is called *complete open* or *blank check* buying. This is done where a supplier must have complete free-

FISH	UNIT	Suppliers	
		City Market	Seafood, Inc.
Jack salmon dressed	50#	(.38)	.39
Filet sole	50#	.42	(.40)
Butterfly whiting	30#	(.30)	.31
Filet ocean pike	30#	(.36)	.37
Halibut—1 fish	35#	.40	(.38)
Shrimp—headless	20#	(.60)	.62

PERISHABLES	UNIT	Suppliers	
		Green Co.	Acme Co.
New cabbage 100# Bg.	3	($ .09)	$ .10
Carrots, bunches	10	.03	.03
Cauliflower 45/50# Ct.	3	(3.25)	3.35
Celery 72/92# Ct., pascal	3	(4.25)	4.30
Lettuce iceberg 24's Ct.	2	2.40	(2.20)
Mushrooms 4 qt. basket	3	(2.00)	2.10
Onions, Bermuda 50# Bg.	3	3.25	3.25
Lemons 360's	2	.40	(.35)

MEATS	UNIT	Suppliers	
		Smith Co.	Higgins Bros.
Pork loins 10/12#	6	(.45)	.46
Bacon hotel slice	50#	.45	(.43)
Boiled ham 8#	6	.62	(.61)
Corned beef brisket	50#	(.39)	.41
Calves liver	10	.55	.55
Hamburger	50#	(.35)	.38
Square chuck	150#	.39	(.38)
Round "good"	150#	.54	.54
Lamb 50-55# Aa	3	.42	(.41)

tional column immediately to the right of the item desired, where this information can be recorded, is recommended. Courtesy *Volume Feeding Management Magazine*.

dom of action in obtaining items for buyers. This may happen where there is an extreme shortage of supply. A seller may learn of scarce goods and purchase them immediately. Only reputable dealers should be trusted with this privilege.

In some instances it may be desirable to purchase on a *cost-plus* basis. In this procedure the seller is paid his purchase cost, plus an approved markup for his services. This type of buying may be required under unstable market conditions or where the basic price is not known and must be ascertained later. In some cases cost-plus may be used if a large volume is given to one reputable seller who agrees to add a markup less than his normal markup on goods. Cost-plus buying could be used also in formal buying.

2. Formal buying may vary from an informality almost equal to that used in call sheet buying to formal advertisement and public opening of bids. Formal buying is usually distinguished by having negotiations in written form.

A semi-formal purchase method called *negotiated* buying may be used: (*a*) if there is a restriction in time, (*b*) if restriction is desired among those from whom prices will be obtained to close off competitive action, (*c*) because of the small size of the purchase, (*d*) because of its perishability or (*e*) because it is otherwise impractical to secure competitive bidding from a number of dealers. Negotiated bidding may be necessary if dealers are hesitant to bid because of time restrictions or perishability of the product. Negotiated bidding allows the buyer to search the market among a restricted few sellers and make a quick purchase.

Procedures for negotiated buying vary. The buyer usually contacts vendors either orally or by written instrument. The seller's response will be in writing, and the writing may merely formalize an already verbal agreement. The buyer compares vendor's prices, quality and other factors. The responsibility for authorizing purchase on the basis of a negotiated bid may vary. The buyer himself may make the decision of award, or a buying office may make the decision and notify the buyer. Sometimes a buying office may require at least three negotiated prices before an award can be made.

Bid buying means that a formal, written notice of requirements is sent to vendors inviting them to submit prices on items required. As the degree of formality increases in bid buying, more and more of the conditions of sale are specified in writing. Invitations to bid can be simple or elaborate. Some buyers and sellers may know each other sufficiently well so that there is no need for elaborate general requirements. The important thing is to describe the items required in such precise and understandable language that all parties understand what is required.

It is suggested that the forms be printed so that items for purchase may be typed or mimeographed in the appropriate columns. A simplified invitation to bid might follow the pattern illustrated in Figure 1–8.

Requests for bid usually contain two parts: (1) general conditions and (2) specifications.

1. General conditions will cover such provisions as furnishing bid and performance bond by the seller, error in bid, alternate or partial bids, discounts, term of contract and time of performance. Submission of samples, delivery points, inspection and certification of quality, packaging, billing instructions and methods of payment and other factors may also be listed. A requisition and method of payment and other factors may also be listed. A requisition number may be given and this must be

INVITATION, BID, AND AWARD

Issued by	Address	Date _____
Manager Ever-ready Restaurant	1122 Supply Street Happy Haven, Maryland	

Sealed bids in duplicate will be received at the above office until _____
_____ , 19___ for the items and in the quantities indicated for delivery on the dates indicated. Quantities indicated are approximate and may be reduced on instruction of the buyer. Increases up to 20 percent will be binding at the discretion of the buyer.

All items to be officially identified by the U. S. Department of Agriculture for class and quality. Costs of such service to be borne by vendor.

Items	Supplies	Quantity	Unit	Unit Price	Amount
1.	Chicken, fresh chilled fryer, 2-1/2 - 3 lb, ready-to-cook - U.S. Grade A To be delivered_ _ _ _ _ _ _ _ _	500	lb		
2.	Chicken, fresh chilled fowl, 3-1/2 - 4 lb, ready-to-cook, U.S. Grade B To be delivered_ _ _ _ _ _ _ _ _	100	lb		
3.	Turkey, frozen, Young Tom 20 - 22 lb, ready-to-cook, U.S. Grade A To be delivered_ _ _ _ _ _ _ _ _	100	lb		
4.	Ducks, frozen roaster duckling, 5 - 5-1/2 lb, ready-to-cook, U.S. Grade A To be delivered_ _ _ _ _ _ _ _ _	50	lb		

Vendor_____

FIG. 1–8. A type of bid form that may be used in an institution for obtaining price quotations from vendors.

listed on all bills of lading and invoices associated with the bid. A specified date for the return of sealed bids may be given and the date at which bids will be opened and awards made announced. Bid openings may be public or private. Bids are usually sent under certified mail, with the date and hour of bid opening, bidder's name and return address on the upper left-hand corner.

Bid conditions should be provided, such as: Merchandise should be guaranteed for its normal shelf life, provided proper care and storage are given. Canned goods are usually required to be guaranteed 12 months against swells, flippers and other defects. Type of packaging specified should be adequate to protect the product during shipment and shelf life. Expected length of shelf life may have to be specified. Buyers should take care to specify that commodities be delivered in standard sizes. Changing package size to meet specified conditions may increase cost to the buyer.

Failure to perform faithfully in any manner with bid provisions should be cause for contract cancellation. Bids should stipulate that the seller is responsible for merchandise until accepted upon delivery. Methods to provide satisfaction should be stated in case of short weight or where drained weights of canned goods do not come up to specifications. Penalties for these or other defaults should be stated. Cancellation of contracts may be desirable. Some call for a provision for deduction for deficiencies from the bill or a requirement that the bidder perform and meet the deficiency may be included. It is sometimes provided that the buyer may enter the market and buy equal merchandise, charging the excess cost to the bidder or against his performance bond. Relief to bidder in case of failure to perform because of acts of God, fires, floods, epidemics and so forth should be provided. Bidders who fail to perform or who are in any way unsatisfactory should also be removed from a list of acceptable bidders.

2. Specifications are precise statements of quality and other factors required in a commodity to suit production needs. They resemble the federal standards except that federal standards are usually much broader. Quality, value and use should be three factors considered in establishing specifications. All foods purchased should be covered by specifications.

Copying specifications developed by others is not recommended. Specifications should reflect specific needs of an operation. A club may desire ribs of beef cut from heavy U.S. Choice steers, while a college dormitory may select ribs from lighter animals of lesser quality. The type of patron, price paid, size of portion and many other factors must be considered. A sandwich house may find that a 5-by-6 pack fresh tomato gives a slice suited for use in sandwich making but a tomato too large for a stuffed tomato salad.   Each food will have its own individual requirements.

Specifications should be brief and simple, giving only the amount of detail required to assure proper definition of the item.   Use of terms commonly accepted in the trade will reduce the amount of detail required.   Frequently specifications are written in too much detail. Merely stating in a specification "U.S. Grade A," "very young," "sieve size 3," or "100 count" will state much to purveyors and reduce the need for detailed explanation.   It is better to have specifications written in too much detail, however, than lacking in necessary essentials.   Items required by law, such as standard of fill and wholesomeness, may be omitted, but some buyers like to remind sellers of the need to conform rigidly to regulations.   All specifications should contain:

  a. the trade or common name of the product,
  b. the quantity required in a case, pound, carton and so forth,
  c. the trade or federal grade or the brand desired,
  d. the size of the container and perhaps number of pieces in a shipping container,
  e. the unit on which prices quoted shall be based (lb, 24/2's, 12 to 14 lb hams and so forth),
  f. the specific factors required to complete a specification for specific commodities.

The specific factors in *f* will vary with different products.   Buyers should check carefully to see that all essentials are covered.   In many instances in the material covered for some food groups these essentials are indicated.   Frequently the grade of the product normally purchased for institutional use is indicated by an asterisk (*).   Some of the specific factors that may be required in *f* are:

Geographical area of production: Qualities differ because of growing conditions or other factors in different areas.   Bluelake string beans grown in Oregon have special qualities.   Florida limes, Hawaiian pineapple, Salinas Valley lettuce, Louisiana rice, Nebraska wheat and Virginia apples all differ from products from other areas, and buyers may wish to define closely the quality desired by specifying that they shall come from a specific region.

Feed: Corn-fed or grass-fed steers, Smithfield or Iowa hams, milk-fed chickens, and so forth.

Variety: Different strains may differ considerably in flavor or ability to perform in cooking.   Gravenstein apples make an excellent applesauce but are too soft for baking.   Telephone peas are satisfactory for frozen but not canned peas.   Marshall strawberries are prized as frozen strawberries.

Type and style: Sticks, slices or tidbits in pineapple, cream-style or whole kernel corn, butterfly fillets or plain fillets in fish, long-cut or short-cut hams, skinned or unskinned hams, fresh-chilled or frozen poultry.

Size: Statement of sieve size may be necessary to obtain the size bean, pea or other canned item required; size may be necessary in meats, such as "from 1000 lb steers", "25 to 28 lb watermelons".

Count or portion size: Number olives per gallon, veal cutlets weighing 4 oz not varying more than ¼ oz over or under, 83 count oranges and so forth.

Sirup density: Water, light, medium, heavy or extra heavy sirup pack.

Packing medium: Sirup, sugar, juice or water, dry or wet pack for shrimp or corn, brine or dry pack for cured meats.

Concentration or specific gravity: Used mostly in tomato products.

Percent mixture: Percent fat in ground meat, percent pork and beef or cereal in sausage meats, percent fruits in fruit salad or cocktail.

Container: Cans, glass, kegs, barrels, paper bags.

Weight tolerance or fill of container: May be fixed by law by standard of fill but in fresh vegetables specification may read *struck full* or *rounded fill* on bushel baskets, *fill equal to facing* in cherries, tomatoes, peaches or other commodities where a selected layer of items is placed in even layers on the top of the package, drained weights for canned goods, pounds per case in eggs, maximum and minimum weights permitted in meats, count in container and so forth.

Age: Terms such as *yearling steers, tree ripened, fryers* and *very young.*

Cut: Side, quarter, primal cut, portioned or oven-ready for meats; sliced, diced, julienne, short cut for canned items.

Cutting style: Chicago cut for cattle, Boston cut on pork shoulder.

Type processing: Type rendered lard, aging in meat, dry salt cure in meat, smoked, hand-peeled, canned, frozen.

Depth of fat permitted: ½ in. on rib roast, ½ in. on lamb chops .and so forth.

Condition upon receipt: Hard frozen, fresh, interior temperature 40° F.

Pure or imitation: Pure jam or jelly, imitation vanilla.

Type flavor or other: Sweetened or unsweetened, salt free.

Sex: Cow, steer, capon.

Manufacturers, processors, salesmen, trade associations or governmental agencies can be of assistance in writing specifications. Although the task of writing a set of specifications may look formidable, if one or two are written occasionally, the accumulated group soon assumes sizable proportions.

If a commodity lacks established quality standards and purchase policies of the operation prohibit the specification of brand, buyers may be forced to write their own specifications in detail. Many buyers may not request a brand even though the term "or equal" is added after the brand designated. (Usually the buyer determines what is or is not the equal.) Then the problem of eliminating unsatisfactory products becomes most difficult. Boards of judges may be established to evaluate and select from samples offered and award made on this basis. Laboratory testing may be done and taste panels used. Selection may in some instances be restricted to three top ranking products after this evaluation. In one instance, undesirable baking powders were eliminated from consideration by careful detail of the chemical formulas in the specifications.

Inspection and Receiving

No matter how well planned buying procedures may be, if care is not taken in receiving the items at the place of business, the entire buying program may lose effectiveness. Quantity and quality must be verified upon receipt of all items. This may be checked against the purchase order or call sheet. Clerks and others may not be able to judge quality and, where this is true, qualified members in the establishment should make this inspection. Receipt should be given for only the quantity received. Shortages, shipping damages or other important variations should be noted on the delivery slip. After the delivery slip has been signed, one copy is returned to the delivery service and one copy retained. If the buyer and seller agree that inspection after delivery will be acceptable, drivers may be permitted to leave without inspection and with only a signed receipt showing that a listed number of packages were dropped off. Because of the increasing costs of deliveries, many sellers or public carriers are reluctant to have drivers wait while detailed inspections are made. Under circumstances where inspection is agreed upon after the driver leaves, the seller should agree that the results of later inspection and any discrepancies will receive prompt attention and correction.

Where reference samples are held for inspection against goods delivered, comparison should be made at delivery or soon after. If a question arises, federal inspection may be requested; the cost to be borne by the seller if the items do not meet sample qualities and by the purchaser if they do. General conditions should state that this procedure will be followed in case of dispute. Acceptance of goods should not mean that the buyer does not have recourse against the seller for latent defects found, fraud or gross mistakes that amount to fraud.

Where goods are certified as to quality before delivery, the certification may be accepted and quality evaluation eliminated in inspection and receiving. Products that are, however, subject to rapid deterioration should be inspected, even though a certificate accompanies the delivery.

Procedures to be followed when goods are rejected should be stated in the general conditions. This may require notice of rejection, time elapse for such notice, pick up of goods by the seller and so forth.

Fresh Fruits and Vegetables

Fresh fruits and vegetables are important as foods, both from an economical and a nutritional standpoint. About 340 pounds are consumed per year per person. Of the total quantity produced, 15% is used by the food service industry. This amounts to about one billion dollars a year.

The fresh-produce market is one of the most difficult markets in which the buyer must operate. This is because: (1) it is a highly dynamic market and changes may occur very rapidly, (2) the product is highly perishable and (3) there is great variation in market practices, grading and products.

1. The fact that supply and demand may change rapidly on this market and that the product is highly perishable accounts for the produce market's rapid shifts and changes. A heavy frost, a drought, unfavorable weather or other conditions may cause a scarcity, with resultant higher prices and lower quality. Favorable conditons may suddenly produce a market glut. Growers must estimate market needs months, seasons or even years ahead. At harvest time they have no choice other than to ship to market or let their crop rot regardless of demand. New strains may be developed or new growing areas opened, and these may suddenly take over the market. Changes in processing may cause a formerly plentiful item to become suddenly scarce. Fresh peas from Utah or winter spinach from Texas were on the market in full supply one year and disappeared the next because of the introduction of freezing plants in the growing areas. The market has always been highly competitive, and this has led to some instability and rapid change.

Some market stability and uniformity have been achieved through the passing of the Perishable Agricultural Commodities Act. Licensing is required for all commission merchants, brokers or dealers buying or selling fresh produce in wholesale or jobbing lots in interstate commerce. These dealers must observe fair business practices. Penalties are provied and licenses may be revoked. Quotas are assigned to growers under the act, and an orderly flow of produce to market maintained. Low-quality products may not be marketed so they will not unnecessarily depress prices of the higher quality items.

Under this law market confidence has been built up and order given where formerly much confusion existed. Futures in market trading are now possible and buyers and sellers may deal from some distance from each other. Under this act it has also been possible to encourage growers to produce items that have better quality and stability for the market.

2. The high perishability of fresh fruits and vegetables causes problems not encountered in other markets. Fresh fruits and vegetables are living organisms. They lose quality rapidly if not given proper handling. Unfavorable conditions may cause sugars to change rapidly to starch and enzymatic reactions cause speedy loss of flavor, appearance and texture. Proper temperatures and good ventilation must be provided to hold quality.

Improved transportation and storage facilities are reducing quality losses. Automation in harvesting and packaging speeds handling and thereby retains quality. Better strains have been developed to withstand rigors of shipping and market handling. Vacuum cooling has been highly successful in improving quality. This is a process in which fresh produce is moved into huge chambers where, for about a half hour, a low vacuum is maintained. This induces rapid evaporation, which quickly reduces field heat. The product is then shipped refrigerated only. No ice is used. This method has been more successful than icing or hydro-cooling in getting products to market in desirable condition. Much more needs to be done, however. It is not possible throughout the marketing channels to maintain optimum conditions, and heavy losses sometimes occur.

Because of this perishability of produce, buyers must learn to know and recognize quality more than on any other market. Reliance upon statement of grade is not enough. A grade may be stated but the condition of the item may not be that grade when delivered. The market makes a distinction between grade and condition, and buyers should state in specifications that the grade indicated should be the condition of the item upon delivery. If an item is graded, it may move through the market with this grade even though it deteriorates in condition. Apples may be graded Extra Fancy when they go into storage and, even

though they come out a low utility grade, they can be called Extra
Fancy on the market. Spinach graded U.S. No. 1 may, in a few hours,
be of U.S. No. 2 quality and yet move under the U.S. No. 1 grade. Unless buyers know this, they may find they are not obtaining items
of the quality or condition designated by the grade.

3. Wide dispersion has made it difficult to bring uniformity to the
markets. High perishability also did not permit shipment at one time
to other markets. Practices thus tended to become different and traditional in each growing area. But wide shipment is now possible and
these local markets still ship produce to the large central markets graded
and packaged according to long-established local customs.

Grade terminology is not consistent on the produce market. In the
meat market "prime" is the only term used to indicate the top grade
of beef. In canned goods "fancy" means top grade. In the produce
market "fancy" may mean top grade, second or third grade. Top grade
in the fresh produce market for different items may be indicated by
"extra fancy," "fancy," "extra No. 1," "Grade AA," "Grade A" or
"No. 1." This means that buyers must learn, for every item on the
market, its own grading terminology. The buyer's job would be simplified if terms that are consistent for first, second and third quality could
be developed.

As a general rule, buyers will find U.S. No. 1 produce good average
quality representing about 50% of the crop. This grade is recommended for ordinary institutional purchase. U.S. No. 2 is usually that
quality considered practical to market under standard conditions.
Grades may exist above U.S. No. 1, such as Extra Fancy or Fancy, but
the quantity in these grades is limited. During off seasons or under
special conditions buyers may purchase in these higher grades. In peak
season adequate quality might be obtained in the No. 2 grade.

The grade standards in the produce market are necessarily broad.
There are many varieties of one type of fruit or vegetable on the market.
Wide variation in growing conditions may also cause wide differences.
Federal standards must have broad tolerances to encompass all these
variations. In some instances, different grade standards have had to be
developed for items marketed from different areas. Citrus fruits, for
instance, will be graded differently, depending upon whether they come
from Florida, Texas or California. Because appearance heavily weights
a buyer's decision on the consumer market, appearance factors in grades
are frequently emphasized in federal grades. Although this may be
desirable for the consumer market, it is not for the industrial purchaser
where utility factors other than appearance may be more important.
Buyers should not be confused by the fact that there are consumer and
manufacturing grades in addition to the wholesale grades he may use.

Because of the wide variation in vegetables and fruits, buyers may have difficulty in properly estimating quantities required. Proper estimate is required so that the amount needed will be obtained and costs may be calculated. In the discussion on specific fruits and vegetables, average wastes in preparation are given but variation found in practice may vary widely. Table 2-14 gives approximate quantities required.

Buyers may also find that federal grades are lacking for some items or that a market does not use the federal grade but uses state or local grading or trade grades. Where no grades exist, buyers may be forced to use commonly accepted terms, such as "good merchantable," "fair" or "ordinary to fair" in defining quality. The need to resort to such indefinite terms leaves much to be desired.

In this chapter only the most important quality factors are summarized. Tolerances allowed, enumeration of quality factors for specific variety and similar details have been omitted for the sake of brevity. Buyers should consult federal grade or trade standards for a specific item if they wish more information. Buyers should compile their own information as they learn their market. It is difficult to delineate quality by words. Written descriptions can only be guides. Actual experience is necessary to give them meaning.

A grade is recommended for purchase later in this chapter. This will usually be satisfactory for most institutional purposes, but at times qualities above or below this recommended grade should be purchased. Buyers will have to make this decision as the need arises. Illustrations are presented in this chapter wherever possible so that the buyer may identify items or see some quality factors that affect grade.

The buyer in the produce market is also confused by the wide variation found in packaging. More standarization in packaging is needed. Prices should be quoted more on the basis of pound than per container. Standard container weights have been listed in the material that follows, but the wide variation found on the market make these somewhat academic. Buyers should be sure to define quantities expected in open containers. When a container is specified as "struck full," it should be evenly leveled across the top. "Bulging pack" means a tight fill rounded over the top level of the container. Loose packs should be watched for short weights and bruised products. Fill of containers should always be specified as equal to facing. Facing assists in improving appearance and in giving a tighter pack.

Packaging methods are also changing rapidly. This makes it difficult for buyers to know the quantity of an item in a container. The huge volume of produce moving through the supermarkets and the pressure of labor unions for lighter containers are increasing the demand for smaller containers. Fiberboard, plastic bags and other materials are rapidly replacing nailed of wirebound wooden boxes. Automatic machine packing is rapidly bringing changes in packaging methods. Counts may now be by electronic device. Other counts may be determined by filling a box and shaking it down. This is called volume filling. The count in volume filling may vary, but the labor saved is sufficient to make this desirable.

Counts actually in containers and the count terms used on the market may differ. A count term on the market may mean the size of an item and have no relationship to the count in the container. At one time the term did indicate both, but as the container changed and, with it, the number of items in the container, the market tended to keep the term as an indicator of size only. Frequently the terms "176" for oranges, "300" for lemons or "5 x 5" for tomatoes may not be indicative of the container count but only of a standard size.

FRUITS

Apples

While there are over 8000 varieties of apples, only about 30 have commercial importance. They are second to oranges in quantity of fruits grown. Extensive growing areas are found in the Pacific Northwest, Appalachian, Great Lakes, Ozarks, Missouri Valley, New York and California. Many apples that are locally grown also appear on the market.

Selection factors. Buyers should classify apples in several ways for purchase. This may be: (1) by maturity, (2) by use, (3) by size and (4) by grade.

1. Apples are known as summer, fall and winter varieties according to the time they are at best quality for use. Summer apples come onto the market in midsummer and last until early fall. They do not keep well and are on the market only a short time. The fall and winter apples keep better, and the winter varieties are available until late spring. To be best for use, apples should be selected at proper maturity. Maturity is indicated by brown seeds, yellowing of the unblushed color or the development of the blush color on red or blushed varieties and softening of the flesh. Properly matured apples possess a rich, fruity apple aroma. The texture softens in turning from green to ripe. Texture may be too hard in immature apples and too soft in mealy, overripe ones. Large apples tend to ripen more rapidly than smaller apples of the same variety.

Short-time storage should be at 36 to 38° F but long-time warehouse

FIG. 2–1. Quality and identification of apples are made by outside and inside characteristics. The top apple shown here is a Winesap. It is a medium-sized apple, red-streaked
with darker stripes and a crisp, white flesh. Note slight lobing. The middle apple is a
Roman Beauty, large in size, red-flecked with white spots. The flesh is clear, white and
fine grained. The Newtown Pippin on the bottom is also called Yellow Newtown. It can
be identified by its yellow exterior, with red blush at the base, and its yellowish flesh.
Courtesy National Apple Institute.

Jonathan is bright red with deep yellow background; used raw is crisp and mildly tart; bakes up fast, holding red color and has juicy, soft-textured, pleasant, tart flesh; holds shape in pie slices. Small to medium size and deep shiny red. September to January.

McIntosh is good for all purpose; aromatic, white, juicy, crisp flesh, good raw; bakes up soft, rather sweet-flavored, juicy, mild, holding characteristic aroma. Cooks smooth. but loses volume in pies. Highly red blushed. September to March.

Cortland has white flesh, high juice, is crisp; bakes well, holding shape. Flesh cooked is juicy, mildly tart, slightly firm and dry. Not a prime pie apple. Deep solid red. September to February.

York Imperial is good raw, bakes well, giving a quite firm flesh, tart flavored, neither juicy nor really dry. Holds shape in slices for pies. Lopsided, pinkish blush. October to May.

Stayman has yellow flesh, juicy and crisp; bakes quite firm, tart flavored and neither juicy nor dry; holds shape in pie slices with firm mellow flesh. Has deep white skin dots over red. Excellent keeper and all-purpose apple. December to May.

Roman Beauty lacks some crispness for use raw, but has excellent flavor, color and acidity; top baker, cooking up fast, moderately tart, soft textured and flavorful; in pies is medium dry, fairly tart, holding shape in slices. Red striped, white dots over red. November to May.

FIG. 2-2. Some common market apples. Note how shape of the apple is an excellent means of identification.

FIG' 2-3. The Delicious and the Golden Delicious are two of the most popular apples used as raw apples. They can be easily identified by the five points on the bottom. The Delicious is red while the Golden is yellowish. The Golden Delicious will not tarnish when cut and exposed to the air. Both are excellent keepers. Courtesy National Apple Institute.

storage should be at 31 to 32° F and relative humidity should be 85 to 90%.[1] If inert nitrogen gas is introduced in place of air, the storage life is extended. At an established time an apple variety will start to ripen. At that time it is at its best and should be selected for use. Apples at

[1] Apples can absorb odors. Keep them away from potatoes, onions, oil and other products that might give off-flavors. Apple odors also may be absorbed by dairy products and other foods.

FIG. 2–4. The Roman Beauty is one of the finest apples for use in baking. Courtesy USDA.

the end of their storage life pass peak maturity rapidly, and these may appear at reduced prices as warehouses are emptied before quality declines to the point the apples are unmarketable. Overripe apples will yield easily to pressure and may show interior brown rot, decay or wilt. Immature apples may shrivel.

Flavor is usually lacking in immature or overripe apples. When an apple is overripe it loses acidity and flavor. Summer apples are juicy, crisp, sweet and slightly acid and full flavored at ripeness, but lose this quality quickly. The fall varieties hold quality longer and winter varieties longest of all. Apple supplies are lowest in June through August.

2. Apples vary in their suitability for use according to variety. A red Delicious is excellent for use raw but performs poorly in cooking. Apples for use raw should be crisp, juicy, have moderate-to-low-acidity and high sweetness. A good baking apple should bake to a soft, moist, firm texture and should possess a sufficiently tough skin to hold the apple's shape. It should possess moderate acidity and good sweetness. Cooking apples should possess high to moderate acidity and have a good texture. In applesauce, a mealy, clear sauce with good tartness is sought. For pies, apples with some texture are desired so that they do not break up, although the famous green apple for summer apple pie has

Table 2–1
Marketing Data for Leading Apple Varieties

Variety	Growing Areas	Marketing Season	Use Raw	Cooking Quality
Arkansas Black	Wash., Oreg., Ill., Me.	Nov. to May	Fair	Good for all
Baldwin	N.Y., N. Eng., Mich., Ohio	Nov. to Apr.	Fair	Good for all
Ben Davis	N.Y., N. Eng., Cumber-land-Shenendoah, Mid-west, Colo.	Nov. to June	Poor	Good for all
Cortland	N. Eng., N.Y., Pa., Ohio	Sept. to Feb.	Good	Good for all
Delicious	Northwest, Midwest, Cumberland-Shendoah	Sept. to Apr.	Excellent	Poor for all
Golden Deli-cious*	Northwest, Midwest, Applachian area	Oct. to Apr.	Excellent	Poor for all
Gravenstein†	Calif. and others	July to Sept.	All purpose except baking	
Grimes Golden	Cumberland-Shenendoah, Midwest	Sept. to Dec.	Good to excel-lent	Good for all
Jonathan	Midwest, Northwest, Colo.	Sept. to Dec.	Excellent	Good
McIntosh	N. Eng., N.Y., Mich., Mont.	Oct. to Apr.	Excellent	Good
Northern Spy	N.Y., N. Eng., Pa., Mich.	Nov. to Feb.	Good	Excellent for all
Duchess (Olden-burg)	Mich., Ill., N.Y., N.J.	Aug. to Oct.	Poor	Good for all
R. I. Greening	N.Y., N. Eng., Mich.	Oct. to Jan.	Fair	Excellent for all
Roman Beauty	Northwest, Ohio, W. Va., Calif., N.J., Idaho	Nov. to Mar.	Good	Excellent, good baking
Stayman Wine-sap	Cumberland, Shenendoah, Ohio, Washington	Dec. to Apr.	Good	Good for all
Wagoner	Mich., N.Y.	Nov. to Jan.	Excellent	Good for all
Wealthy	N.J., Midwest, N.Y.	Aug. to Dec.	Good	Excellent for all
Winesap	Northwest Va., Ill.	Dec. to May	Excellent	Excellent for pies
Winter Banana	Northwest	Sept. to Jan.	Good	Fair for all
Yellow Newtown	Northwest, Calif., Va.	Nov. to June	Excellent	Good for all
Yellow Trans-parent	Ill., Pa., Del., W. Va.	July to Aug. July to Aug.	Poor	Good for pies and sauce
York Imperial	Northwest, Midwest, Appalachian area	Oct. to Mar.	Excellent	Poor for all

*The Golden Delicious does not tarnish easily after peeling.

†Other summer apples good for cooking when slightly immature but good eating raw when at exact ripeness: Strachan, Starr (good also for sauce and pies), Summer Rambo (all purpose), Williams Red (best raw), Lodi (similar to Yellow Transparent).

Table 2–2
Appearance of Leading Apple Varieties

Variety	Size	Predominating Color	Cold Storage in Days*	Tendency to Storage Scald
Arkansas Black	Med to large	Deep medium to dark red	120–180	Severe
Baldwin	Med to large	Bright red carmine stripe	120–200	Med to severe
Ben Davis	Med to large	Striped medium red	120–240	Medium
Cortland	Med to large	Red to deep red	120–200	Medium
Delicious	Med to large	Medium red	90–120	Slight
Golden Delicious	Med to large	Bright yellow or golden	90–160	Med to severe
Gravenstein	Medium	Striped bright red	30–45	Slight
Grimes Golden	Medium	Yellow	60–120	Severe
Jonathan	Med to small	Yellow, with bright red over	60–120	Slight
McIntosh	Medium	Medium red blush	60–150	Severe
Northern Spy	Large	Striped bright red	120–180	Slight
Duchess (Oldenburg)	Medium	Striped medium red	30–90	Slight
R. I. Greening	Med to large	Yellowish green	90–180	Severe
Roman Beauty	Large	Medium red, striped with white dots	120–210	Medium
Spitzenburg	Med to large	Bright red	90–150	Slight
Stayman Winesap	Med to large	Medium red, solidly colored	120–180	Med to severe
Wagoner	Medium	Bright red	90–150	Severe
Wealthy	Medium	Medium red	30–90	Slight
Winesap	Med to small	Dark red	150–240	Medium
Winter Banana	Med to large	Yellow red blush	90–150	Slight
Yellow Newtown†	Medium	Yellow, with blush at base	150–240	Slight
Yellow Transparent	Med to small	Yellow	30–90	None
York Imperial	Med to large	Light red, yellow blushed	120–180	Severe

*Common to maximum time.
†Also known as Newtown Pippin.

a very soft texture and loses shape easily. Some apples may be all purpose, good for eating raw, for cooking, baking or other purposes. Such an apple is the McIntosh, the Stayman Winesap or the Roman Beauty. The Roman Beauty is famous as a baking apple, and some buyers feel the western Rome bakes better than the eastern.

Tables 2–1, 2–2 and 2–3 summarize information of interest to buyers of apples.

3. The size of the apple will affect its usefulness. Sizes of apples on the market may vary from 56 to 252 per western apple box. Figure 2–5 lists standard apple sizes. Apples may be sized by count per box or by diameter as measured not around the girth but from stem to blossom end

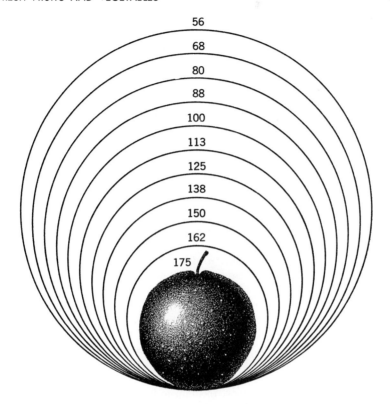

56
68
80
88
100
113
125
138
150
162
175

Count per Western Box	Minimum Diameter Size*
175	$1\frac{1}{4}''$
162	$1\frac{1}{2}''$
150	$1\frac{3}{4}''$
138	$2''$
125	$2\frac{1}{4}''$
113	$2\frac{1}{2}''$
100	$2\frac{3}{4}''$
88	$3''$
80	$3\frac{1}{4}''$
68	$3\frac{1}{2}''$
56	$3\frac{3}{4}''$

*As measured not around girth but from stem to blossom end transversely.
Note: Federal standards call size 88 or less *very large*, 96 to 125, *large*, 138 to 163 *medium*, 175 to 200, *small* and 216 to 252 *very small*.

FIG. 2–5. Apple sizes and counts per western apple box.

Table 2-3
Color, Flavor, and Texture Characteristics of Commonly Used Apples

Variety	Color, Texture and Flavor
Arkansas Black	Nearly white slightly yellow; firm, crisp, moderately fine grained; slightly acid.
Baldwin	Hard, crisp, juicy; medium acid, yellowish flesh; mild.
Ben Davis	Hard, dry tough; medium acid, whitish tinged with yellow flesh.
Cortland	Firm, tender, delicate texture; snow white flesh; mild.
Delicious	Crisp, tender, juicy, rich mildly acid, sweet; yellowish white.
Golden Delicious	Crisp, fine grained, juicy, moderately low acid, rich flavor.
Gravenstein	Firm, crisp, juicy, medium acid; white; loses texture rapidly.
Grimes Golden	Crisp, juicy; medium tender; rich aroma; light yellow flesh; sweet and mellow.
Jonathan	Crisp, juicy; tender; medium to high acid; white to yellowish flesh; rich aroma.
McIntosh	Juicy, mildly acid, pleasant aroma, tender, white flesh, crisp, spicy.
Northern Spy	Firm, crisp, tender, juicy, medium acid; slightly yellowish flesh; tangy.
Duchess (Oldenburg)	Firm, juicy, high acid.
R.I. Greening	Firm, juicy, medium to high acid; yellowish flesh; fine grain.
Roman Beauty	Firm, crisp, medium to low acid; creamy white flesh, moderate grain; bland.
Spitzenburg	Firm, crisp, juicy, tender, medium to sub-acid.
Stayman Winesap	Firm, juicy, crisp, medium acid; creamy yellow flesh, spicy.
Wagoner	Firm, juicy, medium acid.
Wealthy	Firm, juicy, medium acid, tender.
Winesap	Hard, crisp flesh, juicy, medium acid, white flesh tinged with yellow; spicy.
Winter Banana	Firm, tender, medium to low acid; mild sweet flavor.
Yellow Newtown*	Hard, crisp, high juice, medium acid, high aroma; yellowish flesh.
Yellow Transparent	Medium tender, juicy, high acidity unless fully ripe; white flesh.
York Imperial	Hard, crisp, juicy, medium acid, slightly coarse, yellowish flesh.

*Also known as Newton Pippin.

transversely. Diameter sizes are usually given for apples packed in hampers and bushels and by count in western boxes. All packages should show count or diameter. Approximately three medium-sized apples (113 count) equal a pound. This size is considered best for all-round use, giving good yield and, usually, best flavor. Small apples are apt to lack flavor and color and have a tight rubbery texture, while large apples will also lack flavor and be loose grained. The best size for baking in the commercial operation is usually the 88's (3 in. diameter), but smaller sizes may be used for the non-commercial type institution. Normally an eastern apple box will contain 50 to 54 lb, a western box 41 to 47 lb, and a bushel 42 to 52 lb. The paring waste of a good grade should be approximately 24%, and a box weighing 40 lb should yield 30 lb EP.

4. Buyers should state the grade of the apple desired. They should add that the grade should be the condition of the apple upon delivery and not when it goes into storage.

Color is significant in assigning grade. The apples from the State of Washington must meet higher color standards than apples from other areas. Different varieties must also meet different color standards.

Buyers should watch for such defects as decay, internal browning, internal break-down, scab, bitter pit, Jonathan spot, freezing injury, broken skins and bruises. Russeting, sunburn or spray burn, limb rubs, hail or drought spots, scars, cracks, insect, or mechanical or other damage are considered defects. Scald, a common defect found in apples

FIG. 2–6. Apple scald may seriously damage apples held in storage unless they are wrapped in oil paper. Courtesy USDA.

from December to late spring, is caused by apple gases developed in storage. Less scald appears in oil-wrapped apples. Watch for bruising, especially if the apples are very closely packed. Tight packing will be indicated by bulging packs. The grading standards accepted on most markets are either those for apples from the State of Washington or federal standards. A summary of these two grades is given in Table 2–4.

Apricots

Apricots are usually produced in those areas common to peaches. California, Utah, Colorado and the Pacific Northwest produce the bulk of the crop. The main varieties are the Blenheim, a large fruit with light flesh but slightly tart, the Moorparks, medium size with a light amber, sweet flesh and the Royals, a small, sweet fruit with reddish amber flesh. Hemskirk, Tilton, Newcastle and Wiggins Seedling also appear on the market.

The main production period is short. June to July are peak months, with some apricots appearing on the market in May and August. Imports may be found on the winter market from South America and South Africa. Only tree-ripened fruit is of highest quality, and since the ripened fruit is not a good shipper, the quality of the fruit, except for that produced locally, is usually not as high as desired. Immature apricots have a hard flesh and a slightly bitter and acid flavor. The color is greenish yellow. The bulk of the crop goes to canners and driers.

Select apricots that are full, plump, fairly firm and juicy with good flavor and tenderness. They should be kept cool, dry and out of the sun since heat and moisture encourage spoilage. The maximum storage time for good quality fruit is 7 to 10 days under refrigeration.

California lugs holding approximately 24 lb and small baskets or tills of four to the crate (24 lb) are found mainly on the market. These latter are frequently marked to show the number of rows each way in the tills, such as 4 x 4, 4 x 5, 5 x 5, 5 x 6 and 6 x 6. Rows packed in lugs may be stated as 6, 7, 8 and 9 row packs. Buyers should know that in tills the bottom rows will be less in number. A 4 x 4 till will have 4 x 4 on top and center layers, and 3 x 4 on the bottom. A crate of 4 x 4 tills will hold 176 apricots. The fill of fruit should be equal to facing. Eight to 12 apricots weigh a pound.

Examine for overripe, decayed or shriveled fruit. Watch for worms, skin cracks or other blemishes. Select U.S. No. 1. Loss in pitting and peeling is 6%.

Table 2–4

Federal and Washington Grades for Apples

Rank in Quality	Grade Name		Grade Characteristics	
	Washington	Federal	Washington	Federal
1st	Extra Fancy	U.S. Extra Fancy	Sound, clean, fully-matured smooth, well-formed, free from defects. All good mature fruit; good color, shape and condition for variety; carefully packed.	Mature, not overripe, carefully hand picked, clean, well-formed, free from defects, amount of color specified for variety.
2nd	Fancy	U.S. Fancy	Clean, fully matured and of good color for variety; free from defects, fairly well formed.	Mature, not overripe, carefully hand picked, fairly well-formed, free from defects; amount of color specified for variety.
3rd	Grade C	U.S. No. 1	Clean, fully matured fruit, fair color and fair shape; condition good, fairly free from defects.	Same as U.S. Fancy except color may be lower than U.S. Fancy.
4th	None	U.S. No. 1 Early	None	Shall meet all requirements of U.S. No. 1 except for color. This grade is provided for Duchess, Gravenstein, Red June, Twenty Ounce, Wealthy, Williams, Yellow Transparent and Lodi or other varieties normally marketed during the summer months.
5th	None	U.S. No. 1 Cookers	None	Same as U.S. No. 1 except color; grade provided for apples which are mature but lack sufficient color to meet color standards of U.S. No. 1.
6th	None	U.S. Utility	None	Lacks color, shape must not be seriously deformed; may have higher waste and labor preparation cost than saved by purchase of this lower grade.

Avocados (Alligator Pears)

The main producing regions for avocados are Florida, California (70% of the crop) and some of the Caribbean areas. The main varieties are the Fuerte and the Lula.

The Fuerte, grown largely in California, is green and pear shaped. It weighs about 8 to 16 oz. It has a thin, pliable skin. The color may be green or greenish-black. Florida produces the Lula, a heavier avocado averaging 1½ lb. It too is pear shaped, with smooth or slightly corrugated greenish rind flecked with tiny yellow dots. A Nabal avocado comes onto the market at times from Central America. These and other varieties of avocados are more round than oval.

Avocadoes will be found on the market all year, with a high peak in October, November and December. There is a second peak, February to April, with lightest supplies appearing in the summer. While California ships the entire year around, its peak months are in the winter. Florida also has its peak production in the winter, with no supplies appearing April through June. Cuba ships some in the summer months.

Good quality fruit should be fresh and bright appearing, with a flesh that is just beginning to be soft and buttery. Ripeness can be detected when the avocado is placed in the palm of the hand and yields slightly to pressure. The fruit should be heavy for size, with a waxy shell. Soft, mushy, bruised or decayed fruit, detected by dark sunken spots, should be rejected. If hard, an avocado can be ripened in 1 to 5 days by placing in a warm humid place (70 to 80° F). Store at 50° F.

The number of fruit packed in a 13-lb flat may vary from 8 to 35, with the best size for institutions varying from 8 to 12 oz (16 to 28 per flat). Florida may ship in boxes (wood or fiberboard) containing 38 lb. Other shipping containers may hold 12 to 15 or 16 to 17 lb. The Calavo growers of California (Cal-avo = California avocados) grade the fruit No. 1 or 2. Florida grades are No. 1, No. 2 and 3. The California law prohibits the marketing of fruit having less than 8% oil content. There are no federal grades. The fruit appears on the markets in maturity as firm, breaking and ready-to-eat. Fruit can generally be taken from the firm to breaking stage and ripened in 4 to 5 days. Breaking fruit may be ripened in 1 to 2 days. The yields of flesh are Lula, 62%, and Fuerte, 76%.

Bananas

Bananas are a Central American fruit, usually of the Gros Michel or Cavendish varieties.[2] They are shipped green. If allowed to ripen on

[2] The Plaintain is a banana that is usually baked or boiled. It is reddish in color but is not commonly found on the market.

**FIG. 2–7.   View of a 2-year old Cavandish banana plantation in lower Florida.   Courtesy
USDA.**

the tree, they are insipid in flavor.   Ripening may be controlled, and
this is usually done in banana ripening rooms where temperature,
humidity and, sometimes, ethylene gas are used to produce desired
ripening results.   Fast ripening may be accomplished in 3 to 4 days,
medium in 5 to 7 days and slow ripening in 8 to 10 days.   Properly
ripened fruit will have a bright, attractive, yellow color.   The fruit
should be fresh appearing, firm, plump and have good strength of peel.

Ripeness desired may be indicated by three terms.   *Full ripe* means no
trace of green, with typical ripe-banana color, well flecked with light-
brown to dark-brown specks of a size from pinpoints to spots $\frac{1}{8}$ in. in
diameter.   Consumption must be within 24 hours.   *Hard ripe* means
bright banana color with no trace of brown, firm texture, some astringency in flavor, indicating approximately 3 days of storage at room
temperature to ripen.   *Turning ripe* means pale banana color with green
tip, little flavor, with sharp astringency.   These take 5 to 6 days at room
temperature to ripen.

Examine for size, fullness of fruit and degree of maturity.   Look for
bruised fruit or riper fruit than specified, poorly colored skin and mold.
Chilling discolors the fruit.

Bananas are usually sold cut from the stem or bunch in 40-lb cartons.

FIG. 2-8. Bananas require special treatment. They are picked green and kept at 56 to 58° F in transport from Central America. Green bananas will ripen rapidly in 4 days in banana rooms held at 70° F and high humidity. Normal storage temperature of bananas should be around 58° F. Courtesy USDA.

About three medium-sized bananas will equal a pound. Grade refers to fullness of the fruit when harvested. There are no federal grades. Peeling loss averages 32%. Bananas are on the market through the year in good supply.

Berries

Berries are highly perishable, and buyers should make purchases with care. Stained boxes or moist-looking fruit should be carefully examined for spoilage or overmaturity. Molds or rot are easily introduced. Good ventilation and temperatures around 40° F are recommended; storage should only be 1 to 2 days.

Blackberries, youngberries, raspberries, loganberries, boysenberries and dewberries are in season from early June through mid-August. Select bright-appearing, clean fruit free from dirt, good flavored, plump, full size, firm and sweet. Dull color or leakiness may indicate soft or rotten fruit.

Specify U.S. No. 1. Fruit in interstate shipment will be marketed in ½ pt, pt or qt tills. Crates may hold 8, 16, 24 or 32 tills. One quart

FIG. 2–9. Dewberries on the vine at various stages of maturity. Courtesy USDA.

equals about 1¼ lb net. The average waste in preparing to EP is about 5%.

Strawberries appear on the market from April to July, but some early Florida, Louisiana or Texas berries may appear in February. Imports may be obtained in off-season.

FIG. 2–10. The red raspberry. Courtesy USDA.

FIG. 2–11.   A giant blackberry especially developed to give a higher proportion of richly flavored meat to seeds.   Courtesy USDA.

Mature berries should be fully red, plump, firm and free from dirt, bright and clean, free from insect or other damage.   Dull fruit may be spoiled or deteriorated and have poor flavor.   Berries should be picked with stems or at least hulls on.   Purchase from locally grown supplies. Berries must be marketed in interstate commerce in ½ pt, pt and qt tills, usually 16 or 32 to the crate.   One quart weighs 1½ lb.   Preparation waste is 8%.

Cranberries are marketed in crates of 25 and 50 lb as well as 5-lb packages.   Barrels are 100 lb.   Cranberries are grown in Massachusetts,

FIG. 2–12.   Gooseberries on the bush.   Courtesy USDA.

FIG. 2–13. Two types of strawberries showing good quality. Note that fruit is bright, clean, and gives the appearance of firmness of texture and good fruit development.

New York, New Jersey, Wisconsin, Oregon and Washington appearing on markets from September to November. Maturity is indicated by color, which may range from a bright red to almost a black. Good quality berries bounce when dropped from $1\frac{1}{2}$ to 2 ft in height onto a hard surface. Watch for worm, insect damage, rot and frostbite. Purchase U.S. Grade A. Preparation waste is 4%.

Blueberries are on the market from May to September, with the peak in July. Many are frozen. Huckleberries are a different species from

FIG. 2–14. The Early Black Cranberry, one of the most popular varieties. Courtesy USDA.

FIG. 2–15. A newly developed blueberry called the Colville is compared with regular blueberries on left. Courtesy USDA.

blueberries and are on the market during July and August. There are no federal grades for either blueberries or huckleberries, but some trade grades exist for blueberries. These are mainly based on size of berries required to fill a half pint. Some varieties may go 70 or less, but the four main grades are 90 or less, 90 to 130, 130 to 190 and 190 over. Federal market reports generally list these berries as large, medium or small, and omit counts.

Cherries

There are two types of cherries on the market, the sweet and the pie. Pie cherries are seldom used fresh because of the cost of pitting. Canned pitted cherries are readily available.

Dessert cherries, the sweet variety, may be used for eating-in-hand fruit or for salads, desserts and other preparations. Bing, Black Tartarian, Lambert, Republican or the Schmidt are black or blackish-red and possess firmness and durability, which permits shipping. The Chapman is a black cherry that appears on the market early. The Royal Anne is a cream-colored cherry with a red blush. It has a delicate flesh that does not permit shipping.

The cherry season is usually from mid-June to mid-August. Select for size, firmness, well colored for variety, juicy and highly flavored. Immature fruit has a bitter tang and lacks color.

Packaging may be in pint or quart baskets packed 16, 24 or 32 baskets to a crate. Some flats faced and filled will contain 8 to 10 lb. Other lugs will contain 15 to 16 lb, 18 lb, or 20 to 27 lb. California requires non-standard containers to be labeled "irregular pack." Fill should be specified as equal to facing.

Cherries should be picked with stems to prevent mashing. Examine for wormy fruit, soft, overripe or shriveled cherries, and mechanical and insect damage. The cherries should be bright and fresh in appearance, full and plump, firm, juicy, sweet and full flavored. Watch for brown color, dull appearance, mold and bruises. Specify U.S. No. 1.

Citrus Fruit

Approximately 10 billion lb or 60 lb per capita of citrus fruits are consumed yearly. Oranges and grapefruit make up the major portion of the crop, but lemons, limes and some hybrids are also produced in good quantity. There are two main growing areas: (1) Florida and the Gulf states and (2) California and Arizona. Some citrus fruits are imported.

Table 2–5 indicates main production seasons for citrus crops in this country. At times other than these, the quality is apt to be lower and the price higher.

Oranges. There are three main groups of oranges, the sweet, the mandarin or kid-glove type, and the Seville or the sour or marmalade orange. The last named is commercially unimportant but is grown for marmalades. It has a slightly bitter flavor and high acid content.

FIG. 2–16. The Valencia orange, a summer orange produced heavily in both eastern and western growing regions. Courtesy USDA.

Table 2–5
Main Production Seasons for Citrus Fruits

Citrus Fruit	State	Variety	Main Marketing Months
Oranges (sweet)	Florida	Pineapple and Homosassa	December to March
		Hamlin and Parson Brown	October to December
		Temple (hybrid)	December to March
		Valencia	February to August
	California and Arizona	Navel	November to June
		Valencia	March to January
		Temples	November to February
	Texas	Valencia and Temples	February to June
		Navels	November to February
Oranges (mandarin or kid glove)	Florida	Dancy	November through January
	Texas	Clementine	November to March
	California	Dancy mainly	November through January
Grapefruit*	Florida	*	October to June
	Texas	*	November to July
	California	*	March to August
	Arizona	*	December to July
Lemons	California	Lisbon and Eureka	All year, with June to September main peak in production
Limes	Florida	Tahiti (Persian)	All year, with June to September main peak in production (Mexican limes come onto market earlier and later than this)

*The Duncan or Florida Common grapefruit appears on the market early in October and bears heavily until January. The Marsh then appears in December and bears heavily in the late winter and spring. There are very few grapefruit on the market in August and September. The best grapefruit months are those from November to May.

The bulk of the crop is sweet oranges, a type characterized by a skin rather difficult to remove but with membranes easily removable. The Valencia, a summer orange, and the Navel, a winter orange, comprise about 50% and 10%, respectively, of the total sweet orange crop. The Navel is better suited to the dry California climate. Florida grows large quantities of Parson Brown, Hamlin, Pineapple and Homosassa oranges in the winter. The California sweet orange is bright in color, sweet and spicy in flavor. Because of its firmness and lighter juice content, it will segment more easily. Florida oranges are heavier in size and contain more juice than California oranges. They are not as bright in color and are less sweet than California oranges, but carry a fuller flavor. The Temple orange, a cross between the sweet orange and the tangerine, is produced in quantity in the winter months especially in Florida.

Mandarins. The mandarin or kid-glove oranges are characterized by a skin that is easily removed, but membranes that are removed only with difficulty. The skin is wrinkled and apt to be somewhat puffy. Most of these oranges have a coarse texture, a high juice content, good sweetness but less acid than the sweet orange. They have a high aroma. The flavor is full and rich. To this group belong the Kings, a rather large flat-shaped orange; the tangerines, with an orange-red peel; and the Satsumas, with a lighter yellow peel. The last named are much like the tangerines but usually are not quite as juicy and have tougher membranes. They also come onto the market later. Sometimes the Satsuma orange is called the mandarin orange, but the term mandarin is usually applied to all the kid-glove or loose-skinned varieties and not to a specific orange.

The Clementines and the Dancy tangerines are the two main tangerines on the market. Florida and Texas are big producers, with California following.

The kumquat is a small citrus fruit that looks like a tiny orange. It

FIG. 2–17. Tangerines. Courtesy USDA.

Table 2-6
Important Characteristics of Orange Varieties

Variety	Size	Color	Shape	Rind	Seeds	Flesh	Flavor
Sweet orange varieties							
Hamlin	Med to small	Yellow-orange	Oval to round	Smooth, glossy	Few seeds	Medium juicy	Sweet and mild
Parson Brown	Medium	Rich yellow, orange	Oblongish round	Smooth, $\frac{1}{8}$ to $\frac{3}{16}$" thick	10 to 19	Medium fine	Juicy, sweet
Washington Navel	Large	Rich reddish orange to orange yellow	Round to tapering at base	Thin, $\frac{1}{8}$ to $\frac{1}{4}$" thick, smooth. Large oil cells.	None	Medium coarse	Medium juicy rich, sweet
Pineapple	Med to large	Deep orange with reddish tinge	Round	Smooth, glossy, $\frac{1}{8}$" thick	Large, 8 to 15	Medium fine	Rich and juicy
Homosassa	Med to large	Deep orange	Round and oval	Smooth and glossy	15	Medium fine	Excellent, rich fragrant
Valencia	Large	Pale orange to yellow orange with tendency to show green	Slightly oval	Smooth or slight pebble; thin, not tough	2 to 5	Good	Excellent, med juicy
Ruby Red	Medium	Deep orange; red at apex.	Roundish thick	Medium smooth; thick	Many seeds		Rich, sweet almost spicy
Mandarin varieties							
Satsuma	Med to small	Pale to bright orange	Flat to oblate	Rough, large oil cells	Few	Coarse	Juicy, spicy
Dancy Tangerine	Medium	Deep orange	Oblate flat	Thin, glossy	Few	Medium	Rich, juicy aromatic
King	Large	Light to deep orange	Roundish oblate	Very rough	Few	Coarse	Juicy, spicy
Temple	Medium	Deep orange	Oblate	Rough	Few	Moderate	Rich, aromatic, spicy

FIG. 2–18. The Marsh grapefruit. Its full-flavored, juicy flesh and lack of seeds are good reasons for its popularity on the market. Courtesy Florida Citrus Commission.

has smooth, tightly adhering skin and is usually eaten raw with the skin on. It makes excellent preserves.

Grapefruit. The two main varieties of grapefruit grown are the Marsh and the Florida Common or Duncan. Closely related to the Duncan are the Hall, Walters, McCarty and Excelsior. These are all frequently

FIG. 2–19. The Duncan or Florida common grapefruit, one of the main market varieties. It is a high producer of fruit that is full-flavored, rich and juicy, but it is seedy. Courtesy Florida Citrus Commission.

Table 2–7
Purchase Characteristics of Some Common Grapefruit

Variety	Size*	Color	Rind Depth	Flesh	Flavor
Marsh	Medium 3½″	Light yellow	⅛″ thick	Greenish-gray; 11 to 13 sections, no seeds	Medium acidity and sweetness, faint bitterness
Hall	Large 4½″	Light yellow	3/16″ thick	14 sections, 32 seeds, high juice	Acidity, sweetness, and bitterness strong
Walters	Medium 3¾″	Pale yellow	¼″ thick	13 sections, 58 seeds	Acidity, sweetness, and bitterness strong
Duncan	Medium to small 3½″	Light yellow	1/16″ thick	Greenish-gray; 14 sections, many seeds	Acidity and sweetness medium with noticeable bitterness
Triumph	Small 3¼″	Light yellow	⅛″ thick	11 sections, 37 seeds, very juicy	Mild in acidity, sweetness, and bitterness; delicate flavor

*Inches refer to average diameter or fruit.

called Florida Common with the Duncan. The Marsh is seedless or nearly so and outranks all others in quantity produced. The Thompson Pink is actually a pink Marsh. Varieties with pink flesh can be detected by the slight pink blush that appears on the rind.

Florida and Texas grapefruit are heavy in size, juicy, full flavored, with a thin skin and tender, delicate flesh. Some areas, such as the Indian River country in Florida or the lower Rio country of Texas, grow fruit that commands higher prices on the market because of their fine quality. The Marsh and pink grapefruit types are increasing in acreage. California and Arizona grapefruit have a bright clear color but thicker skins, less juice and lack the full body and flavor of the eastern grapefruit.

The tangelo, a cross between the tangerine and the grapefruit, is appearing more and more on the market.

Lemons. Lemons are next to grapefruit and oranges in importance among citrus crops. California and Arizona produce almost 99% of the lemon crop. The moist Florida climate tends to produce a spongy lemon of coarse texture. Its juice also lacks quality. Agricultural research may, however, bring Florida lemons into more prominence. Italian imports are apt to be more coarse than California lemons and lack some of their full spicy flavor.

The main lemon varieties are the Eureka and the Lisbon. While the

FIG. 2–20. Cluster of sweet limes. Courtesy USDA.

latter is a heavier producer, the Eureka comes onto the market at times when lemon prices are higher, and plantings have increased lately with this variety for that reason.

Limes. Limes are produced almost entirely in Florida or off-lying Caribbean islands and Mexico. There are two kinds of limes, the acid and the sweet. The sweet varieties are not commercially important. Of the sour limes, the Tahiti (Persian) lime is heavily produced in Florida. The Mexican lime, a smaller lime with less resistance to cold, is produced in the Caribbean area and Mexico. Its production season is longer than the Tahiti lime.

Quality factors. The best way to judge the quality of citrus fruit is to cut a sample and taste. Buyers should select firm, well-formed fruit with fine-textured, thin skin, free from blemish, hard, dry or broken rinds, bruises, scab or other defects. Note shriveling or any traces of decay. Immature fruit will have high acid, low sugar and lack flavor and juice. Fruit will be heaviest in weight at the beginning and middle of the growing season. The rind will be thick and the shape pointed on late season fruit. Size also grows smaller as season extends. California winter grapefruit is packed 27, 32, 36, 40 and 48 per carton while summer grapefruit (mid-May through mid-September) is packed 32, 36, 40, 48 and 64 per carton.

California and Arizona fruit will have a brighter color than eastern fruit because of the bright sunshine and low humidity of the climate. A small mite that taps the oil cell is the cause of russeting or discoloration on the rind of citrus fruit of Texas and especially Florida. While the

FIG. 2–21.   The difference in rind and texture is evident with late bloom grapefruit on the left compared with regular bloom at the right.   Frequently, toward the end of the season, peaked-shaped and thick-rind fruit are found on the market.   Courtesy USDA.

blemish in no way interferes with quality, it does detract from appearance.   The quantity of russeting is used as a factor to differentiate fruit *within* grade for Texas and Florida fruit.

Citrus fruit must be picked ripe.   Inspectors establish the time citrus fruit may be picked.   The color does not necessarily indicate ripeness. The fruit is heaviest at peak maturity.   The total solids and sugar-acid ratio in the juice are best indicators of ripeness.   Citrus trees may bear flowers, green fruit and ripe fruit at the same time.   Fruit as it ripens may turn a ripe color and then if not picked may turn green again and still be

FIG. 2–22.   Freezing damage on a Valencia orange compared with an undamaged orange on the right.   Courtesy USDA.

ripe. Grapefruit may stay ripe and be of good color on trees for 12 to 15 months. Some varieties of citrus fruit may never completely turn to a ripe color but may show some green even when ripe. This "greening" is prevalent in the Valencia orange, especially the Florida Valencias. Federal standards make allowance for some green color in fruit from here.

Greening may be removed by sweating, a process where ethylene gas or partially burnt kerosene fumes are introduced with warm humid air. This turns the green to a bright ripe color. Much California fruit is sweated and responds well, but Florida fruit does not. Frequently after sweating, color is rubbed on Florida fruit. If this is done the fruit must be labeled "color added." Greening is considered desirable in some fruits. Limes command a better price and are of better quality when they are deep green rather than a full ripe yellow. Some buyers prefer to select lemons that show some green claiming they have higher acidity and better flavor.

Selection factors. Select fruit with thin skins. Puffy or spongy fruit with wrinkled, coarse rinds and pointed sharp necks will lack juice and flavor. Wrinkling and coarseness of texture in kid-glove varieties should not be confused with lack of quality. Fruit that is plump, firm, not soft and flabby, and fine textured, with tiny oil sacs on the rind, should be selected. Western citrus fruit will have thicker skins than the eastern fruit. Recognition of this factor is given in the federal standards.

Fruit should be watched for blue mold, white mold or mechanical damage. Storage of citrus fruits should be at a relative humidity of 80 to 85%, with 37 to 39° F for oranges, lemons 45 to 48° F and grapefruit 48 to 50° F. Eastern citrus will store for longer periods than western citrus.

Packaging and size. Until several years ago much citrus moved to market in $1\frac{3}{5}$ or $1\frac{2}{5}$ bu wirebound wooden crates. Today almost all citrus fruits are marketed in cartons or wooden boxes about one half this size. Some fruit appears in bushel baskets, especially from Texas, and more and more mesh bags, plastic bags and other containers are being seen on the markets. In addition to packaging changes, automation of the industry has occurred, and washing, packing, sorting and handling of the fruit have become completely mechanized. Sorting for size, color and shape is done electronically at the rate of 40 per second. Transistors count the fruit, and, when the required number is in the box, the box moves on and the next one comes up to be filled.

The standard $\frac{4}{5}$ bu carton, filled with California lemons or oranges, will have a net weight of 38 lb and California grapefruit, 33 lb. This carton, filled with Florida oranges, will have a net weight of 45 lb and, with Florida grapefruit, 40 lb. The Texas $\frac{7}{10}$ bu container will average 35 lb when filled with grapefruit.

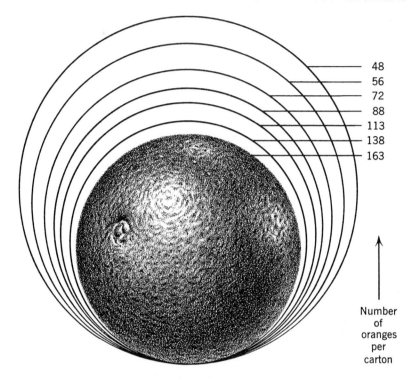

48
56
72
88
113
138
163

Number
of
oranges
per
carton

**FIG. 2–23.   California-Arizona sizes for oranges in standard ⁴/₅ bu fiberboard cartons.
Courtesy Sunkist Growers.**

The federal government classifies oranges as large, medium and small,
based on $1\frac{3}{5}$ bu crate counts, as follows:

Large $3\frac{3}{8}$ in. diameter,* 326 grams each, 126 to box
Medium $3\frac{1}{2}$ in. diameter,* 315 grams each, 215 to box
Small $2\frac{1}{2}$ in. diameter,* 150 grams each, 288 to box

*Greatest dimension as measured at right angles to a line from stem to blossom
end.

Table 2–8 compares standard counts found in the old and new packaging.
In purchasing for juice, the best buy is the lowest price per pound or
carton for similar variety because juice yield is approximately the same
for all sizes, although some buyers state that 176 to 250 oranges, 72 to 96
grapefruit and 360 to 432 lemons ($1\frac{3}{5}$ bu counts) yield higher quantities
of juice than other sizes.   If a half orange is to be served, 48's are about
as small as can be used to make an adequate serving, but 72's may be

used if two halves are served. In grapefruit, 64's in the $1\frac{3}{5}$ bu crate give good standard half servings. Extra large fruit is apt to lack flavor, have coarse texture and soft flesh. Very small fruit will be insipid in flavor, apt to have high acidity and lack sweetness.

Grading. Because of climatic and varietal differences, there are a number of different federal standards for the same type of citrus fruit.

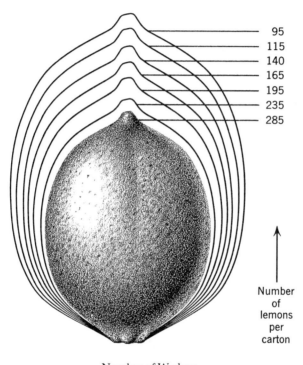

New Size Number	Number of Wedges per Carton	
	Quarters	Sixths
95	380	570
115	460	690
140	560	840
165	660	990
195	780	1170
235	940	1410
285	1140	1710

FIG. 2–24. California-Arizona sizes for lemons in standard ⁴/₅ bu fiberboard cartons. Courtesy Sunkist Growers.

Table 2-8
Approximate Counts and Diameter Sizes of Some Citrus Fruits*

| Type Fruit | Count | | Size |
	1⅗ Bushel	⅘ Bushel	Minimum Diameter, in Inches
Oranges	96	48	3 6/16
	126	56	3 3/16
(Temple oranges	150†	72†	3†
and Tangelos	176	88	2 14/16
will vary	200	100	2 12/16
slightly from	216	113	2 10/16
these counts.)	252	126	2 8/16
	288	138	2 6/16
	324	162	2 4/16
Grapefruit	36	18	5
	45 or 46	23	4 11/16
	54 or 56	27	4 6/16
	64†	32†	4 3/16†
	70 or 72	36	3 15/16
	80	40	3 12/16
	96	48	3 9/16
	112 or 113	56	3 7/16
	125 or 126	63	3 5/16
Lemons	180	85	2.57
	210	115	2.41
	240†	140†	2.24†
	300†	165†	2.13†
	360	195	2.01
	432	235	1.88
	490	285	1.77
Tangerines	100		2 15/16
	120		2 11/16
	150		2 8/16
	176		2 6/16
	210		2 4/16
	246		2 2/16
	294		2
Limes	Usually marketed in flats containing 8 to 10 lb net; varying in count from 40 to 80 limes, depending upon size.		

*It is difficult to generalize too much on standard counts. For instance, the counts given here are for Florida grapefruit. Texas which grows a slightly smaller grapefruit uses a 1⅖ bu or 7/10 bu container which holds by count the same number as held in the Florida 1⅗ bu and ⅘ bu containers. Thus, Texas 54's are not the same size as Florida's but are the equivalent of Florida's 64's, and Texas 64's are the same size as Florida's 70 or 72 pack. Buyers should learn counts and weights of containers appearing on their markets.

†Normally the best size for quantity food production use.

Oranges and grapefruit have three standards: (1) Florida, (2) Texas and states other than Florida, California and Arizona and (3) California and Arizona. The grade nomenclature in all three are U.S. Fancy, U.S. No. 1, U.S. No. 2 and U.S. No. 3. Florida may have a grade at times between No. 1 and No. 2 called Special.

Wider tolerance is allowed for greening in eastern oranges. The western standards make allowance for slightly rougher rinds, although Texas fruit may have slightly rougher rinds than Florida fruit. Thickness of rind is a quality factor in western grapefruit. The eastern standards consider russeting as a factor within grade. The provisions for russeting in Florida oranges are:

U.S. Fancy:	No more than $\frac{1}{10}$ surface discoloration.
U.S. No. 1, Bright:	No more than $\frac{1}{10}$ surface discoloration.
U.S. No. 1, Golden:	No more than $\frac{1}{3}$ surface discoloration in 30% of the fruit or less.
U.S. No. 1, Bronze:	No more than $\frac{1}{3}$ surface discoloration in 75% of the fruit or less.
U.S. No. 1, Russet:	More than 75% have excess of $\frac{1}{3}$ surface discoloration.

Texas has only two classifications of russeting: Bright and Bronze. The classifications for russeting in other citrus fruits may vary but grapefruit in Florida and Texas follow those for oranges.

Only one federal standard for grades exists for lemons. Grades are U.S. No. 1, U.S. No. 2, and U.S. No. 3. Grades for limes are U.S. No. 1 and U.S. No. 2. Institutions will usually find U.S. No. 1 citrus fruit of adequate grade for general use.

The State of Florida has attempted to correlate quality of citrus fruit to the quality of the juice. A U.S. Grade AA orange juice is one having a high solid, acid and sugar content, with 5 gal of orange juice minimum yield per $1\frac{3}{5}$ bu box. A U.S. Grade A orange juice has a slightly lower solid, acid and sugar content and a yield of $4\frac{1}{2}$ gal of juice per $1\frac{3}{5}$ bu box. Florida has established slightly lower yield requirements for grapefruit. Lemons must have a juice content of 30%. To meet federal standards limes must have a juice content of not less than 42%.

In some instances marketing agreements under the Perishable Commodities Act have set higher standards than those used for federal standards. Persian limes, for instance, in Florida may not be marketed less than $1\frac{5}{8}$ in. in diameter and, if between this and $1\frac{7}{8}$ in. in diameter, must possess a juice content of 48%. If over $1\frac{7}{8}$ in. in diameter, they must contain 44% juice. The 44% minimum juice content applies to Mexican limes. Under marketing agreements, oversupply is regulated, and growers receive prorating allowances for market shipment. Ripe-

Table 2-9

Average Yields of Flesh and Juice from Citrus Fruits, by Percent of Total Weight

Type Fruit	Flesh (no membrane)	Juice		
		Arizona	California	Florida
Lemons	64%	44%	44%	
Oranges	65%	48%	47%	54%
Grapefruit	47%	45%	42%	46%
Limes	57%			35%

ness and other factors relating to quality are also controlled under this act.

Coconuts

Most of the coconuts used in this country are imports from the Caribbean, although Florida produces some. Coconuts are found on the market all year, with a peak from October through December. There is a second subpeak February to April. They come on the market in sacks containing 60 to 100 lb net. Quality is indicated by heaviness for size and good shape. Shake to hear milk inside, for coconuts that are dry are apt to be moldy. Examine for cracks, molds or wet eyes. There are no federal standards for coconuts. Purchase by the pound. Waste in preparation is 47%. If the coconuts are cracked and placed into a 350° F oven for a short time, the meat comes easily from the shell.

Dates

Fresh dates are usually purchased in pitted form for institutional use. There are no federal standards. When selecting, watch for waxy, golden color, plumpness and smooth skin. These factors indicate quality. Dull color, dirt or extraneous matter are defects. Fresh dates appear on the market in the fall.

Figs

California-grown fresh figs appear on the market from June to October, usually in baskets weighing 5 lb net, with four baskets to a crate. They are highly perishable. Overripe figs can be detected by their sour odor. Look for bruising, rot and insect damage. For best quality, figs should be fully ripe. The Calmyrna fig is light green, soft and sweet when ripe. Black Missions are stronger in flavor. Calmyrna figs are usually peeled for service. The peeling loss is 18%.

Grapes

Two types of grapes are grown in this country, the American and the European. The former are native to the United States. These have loose skins that separate easily from the pulp. Because of this they are frequently called "slip-skin" grapes. The European grapes have been transplanted from Europe. Their pulp and skin are not easily separated.

American grapes are Concord, Catawba, Moore Early, Worden, Niagara and Delaware. Varieties are found in the East, Midwest, Mississippi and Gulf areas. The Muscadine-type American grapes, the most important variety of which is the Scuppernong, grow along the Gulf Coast and the Mississippi River areas. Vast Concord, Catawba and other American grape growing areas are found around the Great Lakes. The European grapes most popular for table use are the Emperor, Thompson Seedless or Sultanina, Flame Tokay, Red Malaga, Ribier, Almeria, White Malaga, Cardinal, Muscat and Cornichon. California produces most of our European grapes.

American-type grapes appear during the summer and early fall seasons. They are not good keepers. European grapes appear about the

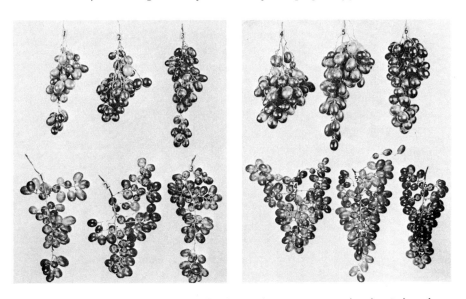

FIG. 2–25.   Structure of bunch is considered in grading grapes.   Here bunches 1 through 6 are photographed hanging, with the same bunch underneath spread out on flat surface. Bunches 1, 2 and 3 are straggly.   Bunch 3 is just below requirement for U.S. No. 1. Bunches 4 and 5 are not straggly but do not meet standard of "fairly well filled" because of lack of filling on upper portion.   Bunch 6 meets minimum standards for "fairly well filled."   Courtesy USDA.

same time but keep better and are on the market for longer periods. They may be stored 4 to 6 months at 31 to 32° F. Imports are on the markets from February to May.

Grapes should be picked near full maturity for best quality. If picked sooner, they will lack flavor, sweetness and best texture. Fully ripe grapes should have cluster stems that are brown. Overshriveling of the cluster stems indicates excessive age, however. The seeds should be brown, not green, and should separate easily from the pulp of both the American or European varieties. A milky opaque pulp indicates freezing and flat flavor. Watch for decay, mold, wet or sticky berries. The fruit should be plump and full. Look for full, not straggly, bunches. Pick up a stem of grapes and shake them. If a number fall off, they are old and will have short storage life. Emperor varieties should have distinctly yellowish green or yellow stems. Freezing damages grapes, and if they have a dull, dead color and the stem attached to the grapes pulls out without meat or brush attached, they have probably been frozen. Yields: American, pulp and juice 57%, European, unstemmed 89%.

Mangos

Mangos are eaten fresh, much as cantaloupe. When green, they are used to make preserves, especially the East Indian chutney. They have a soft melon texture and a flavor resembling a blend of the flavor of apricot and pineapple. They may vary from 4 oz to a pound in size. Look for plump, fresh fruit, firm, clear in color. Taste before accepting, for some mangos may have a turpentine-like flavor. There are no federal standards.

Melons

Most melons do not increase their sugar content after picking and should be picked ripe. Sweetness of flavor, heavy aroma, color and softening are indications of maturity. Netting in some varieties also indicates ripening. Tasting or plugging is one of the best ways to ascertain quality.

Cantaloupes. Cantaloupes or muskmelons appear on the market as early as March as Mexican imports. Peak production occurs in this country from July to October. Late varieties may be obtained until November. Harvest at ripeness is indicated by the manner in which the stem has been broken from the melon. If the scar at the stem end is smooth and clean, it is called a *full slip;* if the stem is partially attached, it is called *half slip.* If the stem did not come free at all but is cut or broken, the melon was green when picked. Early in the season

FIG. 2–26. Cantaloupe picked at full-slip stage of maturity shows a stem pulled away from the melon, leaving a clean, cuplike hole. Courtesy USDA.

specify full slip and in warmest weather half slip. There are three stages of full slip, and buyers should select on the basis of time to be held before service. *Full slip, hard ripe* melons show a yellow green color outside; *full slip, choice* show more yellow and a beginning softening at the blossom end; *full slip, full ripe* are completely yellow and at full ripeness. California and Arizona produce nearly 70% of the cantaloupe crop. Purchase grade U.S. No. 1.

The type of packaging used for cantaloupes will depend upon the producing area. The western jumbo crate is used considerably and will

FIG. 2–27. Cantaloupe picked at half-slip stage shows stem slipped easily but left a part of the stem broken in the hole. Courtesy USDA.

FIG. 2–28.   Moist, sweet, luscious eating quality is indicated in this cantaloupe.   Note prominent netting indicating ripeness.   Courtesy USDA.

hold 18, 23, 27, 36 or 46 canteloupes and weigh 83 lb net.   The stand-ard crate holding 27, 36 or 45 melon is also common.   A bushel will hold between 1½ to 2 dozen and weigh net, 60 to 65 lb.   Local supplies may be found in hampers, boxes or sacks.   Buyers should purchase by the pound.   Canteloupes average ¾ lb to 4 lb.   The 45 count in the western jumbo crate weight 1¼ to 1½ lb each.   These will have about a 5 in. diameter and are good for serving as half portions.   Preparation waste to EP is 50%.

There are a number of cantaloupes or muskmelons.   These are fre-quently classified according to the color of the flesh.   Rich, salmon-colored flesh varieties are: Hales Best, the most important commercial variety, medium size, weighing 2½ to 3½ lb, heavily netted, little ribbing, a good shipper even when picked full slip.   There are many subvarieties of the Hales.   The Bender is another family of commercial importance.   It grows better in cold climates than the Hales but is not as good a shipper.   It is round or oblate, medium to large, weighing 2½ to 4 lb, sparsely netted, with distinct ribbing and broad sutures.   There are also many subvarieties of Benders.   The Hales and Benders are thick fleshed, sweet and juicy, with a rich aroma.   Hearts of Gold is one of the finest of cantaloupes. It has a richly colored flesh varying from an orangy-pink to salmon color. It is an excellent shipper. It will not change color in ripening but retains a natural green. A heavy aroma and softening of the stem end will indicate ripeness. Pink-meated varieties are: Burrell Gem, a medium-sized, oval melon with heavy netting on the ribs and well-defined sutures. The flesh is rich and spicy, and the melon is a good shipper. Tip Top is a medium-to-large melon that may weigh as high as 8 lb. It is slighly oval and has well-defined ribs covered with a light netting. The flesh may vary from pink to a deep yellow. A poor shipper, it is usually found only on local markets. Those having green meat are: the Netted Gem, an eastern melon of medium size weighing 2 to 3 lb. It is slightly oblong, ribbed and covered with fine netting. The aroma and flavor are rich and the flesh is juicy. The Hackensack is a large eastern melon, prominently ribbed and coarsely netted. The flesh is juicy and sweet. The green-meated melons appear fairly late in the summer.

Buyers will hear many names for different varieties of cantaloupes. Usually these are subvarieties or varieties having local importance.

Other small melons. The Honeydew melon is related to the cantaloupe. It is about 6 to 6½ lb in weight and about 6 in. in diameter. The shape is slightly oblong. It has a smooth, greenish-white rind, which, at maturity, is a creamy yellow. The best melons will show full or half slip. The flesh should be thick, greenish, fine grained, juicy, sweet and mild in flavor. Softening at the blossom end and odor may also indicate ripeness. Imports from Chile are on the market from January to June. American production reaches a peak July to October. Specify U.S. No.

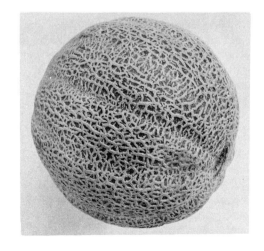

FIG. 2–29. The Rocky Ford cantaloupe, sometimes called the Netted Gem. Average size is about 5½ by 5 in. The fruit has faint ribbing, with a hard gray netting. The seed cavity is fairly large, and the flesh is green with a spicy, sweet flavor. It is a good shipper. Courtesy USDA.

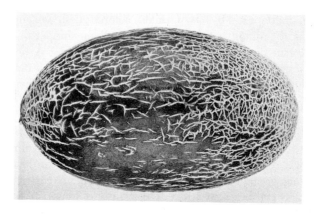

FIG. 2–30.   The Santa Claus melon.   The fruit is oblong, about 12 by 6 in., and weighs around 6 lb.   Rind is green and gold, usually with a trace of netting.   Flesh is light green, with a Casaba flavor.   Good keeper and may be obtained at times in midwinter.   Courtesy USDA.

1.   Waste in preparation to EP is 59%.   Watch for such decay as pink or black dots on the melon.   A sour smell indicates overripeness and spoilage.

The Honey Ball is a slightly netted melon with greenish-white to light-yellow color.   Its flesh resembles the Honeydew but it is slightly smaller in size.   It is a firm, thick-fleshed melon and ships well.

The Persian melon resembles the cantaloupe in outer appearance and in flesh characteristics.   A medium-size melon weighing about 7 lb, it is round with a diameter 7 to 8 in. across.   The rind is dark green covered with fine netting.   The flesh is orange, sweet, juicy and full-flavored.   Purchase on the basis of those selection factors listed for cantaloupe.   The Persian melon does not slip.   Eight to 15 melons are shipped in the standard crates and 12 to 15 in the jumbo.   There is only one federal grade, U.S. No. 1.   Waste to EP is 50%.

The Cranshaw melon is a high quality melon.   Specify full or half slip.   They store well and may appear late on the market.   Some imports are found in midwinter.   They weigh 4 to 8 lb and are pointed at the stem and rounded at the base.   The rind is smooth with little netting and very little ribbing.   It is mottled with a gold and green color.   The flesh is sweet, rich in flavor and mellow.

The Casaba melon is a late variety melon usually ripened on the vine.   It has a soft, creamy white, sweet, juicy flesh but little aroma.   Ripeness may be indicated by a yellow color of the rind and by blossom-end softening.   It is medium size, with a diameter 7 to 10 in. and weighs

6 to 10 lb.   The rind may be rough appearing and it is deeply furrowed.
The Casaba keeps well and may be on the market until Thanksgiving or
later.

The Santa Claus melon is another late melon and an excellent keeper.
It may be on the market until Christmas.   It is oblong, having a 6 to 8
in. diameter and a length of 12 to 14 in.   The rind is green with broad
bands of slight netting.   The flesh is white or light, yellowish-green,
sweet and juicy.

When purchasing crated melons, buyers should require stamped on
the crate the size of crate, the number of melons in the crate and the
federal grade.

Watermelons.   Watermelons are on the market from June to September.
They are grown mostly in the southern states.   Red and yellow-fleshed

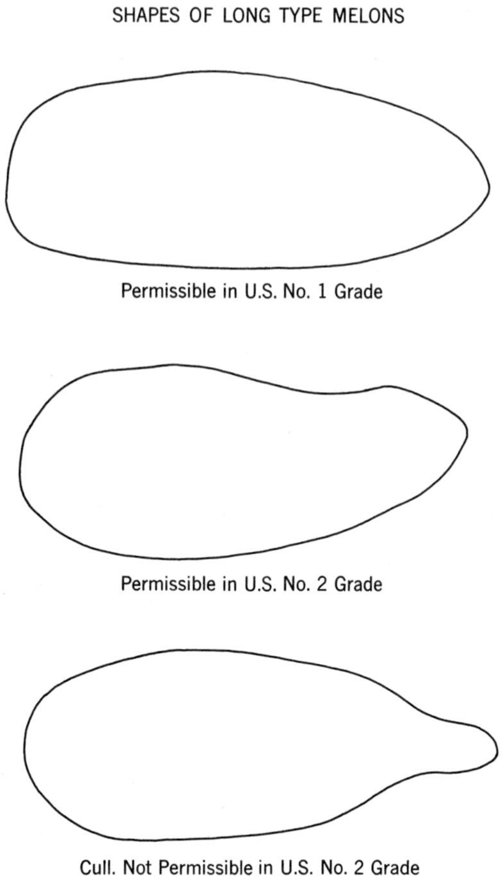

SHAPES OF LONG TYPE MELONS

Permissible in U.S. No. 1 Grade

Permissible in U.S. No. 2 Grade

**FIG. 2–31.   Shapes of water-
melons   permitted   within
grades.   Courtesy USDA.**

Cull. Not Permissible in U.S. No. 2 Grade

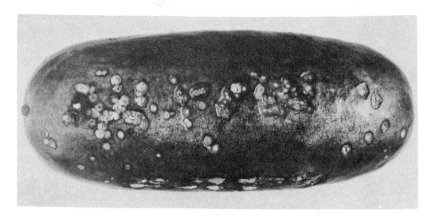

FIG. 2–32. Watermelon seriously spotted by anthracnose fungus. Courtesy USDA.

melons are grown but because the latter is a poor keeper and shipper it is usually seen only on southern markets.

Watermelons should be mature when purchased. Ripeness is indicated by firm, symmetrical shape, fresh and attractive appearance and good color, which may vary from a deep, solid green to a gray, according to the variety. A bloom should be over the surface, lending a somewhat velvety appearance. The lower side of the melon should be yellowish in color. A ripe melon should have a crisp, sweet and juicy flesh. Thumping may indicate degree of ripeness. Immature melons have a hard, greenish, unripe appearance, with a white or pale green underside. Overmaturity is indicated by a dull, lifeless appearance and a soft or springy feel when pressure is applied. Melons having a hard white streak through the length of the flesh have "white heart," which indicates a poor melon that, unfortunately, cannot be detected until the melon is cut.

The type of watermelon appearing most commonly on the market is the Charleston Gray, a good shipper, about 24 in. long and 10 in. in diameter, weighing 25 to 35 lb. The rind is a pale green with a grayish cast and dark green veins. The flesh is deep pink to red; it is crisp and sweet. The seeds are brown with dark veins. The Cannonball (also called the Black Diamond, Blackstone, Black Diamond Yellow Belly) has been replaced as first in market importance by the Charleston Gray and is now second. It is a large oblong melon that may reach 50 lb. The rind is a glossy, dark green, thick and firm. It is a good shipper. The Congo is a striped oblong and blocky melon weighing 30 to 35 lb. It has faint stripes of darker green. The Garrison is a striped melon of commercial importance. It is oblong in shape and may weigh on the average 40 lb. Institutions find that watermelons weighing around 28 lb cut to best advantage. Waste in preparation to EP is 54%.

Nectarines

The nectarine is a smooth-skinned peach and may be either cling or freestone. It is erroneously believed that the fruit is the result of a cross between a peach and a plum. The fruit may be red, white or yellow fleshed. Select for plumpness and firmness, with a good creamy base color flecked with a red blush. The red coloring, except for the John Rivers, an early variety, should cover at least 75% of the surface. Diameters as measured at right angles to the greatest dimension line from stem to blossom end may be between 2 to 3 in. They are frequently packed in four-basket crates 3 x 4, 3 to 4 x 4, 3 to 4 x 5, 4 x 4, and so forth, three layers deep per basket with the bottom layer having one row less each way. Straight, offset and diagonal packs are permitted. (See tomatoes for definition of these packs.) They may also be marketed in bushel or half-bushel baskets. California, the largest producer, ships either in the peach box or in lugs containing approximately 80 to 140 fruit. Specify U.S. Fancy. Preparation waste to EP is 14%.

Papayas

The papaya is also called the tree melon. It is spherical to oblong with a large central cavity packed with seeds. The flesh about ¾ to 2 in. is a yellow to deep orange. The flavor is sweet and mellow, somewhat like a bland cantaloupe. The skin is thin and smooth and turns yellow to orange from green when the fruit is ripe. The average weight is between 1 and 2 lb. Most of this fruit comes from Florida and Hawaii, with a few from Texas. If overmature, the papaya will be soft and lack flavor. Taste before purchase. Papayas are packed usually 10 lb net to a flat. There are no federal grades. EP is 67%.

Peaches

California and Georgia are the leading peach-producing areas, but peaches are also produced extensively in the Great Lakes regions, New York, mid-Atlantic and Pacific Northwest areas. It is a perishable fruit and will store at temperatures just above freezing for only about 3 weeks. Peaches are picked just before maturity and mature rapidly. They do not keep well and amounts purchased should be those that can be used within a short period of time. Cling varieties have little use in institutions since they require more labor in preparation than the freestone varieties.

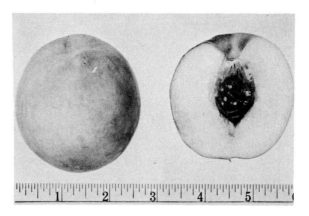

FIG. 2–33. Buyers should cut fruit and note quality inside as shown on this peach. Appearance factors on the outside may sometimes be of little value in indicating texture and flavor inside. Courtesy USDA.

Peaches will be found on the market from May through September, with a peak from mid-July through September. The white-flesh varieties are usually early, with the yellow or creamy colored flesh varieties appearing later. Peaches should be selected on the basis of plumpness, well colored for variety, freedom from blemishes, and firmness of flesh. Immature peaches have a pale yellow color and may show green. They will have poor flavor, high acidity and a hard rubbery flesh. Coloring may not always indicate maturity but the disappearance of green and yellowing with a full flush of pink and softening of the flesh are an indication of maturity. Some of the common peaches on the market are listed in Table 2–10.

Wide variety is found in packing peaches. The most common package is the Los Angeles lug holding 32 to 96 peaches in two layers. Net weight is around 20 lb. The bushel basket is commonly used by eastern and midwestern growers. It averages net between 45 and 48 lb. Hampers holding 16 or 20 qt are also used. Six basket carriers are common in the Carolinas and north and south Georgia. Approximately 3 to 4 peaches per pound is a common size. Buyers should familiarize themselves with market offerings, for practices of packing vary so widely. Percentage waste in skinning and pitting is 24%.

Cut peaches and examine for flavor and maturity. Examine for worms and decay. If gum exudes from the skin over a tiny mark, insect damage is indicated. Watch for mold or rot, growth cracks and bruised fruit. Federal grades are U.S. Fancy, Extra No. 1, No. 1 and No. 2.

Buyers may have to move into grades above U.S. No. 1 to obtain the quality they desire.

Pears

Pears, like apples, should be purchased on the basis of maturity or their use. Early varieties are on the market during the late summer and early fall, while late varieties will be found on the market until spring. Table 2–11 indicates some factors of interest in buying pears.

Pears are picked when slightly immature. If tree ripened, they are apt to be coarse and have a rough appearance. Full ripeness after storage is indicated by a coloring specific to the varieties and softness

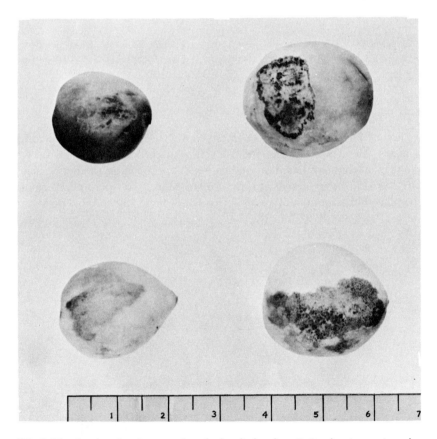

FIG. 2–34. Peaches showing scars from leaf or limb rubs. Fruits showing various degrees of this injury may be admitted into U.S. Grades No. 1 or No. 2 according to tolerance allowances for this defect. Courtesy USDA.

Table 2–10
Some Purchasing Characteristics of Common Peaches

Variety	Flesh Color	Size and Shape	On Market	General Characteristics
Elberta	Yellow, red blush	Large, oval	August to September	Good shipper and keeper
Hale	Yellow, red blush	Large, round	August to September	Excellent flavor; excellent shipper and keeper
Halehaven	Yellow, high blush	Medium to large, round	August	Excellent flavor
Golden Jubilee	Yellow, slight blush	Large, oval	August	Juicy; good flavor; bruises easily
Hiley	White	Medium large	August	Excellent flavor; juicy
Cumberland*	White, high blush	Large, bell shaped	July to August	Excellent flavor; high quality
Carman*	White	Medium to large	August	Good quality

*Semi-clingstone; may for this reason have limited use in institutions because of extra labor and higher waste.

of flesh. The Bartlett pear becomes yellow, with a red blush indicating ripeness; the d'Anjou turns greenish yellow, and the Bosc a yellow brown. Softness at the stem base is an indication of approaching ripeness. Pears are stored for long periods of time at 30 to 32° F. To ripen, pears should be placed in a room at 60 to 65° F for 3 to 5 days. Since most pears are

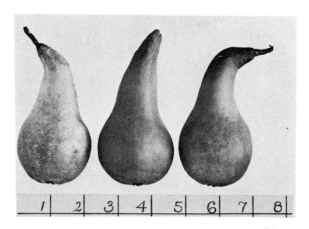

FIG. 2–35. Misshapen Bosc pears. Note slight shriveling on pears. Both defects are factors affecting grade. Courtesy USDA.

Table 2–11
Characteristics of Common Pear Varieties

Variety	Main Producing Regions	Maturity Season	Size	Color Ripe	Best Use	General Characteristics
d'Anjou	N.Y., Northwest and Southern states	Oct. through Apr.	Large	Creamy Yellow-green	Dessert Canning	Good keeper; good flavor.
Bartlett	N. Eng., N.Y., mid-Atlantic, Great Lakes and Midwest, Northwest and Calif.	Mid-July through mid-October	Large	Yellow, red blush	Dessert Canning	All purpose pear, soft and flavorful; medium keeping quality. Susceptible to blight.
Bosc	Northwest, Calif., N.Y.	Sept. to Jan.	Large	Yellow covered with brown russet	Dessert	Juicy, well-flavored; subject to blight. Good keeper.
Gorham	N. Eng., N.Y., Northwest, Calif.	Aug. to Nov.	Large	Yellow	Dessert Canning	Good all round purpose pear. Resistant to blight.
Hardy	Calif., mid-Atlantic; some in Midwest	July to Dec.	Medium	Green to yellow	Dessert	Good keeping quality.
Du Comice	Northwest and Southern states	Oct. to Mar.	Large	Light greenish-yellow	Dessert	Easily bruised, tender skin; soft flavorful flesh.
Winter Nelis	Northwest and N. Eng.	Oct. to Apr.	Small	Green-yellow with dark brown russet	Dessert	Excellent keeper; soft fine texture; juicy; good flavor.
Seckel	Midwest and Southern States	Oct. to Apr.	Medium	Yellow	Dessert, Canning Pickling	Good flavor and quality; watch for grittiness.
Kieffer	N. Eng., N.Y., Mich.	Oct. to Dec.	Medium to large	Yellow	Cooking Canning	Not a good fresh item. Good keeper. Gritty.

Note: The term "blight" as used here means, "scald" or "russeting."

now packed in boxes in polyethylene wraps, the wrap should be broken to permit air to enter. Some late varieties do not ripen until late fall or winter. Pears may be ripened in ripening rooms, much the same as bananas are ripened for market.

Pears appear on the market in the standard pear box or in bushel baskets. Pears are sized per box 70, 80, 90, 100, 110, 120, 135, 150, 165, 180, 195, 210, 228 and 245. The best size usually for institutional use are 110 to 135 counts. The paring and coring waste averages about 26%. Boxes should weigh approximately 45 to 46 lb, and bushel baskets will weigh just slightly higher than this.

Select pears that are clean, bright and typically colored for variety. Misshapen, soft or wrinkled fruit should be avoided. Watch for scars or damage, insect or worm injury. Pears appearing late in the season may show scald or russeting similar to scald found on apples after extended storage. Some pears like the Kieffer may be gritty and should be avoided for fresh use. The summer varieties are highly perishable, and only those quantities that can be used immediately should be purchased. Winter pears are graded U.S. Extra No. 1, No. 1 and No. 2. Summer pears are graded U.S. No. 1 and No. 2. Institutions should usually purchase U.S. No. 1 for either summer or winter pears. Washington state grades are commonly used. Its first and second grades are Extra Fancy and Fancy. Yield EP 78%.

Persimmons

The persimmon must be completely ripe and slightly soft before it is good for use. Buyers should watch for excessive softness and rot, however. The persimmon is a glossy, orange-colored fruit, oblong in shape, with a deep yellow or orange flesh. California produces the Oriental or Japanese persimmon, which is larger than that grown in the southern states. It has a rounded apex ending in a black spot. The southern-grown persimmon is almost red, is frequently seedless and has a drier texture, somewhat pasty in contrast to the California persimmon, which has at extreme ripeness a sloughy quality. The Southern persimmon is not of great market importance.

Persimmons vary in size, running as high as a pound to several ounces. The average is three or four to the pound. One pack common on the market is a flat holding approximately 11 to 13 lb of persimmons.

Select fruit that is well shaped, plump, smooth, soft, of a good color and with stem cap attached. Reject those with broken skin. A slight wrinkling is acceptable, since this indicates ripeness. There are no federal grades. The EP yield on these is 79%. Native southern persimmons, with seeds and calyx only removed, yield 82%.

Pineapple

The market may have fresh pineapple for sale almost any month of the year because so many areas produce it for shipment. Peak supplies will be on the market in April and May. Florida pineapple appear on the market in February. Shipments are made from the Caribbean islands and Mexico from March through June. Hawaii and the Philippines also ship pineapple.

The appearance and odor of pineapple will indicate maturity, and pineapple must be picked mature since the sugar develops in the fruit only during the last two weeks before complete ripeness. The fruit should have a distinct orange-yellow color with more whiteness at the base. It should have a fragrant aroma and a clean, waxy shine on the outer surface with fully developed eyes or surface squares. Immature fruit may be indicated by small size, purplish-green color and only partially developed eyes. Plant-ripened fruit is difficult to ship but is superior in flavor. Good quality is indicated by a dry bottom, firm eyes

FIG. 2–36. A persimmon and pomegranate are shown in this illustration. The persimmon is the pointed tipped fruit shown in the foreground in the bowl while the pomegrante is shown cut on the right.

and a well-developed, plump fruit. The base should be well trimmed. The fruit should feel heavy for its size. Mold first appears at the base and may be indicated by a softness and a sour smell. A darkening under the skin surface may indicate rot. The best stage of maturity for institutional purchase is when the fruit is not quite ready for immediate use. Buyers may indicate this condition by specifying *yellow ripe* in their specifications. The fruit will be still firm and require 3 to 4 days for conditioning. *Hard ripe* fruit must be held for a longer time. Half crates holding 15 pineapple on the average are common on the market, but the number may vary in this container from 9 to 21. Net weight is approximately 35 lb. Full crates containing twice the quantity and weight are still found on some markets. On U.S. No. 1 fruit the length of the tops "shall not be less than 4 inches nor more than twice the length of the fruit." Crates should plainly state count. Yield EP in flesh 52%.

Plums and Prunes

There are over 2000 varieties of plums, which include prunes as a family group. Only a few have commercial importance in this country, however. Plums will appear on the market from May through September, with a peak during July to mid-September. Prunes will appear on the market in July, reach their peak in August and be on the market until October. Plums are grown in the northeastern states, Great Lakes region, Pacific Northwest and California. Imports appear on the market in the winter from Chile and Argentina. The main producing prune areas are Oregon, with its Italian or slightly tart prune, and California, with the French (Imperial) or sweet prune. Most prunes are processed as dried fruit. Plums may have limited use in institutions but they are good as eating-in-hand fruit, in salads and for use in cobblers, pies and other cooked desserts. Market packages are frequently in tills 4 to 6 per crate with a net of 22 to 29 lb containing about 170 to 260 plums, or the Los Angeles lug holding approximately 20 lb net and bushel baskets holding around 56 lb net. Plums and prunes may be classified according to color:

Purple or blue: Italian or French prune; Damson plum.
Red: Clayman, Climax, Hungarian, Santa Rosa and the Beauty (one of the earliest on the market).
Yellow or green: Yellow Egg, Beauty, Wickson, Kelsey, Green Gage.

The largest plum is the Yellow Egg, which may be 2 in. in length. The smallest is the Black Damson, which may be the size of a cherry. The Green Gage plum is a popular variety for canning or for cooked desserts, for it has a fine flavor and a sweet, juicy flesh. Damson plums make excellent jellies.

Mature plums of good quality are plump, firm, full colored for their variety. Color is not necessarily an indication of ripeness but a softening at the end of the tip may be, if the plum is not bruised. Purchase U.S. No. 1 grade. Examine for insect damage and soft, overripe fruit or rot. Yield after pitting and peeling is 85%.

Pomegranates

The pomegranate, known since biblical times, is grown on a bush or small tree. It is about the size of an orange, with a thin skin that is quite leathery. (See Figure 2–36.) Inside is a white pulp in which is encased seeds surrounded by red pulp. This flesh or pulp is sweet in flavor, slightly acid and rich in aroma. The juice is the base for grenadine. It is in season September through December, with a peak in October. Pomegranates are usually marketed in Los Angeles lugs containing 27 to 28 lb net. Select medium to large fruit, colored pink to bright red, with a thin and tough rind. Open and note plumpness of seeds. The seeds should be tender and the flesh should have a rich, full flavor and a good, red color. There are no federal grades. Red pulp yield with seeds is 64% of the fruit and red pulp alone is 56%.

Rhubarb

Although botanically a vegetable, rhubarb is classified with fruits because of its use as a sweetened item much the same as fruit is used. Rhubarb may be field grown or hothouse grown. The latter is usually more delicate and frequently red in color because it is grown at colder temperatures. Cold tends to retard the development of green color in the plant and encourage the development of a red color instead. This red rhubarb is frequently called strawberry rhubarb because of its red color. Hothouse rhubarb appears on the market from the first of January to mid-May. Field rhubarb may appear in April through the summer. Hothouse rhubarb is more slender than the field grown and has an underdeveloped leaf blade. There are a number of varieties.

Most of the rhubarb purchased on the market comes from Michigan or Washington. Michigan hothouse rhubarb usually appears on the market in 5-lb packs, while Washington rhubarb comes in 20-lb lugs. Other states may market in various size containers. Select rhubarb that is fresh, firm, crisp and tender, with good substantial stalks, not weak or shriveled. Note the leaves if still on, since size of leaf will indicate maturity of the stalk. Break or puncture to note stringiness. Purchase U.S. No. 1. Michigan grades are Extra Special Fancy, Extra Fancy and Fancy. Washington grades are Extra Fancy and Fancy. Raw rhubarb without leaves will yield about 86% EP.

FIG. 2–37. The anise bulb only
is cooked and eaten. Courtesy
USDA.

VEGETABLES

Anise

The vegetable anise is a bulb with a flavor resembling a combination of celery and anise seed. It is marketed in stalks in crates containing 2 to 4 dozen stalks holding 70 lb net or wirebound crates holding 2½ to 3 dozen stalks. Other containers may be used. Buyers should purchase by the pound. It is in best supply October through December but appears on the market as early as April.

Specifications should state that bulbs under 2 in. in diameter are not acceptable. Purchase U.S. No. 1. Watch for split bulbs, decay, pithy branches, yellow or brown tops, wilt, disease, insect or mechanical damage. The stalks may be marketed full length or cut back to not less than 10 in. Good quality is indicated by fresh, clean, crisp, solid bulbs and stalks and characteristic color. Anise is sometimes confused with the vegetable sweet fennel, which is eaten in salads or as a boiled vegetable similar to anise. Fennel, however, does not form a bulb.

Artichokes

There are two types of artichokes. The Jerusalem artichoke is a tuber resembling potatoes. It is used grated raw for salads and also as a pickled and cooked item. The other is the globe, a flower bud of a plant belonging to the thistle family. The Jerusalem artichoke is relatively unimportant, but the globe artichoke is marketed in substantial quantities. It is boiled and served cold as a salad or hot as a vegetable. The flavor of the Jerusalem artichoke when cooked resembles that of the heart of the globe artichoke. This heart on the globe and the ends of the leaves are the edible portion. The choke is a covering of tiny, sharp, undeveloped leaves covering the heart.

Quality in the globe artichoke is indicated by compactness of leaves, plumpness, good symmetry and heaviness for size. The color should be a bright, dark green. This color browns with age or injury. Over-maturity is indicated when the artichoke opens and the petals spread with the center becoming fuzzy and a dark-pink or purple color. The sharp point at the tip becomes hard, thorny and projecting.

Globe artichokes are on the market from September to June, with a major peak November to December and a subpeak March into May. Two varieties are marketed, the Italian or long-head variety and the French or the round-head variety. Size is not related to quality. Flats may contain 4 to 10 dozen, with 3 or 4 to the pound preferred for one portion, or about a 6 dozen size per box. Boxes holding about 40 lb net are also marketed holding 48 to 200 artichokes. Watch for worm holes or rot at the base. Purchase U.S. No. 1. Yield in pulp after cooking is 48%.

FIG. 2–38. The globe artichoke. Slight spread of leaves indicates overmaturity. Select those that are tight and compact with a bright green, fresh color. Courtesy W. Atlee Burpee Co.

FIG. 2–39. Asparagus shoots should be cut a few inches below the surface to obtain some of the white woody portion, which helps to retain quality in passing through market channels. Courtesy USDA.

Asparagus

Fresh asparagus is on the market from early March through June, with California marketing a second crop in October and November. Select green asparagus with about 2 in. of white, woody portion. This white portion draws moisture from wet moss on the bottom of the crate and holds quality.

The color should be bright green and the grass should be fresh appearing and firm, with close, compact tips. It should snap or break with ease at or slightly above the white, woody portion. Avoid too much white, woody stem, and specify minimum length of stalk at 7½ to 8½ in. and never over 10½ in. Wiry, tough asparagus will have a dull, dried, shriveled look, with dark color and open tips. Some varieties when young have purplish tips. Some white or bleached asparagus may be obtained fresh.

The asparagus may be bunched in 1, 2 or 2½-lb bunches or packed without bunching. Much western asparagus is placed in pyramidal crates with two compartments, each holding six 2 or 2½-lb bunches. Other areas may market in a variety of containers. Vacuum cooling has been found to give a higher quality asparagus than other methods of cooling before shipment. Federal grades are not generally used. The State of Washington's No. 1 grade is the equivalent of U.S. No. 1. The Washington grades are used more commonly than the federal grades.

Asparagus may be field run (all sizes) or may be sized. Considerable confusion exists on sizes. Various market sizes are shown in Table 2–12.

Size is not a criterion of quality, but U.S. No. 1 asparagus should not be less than ½ in. in diameter, with ⅔ of the stalk green. Store at 32° F at 85 to 90% relative humidity. Asparagus is highly perishable and

Table 2–12
Some Market Sizes of Fresh Asparagus

Diameter Size in 16's Inch	Number Spears per Pound	Market Grade Terms			
		Federal	New Jersey	California	Imperial Valley
14 or over	7 to 8	Very large	Colossal	Colossal	Mammoth
12 to 14	8 to 9	Very large	Jumbo	Jumbo	Giant
11 to 12	about 9	Large	Extra Select	Extra Select	Fancy Regal
8 to 11	9 to 10	Medium	Extra Fancy	Select	Regal
5 to 8	11 to 12	Small	Fancy	Extra Fancy	Fancy Standard
less than 5*	12 or more	Very small	Prime	Fancy	Standard

*Also called Pencil Grass on some markets.

should be used soon after delivery. Yield is 56% EP. Do not remove butt ends until ready to use or shortly before.

Beans, Lima

There are three types of lima beans on the market: the Fordhook or butter bean, the Potato or Baby, and the Fava or Faba. The last is relatively new on our markets. It is also known as the English or Windsor broad bean.

Most limas are shipped in 1-bu hampers or 1-bu baskets holding 32 lb net. Some may be found also in 16 and 24-qt splint baskets. The pods should be well filled and have a bright, fresh, good green color. The beans should be well defined but not bulging in the pod, and the pod should be crisp, not dry and loose around the beans. Watch for rot or mold.

Shelled beans should be plump, with tender skins of a light, whitish-green color. Watch for hard, tough skins and insect injury; test for tenderness by puncturing the skin. Watch for souring, rot or mold. Because lima beans are highly perishable and because of labor in shelling, fresh limas are not usually purchased for institutional use. Purchase

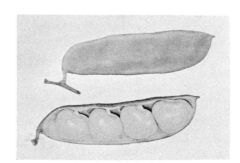

FIG. 2–40. Well-filled lima bean pods should be one of the major selection criterion. Courtesy USDA.

U.S. No. 1.   Loss in snelling is 61%.   California is the biggest producer
and ships all year, but the peak crop appears on the market from August
to September.

Beans, Snap or Common (Green or Wax)

Snap beans are usually stringless, although some varieties may have
strings until maturity.   There are many different varieties, both in the
green and wax types.

Select beans that have a fresh, bright appearance and velvety touch.
They should snap with a distinct, clean break without strings.   The texture of the flesh should be fine and lack fiber in the walls.   All beans of
a lot should be of the same maturity and be full size and plump.   Few
beans should have tails or be misshapen.   Length is not important to
quality.   Reject beans having a dull, dead or wilted appearance or
that are tough, woody or stringy.   Purchase U.S. Fancy but U.S. No. 1
may be acceptable at season peaks.   State condition upon delivery shall
meet the grade specified.   Beans are marketed in bushel containers

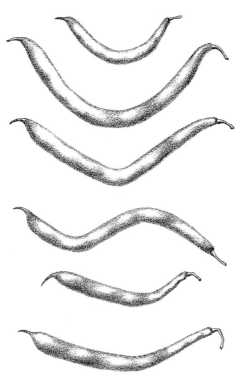

FIG. 2–41.   Lower limits of fairly
well-formed string beans permitted
in U.S. No. 1 grade.   Courtesy
USDA.

holding about 30 lb net. Some 16 to 24-qt splint baskets are also used. All packs should be tightly filled with solid, rounded tops. Trimming waste is 12%.

Beets

Beets are available all during the year. The winter supply is shipped from Texas and California or comes from storage stocks. Early beets are frequently marketed bunched, with 3 to 5 beets per bunch. The bunch should weigh around 1¼ lb. Crates holding 5 dozen bunches or about 75 lb net are used, or bushel baskets or hampers are used. Late beets are usually marketed topped. Topped beets should have not more than 2 in. of stems, although some early beets may be acceptable with 4 to 6 in. stems. Topped beets are usually marketed in bushel baskets or 50- or 100-lb bags. Specify beets with short trim; that is, 2 in. or less of

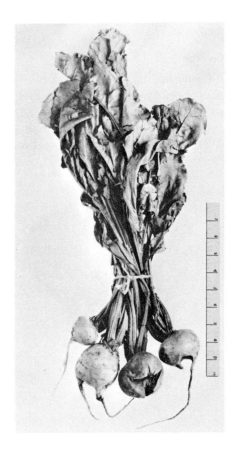

FIG. 2-42. Split growth cracks - on beets will lower grade. Courtesy USDA.

stems. Some stem is desirable to prevent bleeding in cooking. Market
sizes are:

Bunched		Topped	
Small	less than 2 in. diameter	Small	less than 2 in. diameter
Medium	2 to 3 in. diameter	Medium	2 to 3½ in. diameter
Large	3 in. or more diameter	Large	3½ in. or more diameter

Beets that are rough or ridged, or that have deep growth cracks, are
wasteful and may be tough and woody. A short neck covered with deep
scars or by several circles or leaf scars around the top indicates age. Cut
beets with a knife. Pronounced ridges inside and a grating sound in
cutting indicate toughness. Beets that are soft, flabby or shriveled are
lacking in quality. Note freshness of leaves, although sometimes wilted
leaves do not indicate poor quality of the beet. Purchase U.S. No. 1.
Waste from AP to EP cooked is: with tops, 60%; part tops, 51%; and no
tops, 24%. If the quality of the greens is good, the greens may also be
used.

Broccoli

California is a big shipper of broccoli all year around. Heaviest supplies appear October to April. Much of the fresh crop for institutional
use is frozen.

Quality in fresh broccoli is indicated by a fresh, clean, deep-green
color and compact buds. Some broccoli may be slightly purple when

FIG. 2–43. U.S. Fancy bunch of
Italian sprouting broccoli. Note
tightness of buds indicating
quality. Courtesy USDA.

FIG. 2–44. Broccoli that has a "ricey" appearance indicates some maturity. Courtesy USDA.

quite young. U.S. Fancy broccoli should be bunched in 2 or 2½-lb bunches and have stalks not less than 2¼ in. in diameter and length not more than 8½ in. nor less than 8 in. Diameter is measured at the base of the stalk. Watch thick stalks and test by puncturing to see if tender. There are no diameter requirements for U.S. No. 1, but lengths shall not be less than 5 in. and not more than 9 in. A compactness is required in this grade. Some eastern broccoli appears on the market in 1½-lb bunches. Packaging is usually in crates holding 14, 18 or 28 bunches. They run around 42 lb net. Bushel baskets or hampers may contain 14 bunches on the average and hold around 25 lb net. Wilted, flabby broccoli with yellow leaves should be rejected. Opening of the buds or the development of yellow in them indicate overmaturity. Trimming of the base should be even and excess leaves should be removed. Watch for cabbage worms and gray plant lice. Shake broccoli to see if the buds are firmly attached. Yield from AP to AS is 60%.

A heading broccoli different from the more common Italian sprouting variety is sold on the market as cauliflower.

Brussels Sprouts

California and New York's Long Island are the heaviest shippers of Brussels sprouts. They are on the market August through March, with peak months October through January. Quality is indicated by a hard, compact, fresh, bright appearance and good, cabbage-green color. Yellowed or wilted leaves indicate age. A smudgy, dirty appearance under the outer leaves may indicate plant lice. Watch for worm damage. Western sprouts usually appear in 25-lb drums and some pliofilm bag packs are becoming more common. Eastern sprouts are usually sold in bushel or half-bushel baskets holding, respectively, 48

FIG. 2–45. Brussels Sprouts. The small clusters or heads on the stem are harvested. Courtesy USDA.

and 24 lb net. Look for well-trimmed, solid, not burst heads. The base should be free from rot or damage. Uniform, even heads and fill equal to facing should be specified. Specify U.S. No. 1 with diameters not less than $\frac{3}{4}$ in. and length not more than 2 in.

Cabbage

Heavy supplies of Early cabbage appear on the market from December to May. This cabbage has a pointed and not too tightly packed head. It has a conical-shaped head and comparatively smooth leaves. The color is soft green. The Domestic cabbage comes to market about the end of the Early cabbage season. It is identified by flatness at the top, moderately green color and smooth, round heads that are firm and tightly formed. The leaves are brittle and crisp. It is on the market until fall. The Domestic and Early cabbages are not good keepers.

The Danish cabbage is a good late variety that keeps well in storage and ships well. It has a smooth, round, very hard, compact head. The color is almost white and the leaves are tightly wrapped. Savoy cabbage is on the market October through December. It has crinkled leaves, with heads loosely formed and usually flattened. The color is yellowish-green. Red cabbage has a pointed head and is purple-red in color. This cabbage is usually smaller than the white varieties. Chinese cabbage or celery has a long tapering head with crinkly leaf ends on a

FIG. 2–46. Comparison of Danish (left) and Domestic (right) cabbage. Note smooth, circular outline of Danish head and the irregular, angular outline of the Domestic head. Courtesy USDA.

solid core. It is about 4 in. thick and 18 to 20 in. long. It is used mostly as a salad green.

Cabbage is marketed in many containers and buyers should purchase by the pound. A struck-full bushel will weigh around 40 lb net. Cabbage is frequently sold in mesh sacks weighing 50 lb net. The size of cabbage may be described as small, medium and large. For Early cab-

FIG. 2–47. Chinese or Michikli cabbage. Courtesy W. Atlee Burpee Co.

FIG. 2–48. Well-trimmed and poorly trimmed heads are illustrated here. Courtesy USDA.

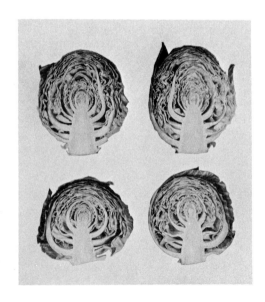

FIG. 2–49. Lower limit of reasonable solidity for U.S. No. 1 Domestic cabbage. To be of U.S. No. 1 Grade, heads shall be at least fairly firm. Courtesy USDA.

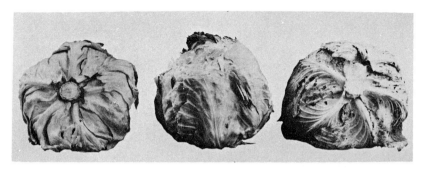

FIG. 2–50. Head on left is overripe, as indicated by base leaves separating from stem. Center head shows seed stem breaking through crown. Where this breaking does not occur, a bulge with excessive hardness may indicate seed stem buried in head. The head on the right shows bad worm injury. None of these heads are U.S. No. 1. Courtesy USDA.

bage, this means, respectively, under 1½ lb, 1½ to 3 lb (best institutional size), and over 3 lb, and for Domestic and Danish, respectively, under 2 lb, 2 to 5 lb (best institutional size), and over 5 lb. Trimming in Early and Domestic cabbage will not be as close as in the late varieties, and close trimming must be given the latter to meet top grades.

Watch for worms, decay, yellowing of leaves and broken or burst heads. Rub across the stem end to see if dry. Look for crispness in leaves. The head should be heavy for its size and solid for the variety. The color should be typical also for the variety. Yellow or wilted leaves indicate age. Look for seed stems inside the head. These can be detected by pressing on the head and feeling a hard, resistant core inside. Burst heads should be rejected. Note also broken sections around the base of the stem. Excessive softness indicates poor quality and high waste. Purchase U.S. No. 1. Waste in trimming and removing core is 20% except for Chinese Cabbage, which will be 38%.

Carrots

Carrots are in good supply during every month of the year. Because of the increased supply of fresh winter carrots, carrots stored in the fall and held for winter use are being used less and less. Early carrots do not keep well since they are not mature, but they have better flavor and are crisper than late carrots.

Like beets, carrots are marketed with tops, short-trim tops or well-trimmed tops. Institutions should purchase carrots with tops cut back less than 1 in. Federal standards state that well-trimmed carrots should have stems not over 1 in. long, short-trim not over 4 in. long, and carrots

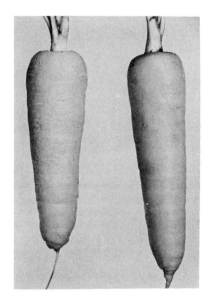

FIG. 2–51. Select blunt, full carrots that will have low peeling loss, as indicated in these carrots. Courtesy W. Atlee Burpee Co.

with tops may have tops 12 to 20 in. long. "Snap top" means broken off close to the carrot. "Clip top" means 2 to 3 in. of stem left on the top. These two latter terms are not in the federal standards. Carrots should not be less than 3 in. in length and of the blunt-end type, not tapering since these will have a high peeling waste.

FIG. 2–52. Minimum permissible shapes in U.S. No. 1 carrots. Courtesy USDA.

Diameters should not be less than ¾ in. nor more than 2 in. at the widest end, and carrots should be all nearly of the same diameter. Carrots will be found on the market in 25, 50 and 100-lb bags and bushel baskets holding approximately 50 lb net of topped carrots. Crates holding around 55 to 60 lb of topped carrots may also be found.

Watch the color of carrots. California, Arizona and Texas carrots, which are sweeter than many locally grown varieties, are light in color. Watch for flabby, wilted, soft or shriveled carrots. Excessively thick masses of leaf stem at the top indicates large cores or hearts and toughness. Freshness of appearance, smoothness and good shape should be sought. The carrots should break with a crisp snap when bent. Loss in paring will be: with tops, 41%; part tops, 28%; no tops, 20%. Purchase U.S. No. 1.

Cauliflower

Heaviest supplies of cauliflower are on the market from October through December, but it is available all during the year on some markets. Whiteness in the flower or head is obtained by tying over the outer leaves to protect the heads from the sun, thus keeping them from turning green. For shipment the leaves should be trimmed down to within 1 to 2 in. from the curd or head.

Size has no relation to quality. Quality is indicated by white or creamy-white, clean, heavy, firm, compact curd, with the jacket (outer leaves) fresh and green. The curd or flower will develop as maturity occurs. Spreading of the curd into a loose mass is called "riciness," "fuzzy," "barber" or "old man" in the trade. Brushing the hand

FIG. 2–53. Grade U.S. No. 1 cauliflower with somewhat enlarged bracts. Courtesy USDA.

FIG. 2–54. An example of a ricey head of cauliflower. This head is graded U.S. No. 2 because of this defect. Courtesy USDA.

roughly over the top will indicate riciness. Higher yields are usually obtained from larger heads. Good, fresh wrapper leaves may be used for chopped greens.

Cauliflower is frequently marketed in western pony crates holding 12 to 15 heads. Net weight is about 42 lb. Age may be indicated by yellow leaves, but, if the head is white and firm, quality is still good. Watch for plant lice, which appear as smudgy, dirty spots on the cauliflower. Spotted, speckled or bruised curds should be rejected. Purchase U.S. No. 1. Waste in trimming and preparation to EP is 65%.

Celery and Celeriac

Most celery marketed today is the green or Pascal type, which has crisp, juicy stalks but heavy strings or midribs. The white or blanched

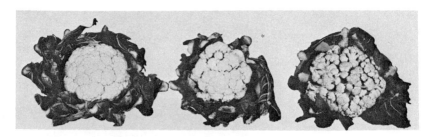

FIG. 2–55. Three stages of maturity in cauliflower found on the market, especially in the later part of the season. The one on the right will be called badly spread, the one in the center, slightly spread and the one on the left, compact. Courtesy USDA.

types (also called yellow or golden celery) are hilled or covered with dirt as the celery grows to bleach the stalk. They are more tender and more delicately flavored than the green types but less in demand. Celery appears on the markets all year but heaviest supplies are November through May.

Clean, brittle stalks with bright green leaves should be selected in the Pascal type. The length should be 16 in. and the stalk should be well trimmed, having good thickness and solidity. The celery should have good heart formation. Stalks should be fairly straight and not twisted. The stalks should be solid and not spongy from pithiness. Twist the stalks or press to note pithiness. The best size for institutional use is 1 to 1¾ lb stalks and the outer whorl of branches should be not less than 6 in., insuring a good stalk. The term *green* in a specification means that

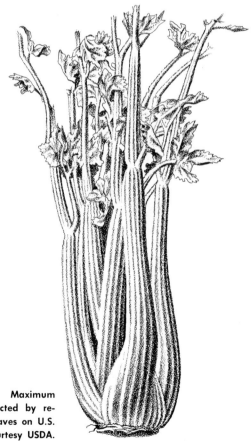

FIG. 2–56. Well-trimmed celery. Maximum extent appearance may be affected by removal of leaves or portions of leaves on U.S. Extra No. 1 and U.S. No. 1. Courtesy USDA.

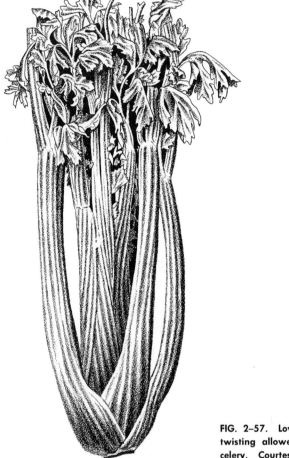

FIG. 2–57. Lower limit of bowing and twisting allowed in U.S. Extra No. 1 celery. Courtesy USDA.

the outer branches should be green to a light-green color. Blackrot can be detected by separating the branches and examining the heart. Look for insect injury or insects. Watch for the formation of seed stems by separating the stalks or branches. Bowing is considered a defect. To ascertain crispness, bend until the celery snaps. Excessive stringiness is a defect. Reject excessively dirty celery. Wilted or yellow leaves indicate age.

Celery is seldom shipped in the rough. It is usually well trimmed or clipped with outer branches removed. Celery is sized, and the number of stalks in the crate or shipping container desired should be indicated. In the standard 16 in celery crate the lowest number of bunches will be one dozen. Sizes of 10 dozen or more to the crate are called "hearts." Institutions find crates containing 2½ to 4 dozen most suitable. The standard crate will contain net from 60 to 65 lb of celery, but many different containers are used, and buyers should ascertain what is on the market to be informed on the quantity they are getting if they purchase celery by the container. Specify U.S. No. 1 for insitutional use. Consumer grades have been developed and U.S. A is the equivalent of U.S. No. 1. The trimming provisions are more stringent in the consumer grades. Waste in untrimmed stalks as purchased normally by institution is 25%.

Celery roots or knobs may be marketed but most of the items called celery root are celeriac, the turnip-rooted celery, which forms a large bulb under the surface. Used for soups and stews, it is seldom eaten raw. The root is 2½ to 4 in. in diameter and is a creamy dark white. It is usually marketed in bushel baskets about 45 to 50 lb net.

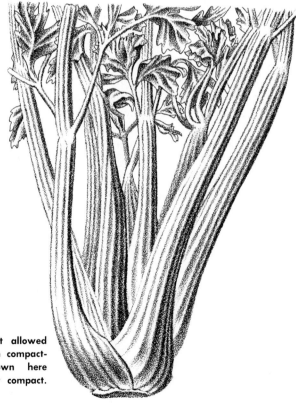

FIG. 2–58. Lower limit allowed in U.S. No. 1 celery in compactness. Condition shown here would be called fairly compact. Courtesy USDA.

Chives

Institutions may purchase chives fresh in bunches but purchase in 1 lb lots frozen is recommended. (See Figure 2–86.)

Corn

Fresh corn is available on the market all during the year but best shipments come to the market from late May to October. California and Florida are the heavy off-season shippers. Long shipment deteriorates quality and 72 hours is considered maximum from harvest to use for acceptable quality, unless refrigerated conditions exist from time of harvest to use. Corn at harvest should have 5 to 6% sugar and 10 to 11% starch. A 2 to 5% loss in sugar can occur in several hours at room temperature.

Shipment is frequently in 50-lb bags holding around 5 dozen ears. A crate holding 5 dozen ears, or 40 to 45 lb net, is also commonly used. A bushel basket of corn weighs about 35 lb and will hold around $3\frac{1}{2}$ to 4 dozen ears. Quality may be indicated by the tassel or silk, which should be brown and silky. A green-colored tassel indicates age. The shuck should be fresh appearing, not dry, and the cob should be free from worms or other damage. The grains should be plump and yield easily to pressure, with milk spouting from the kernels. Watch for ears that are only partially covered. Corn heats rapidly and inspection for rot or fermentation should be made. Use U.S. No. 1 at season's height and specify U.S. Fancy at other times. Specify that sweet corn only, and not field corn, is acceptable. The term "roasting ears" on the market may mean immature varieties of field corn.

Cucumbers

There are two peaks in the cucumber market, the heaviest being August to October, and another April through June. Hothouse cu-

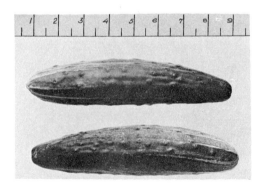

FIG. 2–59. Field-grown cucumbers showing good shapes in this category. Courtesy USDA.

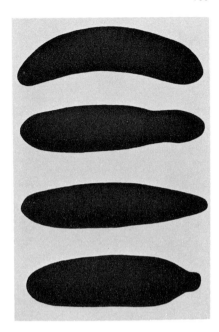

FIG. 2–60. Minimum cucumber shapes permitted in U.S. No. 1 Grade. Courtesy USDA.

cumbers are shipped off season from Indiana, Iowa, Ohio and Michigan. The southern states also market cucumbers during this time. Market containers may vary but most common are bushel baskets, bushel hampers or boxes containing about 2 dozen cucumbers. Fill should be equal to facing in all containers. Quality is indicated by fresh appearance, crispness, good shape, medium size and dark-green color formation over at least $\frac{2}{3}$ of the length. The cucumber should have a shiny, waxy appearance. Withered or shriveled cucumbers have a tough or rubbery flesh and a bitter flavor. Watch for good even shape. Overmaturity is indicated by a dull-green or yellowish-green color, yellow underside and a puffy, soft texture. Seeds should be tender in an almost translucent center that is firm and not jellylike. Decay shows as dark, sunken, irregular areas. A bushel of cucumbers should weigh around 48 lb. Grade and size are correlated. A U.S. Fancy and U.S. No. 1 cucumber must not be more than $2\frac{3}{8}$ in. in diameter and not more than 6 in. in length. Hothouse cucumbers in this grade have no diameter restrictions but may not be less than 5 in. in length. Institutions should specify market type or slicing type cucumbers to avoid obtaining pickling types. Specify U.S. No. 1 large. During off seasons U.S. Fancy may be required.

FIG. 2–61. Quality is indicated in this eggplant by its soft sheen, good appearance and well-filled, plump character. Courtesy W. Atlee Burpee Co.

Eggplant

Mature eggplant of good quality should have diameters of 4 in. or more. The color should be uniformly dark purple. The body must be heavy, plump and free from blemishes. The surface should have a soft, silky sheen. Wilting, shriveling, softness or flabbiness may result from extended holding or immaturity. Watch for worm injury.

Eggplant are on the market all year, with the market peak occurring August through September. They are frequently marketed in bushel baskets weighing 33 lb net. Crates hold 16, 18, 24 and 36 eggplant. The 24 or 30 size, weighing around 1½ lb each, are best for institutions. Specify U.S. No. 1. Eggplant need not be pared for grilling, broiling or deep frying. Paring waste is 20%.

Garlic

U.S. No. 1 garlic should be selected for instituional use. Purchase should be by the pound. Look for well-filled bulbs, heavy for their size. Brown, shriveled or dried bulbs should be rejected. Shake the garlic in the container or bag to hear if there is a dry, rustling sound. The dry rustle should indicate lack of rot. Check to see if the garlic is covered with a dry, outer sheath and if the interior is of good quality.

Garlic may be pink or white. Creole garlic, a white variety is strong in flavor. The Italian variety is pink and has many cloves requiring

more labor to prepare. Tahiti garlic is large, yielding good size cloves.
It will measure 2 to 3 in. in diameter. Specify U.S. No. 1. This grade
has a minimum diameter for each bulb of not less than 1½ in. Purchase by the pound. Preparation to EP in waste is 12%.

Greens, Cooking

There are a number of leaves of plants, which, when cooked are edible
and may be classified under one heading of cooking greens. Freshness
and tenderness are prime quality factors. Immature leaves will be
tender but will lack sufficient body to give good yield and lack adequate
texture to give good eating quality. The leaves should be bright green
without yellowing, wilt, toughness, coarseness, stringiness, or insect or
worm damage. Bruised, broken, or frozen leaves will tarnish quickly.
Slime and mold indicate severe deterioration. Heavy ribbing and seed
stems indicate age. The leaves should be fresh and be sufficiently crisp
to snap when bent. Stalks should be fresh and crisp. Color should be

FIG. 2–62. Well-filled bulbs of Creole-type garlic. Courtesy USDA.

FIG. 2-63. Swiss chard with its outer leaves ready for harvest. These plants average about a foot in height. They should not be coarse and overgrown. Courtesy USDA.

FIG. 2-64. A large, well-developed specimen of the low-growing type collard. Courtesy USDA.

FIG. 2–65. The dandelion is sometimes called "French chicory." It is used raw for a salad green or cooked for boiled greens. Courtesy USDA.

typical for the variety. Watch for grit, dirt, sand and extraneous material. A bushel of greens will weigh 18 to 20 lb net. They are best purchased by the pound.

Beet greens are the tops of young beets. They appear on the market in hampers or bushel baskets. Federal standards for beets may be used if small, tiny beets are desired on the greens. The specifications in this case should state that greens are to be of high quality, not longer than $6\frac{1}{2}$ in. and the beets not over $\frac{5}{8}$ in. in diameter. Peak season is spring and early summer. Specify U.S. No. 1 for beet greens. The waste in preparation to EP is 44%.

Swiss chard comes from a variety of beet grown only for its leaves. Peak season is in the fall and winter but some may be obtained from June to August. Pithiness or toughness can be detected by twisting the stalk. Chard may be shipped in crates, boxes or bushel baskets. There are no federal grades. Waste in trimming to EP is 30%.

Collards are greens closely associated with kale. They have slightly curled leaves lightly folded at the heart. Light supplies are found in

FIG. 2–66. Giant green-curled
Scotch kale. Courtesy W. Atlee
Burpee Co.

the summer and peak quantities in the fall. Best flavor usually develops
after a frost. A type of broccoli is sometimes sold as collards or turnip
greens. Specify U.S. No. 1. Waste in trimming to EP is 23%.

Dandelion greens are on the market most of the year but peak production is in the spring. They may be used also for salad greens. Specify
U.S. No. 1. Waste to EP is 19%.

Kale or borecole is related to the collard and cabbage. There are two
types, the curly or krinkly leaved and the smooth leaved. The latter is
also called spring kale. The curly type may be called Scotch or green,
or Liberian or blue kale. Kale should be purchased washed. Kale may
be purchased whole plant, bunched and stripped. Bronzing or browning caused by cold weather during growing does not harm flavor but

FIG.   2–67.   Dwarf Liberian
kale, a smooth-leaved variety.
Courtesy W. Atlee Burpee Co.

FIG. 2–68. Mustard greens. Courtesy USDA.

does harm appearance. It is usual to pack kale with ice. If purchased by weight, buyers should be sure they are not purchasing ice for the price of kale. Well-packed kale will weigh 20 to 25 lb net per bushel. Specify U.S. No. 1. Waste to EP 30%.

Mustard Greens are especially popular in the South. The young tender leaves may also be used for salad greens. There are several varieties, some of which are smooth leaved while others are curly. Color may range from a light to a dark green. Seed stems indicate age and toughness. Purchase U.S. No. 1. Preparation waste to EP 30%.

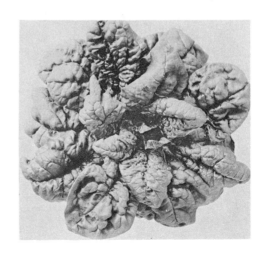

FIG. 2–69. The Savoy-type spinach is a good shipper. The curled leaf prevents packing and heating of the green during shipping and holding on the market. Courtesy W. Atlee Burpee Co.

FIG. 2–70.   Turnip greens.   Either the entire plant or only the shoots are marketed.   As shoots are removed, the plant has a tendency to send up a number of new shoots successively.   Courtesy USDA.

FIG. 2–71.   Sprouting broccoli, a type sold as greens.   It is sometimes confused with turnip greens on the market.   Courtesy USDA.

Spinach is on the market all year but the production peak is March to June. The Savoy variety is almost universally shipped to market because its crinkly leaves make it a good shipper. The smooth-leaved varieties are grown for canning but are highly perishable shipped because they pack and heat in shipment. Sprouts or buds or crowns may indicate poor quality and texture. Select U.S. No. 1 or U.S. Extra No. 1, the latter when quality is low on the market. A consumer U.S. Grade A, equivalent to the U.S. Extra No. 1, exists.

Turnip greens are graded by federal standards under mustard green standards. A broccoli green may sometimes be sold for turnip greens and is a turnip grown for its greens. If turnip greens are sold with the roots, the maximum diameter of the root should be limited to 1½ in. Specify U.S. No. 1.

Greens, Salad

Leaves of plants are also eaten raw as salad greens. Selection should be based on factors similar to those used for cooking greens. Solidity or firmness of head is a factor that is used to judge quality of some. Some plant leaves, such as lettuce, parsley and watercress, may also be used as garnishes. Raw spinach, cabbage, turnip greens and others may also be used for salad purposes.

FIG. 2–72. Chicory may be used for salads or as a cooked green. Courtesy USDA.

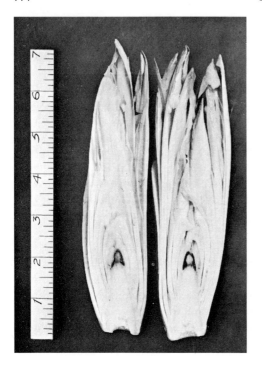

FIG. 2–73. Lengthwise section of chicory, also called Whitloof, or Belgium or French endive. Note discoloration at the heart, possibly caused by rapid growth. Courtesy USDA.

Chicory, endive and escarole are often confused. Chicory is a broad-leaved green with an upright, spreading growth. French or Belgium chicory (also called French or Belgium endive or Witloof chicory) is a solid, small, firm-headed green used for salads. It is usually on the market in the winter months and is not plentiful. It is slightly bitter, like broad-leaved chicory. The leaves of the French or Belgium chicory are tightly folded around a core or heart to form a solid, elongated head or stalk.

Endive is also called curly chicory. It is a flat spreading plant with an almost white heart. The outer areas are green but the spine or center is white. The leaves are narrow, finely divided and curly. The finely curled endive may be 12 to 13 in. in diameter. Some varieties have broad ribs slightly rose-tinged and creamy white at the heart. Varieties include Pancalier, Green Curled Ruffec and the White Curled. It will be found on the market from fall into spring.

Escarole resembles endive or curly chicory. It is a flat, spreading plant with an almost white heart. The spine of the leaf is white and the outer areas of the leaf are green but a deeper green, usually, than endive. The leaf also is broader. Escarole is available almost the year

FIG. 2–74. Heads of curly-leaf endive, sometimes called curly chicory. Courtesy USDA.

around but the peak production occurs in December, about the same time that endive is plentiful on the market.

Federal grades for chicory, endive and escarole are the same. Institutions should select U.S. No. 1. No federal grades exist for French or Belgium endive. Crispness, freshness, cleanliness and bright appearance are selection factors. Toughness or tenderness can be determined by breaking or twisting a leaf. They may be packed in bushel baskets or hampers, crates packed 2, 3, 4 dozen per basket or crate or other

FIG. 2–75. Heads of escarolle showing stem and leaf characteristics. Courtesy USDA.

FIG. 2–76. The Iceberg is a crisp, large head lettuce. Courtesy USDA.

methods of packing may be used.   A western crate holding 2.4 bushel is also found on the market.   A bushel weighs about 25 lb.   Spread to see if white inside.   Select those free of rot and damage and that indicates freshness and tenderness.   Specify U.S. No. 1.   Waste in trimming to EP 25%.   Another chicory is on the market, but this is sold for its roots and is cooked much as turnips, parsnips and other root vegetables.

Lettuce may be of several varieties.   The most popular is the Iceberg or crisp-head lettuce.   Other varieties are the butterhead, bibb, cos or romaine, leaf or bunching and stem.

The Iceberg or crisp-head lettuce is usually a pointed-head variety if grown in the East, and a round, more firm head if grown in the West. The outer leaves should be pale, with the interior crisp, white and tender.   Peak production is May through July, but the lettuce is in good supply throughout the year on most markets.   Weather may at times slow supply.   California's Salinas Valley, the biggest producing area in this country, ships heavily May through October.   California's Imperial

FIG. 2–77. Typical head of Big Boston or Butterhead lettuce. The heads are less solid than Iceberg lettuce, and the leaf is somewhat silky, soft and not crisp.   Courtesy USDA.

FIG. 2–78. A Boston lettuce variety called White Boston lettuce. Courtesy W. Atlee Burpee Co.

Valley will generally have heavy shipments December through April. Other southern California areas ship in the winter and spring. Arizona's Salt River area ships December through March and in the Yuma area, fall, winter and spring. Texas ships from the Herford (Yvalde) area September through October and the Lower Rio Grande area ships December through February. Many other areas come into production in the early summer, summer and fall. Iceberg lettuce is an excellent shipper and a good keeper. With vacuum cooling icing has been discontinued for shipment, and the lettuce now is more closely trimmed and placed into fiberboard cartons 2 to $2\frac{1}{2}$ dozen heads per carton, vacuum cooled and shipped in refrigerated cars. Number of small heads per carton may be as high as 5 dozen.

The Boston or Butterhead lettuce is a softer headed variety, with leaves of fine, soft texture, oily to touch and very tender. 'It is greener than Iceberg lettuce, with a yellow-whitish inner leaf. Bibb or Limestone lettuce is a butterhead type lettuce. The head is cup shaped, small headed, about twice the size of a tulip. It has a deep, rich, green outer leaf that blends into white at the core. It is crisper than the larger Butterhead lettuce.

FIG. 2–79. Burpeeana lettuce, a smooth, soft-textured lettuce, a variety related to the Boston-type lettuce. Courtesy W. Atlee Burpee Co.

FIG. 2–80. Leaf lettuce. This particular variety is called Salad Bowl lettuce. It ships better than smooth-leaved varieties of leaf lettuce. Courtesy W. Atlee Burpee Co.

Leaf or garden lettuce is not headed but frequently comes cut in bunches with the main stem attached or just leafed. The leaf is curled or smooth, depending upon the variety, and the color may be a pale green or a leaf touched with rusted red. It is not as durable as the head lettuce and cannot be shipped great distances. It is on the market in fairly plentiful supply as hothouse lettuce in the winter and from local sources in the summer.

Stem lettuce is grown for its stems and not for the leaves. The stems are eaten raw or cooked.

Cos or Rómaine is a cylindrical, elongated-headed lettuce with a coarse, stiff leaf. It has a slightly stronger flavor than Iceberg lettuce but is somewhat sweeter. It is quite crisp and will be almost completely green throughout. Romaine is shipped in $\frac{2}{3}$ crates from California and this container holds 2 dozen heads or approximately a bushel.

Bibb and leaf lettuce from Michigan appear on the markets in 24-qt basket crates (about 10 lb net) or 12-qt basket crates holding half that quantity. Much eastern lettuce appears in crates holding 18 to 24 heads. Boston or Bibb lettuce is packed in 1 and $1\frac{1}{2}$ bushel hampers or in crates holding 18 to 36 heads. A 4 dozen pack in a standard crate should be packed 4 to a row, 12 to a layer, 4 layers deep. A standard crate contains about 45 lb of lettuce net.

Look for rot, decay, tip burn, ragged leaves or excess wrapper leaves, and a small head. The color should be bright and fresh. The greens should be clean. Seed stems developing in the head can be distinguished in solid heads by pressing down and feeling the hard core inside.

FIG. 2–81. Stem lettuce is grown only for its stem, which is cooked and eaten. Courtesy USDA.

Sometimes soft rot that penetrates the interior of the head is found. A distinct reddish tinge or rust appearing on the broken surface indicates age, but vacuum cooling is rapidly eliminating this defect. The butt or stem end should be small and light in color, either white or a light pink. Deep red indicates age and bitterness. Watch for aphis, freezing and

FIG. 2–82. Untrimmed Cos or Romaine lettuce. This particular variety is called Paris White. Courtesy W. Atlee Burpee Co.

FIG. 2–83.   Well-trimmed heads of dark green Romaine, a Cos variety of lettuce.   Courtesy USDA.

sun burn.   Purchase U.S. No. 1 for headed lettuce and U.S. Fancy for greenhouse leaf lettuce.   When the term "fairly well headed" is used in specifications for romaine it means that four or more inner leaves overlap each other at the top of the plant.   "Well trimmed" with all types of lettuce means that there are no more than 3 wrapper leaves, none of which are excessively large and coarse.   If lettuce is to be used for lettuce cups, do not select too firm heads or use leaf lettuce.   Endive (curly chicory) and escarole also make good underliners for salads when lettuce is high in price in the winter time.   Trimming waste varies for different types but a general average to EP would be around 30%.

Watercress is used for a garnish as well as for salad greens.   It is available all the year but peak production occurs May through July. Select fresh, bright, green, crisp and clean cress.   Watch for worms and insects, yellowing of leaves or wilting.   A bunch usually weighs 3 to 5 oz.   A large bunch may weigh 2½ lb.   Watercress is frequently found on the market in 10-dozen bunches to the box, containing about 30 lb net of watercress.   Barrels of cress may be shipped holding 25- to 30-dozen large bunches.   There are no federal standards.   Loss in preparation to EP 8%.

Kohlrabi (Cabbage Turnip)

Kohlrabi is related to the cabbage family but the bulb is a swollen stem that grows above the ground.   This bulb resembles a turnip.   The name "kohlrabi" means "delicate cabbage turnip."   The color may vary from that of purplish white, as in a turnip, to white and light green. The former, called the Purple Vienna, are most often seen on the market. The tops or leaves may be used as greens if they are fresh, green and tender. Bulbs about 2 in. in diameter are preferred, and specifications should state bulbs over 3 in. in diameter are not acceptable. The condition of the tops is an indication of the condition of the bulb. Most on the market are topped, however. The stem should be crisp and firm. Cut and note any stringiness or woodiness in the bulb. They are usually sold by the pound or in bushel baskets or hampers. There are no U.S. grades. They are on the market May through November, with peak production June and July. Waste to EP after paring 45%.

Leeks

Leeks resemble green onions in appearance but they are larger. They also have flat leaves. They do not form enlarged bulbs on the end but like shallots, have a straight end with little or no rounded bulb development. (See Figure 2-86). Buyers should look for fresh green tops and medium-sized necks. The bulb and top should be young, crisp and tender. A white color should appear up to 2 to 3 in. from the root.

FIG. 2-84. Early purple Vienna kohlrabi. Courtesy W. Atlee Burpee Co.

Specify bulbs not under ¾ in. in diameter.   If bruised, wilted, yellowed or otherwise damaged, flabby, tough, or fibrous, the leeks will lack quality.   Puncture with a thumbnail to ascertain tenderness.   Watch for silt and grit.   They are on the market the year around but the peak is September through November.   They are bunched usually 12 to 25 leeks to a bunch.   Market containers are bushel baskets or hampers.   A bushel weighs around 24 to 30 lb.   There are no federal grades.   Preparation waste to EP 48%.

Mushrooms

Mushrooms are usually sold by the pound or in 2-qt baskets for the institutional trade.   The caps should be white and firm and be closed at the stem, with the veil joining the cap unbroken, leaving the gills unexposed.   Stems should be properly trimmed and should not exceed $1\frac{1}{4}$ in. in length.   Sizes for caps may be used as follows:

Small	under 1″ in diameter
Medium	1″ to $1\frac{5}{8}$″ in diameter
Large	$1\frac{5}{8}$″ to 3″ in diameter
Extra large	over 3″ in diameter.

Watch for misshapen, dark mushrooms, bruising, mold or other defects. The cut surface of the stems should be white or delicately pink, not dark or black, which would indicate age.   The peak of the season is November through December, with a low point in August, but mushrooms are usually available all year around.   Select U.S. No. 1.   There are about 20 to 30 medium-sized mushrooms to a pound.   Waste in trimming to EP unpeeled 9%.

Okra (Gumbo)

Green and white okra is on the market but the green is much more common.   There are long and short varieties.   Okra is available on the market all year but the peak harvest is July through October.   Cuban imports start in November.   California also furnishes some okra in off seasons.

Select pods 2 to $3\frac{1}{2}$ in. long.   Look for tender, crisp pods with soft, white seeds.   A woody pod with hardened seeds indicates over-maturity. Dull, dry or shriveled pods are apt to be tough.   Misshapen pods, damage or decay should be cause for rejection.   Watch for dirty pods, foreign matter, disease, insects or mechanical damage.   About thirty-five 3 in. pods make a lb.   Okra or gumbo is marketed in hampers, in 6-basket crates, bushel and half-bushel baskets and tills.   Specify U.S. No. 1.   Waste in preparation to EP, 22%.   Frozen okra is rapidly replacing fresh okra for institutional use.

FIG. 2–85. Okra. This variety
is called the Patomas Flats and is
a dwarfed, short-pod type. Courtesy USDA.

Onions

Purchase criteria for onions should be divided between those for green
or immature onions and shallots and between dry or mature onions.

Green onions and shallots. Green onions are sold in bunches, with the
green leaves attached to the undeveloped bulb. Onions may be differentiated from shallots by noting the bulb end. Onions will have only
slightly rounding or bulb formation in the top grades and considerably
more in the lower grades. A scallion is a very young green onion, so
young that it shows no bulb development. Shallots are similar to green
onions except they do not develop enlarged bulbs. They also grow in
oblong clusters and not individually as do onions.

In all these, look for fresh, green tops and medium-sized necks. Two
to 3 inches of the root should be clean, clear white, full, plump and
tender. Crispness and tenderness can be ascertained by twisting and
puncturing with a thumbnail. Yellow, bruised or wilted leaves are apt
to indicate deterioration. Some green onions and shallots appear on the

FIG. 2–86.   Leeks, onions, chives and shallots shown from left to right.   Courtesy USDA.

market with trimmed tops.   The term "clipped tops" in a specification means all onions or shallots are clipped back evenly.

Onions and shallots are frequently sold in massed bunches of 20 to 48 small bunches to one large bunch or in crates holding bunches of 6 individual bunches each, with each individual bunch containing 10 to 12 onions or shallots.   Normally, 12 bunches of shallots or young onions should weigh 4 lb or over.   U.S. No. 1 green onion standards state that the overall length of unclipped bunches shall not be over 24 in. nor under 8 in. and not less than $\frac{1}{4}$ in. nor over 1 in. in diameter.   The terms small, medium and large for green onions indicate, respectively, less than $\frac{1}{2}$ in. in diameter, $\frac{1}{2}$ to 1 in. in diameter and over 1 in. in diameter.   Onions and shallots are available the year around but peak production appears on the market May through August.   Waste to EP is 65%.

Dry onions.   Dry onions are our fifth largest vegetable crop.   New York, Michigan, Utah, Texas, California, Idaho and Washington are heavy producers.   There are a number of different varieties and buyers should learn to classify them according to use.   There are the mild flavored, called the early onion, and the more pungently flavored varieties called the Northern or late onion.

The early varieties are the Bermuda onions and the Spanish.   The latter is also called the Sweet Spanish or Valencia onion.   The Bermuda onion is a flat onion about 2½ to 2¾ in. in diameter, appearing on the market from March to June.   It is not a good keeper.   There are white, yellow and red varieties.

Creole onions are more pungent and have considerable use in the South.   The yellow varieties in cooking have some tendency to turn slightly pink and this is cause for downgrading as a defect.   The red variety is most commonly seen on the market.   They are good keepers.

The Sweet Spanish onion is large, mild and sweet.   There are yellow

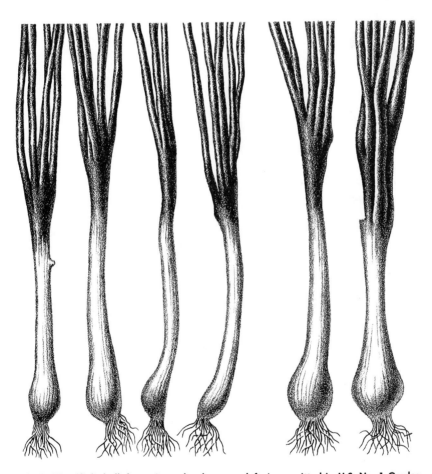

FIG. 2–87.   Slight bulb formation only, shown on left, is permitted in U.S. No. 1 Grades for green onions.   Bulb formation called not excessive permitted in U.S. No. 2 Grade is shown on right.   Courtesy USDA.

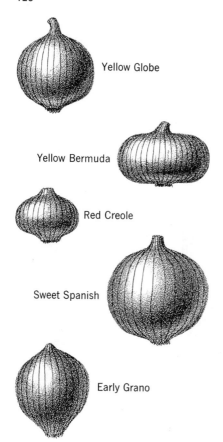

Yellow Globe

Yellow Bermuda

Red Creole

Sweet Spanish

Early Grano

FIG. 2–88. Outlines of some of the most commercially important onions on the market. Optimum shape is shown.

and white varieties. This onion does not keep well. It is a round to slightly oval onion and comes onto the market from irrigated areas in the West and from the South in winter. The Early Grano or Babosa is a yellow onion, mild in flavor, a poor keeper and fairly new on the market. It has a pear-shaped bulb and is a fairly large onion.

The Globe onion is also called the Northern onion or the Domestic onion. It is the most commercially important onion of the group. The yellow globe is most common but there are red, white and brown varieties. The white varieties are considered the most mild. Globes are excellent keepers and furnish a large part of the winter supply. They are strong in flavor. The Australian Brown, a very strong onion but good keeper, and the Ebenezer, a strong, early onion, also a good keeper, are seen on the markets from time to time. There are also hybrids. Some dry mature shallots appear on the market.

FIG. 2–89. The Excel onion, a new Bermuda-onion type. Courtesy USDA.

Onions are on the market all year but there are three peak periods. The first crop comes onto the market in April and May, an intermediate crop appears from June to July and the late crop from August to March. Winter stocks come mainly from storage supplies. About 75% of the total onion crop is marketed in the last period.

Dry onions should be bright, clean, hard, well shaped, with dry skins. When shaken they should give a dry rattle. Look for rot or decay. Interior decay can be detected by noting moist stems at the neck. Seed

FIG. 2–90. The sweet Spanish onion. Courtesy W. Atlee Burpee Co.

FIG. 2–91. The Grano onion, a hybrid fast becoming a leader on commercial markets. Courtesy W. Atlee Burpee Co.

stems or coarse interiors resulting from seed stem growth cause high waste. These seed stem onions are called "seeders" in the trade. Watch for thrips, molds and fungus growths.

Specifications for onions should state size of onion desired. Small onions may be desirable for creaming or pickling; the White Portugal (globe) is suitable for this purpose since it seldom exceeds 1 in. in diameter. Small Bermudas, Globes and Creoles may also be purchased for boilers. Large Bermudas, Sweet Spanish and Early Granos are best for slicing for sandwiches and salads, and medium sizes are best for chopping. There are no market terms used to indicate size, but federal standards U.S. No. 1 for Northern or Globe onions have a minimum size of $1\frac{1}{2}$ in. in diameter with a requirement that 40 to 60%, depending upon type of globe, must be over 2 in. in diameter. U.S. No. 2 standards for these onions hold to a $1\frac{1}{2}$ in. minimum size. This grade may have splits and other deformities and may not be suitable for use unless used for chopping. U.S. No. 1 boilers must be not less than 1 in. in diameter nor over $1\frac{7}{8}$ in. The standards for Creole onions state that U.S. No. 1's shall be not less than $1\frac{3}{4}$ in. in diameter and No. 2's shall be not less than $1\frac{1}{2}$ in. in diameter. Bermuda onions have no minimum or maximum sizes, but buyers can designate size by using the terms *small*, *medium* or *large*, which should be taken to mean, respectively, 1 to 2 in. (boilers) in diameter, 2 to $3\frac{1}{2}$ in. in diameter, and 2 in. minimum, with more than 10% above $3\frac{1}{2}$ in.

Dry onions are sold in open mesh bags containing either 25, 50 or 100

FIG. 2–92. Well-shaped, clean
parsnips grading U.S. No. 1.
Courtesy W. Atlee Burpee Co.

lb. Some onions appear in 50-lb crates. Bushel baskets of onions hold 56 lb. Waste to EP 10%.

Parsley

There are two types of leaf parsley, the moss or curly leaf and the plain leaved. The curly leaf is popular for use as a garniture. Parsley may also be used as a salad green and as a seasoning agent in cooked items. Parsley should be bright, green, fresh, free from dirt and yellowed leaves. Watch for wilting, rot or bruising. A delicate fragrance should be evident in good parsley. Dark green or browned parsley indicates overmaturity and strong flavor. A bunch equals about 2 oz. U.S. No. 1 is the only grade. Parsley is frequently sold on the market packed 4 dozen bunches to a crate. A Hamburg parsley may be encountered by buyers. This is a root vegetable, resembling a parsnip.

Parsnips

Parsnips are sweetest and best when left in the ground until after several hard frosts. Holding two weeks around freezing temperatures

FIG. 2–93. Minimum shapes permissible in U.S. No. 1 Grade parsnips. Courtesy USDA.

FIG. 2–94.   Minimum shapes permissible in U.S. No. 2 Grade parsnips.   Courtesy USDA.

also develops a high sugar content.   Peak supplies are on the market October through January; very few are found May through July.

Select roots that are smooth, firm, small-to-medium size, with good, typical shape and a clear, creamy color.   Softness may indicate decay and flabbiness, or shriveling will indicate poor quality.   Watch for pithy or fibrous roots.   Large parsnips are apt to have woody cores.   Reject those that are misshapen.   The root should be straight.   Four medium-sized parsnips equal a pound.   Select U.S. No. 1.   Parsnips are marketed in bags, sacks or bushel baskets.

Peas

Fresh peas have been largely replaced by frozen peas in institutional use.   Select U.S. No. 1. fresh peas.

Since peas can lose quality rapidly, watch for freshness, crispness and good color.   The pods should be full, with sweet peas inside.   Puncture the pod and the peas with the thumbnail to test for tenderness.   The pods turn yellowish with age.

A special type of pea that is cooked with the pods is grown.   These should be picked before the peas develop, not as done with shelled peas.   While they have always been popular with the Chinese, they are growing in popularity for institutional use.

Southern black-eyed peas may also be purchased in the pod.   Selection should be based on purchasing characteristics used for green peas.

Fresh green peas may be purchased during the entire year but the peak of production occurs May through August.   Green peas are marketed in 1-bu tub baskets holding about 28 to 30 lb net.   Loss in shelling is around 60%.

Green Peppers (Sweet)

Two sweet peppers are found on the market, the bell and the bull-nose. The hot-type peppers are not in the sweet pepper group. Peak production is July through October, but peppers may be obtained throughout the year, although the price varies considerably. Some institutions split peppers, take out the core and seeds, blanch and freeze. They find it pays when peppers may be purchased for $1.00 a bushel in August or September, compared with $12.00 a bushel in January.

Peppers should be a clear, bright green, although some bronze-red or red color may appear as they mature. This reddening of color does not indicate a change to a hot flavor as it does in some of the hot-pepper varieties. Immature peppers should be soft, pliable, good shaped, thin fleshed, and possess a good green color and a soft, waxy sheen. Soft, underdeveloped white seeds indicate proper maturity. Crispness and tenderness may be indicated by pressing with the thumbnail. Shriveling or softness may indicate age or that the peppers were harvested while immature. Watch for deformities or defects. A bleached, discolored area that appears sunken or resembles a water-soaked blister indicates decay. Watch fill of containers; fill should be equal to facing.

Peppers are marketed in bushel baskets and Florida pepper crates, or a variety of containers may appear with locally grown produce. A bushel holds net around 25 lb of peppers and the Florida pepper crate approximately 34 lb. Lack of fill or loose pack, however, may cause a bushel of peppers to weight only 18 lb. California ships some peppers in a Sturdee crate holding about 42 lb net of peppers.

Federal standards state that fancy peppers should have a minimum

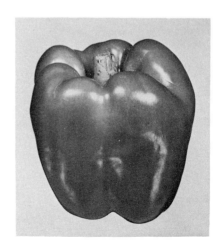

FIG. 2–95. The bull-nose green pepper. Note high, lively sheen, indicating good quality. Courtesy W. Atlee Burpee Co.

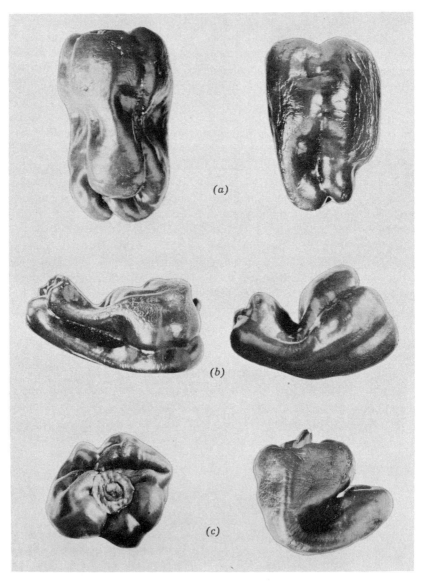

FIG. 2-96. (a) Well-shaped, (b) fairly well-shaped and (c) badly misshapen peppers. Courtesy USDA.

FIG. 2–97. The Katahdin, a large, short, medium-thick potato with shallow eyes, is grown largely in Maine, Long Island and the East. Courtesy W. Atlee Burpee Co.

diameter of 3 in. and 3½ in. length, and No. 1 peppers a minimum of 2½ in. diameter and 2½ in. length. The shape of the pepper affects its grade. Purchase U.S. No. 1 in seasons of good supply and U.S. Fancy when it is difficult to obtain good quality No. 1 peppers. Waste in preparing to EP is 18%.

Potatoes, Irish (White)

The largest vegetable crop of this country is the Irish potato. California, Idaho, Washington, Maine and New York are the main producing states, but many other areas are also of commercial importance.

FIG. 2–98. The Russet Burbank, a large, long, oval potato, heavily netted with numerous shallow eyes. Grown largely in Idaho, Washington and other western states. Courtesy USDA.

FIG. 2–99. The Red Pontiac, a large, oblong to round potato, which may have either a smooth or sometimes netted skin. This potato has medium-deep eyes and will be red or reddish in color. Courtesy USDA.

There are nine leading varieties, the Katahdin, Russet Burbank, Red Pontiac, Irish Cobbler, White Rose, Kennebec, Chippewa, Triumph and Sebago. There are other varieties of local importance. The Katahdin and Kennebec potatoes are produced heavily in the East, the Russet Burbanks and White Rose in the West and the other varieties are found in quantity in the central states. Potatoes are usually classified as follows:

FIG. 2–100. The Irish Cobbler, a popular midwestern potato, is a waxy-type potato. It has medium-blunt ends and shallow-to-deep eyes. It is a medium-to-large roundish type potato. Courtesy USDA.

FIG. 2–101. The White Rose, a large, long, oval potato somewhat flattened, with numerous medium-deep eyes. **Courtesy USDA.**

Round White
 Katahdin—large, short, medium thick, shallow eyes
 Chippewa—large elliptical to oblong, medium thick, shallow eyes
 Kennebec—large elliptical to oblong, medium thick, shallow eyes
 Irish Cobbler—medium to large potato with blunt ends and shallow to deep eyes
Round Red
 Red Pontiac—large, oblong to round, smooth or sometimes netted, medium
   deep eyes
 Triumph—medium to large, round and thick, medium deep eyes
Long White
 White Rose—large, long, oval potato, flattened, numerous medium deep eyes
Long Russet
 Russet Burbank—large, long oval shape, heavily netted, numerous shallow eyes.

FIG. 2–102. The Early Triumph, a medium to large, round, thick potato, with medium-deep eyes. The color will usually be red or reddish, especially in young, immature potatoes. **Courtesy USDA.**

FIG. 2–103. The Chippewa, a large, elliptical to oblong potato, medium thick, with shallow eyes. Courtesy USDA.

Potatoes should be selected on the basis of use. Some varieties perform well as boiled, hash brown or for potato salad. Others are best for mashing or baking. For the former purposes, a moist, slightly waxy potato is suitable, but a dry, mealy potato is desirable for mashing and baking. The moisture and starch content of potatoes will determine their relative qualities for use. Age or maturity, variety and growing conditions will affect the moisture and starch content of potatoes.

New potatoes (immature) will have a high moisture and sugar content and a lower starch content. These properties give a waxy, moist cooked potato. Mature potatoes are drier and have a higher starch content. It is difficult to obtain a good mashed or French-fried potato from a new potato. They are over moist and sloughy for mashing. They fail to color and give a good crisp French-fried potato. They are good, however, for steaming or boiling, for hash browns or for potato salads and similar uses where a waxy-type potato is desirable. During the late spring the mature potato will change some of its starch back to sugar and at this time these mature potatoes lose some of their mealy qualities. Mature potatoes kept in storage around 35 to 40° F will change some of their starch to sugar. When these potatoes are withdrawn from storage they must remain at 50° F about 2 weeks to bring the starch-sugar ratio back to that desired.

The specific gravity of potatoes will indicate their suitability for use. Those potatoes with higher specific gravity will contain more dry matter (starch). A specific gravity of 1.08 indicates a potato good for baking or mashing, 1.07 to 1.08, good for boiling, and 1.07, for hash browns, frying and so forth. Two ounces of salt in one pint of water will permit potatoes at 1.08 specific gravity or higher to sink, but will float those below 1.08. The solution should be at room temperature.

Potatoes will also vary in cooking properties according to variety. The mature Triumph and Irish Cobbler are a moist-type potato, the Katahdin and Kennebec moderately moist, and the White Rose and Russet Burbank are dry. Buyers should learn to know what potatoes are on their market and test by cooking to ascertain their cooking properties.

The area in which the potato is grown also affects the cooking quality significantly. Potatoes that are highest in starch and, therefore, most mealy in quality, must be grown in a light soil with good drainage. Potatoes grown in moist, mucky soil will tend to be high in moisture content. Such potatoes are commonly referred to as "river-bottom potatoes." Potatoes high in starch are grown in the mountain regions of the West, and the Idaho, Washington (Yakima Valley), Montana (Bitterroot Valley) and California potatoes are known for their high quality as mealy potatoes. They are mostly Russet Burbanks or White Rose potatoes. The Maine Katahdin and the potatoes grown on Long Island also have a dry texture. Midwestern potatoes tend to be high in moisture.

Buyers find that, during periods when mealy potatoes are not available, the processed, dehydrated potato, either in granule, flake or chip form, can be used to give desirable quality products. The use of this product has increased considerably in recent years.

Fresh potatoes are available on the market all year, but mature potatoes may be in short supply in the summer months when storage

FIG. 2–104. The Kennebec, a large, elliptical to oblong potato, medium thick, with shallow eyes. It is grown largely in the East and, with the Katahdin, is popular in the heavy Main producing areas. Courtesy USDA.

FIG. 2–105. U.S. No. 1 long-
type potatoes.   Note even
shape, smooth skin and lack of
defects. Courtesy USDA.

stocks run low and the new crop has not yet matured.   Early or new
potatoes appear on the market in January through the summer months.
The mature crop appears on the market September to early June.
Potatoes should be stored at 50° F.   If purchased in small supply they
may be stored at room temperature.   New potatoes are not good keepers;
only immediately required stocks should be purchased.

Potatoes are shipped in burlap or solid-paper sacks in 100 or 50 lb net.

FIG. 2–106. U.S. No. 1 large,
round-type potatoes. Courtesy
USDA.

FIG. 2–107. Growth cracks will lower the grade. Extra labor and high waste result from these potatoes. Courtesy USDA.

More and more high quality potatoes are being shipped in fiberboard boxes carrying 50 lb net. The brand, name and address of the packer, with grade designation and possibly size, should appear on the package. Net contents must also appear.

Sizes may be specified. Federal standards state that size A "for long varieties such as Burbank, Russet Burbank, Early Ohio, White Rose or other similar varieties, the diameter of each potato shall be not less than $1\frac{7}{8}''$ in diameter and not less than 40% of the potatoes in the lot shall be six ounces or more in weight." For round or intermediate-shaped varieties, such as Irish Cobbler, Katahdin, Bliss Triumph and Green Mountain, the diameter of each potato "shall be not less than $1\frac{7}{8}''$ and not less than 60% of the potatoes in the lot shall be $2\frac{1}{4}''$ or larger in diameter." Size B for all varieties shall be "from $1\frac{1}{2}''$ to not more than $2''$ in diameter." Potatoes may be specified as *bakers*, which will indicate an average 6 oz potato, 30 to 60% of which must be over 6 oz. Limitations on size may also be stated as "potatoes shall average 6 oz with variation permitted one-half ounce either over or under." Boxed potatoes in 50-lb lots may be obtained in counts of 50, 60, 70, 80, 90, 100, 120, 125 to the box. A 50 count will contain potatoes weighing

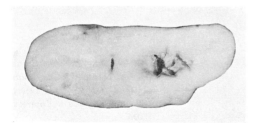

FIG. 2–108. An example of hollow heart in potatoes. This defect is frequently not evident and may appear in some top-grade potatoes. It usually results from too rapid a growth of the potatoes. Courtesy USDA.

about a pound and the 125's, 6 oz. Size may also be designated by diameter, such as 2½, 2¼ or 2¼ to 3¼ in.

Federal wholesale grade standards are U.S. Fancy, No. 1, Commercial and No. 2. U.S. No. 1 is recommended for general food facility use. Standards for No. 1 potatoes state "the diameter must not be less than 1⅞ inches; not more than 3% of the potatoes in any lot may fail to meet the specified minimum size, except that a tolerance of 5% shall be allowed for potatoes packed to meet a minimum size of 2¼" or more in diameter or 6 oz in weight. In addition, not more than 15% can fail to meet any specified maximum size." The minimum diameter size permitted in U.S. No. 2 potatoes is 1½ in., with tolerances allowed. Buyers should distinguish between grade and condition of potatoes. Grade indicates the quality of the potato when it went into storage. Condition refers to the quality at any specific time. Specifications should state that the grade specified should be the condition of the potato at the time of delivery. This similar situation was seen for apples.

Select good, firm, smooth-skinned potatoes. Potatoes with deeply set eyes will have a higher paring waste and require more labor to prepare. New potatoes will have a thin skin that may feather or peel from the flesh easily. Mature potatoes should be dry and possess unbroken peel. Watch for freedom from scab, mechanical, worm or other injury. Wilted, leathery, discolored potatoes should be rejected. A green coloring is sunburn, which gives a bitter flavor to the potato. Black heart is a disease that develops while the potatoes are in storage. Hollow heart is an open area in the interior of the potato that develops in large potatoes, probably because they grew too fast. Frozen potatoes may be detected by wetness or leakiness, or when they are cut across and show a black ring just within the outer surface. Shriveling may occur in potatoes that lack maturity or in mature potatoes as early summer approaches. Heavy sprouting may also occur in the spring. Potatoes held in too warm a storage or in a sprouting condition may be soft and give a

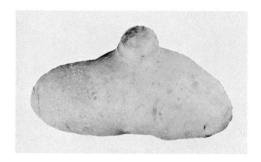

FIG. 2–109. Knobs such as this in potatoes cause high waste in peeling. An excess will lower grade. Courtesy USDA.

FIG. 2–110. Federal inspector inspects representative samples from a lot of potatoes. He cuts some to make sure they are not infected with disease, insects or dry heart. Courtesy USDA.

high paring waste. Sprouting potatoes have a higher sugar content. Normal paring waste on old potatoes is 27% and with new potatoes 20%.

Although pared potatoes should fall under the category of processed foods, perhaps they should be discussed here. These potatoes are pared and treated with anti-oxidants to prevent browning. They may be held for nearly 7 days at 32 to 40° F without deterioration. Federal grade standards exist for peeled fresh potatoes. Grades are U.S. Grade A or Fancy, U.S. Grade B or Extra Standard and U.S. Substandard. Styles are whole (potatoes not less than 1½ in. in diameter), cut and whole, sliced, diced, French or shoestring and cut. Grading is according to score. Maximum total scores are: color 20, uniformity of size 20, defects 40, and texture 20. Increased institutional uses of these potatoes is occurring. Federal standards also exist for frozen French-fried potatoes. Grades are similar to those of fresh peeled potatoes. Strips of potatoes may vary from ¼″ by ¼″ to ½″ by ½″. Scoring is according to color, defects and texture, with maximum points, respectively, 30, 40, and 30.

Potatoes, Sweet

Yams are usually included with sweet potatoes as one type. Yams are thought of as more moist and having a deeper orange or reddish flesh than sweet potatoes, but this may not necessarily be true although for market purposes it is. Yams tend to break up more easily and for that reason sweet potatoes are best for candying and other purposes where the potato is separated from the peel and used.   Some individuals like the dry, mealier sweet potato for mashing.   Yams and sweet potatoes, like the white potato, must be cured or matured before marketing. Select potatoes that are clean, firm and free from blemishes.   Inspect carefully.   Note shape, for shape affects grade.   Potatoes that appear damp may have rot in them.   Potatoes that are shriveled, soft and flabby are usually old, of poor flavor and wasteful.   Cut potatoes to note amount of coarse viening inside.   This will indicate stringiness.   Purchase U.S. No. 1.

Sweet potatoes are on the market during the entire year, but heaviest supplies come in the fall and winter.   Imports from Puerto Rico and

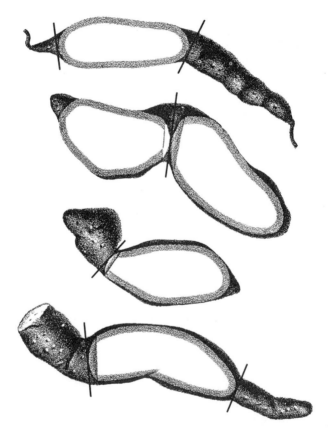

FIG. 2–111.   Buyers of sweet potatoes should note shapes.   These potatoes, called fairly well shaped, show there are one or more pieces of usable potato.   Yield will be materially affected by the shape of the potatoes.   Courtesy USDA.

FIG. 2–112.   Cook sweet potatoes and cut to note shreds indicating stringiness.   Courtesy USDA.

other Caribbean areas come onto the market later than the crop from the southern states.   Machine-pared sweet potatoes lose 25%.

Pumpkin

Pumpkins of good quality have a rich yellow color with no green showing on the rinds.   Select for heaviness for size.   There are no federal grades.   Loss in preparation to EP 30%.

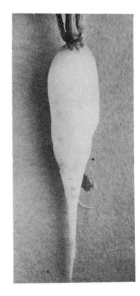

FIG. 2–113.   The white icicle radish is sweet, crisp and delicately flavored when young. It becomes strong flavored and hot when old.   Because it is cold resistant, it may be seen on the market later than some other radish varieties. Courtesy USDA.

FIG. 2–114. The all-red, round radish. This is the giant type. It is an excellent radish when young but becomes soft and pithy as it ages. Courtesy W. Atlee Burpee Co.

Radishes

There are a number of different radishes, but the small, round, red radish with a white tip or all red radishes are most frequently seen on the market. Radishes are on the market all year, with peak supplies coming in the spring and early summer. Radishes should be well formed, smooth, firm, tender, crisp and mild in flavor. The leaves should be fresh, bright and green. Note spongy or soft radishes indicating pithiness. Large radishes are apt to be pithy. Size may be specified as small, less than $\frac{3}{4}$ in. in diameter, medium, $\frac{3}{4}$ to 1 in. in diameter, large, 1 to $1\frac{1}{4}$ in. in diameter, and very large, over $1\frac{1}{4}$ in. in diameter. Styles may be tops full length or topped, which means tops clipped back to not more than $\frac{3}{8}$ in. in length. More and more radishes are appearing on the market topped and packed in polyethylene bags. Specify U.S. No. 1. Waste of radishes with tops to EP 37%.

Salsify (Oyster Plant)

Like parsnips, the flavor of this root vegetable improves after being exposed to heavy frosts and near-freezing temperatures. The roots are also the color of parsnips, but are smaller in diameter and not as tapering. Select smooth, firm, well-shaped roots of medium size and avoid soft, flabby or shriveled roots, for they are usually pithy or tough and woody. Softness may indicate decay. Large, coarse roots may have woody cores. Misshapen roots will have high waste. There are no federal standards. It is found on the market in the fall and winter. Waste in preparation to EP is 30%.

FIG. 2–115. The salsify is frequently pared, boiled and diced, and served in cream sauce. The root has an cyster-like flavor. Courtesy W. Atlee Burpee Co.

Squash

Classification of squash for buying purposes may be made in a number of ways. There are summer and winter varieties. Each variety will perform differently in cooking; some are adapted to one type of cooking while others perform best with another.

Summer squash. Summer varieties are more fragile and are poor keepers. They should be held at 32 to 40° F until used. They are usually soft-skinned and immature squash. Cutting open and inspecting seeds should expose softness in the seed and immaturity. Summer squash are frequently cooked and eaten with the seeds. The pulp is soft and moist when cooked and lacks the mealiness found in the winter varieties. There are some hard-rind summer squash whose flesh is usually yellowish. These squash resemble winter squash more than the summer varieties.

FIG. 2–116. Two varieties of Zucchini, a summer-type squash, frequently sliced and boiled with the skin on. Courtesy W. Atlee Burpee Co.

FIG. 2–117.   The early golden crookneck squash, a
summer variety.   Courtesy W. Atlee Burpee Co.

Select for freshness, heaviness for size, freedom from blemishes and a
rind sufficiently tender to be easily punctured except in the hard-rind
varieties.   A bushel will contain about 48 lb net, small lugs 20 to 30 lb,
cartons 40 lb.   They should be purchased by the pound.   Preparation
waste varies, but most summer squash are merely washed and trimmed as
required and used with the rind on; the preparation waste is around
10%.   Summer squash will be found on the market almost all year, especially such common varieties as zucchini.   Others are on the market
summer until fall.

FIG. 2–118.   The early prolific, a straight-neck squash, a
summer variety.   Courtesy W. Atlee Burpee Co.

FIG. 2-119. Butternut squash, a fall variety but not a good keeper. The flesh is moist and richly flavored. Courtesy W. Atlee Burpee Co.

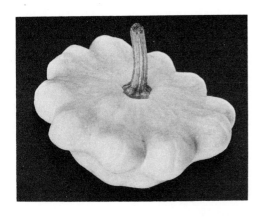

FIG. 2-120. The scallop squash. This is a summer variety. It is usually cut into eighths and boiled. The seeds should be tender enough to be eaten. Courtesy W. Atlee Burpee Co.

FIG. 2-121. The acorn squash, a small, winter variety. It is excellent boiled, stuffed or baked with butter and brown sugar. The flesh is soft, moist and rich. Courtesy W. Atlee Burpee Co.

FIG. 2–122. Buttercup squash, a winter variety of squash and others shaped like it are also called the turban squash because of its resemblance to oriental turbans. Courtesy W. Atlee Burpee Co.

Winter squash. The winter squash usually have hard rinds, a yellowish-orange flesh and hard, white seeds. They are usually fair-to-good keepers. Some may have smooth rinds, others rough. The rinds may be dark green, gray, orange or other colors, depending upon type. The squash should be firm, with a thick, hard rind that is nearly unblemished. They should be heavy for their size. Examine carefully for rot or mold. Press to feel firmness and condition. Split to examine for interior condition. Winter squash may be sold by the pound, and it is common for large squash to be sold in this manner. Others may be sold in bushel baskets, crates or other containers. A bushel will weigh around 50 lb.

FIG. 2–123. Cocozealla squash above and banana squash below. They are hard rind squash and are found on the market in liberal quantities in late summer and early fall. They are only fair keepers. Courtesy W. Atlee Burpee Co.

Specify U.S. No. 1 for both summer and winter varieties. Preparation wastes to EP are: for Acorn, 26%; Boston Marrow, 12%; Butternut, 48%; Hubbard, 34%.

Tomatoes

While peak supplies are on the markets late in the summer and early in the fall, good supplies of tomatoes come from greenhouse production or from California, Florida, Texas, Cuba or Mexico during the winter. The distance that tomatoes must be shipped has increased the need for firmer tomatoes on the produce market, and the softer varieties are usually obtained only when locally raised tomatoes are on the market.

The stage of ripeness at which tomatoes are picked depends upon the distance from the market. Vine-ripened tomatoes are of better quality, but, because of softness, damage may occur in shipping or the tomato may spoil before reaching the market. Tomatoes are picked immature green, mature green, turning, pink or firm ripe. *Immature green* tomatoes show no red or yellow color. The seeds are immature and soft and the skin can be rubbed off. The quality of tomatoes picked at this time is usually low but many are harvested and shipped at this point. *Mature*

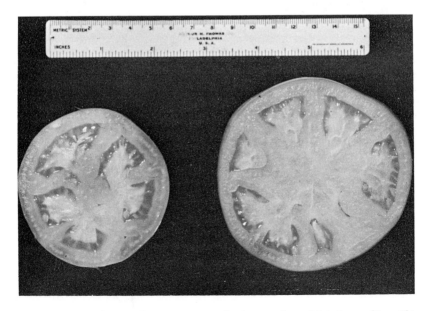

FIG. 2–124. Cut fruit, such as tomatoes and others, to inspect interior quality. This tomato is a variety that ships well. It is reddish pink at full maturity. Courtesy USDA.

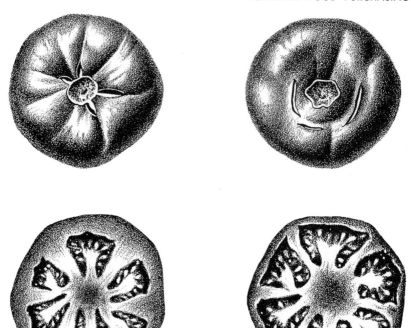

FIG. 2–125.   Limits of growth cracks and puffiness allowed in U.S. No. 1 Grade for tomatoes. The left tomato at the top shows maximum aggregate length of radial growth
cracks permitted on 2½ in. tomato in U.S. No. 1 Grade.   The tomato on the right top
shows concentric growth cracks that affect appearance to same extent as maximum aggregate length of radial growth cracks permitted in U.S. No. 1 Grade.   These limitations
apply in all stages of maturity.   The lower limit allowed of puffiness in U.S. No. 1 tomatoes is shown in the bottom tomatoes.   The proportion of open space permitted is de-
pendent upon the thickness of walls.   Tomatoes with thicker walls may have proportionately greater amounts of open space.   Tomatoes with thinner walls shall have
proportionately lesser amounts of open space.   Courtesy USDA.

green tomatoes have a gloss, no red color but seeds sufficiently hard as
to resist cutting with a knife. A bit of white may appear on the bottom
or blossom end of the tomato. The skin has become waxy and cannot
be rubbed off. A tomato that is *turning* shows a trace of red color or
yellow. This stage of maturity is also referred to as the "breaker" stage.
A *pink* tomato has more than ·50% of the surface colored but is still firm
and not completely colored. A *firm ripe* tomato is well reddened but not
at complete ripeness. It is difficult to ship for long distances but still has

sufficient firmness to be moved farther than just local growing areas to market. *Full ripe* tomatoes are ready for use.

When tomatoes are received at warehouses, they are stored under carefully controlled conditions. Ripening rooms are kept at around 65° F and 88% humidity. Ethylene gas is used to assist ripening. The tomatoes are repacked and moved onto the market. Buyers may specify their tomatoes as pink firm ripe (sometimes also called hard ripe), or full ripe, depending upon the length of time they are to be held. Buyers should also be aware that different varieties of tomatoes are colored differently at complete ripening. Many hothouse varieties are pink when completely ripe. Other varieties may be red and others deep scarlet. Vine-ripened fruit usually has a more natural color, thinness and tenderness of skin and a superior flavor.

Small, medium, large and very large tomatoes are, respectively, those under 3 oz, 2 to 6 oz, 6 to 10 oz and over 10 oz. Greenhouse varieties are called small, medium and large, respectively, when under 3 oz, 3 to 8 oz and over 8 oz. Tomatoes are most frequently marketed in lugs holding three layers of tomatoes. The lug will contain about 30 to 32 lb net. The lugs are most always place packed, and tomatoes are wrapped individually unless double wrap packs are specified. In this case two tomatoes will be wrapped in one wrapper.

Packing in the standard lug may be termed standard, straight, extra row or bridge pack. The standard pack is an arrangement whereby the tomatoes are placed in three layers in established rows, and columns. The tomatoes are sized to have very little variation between individual tomatoes. Packs are indicated by such terms as 5 x 5, 5 x 6 to indicate rows and columns respectively. Thus, a straight pack lug 5 x 5 pack will have 75 tomatoes in it. Table 2–13 indicates the size of tomato according to pack.

Table 2–13

Los Angeles Lug Size Placements	Diameter in Inches*	
	Minimum	Maximum
4 x 4	$3\frac{5}{16}$	$3\frac{15}{16}$
4 x 5	3	$3\frac{10}{16}$
5 x 5	$2\frac{14}{16}$	$3\frac{6}{16}$
5 x 6	$2\frac{11}{16}$	$3\frac{3}{16}$
6 x 6	$2\frac{8}{16}$	$2\frac{14}{16}$
6 x 7	$2\frac{4}{16}$	$2\frac{10}{16}$
7 x 7	2	$2\frac{6}{16}$
7 x 8	$1\frac{14}{16}$	$2\frac{4}{16}$

*A 10% tolerance is allowed.

Straight pack tomatoes may have alternating rows with one more tomato packed. This packing is indicated by 4-5 x 9 indicating 9 rows packed alternately, 4 and 5 tomatoes to the row. This 4 x 5 pack will have 40 to 41 tomatoes to the layer.

Extra row packs may have standard top layer pack, such as 5 x 5, but the lower layers contain more than one additional row one way of the lug. The lower layers may be packed 5 x 6. Only one additional row is permitted in the lower layers, and the lug with a top 5 x 5 pack may not be packed 6 x 5 and 7 x 5 in the lower layers.

It is a common understanding in the trade, however, that reference to a size by a term 5 x 5 refers to the size of the tomato and not to the pack unless reference is made to Los Angeles lug packing. Irregular pack indicates the tomatoes are not packed in any standard manner.

A variety of other containers may be used. Tomato crates, wirebound or nailed, contain around 60 lb tomatoes; standard fiberboard cartons 40 and 50 lb; small, wirebound crates 38 lb; field boxes 60 lb; 1 bushel basket or hamper 53 lb; ½-bushel containers 27 lb; 12 qt climax baskets 18 to 20 lb; 16 qt splint baskets or 16 qt hampers 27 lb; ⅝ bushel hampers 33 to 34 lb; 8 qt splint basket or fiberboard box 12 lb; 4 basket crate 22 lb; 3 at till 5 lb. Tomatoes to be shipped considerable distances do not ship well in bushel baskets or bushel hampers. Greenhouse tomatoes are frequently packed in baskets holding around 10 lb.

Tomatoes should be selected on the basis of flavor, firmness, internal characteristics, color and size. Select tomatoes that are mature but not overripe or soft. Quality is indicated by those that are well developed, fairly smooth and that are free from decay, freezing injury and damage caused by dirt, bruises, cuts, sunscald, sunburn, puffiness, catfaces, growth cracks, scars, disease, insects, hail or mechanical or other means. Watch for worm damage, decay, mold or wateriness. Purchase U.S. No. 1, but at the peak seasons lower grades may be selected to advantage if quality is high. Greenhouse tomatoes should be U.S. Fancy or U.S. No. 1, depending upon quality. Removing skins, hard cores, stem ends and trimming will given an average loss of 12%.

Turnips and Rutabagas

The quality factors for selecting turnips and rutabagas are similar. Federal standards for grades are the same for either vegetable.

Turnips may be white or white with a light purple on the top. Best sizes for turnips are those listed for sizes desirable in beets. Turnips may be sold in bunches with tops. There should not be less than three turnips to a bunch and the bunch should weigh a pound.

Rutabagas are sometimes called Swedish turnips. They are yellow in

FIG. 2–126. The lack of old leaf scars at
the crown of this rutabega indicates immaturity. Courtesy USDA.

color, larger than turnips, have a longer shape and may be almost oval.
Rutabagas also have a more dense flesh. Rutabagas and turnips may be
marketed trimmed (4 in. of top remaining) or topped (not more than
¾ in. top remaining.)

Rutabagas and turnips may be stored in cool, well-ventilated areas
but after extended storage they may become strongly flavored. They
may be marketed waxed and when this is done, these vegetables will
have a high gloss. They are usually marketed in 50-lb bags or in bushel
baskets containing 55 lb net. U.S. No. 1 standard states that turnips
and rutabagas shall have a minimum diameter of 1¾ in. Specifications
should state that turnips over 2½ in. in diameter will be rejected.
Rutabagas may be larger. If turnips come with tops, they should be
fresh and green. Watch for rough skins on the vegetables, puffiness
and leaf scars on the top. Cut and examine for woodiness and crispness.
The medium sizes are usually best quality. Spongy, wrinkled or shriveled
items should be rejected.

Table 2-14
Approximate Quantities Required for Some Common Fruits and Vegetables

Item	Shipping Container	Approximate Net Weight, as Purchased per Container	Miscellaneous Shipping or Portioning Data	Portion Size as Served	Portions per Pound as Purchased	Approximate Amount to Purchase as Purchased for 100 Portions
Fruit						
Apples, whole	Western box, 113's	44 lb		1 each	2.3	44 lb (1 box)
Apples, baked	Western box, 88's	44 lb		1 each	1.8	55 lb (1¼ box)
Apples, for pies	Bushel basket	48 lb	20 pies per bushel; 2½ lb used per 9" pie	1 pie slice*	2.5	40 lb
Apples, rings	Western box, 113's	44 lb	5 rings per apple	2 rings	6.7	15 lb (⅓ box)
Apple salad, Waldorf	Western box, 113's	44 lb		½ c diced	4.5	22 lb (½ box)
Apple slices, small	Western Box, 113's	44 lb	15 slices per apple	3 slices	14.0	7½ lb (20 apples)
Applesauce	Bushel basket	48 lb	16 to 20 qts per bushel	½ c	2.8	36 lb (¾ bu)
Apricots, whole	Till, 60's	5 lb	8 to 12 per lb	2 each	5.0	20 lb (4 till)
Apricots, whole	Los Angeles lug	20 lb	100 apricots per lug	2 each	2.5	40 lb (2 lugs)
Avocados, half	Flat, 18's	13 lb		half	2.0	52 lb (4 flats)
Avocados, sliced	Flat, 24's	13 lb	30 slices per avocado used in grapefruit salad	4 slices	25.0	4 lb (8 avocado)
Bananas, whole	Box	40 lb	3 per lb	1 each	3.0	33 lb (.8 box)
Bananas, sliced	Box	40 lb	2 to 2½ c per lb or 30 slices per banana	½ c	4.0	25 lb
Blackberries	Crate, 24 qts	30 lb		½ c with cream	6.0	17 lb (13 boxes)
Blueberries, for pies	Crate, 12 qts	8 lb	(use 1 qt per pie for pies)	1 pie slice*	7.0	15 lb (24 pt)
Blueberries, pudding	Crate, 24 qts	30 lb	¾ qt per 9" pie.	½ c	12.1	8¼ lb (6½ qt)
Cherries, sweet, whole	Lug	15 lb		12 cherries	5.0	20 lb (1⅓ lug)
Cherries, sour, pie	Bushel	54 lb	1¼ qt per 9" pie	1 pie slice*	3.3	33 lb (⅔ bu)
Cranberries, sauce	Box	25 lb	cooked sauce	¼ c	3.5	7½ lb
Cranberries, sauce	Box	25 lb	chopped raw	½ c	6.0	17 lb
Figs	Flat, 48's	6 lb		3 medium figs	2.8	36 lb (6 boxes)
Grapes, Concord, whole	Basket	6 lb		¼ lb	4.0	25 lb (4 baskets)

Grapes, European, whole	Box	28 lb	70 grapes per lb	½ c	3.6	28 lb (1 box)
Grapefruit	⅘ bu carton, 32's	40 lb		half	0.8	125 lb (3⅛ box)
Grapefruit, sections	⅘ bu carton, 32's	40 lb	12 sections per grapefruit	6 sections (salad)	0.8	125 lb (3⅛ box)
Grapefruit, juice	⅘ bu carton, 40's	40 lb	6½ qt juice per carton	4 oz	1.3	80 lb (2 boxes)
Lemons, juice	⅘ bu carton, 85's	38 lb	for lemonade; 1 pt juice per dozen; 8 qt per carton	2 oz juice	3.6	28 lb (12 doz)
Lemons, slices	⅘ bu carton, 85's	38 lb	8 slices per lemon	1 slice	40.0	2¼ lb (1 doz)
Lemons, wedges	⅘ bu carton, 85's	38 lb	6 wedges per lemon	1 wedge	25.0	3½ lb (1½ doz)
Limes, juice	Dozen		for limeade	1¾ oz (1 lime)		9 doz
Limes, wedges	Dozen		4 to 5 wedges per lime	1 wedge		2 dozen limes
Melons						
Cantaloupe†	Crate, 45's	70 to 80 lb		half	.8 to 1	90 lb (1.2 crates)
Cantaloupe rings	Crate, 45's	70 to 80 lb	8 rings per melon, each ring used to hold chopped fruit for salad	1 ring	4.0	22 lb (13 melons)
Cantaloupe balls	Crate, 45's	70 to 80 lb	30 balls per melon; used for melon ball cup	9 balls	1.8	51 lb (30 melon)
Cantaloupe, diced	Crate, 45's	70 to 80 lb	10 oz meat per melon	3 oz	1.8	51 lb (30 melon)
Casaba‡, wedge	Crate, 8's	50 lb		⅛ melon	1.3	82 lb (13 melon)
Watermelon, slice	Individual melon	35 lb		1 lb	1.0	100 lb (3 melon)
Nectarines, whole	Lug, 120's	20 lb		2 whole	2.4	34 lb (1⅔ lug)
Oranges, whole	Carton, 88's	38 lb		1 whole	2.3	43 lb (8⅓ doz)
Oranges, juice	Carton, 88's	45 lb	10½ qts per carton	4 oz	2.2	55 lb (1¼ cartons)
Oranges, slice	Carton, 88's	45 lb	6 slices per orange for salad	3 slices	4.0	26 lb (50 oranges)
Oranges, sections	Carton, 88's	38 lb	9 sections per orange	6 sections	3.6	28 lb (5½ dozen)
Peaches, sliced	Lug	20 lb	4 per lb; 6 c sliced per lb; 8½ qts sliced per lug	½ c	1.7	60 lb (3 lugs)
Peaches, pie	Basket, 20's	5–6 lb	3 pies per basket; 2 c per pie	1 slice pie*	3.4	30 lb (5–6 baskets) or ⅔ bushel)

*Each pie cut 6.

†Yield on Honeyball melons is same as for cantaloupes if 45 per crate.

‡Yield on Honeydew and Persian melons is same for Casabas if 8 per crate.

Table 2-14 (Continued)
Approximate Quantities Required for Some Common Fruits and Vegetables

Item	Shipping Container	Approximate Net Weight, as Purchased per Container	Miscellaneous Shipping or Portioning Data	Portion Size as Served	Portions per Pound as Purchased	Approximate Amount to Purchase as Purchased for 100 Portions
Peaches, pudding	Bushel	45 lb		½ c	5.5	18 lb
Pears, whole	Box, 120's	40 lb	3 per lb	1 whole	3.0	34 lb
Pears, diced	Bushel	48 lb		½ c	3.0	32 lb (¾ bushel)
Persimmons, whole	Flat, 28's	14 lb	(6 sections can be obtained per persimmon)	1 each halved	2.0	50 lb (8⅓ doz)
Pineapple, diced	Crate, 24's	70 lb	20 oz diced per pineapple	½ c	1.7	60 lb (20 pineapple)
Pineapple, sliced	Crate, 24's	70 lb	10 round slices per pineapple	1 slice	3.3	30 lb (10 pineapple)
Plums, whole	Basket, 5 x 5	5 lb	18 to 24 medium per basket	3 medium	4.4	22½ lb (4½ baskets)
Plums, pies	Basket, 4 x 5	5 lb	2½ to 3 9″ pies per basket	1 pie slice*	3.3	30 lb (6 baskets)
Raspberries	Crate, 24 pt	18 lb		3 oz (⅔ c)	6.3	16 lb (20 pts)
Raspberries, pie	Crate, 16 qt	20 lb	¾ qt per pie	1 pie slice*	6.0	17 lb (13 qts)
Raspberries, cobbler	Crate, 16 qt	20 lb		½ c	10.0	10 lb (8 qt)
Rhubarb, hothouse	Flat	5 lb	used for sauce	½ c	4.0	20 lb
Rhubarb, pie	Crate	40 lb	3 c rhubarb sliced per pie	1 pie slice*	6.6	15 lb
Strawberries	Crate, 24 qt	30 lb	6 servings to qt	⅔ c	5.0	20 lb (17 qt)
Strawberries, pies	Crate, 24 qt	30 lb	1 qt per pie	1 slice pie*	5.0	20 lb (17 qt)
Strawberries, sauce	Crate, 24 pt	18 lb		¼ c	10.0	10 lb (13 pt)
Tangerines	Crate, 125's	40 lb		1 tangerine	3.0	35 lb
Tangerines, sections	Crate, 125's	40 lb	10 section per tangerine; used for salad	5 sections		16 lb (4¼ dozen)

Vegetables§

Item	Container	Weight	Notes	Serving	No.	Yield
Artichoke, globe	Artichoke box, 72's	40 lb		1 each	1.8	56 lb (8⅓ doz)
Asparagus	Crate	29 lb	1 bunch is 2½ lb and contains 24 stalks	3 oz (3–4 stalks)	2.6	38 lb
Beans, Lima, Fordhook	Bushel basket	30 lb	yields 8 qts shelled	3 oz (½ c)	2.1	48 lb
Beans, Lima, Baby	Bushel basket	28 lb	yields 8 qts shelled	3 oz (½ c)	2.2	45 lb
Beans, Lima, Fava	Bushel basket	28 lb	yields 8 qts shelled	3 oz (½ c)	2.1	48 lb
Beans, Lima, shelled	Basket	¼ lb		3 oz (½ c)	5.3	19 lb
Beans, snap	Bushel basket	30 lb		3 oz (½ c)	4.5	22 lb
Beets, with tops	Crate, 36 bunches	45 lb		3 oz (½ c)	2.1	46 lb
Beets, topped	Bushel basket	52 lb		3 oz (½ c)	4.0	25 lb
Beet greens	Bushel basket	18 lb		3 oz (½ c)	2.3	43 lb
Broccoli	Crate, 18 bunches	63 lb	1 bunch is 2 to 2½ lb	3 oz (½ c)	2.9	35 lb
Brussels sprouts	Drum	27 lb		3 oz (½ c)	4.1	24 lb
Cabbage, shredded	Bag	50 lb	cooked 1 lb shredded cabbage yields 2½ c	3 oz (½ c)	4.0	25 lb
Cabbage, shredded	Bushel basket	40 lb	raw 1 lb shredded cabbage equals 3½ c	½ c slaw	6.5	15 lb
Cabbage, Chinese	Bushel basket	40 lb	diced raw	2½ oz (½ c)	4.0	25 lb
Carrots with tops	Crate, 36's (bunches)	45 lb		3 oz (½ c)	2.8	35 lb
Carrots with tops	Crate, 36 bunches	45 lb	strips raw	2 oz (4 strips)	4.3	23 lb
Carrots, topped	Bag	50 lb		3 oz (½ c)	3.9	26 lb
Carrots, topped	Bag	50 lb	strips raw	2 oz (4 strips)	5.8	17 lb
Cauliflower	Crate, 12's	24 lb		3 oz (½ c)	2.0	50 lb
Chard	Bushel basket	18 lb		3 oz (½ c)	3.7	27 lb
Celery	Crate, 30's	30 lb		3 oz (½ c)	3.7	27 lb
Celery	Crate, 30's	30 lb	stalk pieces raw (small)	2 oz (2 stalks)	6.0	17 lb
Cucumbers, pared	Bushel basket	45 lb	75 cucumbers; 1 9" cucumber yields 25 to 30 slices	2½ oz (5 slices)	5.8	18 lb
Cucumbers, unpared	Bushel basket	45 lb		2½ oz (5 slices)	7.6	13 lb
Endive, Belgium, chopped	Basket	5 lb	15 to 25 heads	2 oz (½ or ⅓ head)	7.1	14 lb
Collards	Bushel basket	20 lb	12 bunches	3 oz (½ c)	4.3	23 lb

§All items cooked unless noted.

Table 2–14 (Continued)
Approximate Quantities Required for Some Common Fruits and Vegetables

Item	Shipping Container	Approximate Net Weight, as Purchased per Container	Miscellaneous Shipping or Portioning Data	Portion Size as Served	Portions per Pound as Purchased	Approximate Amount to Purchase as Purchased for 100 Portions
Corn on the cob	Wirebound crate	40 lb	5 doz ears each ear approximately 10 to 12 oz AP	7 oz (1 ear)	1.7	60–75 lb (8⅓ doz)
Corn, kernels from cob	Wirebound crate	40 lb		3 oz (½ c)	1.5	66 lb
Eggplant	Bushel basket	40 lb	24 to 30 eggplant; eggplant pared and steamed	3 oz (½ c)	4.0	25 lb
Eggplant, sliced	Bushel basket	40 lb	unpared, batter fried	3½ oz (1 slice)	4.3	23 lb
Escarole, diced, raw	Bushel basket	25 lb	2 dozen heads	2 oz	5.8	17 lb
Chicory, curly leaf	Bushel basket	22 lb	2 dozen heads	2 oz	6.0	17 lb
Kale	Bushel basket	19 lb		3 oz (½ c)	3.7	27 lb
Kohlrabi	Bushel basket	22 lb	3 to 5 per lb	3 oz (½ c)	2.9	35 lb
Leeks	Bushel basket	18 lb	18 bunches, 3 to 5 per bunch	3 oz (½ c)	2.2	45 lb
Lettuce, Iceberg	Carton, 24's	25 lb	chopped raw underliners for salad;	2 oz (½ c)	5.9	17 lb
Lettuce, Iceberg	Carton, 24's	25 lb	12 per head average		11.1	9 lb
Lettuce, leaf	Bushel basket	18 lb	raw	2 oz	5.3	19 lb
Lettuce, Boston or Bibb	Bushel basket	24 lb	raw	2 oz	5.1	20 lb
Mushrooms, chopped	Carton	1 lb		1 oz (2 T)	11.1	9 lb
Mustard greens	Bushel basket	18 lb		3 oz (½ c)	3.1	32 lb
Okra	Bushel hamper	38 lb	diced and cooked	3 oz (½ c)	5.1	20 lb
Onions, dry	Sack	50 lb		3 oz (½ c)	4.0	25 lb
Onions, dry	Sack	50 lb	French-fried	2½ oz	5.0	20 lb
Onions, dry	Sack	50 lb	raw diced or sliced	2 oz	7.1	14 lb
Onions, green	California ⅔ crate	50 lb	8 dozen bunches to the crate	1½ oz (2 onions)	3.9	25 lb

Commodity	Unit	Weight	Preparation	Serving	Servings/lb	Yield
Parsnips	Bushel basket	45 lb		3 oz (½ c)	4.2	24 lb
Peas, green	Bushel basket	28 lb	8 qts shelled	3 oz (½ c)	1.9	53 lb
Peppers, green	Sturdee crate, 1¼ bushel	30 lb	chopped raw	1 oz	13.1	8 lb
Peppers, green	Sturdee crate, 1¼ bushel	30 lb	halves steamed	2 halves	4.0	25 lb
Potatoes, Irish	Sack	100 lb	whole pared	1 (5 oz)	2.6	39 lb
Potatoes, Irish	Sack	100 lb	baked	1 (7 oz)	2.1	47 lb
Potatoes, Irish	Sack	100 lb	hash brown	4 oz	2.3	44 lb
Potatoes, Irish	Sack	100 lb	mashed	4 oz	3.3	30 lb
Potatoes, Irish	Sack	100 lb	raw fried	4 oz	1.7	59 lb
Potatoes, Irish	Sack	100 lb	French-fried	3 oz	2.7	37 lb
Potatoes, Sweet	Bushel	50 lb	140 potatoes; mashed	4 oz	3.3	30 lb
Potatoes, Sweet	Bushel	50 lb	candied	4 oz	3.4	30 lb
Potatoes, Sweet	Bushel	50 lb	baked	6 oz	2.7	36 lb
Pumpkin	Bushel	40 lb		3 oz (½ c)	3.4	30 lb
Radishes	Dozen bunches	10 lb	raw	1 oz	10.0	10 lb
Rutabagas	Bushel	45 lb		3 oz (½ c)	3.8	27 lb
Spinach	Bushel	18 lb		3 oz (½ c)	3.2	31 lb
Spinach, trimmed and washed	Bushel	18 lb		3 oz (½ c)	4.0	25 lb
Squash, summer	Bushel	40 lb		3 oz (½ c)	4.2	24 lb
Squash, Acorn	Bushel	50 lb	50 squash	1 half	2.0	50 lb
Squash, Boston Marrow	Pound		mashed	3 oz (½ c)	4.1	24 lb
Squash, Boston Marrow	Pound		baked	4 oz	2.9	35 lb
Squash, Butternut	Pound		mashed	3 oz (½ c)	2.4	41 lb
Squash, Butternut	Pound		baked	4 oz	1.7	59 lb
Squash, Hubbard	Pound		mashed	3 oz (½ c)	3.1	33 lb
Squash, Hubbard	Pound		baked	4 oz	2.2	46 lb
Tomatoes, unpeeled	Lug, 5 x 5	30 lb	75 tomatoes; raw	3 oz	4.9	20 lb
Tomatoes, peeled	Lug, 5 x 5	30 lb	raw	3 oz	4.7	21 lb
Turnips, topped	Bushel	50 lb		3 oz (½ c)	4.0	25 lb
Turnips, with tops	Crate, 18's	36 lb		3 oz (½ c)	3.3	31 lb
Watercress	Basket 14 bunches		raw	2 oz	5.9	17 lb

Table 2–15
Federal Standards for Fresh Fruits and Vegetables at the Wholesale Level*

Fruits
  Apples   Extra Fancy, Fancy, No. 1, No. 1 Cookers,
                                              No. 1 Early, Utility
  Apricots   No. 1, No. 2
  Avocados, Florida   No. 1, Combination
  Cantaloupes   No. 1, Commercial
  Cherries, Sweet   No. 1, Commercial
  Cranberries   Grade A (Consumer grade)
  Dewberries and Blackberries   No. 1, No. 2
  Grapes, American Bunch
  Grapes, European, Sawdust Pack   Fancy, Extra No. 1, No. 1
  Grapes, Table   Fancy, No. 1
  Grapefruit (California and   Fancy No. 1, No. 2, Combination, No. 3
    Arizona)
  Grapefruit (Florida)   Fancy, No. 1, No. 1 Bright, No. 1 Golden,
                                              No. 1 Bronze, No. 1 Russet, No. 2, No. 2
                                              Bright, No. 2 Russet, No. 3
  Grapefruit (Texas)   Fancy, No. 1, No. 1 Bright, No. 1 Bronze,
                                              Combination No. 2, No. 2 Russet, No. 3
  Honey Dew and Honey Ball   No. 1, Commercial, No. 2
    Melon
  Lemons   No. 1, Combination, No. 2
  Limes (Persian) Tahiti   No. 1, Combination, No. 2
  Nectarines   Fancy, Extra No. 1, No. 1, No. 2
  Oranges (California and Arizona)   Fancy, No. 1, Combination, No. 2
  Oranges and Tangelos (Florida)   Fancy, No. 1 Bright, No. 1, No. 1 Golden,
                                              No. 1 Bronze, No. 1 Russet, No. 2 Bright,
                                              No. 2, No. 2 Russet, No. 5
  Oranges (Texas)   Fancy, No. 1, No. 1 Bright, No. 1 Bronze,
                                              Combination No. 2, No. 2 Russet, No. 3
  Peaches   No. 1, No. 2
  Pears, Summer and Fall   No. 1, Combination, No. 2
  Pears, Winter   Extra No. 1, No. 1, Combination, No. 2
  Pineapples   Fancy, No. 1, No. 2
  Plums and Prunes   Fancy, No. 1, Combination, No. 2
  Rhubarb   No. 1, No. 2
  Strawberries and Raspberries   No. 1, No. 2
  Tangerines   Fancy, No. 1, No. 1 Bronze, No. 1 Russet,
                                              No. 2, No. 2 Russet, No. 3
  Watermelon   No. 1, Commercial, No. 2

Vegetables
  Artichokes, Globe   No. 1, No. 2
  Asparagus   No. 1, No. 2 (Washington No. 1, Washing-
                                              ton No. 2 are more used in the markets)
  Beans, Lima   No. 1, Combination No. 2
  Beans, Snap   Fancy, No. 1, Combination, No. 2
  Beets   No. 1, No. 2

Table 2–15 (Continued)
Federal Standards for Fresh Fruits and Vegetables at the Wholesale Level*

Beet Greens	No. 1
Broccoli, Italian Sprouting	Fancy, No. 1, No. 2
Brussels Sprouts	No. 1, No. 2
Cabbage	No. 1, Commercial
Carrots, bunched	No. 1, Commercial
Carrots, topped	Extra No. 1, No. 1, No. 2
Carrots, short-trimmed tops	No. 1, Commercial
Cauliflower	No. 1
Celery	Extra No. 1, No. 1, No. 2
Collard or Broccoli Greens	No. 1.
Corn, Green	Fancy, No. 1, No. 2
Cucumbers	No. 1, No. 1 large, No. 2
Cucumbers, Greenhouse	Fancy, No. 1, No. 2
Dandelion Greens	No. 1
Eggplant	Fancy, No. 1, No. 2
Endive, Escarole, Chicory	No. 1
Garlic	No. 1
Kale	No. 1, Commercial
Lettuce	No. 1, No. 2
Lettuce, Greenhouse Leaf	Fancy, No. 1
Mushrooms	No. 1
Mustard Greens and Turnip Greens	No. 1
Okra	No. 1
Onions, Bermuda, Granex	No. 1, No. 2, Commercial
Onions, Creole	No. 1, No. 2, Combination
Onions, Northern Grown	No. 1, No. 1 Boilers, No. 1 Picklers, Commercial No. 2
Onions, Green	No. 1, No. 2
Parsley	No. 1
Parsnips	No. 1, No. 2
Peas, Fresh	Fancy, No. 1
Peppers, Sweet	No. 1, No. 2
Potatoes	Fancy, Extra No. 1, No. 1, No. 2, Commercial
Potatoes, Sweet	Extra No. 1, No. 1, Commercial, No. 2
Radishes	No. 1, Commercial
Romaine	No. 1
Rutabagas or Turnips	No. 1, No. 2
Shallots, Bunched	No. 1, No. 2
Spinach, fresh	Extra No. 1, No. 1, Commercial
Squash, Fall and Winter type	No. 1, No. 2
Squash, Summer	No. 1, No. 2
Tomatoes, Fresh	No. 1, Combination, No. 2
Tomatoes, Greenhouse	Fancy, No. 1, No. 2

*Prefix U.S. before all grades.

Table 2–16
Storage of Fresh Vegetables

Beans, Snap	Temperature range of 40° to 45° F in an institutional refrigerator, with 85 to 90% humidity.
Beets	Temperature 32°F is ideal—35° to 45°F is satisfactory for a short period (beets wilt because of rapid loss of water). Topped beets need very high humidity 95 to 98%. Bunch beets need 85 to 90%.
Cabbage	Temperature 32° to 35° F, humidity 90 to 95%
Carrots	Temperature 32° F, humidity 90 to 95%
Celery	Temperature 31° to 32° F, humidity 90 to 95%
Corn	Temperature 31° to 32° F, humidity 85 to 90%. Tests show Corn can lose as much as 40% of its sugar in 24 hours when not kept cold.
Cucumbers	Temperature 45° to 50° F, humidity 90 to 95%
Eggplant	Temperature 45° to 50° F, humidity 90 to 95%
Garlic	Keep cool and dry—short period.
Greens	All varieties should be kept cold and moist. Temperature 32° F, humidity 90 to 95%. Should be received cold and kept so.
Lettuce	Temperature 32° F, humidity 90 to 95%
Okra	Temperature 50° F, humidity 85 to 95%
Onions, dry	Storage of onions depends on the length of time to be held. Will keep 5 days if kept dry and cool and well ventilated. If held longer refrigerate 32° to 36° F, humidity 60 to 70% or lower, preferably 50%. Do not store with other foods that will absorb onion odor.
Onions, green	Temperature 32° F, humidity 85 5o 90%, keep covered to avoid drying.
Parsley	Temperature 32° to 33° F, humidity 80 to 85%
Peppers, green	Temperature 45° to 50° F, humidity 85 to 90%
Potatoes	*Late Crop* stored for a short time at room temperature. If stored for week or more 55° F, humidity 85 to 90%—this temperature preserves the bland flavor, 40° F and lower will cause some of the starch to be converted to sugar. *New Crop* is more perishable, need to be used quickly. The humidity and temperature should be about the same as late crop.
Radishes	Temperature 32° F, humidity 90 to 95%. Topped radishes in a plastic bag should be kept cold, in this case humidity is not a problem.
Squash	*Winter types*—50° to 55° F, humidity 75%. *Summer types*—32° to 40° F, humidity 85 to 95% for short periods only
Sweet Potatoes	Temperature 55° to 60° F, humidity 85 to 90%. Do not chill. If kept above 75° F, will sprout.
Tomatoes	Ripe tomatoes may be held two or three days at 50° F, or slightly lower.
Turnips and Rutabagas	Temperature 32° F, humidity 90 to 95%. Handled like topped carrots.

3 Processed Fruits and Vegetables

CANNED FRUITS AND VEGETABLES

Nicolas Appert, distinguished French scientist, began the canning industry when his experiments proved that foods could be preserved by subjecting them to heat in sealed containers. Many advances have been made in canning since Appert first developed his equipment and methods. The canning industry is today a vast structure operating throughout the world, and canned foods rank first in quantity of all foods processed.

To preserve quality and reduce costs, canneries are located close to their supply of raw materials. Some fish canneries are even built on ships or barges, and canning occurs out at sea. Many canners work closely with growers and agricultural experts to improve the quality of the raw product. Reduction of harvesting and processing time has favored better quality and nutrient retention. Constant research is conducted to improve processing methods and reduce costs.

Today's cannery is highly mechanized, and little or no handwork occurs in preparing, washing, sizing, grading, peeling, shelling, trimming, loading into cans or other manipulations. After preparation and selection, the food is ready for blanching in boiling water or steam. This is done to fix color, improve flavor, destroy enzymes and bacteria, soften tissues and remove gases and dirt. Blanched asparagus is more pliable for filling into cans, and bulky spinach or other greens are reduced in size so that they can be easily packed into cans. Certain fruits when blanched have a more uniform color and will not turn brown from oxidation. After blanching, the foods are ready for the cans. Only a few require complete cooking at this point. They are covered with a

FIG. 3–1. As cans come out of capping machines they are put into giant cradles and then into steamers at high temperatures. Courtesy USDA.

packing liquid. The cans are then closed and exhausted. Exhausting is done either by heating or by using a mechanical vacuum. Closing is by machine and most canners use 190 and 165° F, respectively, for closing small and large cans under heat treatment. The food is then processed, usually by steam under pressure. The heat destroys enzymes and bacteria. Once the food is sterilized in hermetically sealed cans, there is little chance for spoilage. After processing, the cans are rapidly cooled with running water, water spray or air.

Canners code the tops of their cans with letters and numbers so that the product can be identified and additional information, such as date of canning, can be known.

The development of the crimped double-seam can has made it possible to can foods with far more assurance against spoilage than formerly possible. The development of enamels to prevent foods from reacting with the metals of the container was another important step. Certain enamels or lacquers can be applied in a uniform film over metal sheets and then baked at high temperatures, leaving an insoluble, inert, resinous film on the tin plate. These enamels resist attack from foods upon the metal of the can. One of the most important enamels developed has been the Sanitary, also known as the Standard or "R" enamel. This enamel is used for cans in which highly colored fruits, berries or beets are processed. It prevents tin salts from joining with the acid and anthocyanin pigments (red) which would develop an off-color and off-flavor. C-enamel is another enamel used for canning products containing large quantities of sulfur. This enamel retards development of ferrous sulfide, a dark, undesirable tasting substance. Corn, fish, meats and other products are packed in cans lined with this enamel. Additional types of enamels have been perfected to resist the specific action of fats, meats, acid, alcohol or other products.

Labeling

Although some canners label their own canned foods and market them under their own brands, a majority do not; instead they sell the cans unlabeled or label them for various jobbers or wholesalers with the jobber's or wholesaler's own brand.

The provisions of the Pure Food, Drug and Cosmetic Act must be observed in labeling. This means that the label must list the name of the product, the name and address of the canner or distributor, the net can contents and the common name of the ingredients in the product if the product is not a standard food. If below standard of quality or fill,

FIG. 3-2. An example of a good label. Some of the information is not required by law but it tells the buyer much about the product. The "1.06" refers to the specific gravity of the tomato puree. The use of the term "fancy" indicates that the seller claims his product meets U.S. Fancy quality but makes no claim that federal inspection has established this. Under court rulings, this product, if shipped in interstate commerce, may be considered misbranded if it does not meet standards for U.S. Fancy quality.

NET CONTENTS
6 LBS. 10 OZS.

	DRAINED	WITH BRINE
NUMBER OF 2 OZ. SERVINGS	36	52
NUMBER OF 3 OZ. SERVINGS	24	35

TENDER YOUNG
SWEET PEAS
MIXED LARGE SIZES

SUGAR AND SALT ADDED
ARTIFICIALLY COLORED

DISTRIBUTED BY
GREEN GIANT
COMPANY
LE SUEUR, MINNESOTA

BELOW STANDARD IN QUALITY
ARTIFICIALLY COLORED

ABOVE LEGEND MANDATORY-PEAS ACTUALLY HIGH QUALITY

FIG. 3-3. An example of a good descriptive label. Note the descriptive words, which have precise meaning in relation to quality, quantity and other factors of interest to the buyer. Because the product is colored with an artificial green coloring to make the peas green, it must be labeled "Below Standard in Quality." The food is high in other quality factors.

the label must indicate this. The packing medium must be listed. Style of pack, variety, the use of artificial or imitation flavors or colors must be noted. If the label has any foreign language on it, the language must conform to the provisions of the act as if it was written in English. Special dietary packs must label the nutrient values claimed.

Sometimes voluntary statements may appear on the can, such as the sieve size, or terms indicating size, such as "extra large," "small," or "midget." Some packers make voluntary statements regarding variety and style of pack. This information is not required by federal regulations. Some will use descriptive words, such as "very young," "young" and "mature," to indicate age of the product. Other voluntary statements may include quantities in terms of cupfuls, number of servings, number of pieces in the can and the can size. Methods for using the product may be given. This labeling is called *descriptive labeling* and by encouraging good descriptive labeling canners feel that they give sufficient information to make grading unnecessary. A good example of descriptive labeling is seen in Figures 3-2 and 3-3.

Standards of Quality

The federal government, through the U.S. Department of Agriculture, has established quality standards or grades for most canned fruits and vegetables as required by law. The use of these standards of quality in the trade is voluntary. The grades are:

Fruits	Vegetables
U.S. Grade A or U.S. Fancy	U.S. Grade A or U.S. Fancy
U.S. Grade B or U.S. Choice	U.S. Grade B or U.S. Extra-Standard*
U.S. Grade C or U.S. Standard	U.S. Grade C or U.S. Standard

*California canned tomatoes B grade may appear on the market graded "Choice."

If a canned item does not meet these standards of quality, it must be labeled "Below Standard in Quality," and the reason must be listed why. (See Figure 3-3.) The use of the letters "U.S." before a grade term indicates that the product has been graded by a federal inspector. The use of a federal shield with a grade in it also makes this same claim. The use of the terms in any way of "Fancy," "Choice," "Extra-Standard" or "Standard" on a label does not make this claim but the courts have ruled that if these terms are used in any way on a label of food moving in interstate commerce and the food is not found to be the

FIG. 3-4. Three grades of canned tomatoes. Front tray contains U.S. Grade A or Fancy tomatoes. These are whole, practically uniform, good, red, typical color; practically free from defects; normal tomato flavor and odor. The back tray contains U.S. Grade B or Extra Standard tomatoes. The tomatoes are mostly whole, reasonably good, red, typical color; reasonably free from defects; normal tomato flavor and odor. The tray at the right contains U.S. Grade C or Standard tomatoes. These are mostly pieces, fairly good red, typical color, fairly free from defects, normal tomato flavor and odor. Courtesy USDA.

quality indicated by the term, the food is misbranded. Many producers, therefore, avoid using these terms and attempt to indicate quality by other words.

Grade determination. Federal grades are established by examination of the product and scoring specific factors. The total of factor scores determines grade. If a product scores 90 or above, it may be Grade A or Fancy, 80 to 89 Grade B or Choice or Extra-Standard, 70 to 79 Grade C or Standard, and below 70, Substandard. Substandard does not mean the food is unwholesome. All canned foods must be wholesome under provisions of the Food and Drug Administration. Substandard merely means that the food has some quality defect lower than the Standard grade. It may be considerably broken up, be considerably off-color or it may contain more than an allowed amount of defects, such as peel or uneven cuts. Where food services must meet low cost budgets, Substandard foods may be used. Where form and appearance are not important, Substandard foods, lacking these qualities, may be used in all operations.

Scores establishing grade are not the same for all canned items. Frequently a score of 90 or above is top grade but this may not necessarily be so. A top grade in fruit or vegetable juice may be as low as 85. The number of grades and the minimum scores for determining the grades will be those necessary to adequately move the product through channels of trade. In some instances products may not qualify for a grade even though the total score is at or above the minimum score established for that grade. This occurs because of a "limiting rule." A limiting rule means that, should a product fail to score above a certain level on a factor, it cannot be placed in the grade established by the total score but only in the grade established by the score for that factor. Thus, in the federal standard for pears, if the color score is 14 or 15, the pears "shall not be graded above U.S. Grade C or U.S. Standard . . . regardless of the total score for the product." It then adds, "This is a limiting rule." This means that even though the score total of the product is 89, the pears cannot be graded B or Choice because they have failed to score above 15 for color. A "partially limiting rule" is one where the grader is given some freedom in making a judgment to limit grade if the product fails to score sufficiently high in a specific factor. (See footnotes 1 and 2 in Figure 3-5.)

Most fruits and vegetables are scored on the basis of color, absence of defects and character. Character takes in tenderness, texture, maturity and so forth. Very often, uniformity and symmetry are other factors scored. Flavor is frequently not a scored factor but is considered a characteristic "under the masthead," which means that good flavor and good odor must be present in all products to be eligible for grading.   Examples of score factors and their range are shown in Table 3–1.

Buyers should realize that the range of points within grade is an important factor to consider.   Pears scoring 90 points and pears scoring 89 points may be closely similar in quality but separated by grade and, consequently, price.   Buyers, by requesting certification of canned items,

Score Sheet for Canned Fruit Cocktail.

Three standards are indicated: Grades A, B and Substandard (SStd).

Size and kind of container_____
Container mark or identification_____
Label_____
Net weight (ounces)_____
Vacuum (inches)_____
Drained weight (ounces):
  ( ) Meets fill of container_____
  ( ) Fails fill of container_____
Brix measurement_____
Sirup designation (extra heavy, heavy, etc.)_____
Proportions of fruit ingredients:
  Peach: __ oz ___ % ( ) Meets ( ) Fails_____
  Pear: __ oz ___ % ( ) Meets ( ) Fails_____
  Pineapple: __ oz ___ % ( ) Meets ( ) Fails_____
  Grape: __ oz ___ % ( ) Meets ( ) Fails_____
  Cherry: __ oz ___ % ( ) Meets ( ) Fails_____
    Total __ oz 100 %
Count:
  Pineapple ( ) Sectors ( ) Diced_____
  Cherry halves_____

Factors		Score points	
Clearness of liquid media_____	20	(A)	17–20
		(B)	14–16
		(SStd)	[1]0–13
Color_____	20	(A)	17–20
		(B)	[2]14–16
		(SStd)	[1]0–13
Uniformity of size_____	20	(A)	17–20
		(B)	[2]14–16
		(SStd)	[1]0–13
Absence of defects_____	20	(A)	17–20
		(B)	[1]14–16
		(SStd)	[1]0–13
Character _____	20	(A)	17–20
		(B)	[1]14–16
		(SStd)	[1]0–13
Total score_____	100		

Normal flavor and odor_____
Grade_____

[1] Indicates limiting rule.
[2] Indicates partial limiting rule.

Score Sheet for Canned Asparagus.

Note three standards are indicated, A, C and Substandard.

Number, size, and kind of container_____
Label_____
Container mark or identification_____
Net weight (ounces)_____
Vacuum (inches)_____
Drained weight (ounces)_____
Type_____
Style_____
Size or sizes (Spears, tips, and points)_____
Length of cut_____
Heads (cut) (percent, by count)_____

Factors		Score points	
Liquor _____	10	(A)	9–10
		(C)	7–8
		(SStd)	[1]0–6
Color _____	20	(A)	17–20
		(C)	14–16
		(SStd)	[1]0–13
Defects_____	30	(A)	25–30
		(C)	[1]21–24
		(SStd)	[1]0–20
Character _____	40	(A)	34–40
		(C)	[1]28–33
		(SStd)	[1]0–27
Total score_____	100		_____

Flavor (A, C, or SStd)_____
Grade_____

[1] Indicates limiting rule.

FIG. 3–5.   Courtesy USDA.

Table 3–1

Factors	Score Range from Maximum to Minimum			
	A	B	C	(Substandard)
Peas				
Clearness of liquor	9–10	7–8	5–6	0–4
Uniformity of color	14–15	11–13	8–10	0–7
Absence of defects	27–30	23–26	19–22	0–18
Maturity	40–45	34–39	28–33	0–27
Total score range	90–100	75–89	60–74	below 60
Pears				
Color	18–20	16–17	14–15	0–13
Uniformity of size and symmetry	18–20	16–17	14–15	0–13
Absence of defects	27–30	24–26	21–23	0–20
Character	27–30	24–26	21–23	0–20
Total score range	90–100	80–89	70–79	0–69

may obtain the scores of the products certified. Some factors within a quality standard may not be important for certain production uses, such as uniformity of size and symmetry for peaches or pears that are to be diced or cut up, and if the scoring is low on this point but high on others, the product may be a good buy.

In general, top, middle and lowest grades in canned products will meet the following descriptions:

U.S. Grade A or Fancy products are highest quality. Fancy vegetables must have clear liquor, a typical, uniform color, normal flavor, appropriate size for the vegetable and be tender, succulent, well formed and free from blemishes and extraneous water. Fruits must have typical color without blemish, greenness or tarnishing. Color must be uniform. Shape and symmetry must be good. Crushed, broken, split or other damaged items may be only within established tolerances. Similarly, defects such as stems of fruit, caps in berries, peel, and evidences of poor workmanship, as in coring of pears or pitting of peaches, must be within narrow tolerance limits. Very frequently the term "practically free" is used to indicate quality factors for items in this grade.

U.S. Grade B or Extra-Standard, or Choice products are not usually as tender or succulent, well trimmed or fine flavored as those in the higher grade. This grade in vegetables may have two or three but not all of the following defects: lack of symmetry or form, lack of uniformity of color, lack of the deepness of color found in Fancy products, slight blemishes or spots, larger or smaller pieces than in the Fancy grade or pieces not as uniform. Fruits, similarly, will lack the color, shape and symmetry or character of the higher grade item. "Reasonably free" is the term used to describe quality in this grade.

U.S. Grade C or Standard products are good, edible food, wholesome in every respect but not meeting the standards of the above higher grades. Standard products may lack tenderness, as in peas, corn or cherries. They may also have fewer whole or less uniform pieces than the next grade or lack uniformity of color. More blemishes, or broken or mashed items, may be in them. Greenness or paleness of color may be more evident. They may have several but not all of the following defects: off-color, excessive spots, blemishes, hard portions and other defects that detract from appearance or quality. Lack of uniformity in size or symmetry, insufficient trim, coring or peeling are included in this group. Frequently the term "fairly free" is used to describe characteristics within this grade.

U.S. Substandard (SStd) products are those lacking the required quality of the C Grade. Noticeable variation in characteristics making up quality is cause for grading a canned food substandard.

Some confusion exists on terms to use for substandard foods, and sometimes foods that are above substandard are thought of as that because of the terms used. U.S. Grade D is frequently the same quality fruit as U.S. Grade C except that the fruit is packed in water. If an item is graded U.S. Grade E, it is of lower quality than C or is Substandard, and it is also packed in water.

Solid packs, heavy packs or water packs are not necessarily substandard. They may be any grade, and some Grade A quality fruits are packed in water. A *solid pack* means that the product has had no water added. A *heavy pack* means that the product has had only a small quantity of water added. Sometimes solid or heavy packs are called "pie packs" in the trade, but most frequently a pie pack refers to a U.S. Grade E item. Buyers would be wise to discontinue the words "pie pack" and refer to the type of pack in specifications as sirup (giving density of sirup), water, solid pack or heavy pack. The grade of the item desired should be stated. If a Grade D or E water pack item is desired, this should be so stated.

Standards of Identity

The provisions of standards of identity noted in Chapter 1 must be observed for canned goods. All government standards for quality also include a definition of the identity of the item to be graded. Standard or common foods must meet provisions of standards of identity. Uncommon food mixtures must have ingredients listed on the label in order of greatest to least quantity. Exact quantities of ingredients need not be given. The standard term "Pork and Beans" may be used as the common name, but the list of ingredients below on the label must list beans before pork if more beans are in the pack than pork.

Standards of Fill

Standards of fill may vary. Some canned products must be filled to within $\frac{3}{16}$ in. of the top of the container. Others must be filled to 90% of the water capacity, while still others must be filled as "full as practical" without impairment of quality or breaking or crushing the ingredients. If the product fails to meet the standard of fill, it must be prominently labeled "Below Standard in Fill" or "Slack Fill." The National Canner's Association has recommended the following standards for filling as full as practical without impairment to products.

No. 10 and No. 3 cylinder cans	$\frac{27}{32}''$
No. 2½ cans	$\frac{20}{32}''$
No. 2 cans	$\frac{19}{32}''$

Drained Weight

In most instances drained weight is not a factor influencing grade, but government standards for quality usually state recommended drained weights for products. Drained weight refers to the weight of the product after its liquid content has been allowed to drain for 2 minutes on screens.[1]

The yield in servings from canned items will frequently vary according to the ratio of fruit or vegetable to packing medium. Buyers should state drained weight requirements and should test to see that drained

[1] To determine the drained weight, the contents are emptied on a circular mesh screen, set on a frame with the vertical side higher than the level of the product on the screen. The can contents are distributed over the screen to form a layer of uniform depth, accomplished usually by tilting the open container so as to distribute the contents evenly over the screen, which has been previously weighed. Fruits in halves are turned pitside down during the draining to permit complete drainage, but this is done in such a way as not to express additional liquid. Two minutes from the time drainage begins, weigh the screen and the drained item. The weight, less the screen weight, is the total drained weight. Four types of circular screens are used to determine drained weights: (1) 8 in. screen with 8 meshes to the inch for all goods packed in No. 2½ cans or smaller, except tomatoes, (2) 8 in. screen with two meshes to the inch for tomatoes in No. 2 cans or smaller, (3) 12 in. screen with eight meshes to the inch for all foods packed in No. 3 cylinder, No. 10 or 1 gal cans, except tomatoes and (4) 12 in. screen with two meshes to the inch for tomatoes in No. 10 cans. The bottom of the sieve or screen is woven-wire cloth, which complies with the specifications for such cloth as set forth under "2380 Micron No. 8" in Table I of the Standard Specifications for Sieves, published March 1, 1940, in LC 584 of the U.S. Department of Commerce, National Bureau of Standards.

FIG. 3–6. This instrument, a consistometer, measures the rate of flow of liquids after the end part is filled to an established level and the trap is opened. Courtesy USDA.

weights equal those specified. Vegetables will, on the average, have a higher drained weight than fruits. There is some feeling that the present recommended drained weights for fruits may be too high to meet good trade practices and these may be lowered in the future. Some buyers state that water or light sirup packs have a higher drained weight than the heavier sirup packs. Buyers should compile their own information on yields, such as: "One No. 10 can of sliced, solid pack apples will yield six 9 in. pies" or "one No. 10 can of pumpkin will yield eight 9 in. pies." Table 3–6 gives some of this information. Servings obtained from a can are frequently stated on descriptive labels. If stated in undrained weight and the product is served drained, the information given may be misleading.

With some products drained weight cannot be obtained. Tests for establishing density have been determined for such products as cream-style corn and apple butter. The product is usually stirred and then a small amount is placed in a mounded mass on a smooth, flat surface. After 2 minutes the spread is noted and the amount of separation of free liquid. In other tests the flow is calculated on a consistometer. Some buyers use a large blotter and place competitive products in equally measured amounts on the blotter; then they note the moisture ring formed after 2 minutes. Criteria have been developed for tomato products based on the specific gravity or the percent of solids. Tomato catsup specified as "heavy" has 33% solids (specific gravity 1.15) and "light" has 25% solids (specific gravity 1.11). Usually catsup is concentrated to not less than 25%, tomato paste not less than 24% and puree not less than 25% solids.

Count and Size

Count or size in the can may be important at times for portioning yield. Proper selection of count can be made by reference to the sizes listed in this text. If pineapple slices for 28 or 64 count per No. 10 are the same price, a better appearing and slightly more economical portion is obtained by giving two 64-count slices rather than the one 28-count.

Buyers frequently have difficulty in translating the quantity of food

Table 3–2
Some Common Can Sizes Used in Food Facilities

Can Name	Dimensions, in. Diameter	Height	Canner's Designation	Volume, oz	Approximate Cups	Number per Case
2Z	$2\frac{1}{8}$	$2\frac{1}{4}$	202 x 204*			
	$2\frac{1}{8}$	$2\frac{7}{8}$	202 x 214	$4\frac{3}{4}$‡	$\frac{1}{2}$‡	12, 24, 48
6Z	$2\frac{1}{8}$	$3\frac{1}{2}$	202 x 308	$5\frac{3}{4}$	$\frac{2}{3}$	24, 48
8Z tall†	$2\frac{11}{16}$	$3\frac{1}{4}$	211 x 304	8.3	1	24, 36, 48, 72
No. 1 picnic	$2\frac{11}{16}$	4	211 x 400	$10\frac{1}{2}$	$1\frac{1}{4}$	24, 48
No. 211 cylinder	$2\frac{11}{16}$	$4\frac{7}{8}$	211 x 414	12	$1\frac{1}{2}$	24, 36, 48
No. 300	3	$4\frac{7}{16}$	300 x 407	$13\frac{1}{2}$	$1\frac{3}{4}$	24, 36, 48
No. 1 tall	$3\frac{1}{16}$	$4\frac{11}{16}$	301 x 411	15	2	24, 48
No. 303	$3\frac{3}{16}$	$4\frac{3}{8}$	303 x 406	15.6	2	12, 24, 36
No. 303 cylinder	$3\frac{3}{16}$	$5\frac{9}{16}$	303 x 509	19	$2\frac{1}{3}$	
No. $\frac{1}{2}$ flat	$3\frac{7}{16}$	$2\frac{1}{16}$	307 x 201			48
No. 2	$3\frac{7}{16}$	$4\frac{9}{16}$	307 x 409	19.9	$2\frac{1}{2}$	12, 24
No. 2 cylinder	$3\frac{7}{16}$	$5\frac{3}{4}$	307 x 512	23	3	24
No. $2\frac{1}{2}$	$4\frac{1}{16}$	$4\frac{11}{16}$	401 x 411	28.5	$3\frac{1}{2}$	12, 24
No. 3	$4\frac{1}{4}$	$4\frac{7}{8}$	404 x 414	33.6	4	12, 24
No. 3 cylinder	$4\frac{1}{4}$	7	404 x 700	46	$5\frac{3}{4}$	12
No. 5	$5\frac{1}{8}$	$5\frac{5}{8}$	502 x 510	56	7	12
No. 10	$6\frac{3}{16}$	7	603 x 700	103.7	$12\frac{3}{4}$	12
Gallon	$6\frac{3}{16}$	$8\frac{3}{4}$	603 x 812	130	16	6, 12

*Diameter is represented by first number and height by second; the first digit in each three digit group indicates inches and the second and third digits, sixteenths of an inch. Thus, 303 by 406 is a can $3\frac{3}{16}$ in. in diameter and $4\frac{3}{8}$ in. in height.

†Also called No. 55 or the 8-oz can.

‡One fluid ounce equals $\frac{1}{16}$ pint and one cup equals $\frac{1}{2}$ pint. Net weight of contents not given since foods vary in density and thus in net weight contained in cans.

obtained in various can sizes. In general, it takes two No. 3 cylinder cans, three and a half No. $2\frac{1}{2}$ cans, five and a half No. 2 cans and six No. 303 cans to equal the quantity of food in a No. 10 can. To equal a case of 24/303's, use, respectively, 0.82, 0.57 and 0.74 of 24/2's, 24/2$\frac{1}{2}$'s and 6/10's. To equal a case of 24/2's, use, respectively, 1.22, 0.69 and 0.75 cases of 24/303's, 24/2$\frac{1}{2}$'s and 6/10's. To equal a case of 24/2$\frac{1}{2}$'s, use, respectively 1.74, 1.45 and 1.08 of 24/303's, 24/2's and 6/10's. To equal a case of 12/3 cylinder (46 oz) cans, use, respectively, 1.28, 1.26, 0.87 and 0.94 of 24/303's, 24/2's, 24/2$\frac{1}{2}$'s and 6/10's. To equal a case of 6/10's, use, respectively, 1.35, 1.33, and 0.92 of 24/303's, 24/2's and 24/2$\frac{1}{2}$'s. Common can sizes are listed in Table 3–2.

Sirup Density

The density of the sirup is not a factor in establishing quality. Federal laws require that the label state the type of packing medium. Sirups may be water or juice: plain, slightly sweetened, light sirup, medium sirup, heavy sirup or extra-heavy sirup. The density of a sirup may be tested by using a Brix hydrometer.

There are no general standards for density of extra heavy, heavy or other sirup densities. Standards are set for specific fruits. A light sirup for peaches will be between 14 and 19° Brix, while a light sirup for cherries will be between 16 and 20° Brix. When fruit is canned, a much heavier sirup is put into the can than is obtained when the fruit is opened. Apricots packed in 55, 40 and 25° Brix will "cut out," respectively, 25, 21 and 16°. This sirup density at packing is called the "put in," while the sirup density at the opening is, as indicated, called the "cut out." Fruit, after canning, must stand at least 15 days before "cut out" sirup density is tested. The can may then be opened and a Brix reading taken. Buyers should specify sirup densities desired.

Federal regulations govern the amount of non-sucrose sugars that can be used with sucrose in sirups. Normally, for every degree Brix, the product may be estimated to have a 1% sugar content. Thus, a product cutting out at 21° Brix will be approximately 21% sugar. Because sugar strengthens cellulose, fruits canned in high density sirups are usually firmer than those canned in low density sirups. Berries, freestone peaches, fruit cocktail and other fragile products are best purchased in the heavier sirups. Buyers should be aware, however, that purchasing some fruits in heavy or extra heavy sirup may represent a waste if the sirup cannot be utilized either in serving with the fruit or for making gelatin desserts, punch or other preparations. If the sirup cannot be used, it is wiser to purchase fruits in lighter sirup at lower cost, providing the quality is acceptable.

Defects in Canned Goods

Although modern canning methods have eliminated most of the losses that resulted from can failures or improper processing methods, spoilage does occasionally occur. A can may be dropped and a seam will spring. High acidity in the product may eventually eat through the metal. Other failures unrelated to either the method of processing or the can itself may occur.

A can that develops a leak so that contents run out is called a *leaker.* Even though a can may be properly sealed, a failure to sterilize the contents may result in bacterial action that produces gas to distend the can. Such a can is called a *swell.* A swell may be so mild as to barely distend the ends or so strong as to cause the can to burst. A *puffer* is a swell but is usually applied to a can swelled from meat spoilage. Most food spoilage is accompanied by carbon dioxide, a distasteful odor and deteriorated appearance of the product. Some spoilages may occur without air. When spoilages occur that require air, the can must be a leaker.

Bacterial spoilage in canned foods may be caused by thermophilic bacteria, types of bacteria that resist high canning temperatures and grow best at higher than normal temperatures. Spoilage from these bacteria usually occurs much more slowly at temperatures of 100° F or above. This spoilage is frequently encountered when storage areas are warm. A spoilage caused by flat, sour thermophiles produces an acid but no gas, and, therefore, the can will not swell. The spoilage can be detected by the high acid smell and the disintegration of the food into a sloughy, soft product. Color changes may also be evident. Thermophilic anerobic bacteria—"heat-loving" bacteria that grow without any air or oxygen—are evident by the development of acid plus the development of gas, which distends the can. The odor of the food from this type of bacterial spoilage is described as "cheesy." Some other anerobic thermophiles form hydrogen sulfide. This gas is soluble in the liquid and so the can does not swell. Blackness from iron sulfide formation may be an indication of this spoilage, and the odor may be unpleasant and nauseating.

Clostridium botulinum poisoning is seldom found in commercially canned foods because of the high processing temperatures used. These bacteria produce a highly poisonous toxin under anerobic conditions. They cannot reproduce, however, in acid foods, such as tomatoes, fruit juices, canned fruits and acid vegetables. They may be found in canned beets, string beans, peas and other non-acid vegetables. The clostridium botulinum bacteria have the ability to change into spore form, which makes them able to withstand high temperatures. After the food is processed, under anerobic and non-acid conditons the spore will change back to viable bacteria and develop. A powerful poison results from this growth, a small amount of which is sufficient to cause violent death. Toxins have been developed that may be used to counteract the poison, and not all persons eating food contaminated from this bacteria will die if the toxin is administered quickly. Foods contaminated by botulinum may not have readily detected spoilage characteristics. Boiling foods containing botulinum for 10 minutes will destroy the toxin.

Some cans may become distended from non-bacterial causes; then the can is not called a swell but a *flipper* or a *springer*. An exception is a can distended by acid reacting with metals, thus freeing hydrogen. This type of can may be called a *hydrogen swell*. The food in a hydrogen swell, flipper or springer may be consumed without danger, but the best recommendation is to reject the food in all cans showing distention of any kind. Overfilling, storage at high altitudes, heat, denting of the can or other reasons may be the cause of a flipper or springer.

Discoloration may be caused by metals reacting with food substances, from the effect of high or prolonged heat or from bacterial action. Corn may become blue-gray from copper sulfide formation; peas may turn black when contanimated with copper. Blackening of hominy is caused by a failure to remove all the lye in processing. Copper increases the darkening of canned-milk products. Iron will darken fruits. At high temperatures the sulfur compounds in canned foods break down, and a black deposit may form in the headspace of the can. This black material may also become detached and adhere to some of the food; this is seen sometimes in canned corn where the C-enamel has failed to protect the can lining from attack. Pears may turn a pink color if subjected to too high heat in processing.

FROZEN FRUITS AND VEGETABLES

Rapid handling between the time of harvesting and the time of freezing is necessary to preserve maximum quality in frozen foods. Quick freezing is also required to develop small crystals that do not pierce and rupture cell walls. Three methods of freezing are used: (1) air blown through tunnels at extremely low temperatures, (2) contact—a process whereby packaged food is placed between low temperature plates and rapidly frozen and (3) immersion freezing. The third method is growing in use. Placing foods in liquid nitrogen at $-320°$ F gives extremely rapid freezing and high quality products.

Preliminary preparation of fruits and vegetables for freezing is similar to that used in canning. Like many canned products they are cleaned, sorted, washed, blanched to remove soil, destroy enzymes and bacteria and to make the food more pliable or dense for packing and handling. Blanching fixes and intensifies color in some vegetables. Oxidation or browning of fruits is minimized by using anti-oxidants, such as ascorbic acid or sulfur dioxide fumes. Vegetables are usually frozen with little or no added liquid. About 1% salt is added. Fruits retain flavor and color when frozen with some sugar. Part sucrose and part non-sucrose sugars may be used as sweeteners. Non-sucrose sugars may not exceed the sucrose used. Sirups may be used in place of sugar. Recommendations for fruit-sugar ratios are listed later in this chapter. Packaging for frozen fruits may be 10 or 12 oz, 1, 6, 6½, 25 and 30 lb and larger containers. The larger packs are usually in metal containers. Vegetables may be purchased in 10 and 12 oz, 1, 2, 2½, 3 and 5-lb packages. Some potatoes, peas and corn may be obtained in larger sizes.

Federal grading is the same as for canned goods with total score determining grade. Limiting rules may be effective in withholding a grade from a frozen fruit or vegetable in much the same way as for canned

Score Sheet for Frozen Broccoli.

Size and kind of container_____
Container mark or identification_____
Label_____
Net weight (ounces)_____
Style_____
Count (of stalks)_____

Factors		Score points	
Color _____	20	(A)	17–20
		(B)	[1]14–16
		(D)	[1]0–13
Uniformity of size_____	20	(A)	17–20
		(B)	14–16
		(D)	[1]0–13
Absence of defects_____	20	(A)	17–20
		(B)	[1]14–16
		(D)	[1]0–13
Character_____	40	(A)	34–40
		(B)	[1]28–33
		(D)	[1]0–27
Total score_____	100		

Flavor and odor_____
Grade _____

[1] Indicates limiting rule.

Score Sheet for Frozen Strawberries.

Number, size, and kind of container_____
Label: Style or pack: Fruit-sugar ratio (if shown)_____

Container mark or identification	Containers or sample
	Cases

Net weight (ounces)_____
Style _____
Size or sizes (whole)_____
Under ⅝″ (percent by count)_____

Factors		Score points	
Color _____	40	(A)	36–40
		(B)	[1]32–35
		(C)	[1]28–31
		(SStd)	[1]0–27
Defects_____	40	(A)	36–40
		(B)	[1]32–35
		(C)	[1]28–31
		(SStd)	[1]0–27
Character_____	20	(A)	18–20
		(B)	[1]16–17
		(C)	[1]14–15
		(SStd)	[1]0–13
Total score_____	100		

Flavor and odor_____
Grade _____

[1] Indicates limiting rule.

FIG. 3–7.   Courtesy USDA.

Table 3–3
Allowances for Defects in Frozen Pineapple*

Grade	Score points	Whole slices — Crushed units (By count)	Whole slices — Excessively trimmed (By count)	Whole slices — Blemished units (By count)	Whole slices — Broken units (By weight)	Crushed—Blemished units (By weight)	Half slices and broken slices — Crushed units (By count)	Half slices and broken slices — Blemished units (By count)	Tidbits and chunks — Crushed units (By count)	Tidbits and chunks — Blemished units (By count)
U.S. Grade A or U.S. Fancy	30	None	None	2%	4%	¼%	....	....	2%	2%
	29	None	None	3%	6%	¼%	....	....	3%	3%
	28	None	None	4%	8%	½%	....	....	4%	4%
	27	None	None	5%	10%	½%	....	....	5%	5%
U.S. Grade B or U.S. Choice	26	1%	1%	6%	15%	¾%	....	....	2%	6%
	25	3%	2%	9%	20%	¾%	....	....	3%	9%
	24	5%	3%	12½%	25%	1%	....	....	5%	12½%
U.S. Grade C or U.S. Standard	23	....	....	....	....	....	1%	6%	....	....
	22	....	....	....	....	....	3%	9%	....	....
	21	....	....	....	....	....	5%	12½%	....	....
U.S. Grade D or Substandard	20 or less	More than allowances permitted for 24 points.					More than allowances permitted for 21 points.		More than allowances permitted for 24 points.	

*United States Department of Agriculture.

FIG. 3–8. The quantity of dehydro-frozen apples on the left is the equivalent of the frozen sliced and the fresh apples shown to the right. Courtesy USDA.

items. The weighting of grade factors may vary according to the product. Many packers only process one or two grades. Frozen foods are graded after thawing and vegetables are usually cooked before grading. Good flavor and odor are requirements and are not a part of the total score. The number of points given a factor, such as defects, may be based on percentages of defects found in the product. The following indicates maximum possible scoring for raspberries, blueberries and peas:

	Raspberries	Blueberries	Peas
Color	40	20	20
Absence of defects	40	40	40
Character	20	40	40
Total score	100	100	100

The frozen-food industry has been slow to adopt federal standards for grading, preferring to sell on the basis of brand and descriptive labeling.

The packers of frozen fruits and vegetables have also restricted the number of grades or qualities packed, and buyers will have difficulty in finding three grade levels in frozen foods under one brand, as can be done many times with canned goods.

In addition, packers have had difficulty in maintaining the quality of their product after it leaves their control. Temperatures must be 0 to $-10°$ F to retain quality in a product, and it is not always possible, in shipment and storage, to maintain this low a temperature.

It has been found possible to partially dehydrate fruits and vegetables and freeze them; this is called dehydro-freezing. Besides reducing weight, some higher quality retention is possible. Undoubtedly more and more of these dehydro-frozen products will reach our markets in the near future.

FROZEN COOKED FOODS

Increasing quantities of frozen foods processed outside the facility to a point that they require only final conditioning are appearing on the market. With increasing labor costs and improved quality in such products, more and more interest is being shown in these new foods. As yet there have been no standards established for these products; facilities wishing to purchase them must establish their own. If the quality standard for a conventional product is selected and, from this, a specification developed for these food products, standards can be established upon which good quality products may be obtained. Facilities should be careful in expressing detail so that the products meet standards of quality desired. Use of standards of identity and quality established for canned goods may be of assistance. For instance, buyers might state that the meat portion of meat dishes should be approximately 14% cooked weight or 25% raw weight of the total weight of the product. A stew, fricassee, meat pie portion of 8 oz total should have, therefore, $1\frac{1}{2}$ oz of cooked meat in it or should have had 2 oz of raw meat used in its preparation. This ratio is required by law in these canned products when shipped in interstate commerce.

PROCESSED JUICES

The types of processed juices available for food facility use are fresh chilled, canned single strength, canned concentrated, frozen (usually concentrated) and dehydrated. Canned frozen juices outrank all others in quantities used.

Chilled Juices

Chilled juices are becoming increasingly available in highly populated urban centers, especially those close to heavy citrus growing areas. The ability to improve stability by treating with heat reduces perishability and facilitates marketing. Some chilled juices may not be heat treated but may merely be prepared from fresh fruit or concentrated juices and marketed. These juices may also be purchased sweetened or unsweetened. Canned juices and juices preserved with chemical preservatives do not qualify as chilled juices. Watch for coagulation and material separation. Good flavor and odor should be present without noticeable traces of oil from the fruit. Color should be good for the product. In orange juice the color should be a bright yellow or yellow orange. Dull, dark, murky juice should be rejected. Watch for seed or portions of fruit, rind, cells, pulp or other extraneous material. Excessive sediment should be cause for rejection. Brix readings for density will vary according to the quality, the amount of sweetener added and

Score Sheet for Chilled or Canned Orange Juice.

Size and kind of container_____
Container mark (packages)_____
     or
Identification (cases)_____
Label (including ingredient statement, if any)_____
Liquid measure (fluid ounces)_____
Style _____
Brix (degrees)_____
Acid (grams/100 ml.: calculated as anhydrous citric
    acid) _____
Brix-acid ratio ( )_____
Recoverable oil (% by volume)_____
Degree of coagulation____ { ( ) None_____
                  { ( ) Slight_____
                  { ( ) Serious_____

Factors		Score points	
Color _____	40	(A)	34–40
		(B)	[1]28–33
		(SStd)	[1]0–27
Defects_____	20	(A)	17–20
		(B)	[1]14–16
		(SStd)	[1]0–13
Flavor _____	40	(A)	34–40
		(B)	[1]28–33
		(SStd)	[1]0–27
Total score_____	100		

Grade _____

[1] Indicates limiting rule.

FIG. 3–9.   Courtesy USDA.

whether the chilled juice is made from single or concentrated-strength products. Brix readings may vary from 11.0 to 12.5°. The Brix-acid ratio is also a factor considered in quality, and this ratio may vary, according to product, from 11:1 to 17:1 in high quality juices. Federal standards for quality have been established for orange juice only, with Grades A and B having minimum scores, respectively, of 85 and 70.

Canned Juices

Apple, grape, grapefruit, blended grapefruit and orange, lemon, orange, pineapple, tangerine and tomato juices form the major portion of canned juices on the market. Federal grades for all these products exist. Some sauerkraut, carrot, blended vegetable or blended fruit juices and some tropical fruit juices are also on the market. Federal grades are U.S. Grade A or Fancy and U.S. Grade C or Standard. U.S. Grade D is Substandard. Minimum scores for grades A and C are 85 and 70, respectively.

The juice should possess a bright, sparkling typical color for the product. The color should not be dull, dark or excessively cloudy. The juice should be practically free from sediment or other residue, particles of pulp, seeds, specks, or other extraneous matter. The consistency should be typical for the product. Tomato juice should have some viscosity; while others should not. Flavor should be pleasant and

Table 3–4
Brix and Acid Values for U.S. Grade A Fruit Juices

Juice	Brix Minimum		Anhydrous Acid per ml, in Grams	Type Acid
	Sweetened	Unsweetened		
Canned single strength				
Apple		11.5	0.35 to 0.70	malic
Grape	16.0	14.0	0.45 to 1.40	tartaric
Grapefruit	11.5	9.0	0.85 to 2.00	citric
Grapefruit and orange	11.5	10.0	0.80 to 1.70	citric
Lemon		8.0	5.00 to 7.00	citric
Orange	10.5	10.5	0.75 to 1.45	citric
Pineapple	12.0	12.0	1.10	citric
Tangerine		12.5	0.70 to 1.40	citric
Canned concentrated				
Grapefruit		10.5*		
Orange		11.7*		

*Calculated after rehydration to normal concentration.

that of well-ripened, mature fruit, with aroma typical of the fruit. Because of processing, the flavor may vary from that of fresh juice, but there should be no flavor of fermentation, excess oil from peel or any other off flavors. Brix and acid limits have been established for those juices having federal standards. Some juices must meet a Brix-acid ratio. A U.S. Grade A grapefruit juice must have a Brix-acid ratio of 7:1 when the Brix reading is 10.5° or more. Buyers should watch for coagulation in the juices and tendency to separate. Juices may or may not be sweetened. Blends are on the market. Buyers should specify the ratio of the juices that are blended together. Fill of container should be 90% of total water capacity.

Canned Concentrated Juices

The use of canned concentrated fruit juices is increasing in food facilities. Federal standards exist for canned concentrated grapefruit, orange and tomato juice; although none exist for canned concentrated tomato juice it is used extensively in food services. There are two grades, U.S. Grade A or Fancy and U.S. Grade C or Standard, with minimum scores, respectively, of 85 and 70. The juices are graded after rehydration. Quality, Brix and acid values should be similar to those listed for canned juices. Buyers should state in specifications that juices concentrated for manufacturing are not acceptable for these are not suitable for food production use.

Frozen Juices

Most frozen juices are concentrated so that a water-juice ratio on rehydrating of 3:1 is used; others may vary from 2:1 to 18:1. These juices may be blends of varieties of a single fruit or blends of different fruits. Evaluation of quality is made after reconstitution, and factors considered are similar to those used for canned fruit juices. The flavor, however, should be more nearly that of fresh juice than that represented by canned juice. In addition, buyers should watch to see that the juice reconstitutes properly. Federal juice standards exist for grape, grapefruit, grapefruit and orange, lemon, lime and orange juices. The grades are U.S. Grade A (Fancy) and U.S. Grade B (Choice); minimum scores are 85 and 70 respectively.

Frozen concentrated pineapple juice may be obtained either in 7-gal, polyethylene-fiber containers or $^6/_{10}$ cans in a concentration of $4\frac{1}{2}:1$ water to juice ratio. Sweetened or unsweetened juices are available. Concentrated frozen lemon or lime juices, sweetened sufficiently for use as ades, are on the market.

Dehydrated Juices

Dehydrated grapefruit, orange, tomato and other juices are on the market. Federal standards for dehydrated grapefruit and dehydrated orange juice have been established. Grades are defined in these as U.S. Grade A or Fancy and U.S. Grade B or Choice, with minimum scores, respectively, 85 and 70. After rehydration the juices are evaluated, and the factors considered are similar to those given for canned juices above. The moisture content should not be more than 3%. The juices may be sweetened or unsweetened.

FRUIT SPREADS

A number of products are used as sweetened fruit spreads. These are jels that make up a group called jams, jellies, marmalades and fruit butters. Federal standards of identity state that fruit butters must not be less than 43% soluble solids and that jellies and jams must be not less than 65% soluble solids. Fruit or fruit juice in the ratio of 45 parts to 55 parts sugar is also required except for the fruit butters. The sweetening agents that may be used are also specified in identity standards. Non-sucrose sweeteners may not be more than 25% in ratio to a sucrose of 75%. If there is not a sufficient quantity of pectin or acid to form a jel, these may be added but only in sufficient quantity to make a jel.

Fruit spreads are made by first washing the fruit, sorting it and giving it preliminary treatment, such as peeling, paring, trimming and coring. The word "pure" used with a spread means that only fruit and sugar in required ratios have been used to form the basic components of the jel. The word "imitation" must be used when artificial color, flavor or other non-natural components are used. If juice only is to be used, the fruit is cooked, the juice pressed or extracted from the pulp and clarified for combination with the sugar. One fruit or combinations of two to five fruits may be used for jellies and jams. The soluble solids for jam and jellies must be between 65 and 68%. Special jellies also may be made, such as mint, honey and wine. Wine jelly may be made from 11% apple pectin, 56% sugar and 33% wine.

Marmalades are clear jellies in which slices or cut pieces of fruit or peel are suspended in the jel. Generally the citrus fruits are used for marmalades. Orange marmalade is frequently made from the Seville or bitter (sour) orange. Mixed citrus marmalades are also on the market, as are such items as gingerroot marmalade and carrot marmalade.

Jams and preserves are pieces of fruit suspended in a jel. A jam is usually a jel in which fruit is mashed or broken up in the jel, while a preserve has whole fruit suspended in the jel. The two terms are frequently confused.

Fruit butters are semi-solid pastes made by cooking strained fruit pulp to a desired consistency. Spices may be added. The resulting paste should be smooth, heavy enough to use as a spread and of good flavor. Standards of identity state that fruit butters are "smooth, semi-solid pastes made from not less than 5 parts by weight of fruit and 2 parts by weight of sweetener."

Federal grade standards for jams, jellies, marmalades and preserves are Grade A (Fancy) or Grade B (Choice) except for apple butter (and cranberry sauce if it is included as a spread), which have Grades A (Fancy) and C (Standard). The minimum score for Grade A in both is 85; the lower score minimum (either B or C) is 70.

Packing may be in cans, jars or tubs. No. 10 cans are most frequently used for food facility use. Jars may be 1, 2, 4, 5, 8½ lb and approximately 11 lb or 1 gal. The 30-gal wooden tub is used when large quantities are required for table service or bakeries or others using substantial quantities of these products.

DRIED AND LOW-MOISTURE FRUITS

Reducing the moisture content to below that point where bacteria, molds and decay can occur has been used as a means of fruit preservation since man's earliest history. At one time it was one of the main food processing methods used but with the introduction of modern methods of preservation by canning, freezing and refrigerated storage, the quantity of dried fruits consumed per capita has decreased. Nevertheless, every year in this country over a billion pounds of dried fruits are processed. Two methods of drying are used. Dried fruits are those which have had about 75% of the moisture removed either by drying in the sun or in areas where warm dry air is allowed to extract the moisture. Partial sun drying may be used with the drying finished in drying sheds or rooms. The second method is called vacu-drying and is a recent development. Fruits are dried by placing them in enclosed chambers. Dry warm inert gas under vacuum conditons extracts from 95 to 98% of the moisture. The use of the inert gas reduces flavor changes in drying. Because of the low moisture content, vacuum-dried fruits are less perishable and less liable to insect infestation. Flavor retention in some low-moisture products is also enhanced. Dried and vacu-dried products may be subjected to sulfur dioxide fumes to bleach the fruits and prevent their discoloration. Dried and vacu-dried fruits contain about 50% natural sugars.

FIG. 3–10. Trays of peaches spread for sun drying.

Many fruits are full ripe when selected for drying. Prunes and figs are allowed to drop to the ground from ripeness; then they are carefully gathered and dried. This ripening gives highest sugar content and maximum flavor. Pears are picked just before ripening and ripened in storage. Apples may be picked at good maturity and held. If these apples are removed from storage for drying while in good condition, the quality of the dried fruit will be good.

Because of the high maturity at which most dried fruits are selected, there is a chance of greater damage or defects. Good inspection should be given to see that only desirable fruit is obtained. The character of many fruits is considerably changed by drying, and damage caused by insects, molds or decay may be hidden. Modern methods of cleaning and processing have improved quality; thus, sanitation and defects are of much less concern than they were in the past.

Dried fruits are packed in a number of container sizes. The usual size for food facility use is the 30-lb or 25-lb fiber box, with the fruit protected by a layer of plastic on the outer edges. Many operations find that 4-lb packages, 6 packages to the case, are desirable. If the quantity used is not large, purchase of 1-lb packages may be advisable. Dates are packed in containers holding 60, 10, 5 and 1 lb. The 5 or 10-lb pack has been found best for food facilities. Many dried fruits may be purchased in the slab. If fruits are chopped or if form is not important, this may be more economical. Check quality carefully in slab fruit.

Storage of dried fruit should be in a 40 to 50° F area to reduce the danger from insect infestation. Moths and weevils are attracted to dried fruits. In areas of high humidity and favorable temperature, dried fruits may mold. Some facilities find that storage in refrigerated areas is re-

quired to hold dried fruits. Purchase dried and vacuum-dried fruits by
the pound. Most vacuum-dried fruits are packed in $^6/_{10}$ cans. This
packing, plus their low moisture content, leaves them less susceptible to
molds and insect infestation. Both types of dried fruits may darken and
lose flavor if held in storage for extended periods of time. Purchase in
one-month lots or two at the most.

As in all foods, many quality factors of dried fruits are empirical and
cannot be reduced to writing. Color, uniformity of size and shape,
absence of defects and character, the latter comprising such elements as
texture, tenderness and maturity, are factors indicating quality. Flavor
and odor are important.

Federal standards for quality exist for all dried fruits of market importance and for low-moisture apples, apricots and peaches. Certification for grade may be obtained by application to federal offices. Quality
terms are frequently used on the market as "good," "reasonably good"
and "fairly good" for U.S. Grades A (Fancy), B (Choice) or C (Standard), respectively. Grading for most dried fruits is done by counting
defects and assigning a percentage factor and these factors are added to
obtain total score. Federal standards have size as a factor for grade of
apples and prunes. Trade grades are based almost completely on size.
The California Dried Fruit Association certifies trade quality for fruit
shipped from California. Trade grades are given in Table 3-5. Raisins
have other grades for size, and these are listed under the discussion on
raisins. Dried fruits packaged for retail trade are sized differently than
the grades listed in this text and quantity food buyers who purchase retail stocks should know that this grading differs from that listed here.

Buyers should look for uniformity of color and lack of discoloration or
off-colors. Highest grades have light colors, bright and typical for the
product. Look for indications of unripeness, end cracks, flesh damage,
scars, mold, dirt, extraneous matter, decay, fermentation and other defects. Excessively sugared fruit is undesirable. Insect infestation or

Table 3-5
Size Standards for Dried Apricots, Figs, Peaches and Pears, in Inches

Size Number	Size Term	Apricots	Figs White	Figs Black	Peaches	Pears
1	Jumbo	$1\,^7/_{16}$ up	$^8/_{16}$ up	$1\,^5/_{16}$ up	2 up	$1\,^7/_8$ up
2	Extra Fancy	$1\,^3/_8 - 1\,^7/_{16}$	$1\,^5/_{16} - 1\,^8/_{16}$	$1\,^3/_{16} - 1\,^5/_{16}$	$1\,^3/_4 - 2$	$1\,^1/_4 - 1\,^7/_8$
3	Fancy	$1\,^1/_4 - 1\,^3/_8$	$1\,^3/_{16} - 1\,^5/_{16}$	$1\,^1/_{16} - 1\,^3/_{16}$	$1\,^1/_2 - 1\,^3/_4$	$1\,^1/_2 - 1\,^3/_4$
4	Extra Choice	$1 - 1\,^1/_4$	$1\,^1/_{16} - 1\,^3/_{16}$	$^{15}/_{16} - 1\,^1/_{16}$	$1\,^3/_8 - 1\,^1/_2$	$1\,^3/_8 - 1\,^1/_2$
5	Choice	$^{13}/_{16} - 1$	$^{15}/_{16} - 1\,^1/_{16}$	$^{13}/_{16} - ^{15}/_{16}$	$1\,^1/_8 - 1\,^3/_8$	$1\,^1/_8 - 1\,^3/_8$
6	Standard	under $^{13}/_{16}$	under $^{15}/_{16}$	under $^{13}/_{16}$	under $1\,^1/_8$	under $1\,^1/_8$

Work Sheet for Scoring Processed Raisins.

Size and kind of packages and/or cases_____
Markings_____
Label or brand_____
Net weight_____
Type_____
Size or sizes_____
Moisture content_____

Flavor	A	B	C
Defects	Maximum		
Pieces of stem:			
Thompson Seedless_____	1 per 96 oz____	2 per 96 oz____	4 per 96 oz____
Other types_____	1 per 32 oz____	2 per 32 oz____	3 per 32 oz____
	Maximum (per 16 ounces)		
Capstems:[1]			
Thompson Seedless_____	15	25	35
Muscat_____	10	15	20
Sultana_____	25	45	65
Seeds in Muscat Seeded only[1]_____	12	15	20
Loose capstems: Muscat, uncapstemmed___	20	20	20
	Maximum (by weight) (percent)		
Undeveloped:			
Thompson Seedless "Small size"_____	1	2	3
All other raisins_____	1	2	2
Damaged:			
Thompson Seedless and Sultana_____	2	3	5
Muscat_____	3	4	5
Sugared (all raisin types)_____	5	10	15
	Maximum (by count) (percent)		
Moldy (all raisin types)_____	2	3	4
Shattered (or loose) individual berries and small clusters of 2 or 3 berries each.	Practically free_	Reasonably free	_____
Damaged by fermentation (all raisin types). Affecting appearance or edibility.	Not affected___	No more than slightly affected.	Not materially affected.
Grit, sand, or silt (all raisin types). Affecting appearance or edibility.	None of any consequence.	None of any consequence.	Not more than a trace.

Color	Maximum by weight (percent)	
Thompson Seedless:		
Sulfur bleached and golden:		
Well-bleached (Extra Fancy)_____	$\frac{1}{2}$	
Reasonably well-bleached (Fancy)_____	3	Definitely dark berries.
Fairly well-bleached (Extra Choice)_____	6	
Sulfur bleached: Bleached (Choice)_____	15	
Golden: Bleached (Choice)_____	20	
Muscat: Soda dipped unseeded, and seeded:_____ Grade A__	10	Dark reddish brown berries.
Grade B__	15	
Grade C__	20	

Grade _____

[1] Not applicable to layer (or cluster) or uncapstemmed muscat raisins.

FIG. 3–11. Courtesy USDA.

Work Sheet for Scoring Dried Prunes.

Size and kind of container_____
Container mark or identification_____
Label or brand_____
Varietal type_____
Size: Count per pound   (Average)_____   Uniformity_____
    ( ) Extra large.   ( ) Large.
    ( ) Medium.   ( ) Small.
Moisture content_____percent; Uniformity_____
Varietal characteristics: ( ) Similar. ( ) Dissimilar.

Defects and summary of allowances[1]	Grade A maximum	Grade B maximum	Grade C maximum	Substandard maximum
Total of all defects, including off-color.	10 percent___	15 percent___	_____	No limit except as indicated below.
Total of all defects, including off-color and poor texture.	_____	_____	20 percent___	
Poor texture, end cracks, skin or flesh damage, fermentation, scars, heat damage, insect injury, other means. mold, dirt, foreign material, insect infestation, decay.	But no more than 6 percent.	But no more than 8 percent.	_____	
End cracks,[2] skin or flesh damage, fermentation, scars, heat damage, insect injury, other means, mold, dirt, foreign material, insect infestation, decay.	_____	_____	10 percent[2]__	
Skin or flesh damage, fermentation, scars, heat damage, insect injury, other means, mold, dirt, foreign material, insect infestation, decay.	_____	_____	But no more than 8 percent.	
Mold, dirt, foreign material, insect infestation, decay.	3 percent____	4 percent____	5 percent____	5 percent.
Decay _____	But no more than 1 percent.	But no more than 1 percent.	But no more than 1 percent.	But no more than 1 percent.

Total _____
U. S. Grade (including all factors)_____

[1] Percentages of defects are "by weight."

[2] Except that each 1 percent of end cracks to, and including 8 percent, by weight, shall be considered as ½ percent damaged by end cracks; and any additional end cracks shall be calculated as true percentage, by weight.

FIG. 3–12. Courtesy USDA.

damage is common.   Buyers should check each season to ascertain which size is most plentiful and lowest in price on the market, for this will vary season to season.

In purchasing dried apples, buyers should note that the units are fairly large and are not screenings.   Note core, skin defects.   Bruises may be evident.   The dried apples may have bitter pit or corky tissue.   Slab apricots are the product of mature or overripe fruit, which, in drying, has become flattened and misshapen. They are generally lacking in normal contour. Whole, pitted, dried apricots are available on the market. Natural and steamed apricot kernels may be purchased. All

ORIGINAL

INSPECTION No. 1267

Dried Fruit Association of California
APPLICATION FOR INSPECTION

Shipper___FLEETWOOD PACKING CO., INC._____ SAN JOSE, CALIFORNIA____

For Steamer____SEATTLE_____ ____JOHNSON_____Line

_____Car No._____ Route_____

NUMBER OF PACKAGES	STYLE OF PACKAGE	VARIETY AND GRADE	CROP	SHIPPING MARK
450	48/15 Oz. Cartons	Select Natural Thompson Seedless Raisins	1959	1267 Norway
500	30# Cases	40/50 Santa Clara Prunes	1959	
800	24/1# Cartons	Fancy Blenheim Apricots	1959	

CONTRACT REQUIREMENTS
(State fully all conditions of sale necessary to enable Inspector to properly pass on shipment.)

FLEETWOOD PACKING COMPANY, INC.
Shipper

OFFICIAL CERTIFICATE OF INSPECTION

THIS IS TO CERTIFY, that on the 1 ST day of MARCH, 19 60, an official inspector of this Association, carefully examined and tested the above described goods prepared for shipment to NORWAY, and that the same are of good merchantable quality, equal to or better than the average of the season, in good condition and of the grade and character described in the above application of shipper.

IN WITNESS WHEREOF, this Association by its_____
Secretary duly authorized has this 7 TH day of MARCH, 19 60, issued this certificate in its corporate name and under its official seal.

DRIED FRUIT ASSOCIATION OF CALIFORNIA.

By_____
Secretary

F 2A

FIG. 3–13. A trade inspection certification for dried fruit. Courtesy Dried Fruit Association of California.

grades of black figs should have a typical, natural black or dark reddish-brown color and be reasonably free of serious scar damage. All grades of white figs should be of uniformly good color. Bleached Calimyrnas are lightened in color in processing by using hydrogen peroxide. Tray-dried Kadota figs are picked from the trees, bleached with sulfur and dried in layers. The color should be white to light amber. Dried freestone or dried cling peaches may be obtained on the market. Varigrade peaches are those that contain mixed varieties and slabs. They may be variable in color, appearance and size but should be reasonably free from dark, off-color pieces. Pears that show dingy brown or red discoloration are downgraded.

DRIED VEGETABLES

Federal standards for quality exist for dried beans, lentils and peas. The federal grades are U.S. No. 1, 2 and 3. There are many varieties of dried beans such as red, kidney, Mexican (chili), pinto, marrow, old-fashioned yellow-eye, navy, great northern, or lima. Lima beans are sized baby (small), medium and large. White beans are sized in the trade as small or large.

Peas may be yellow or green and are usually purchased split. The hull is removed in both split and unsplit peas. Dried, black-eyed peas are also found on the market.

Lentils have limited use. They are much like dried peas.

Examination for quality should consider such extraneous matter as sticks, stones and dirt. The product should be full, plump, well dried and mature. Look for weevil damage. Indications of shriveling, broken pieces, split seeds and damaged or crushed units lower quality. Cook the product to ascertain texture, flavor and color. Beans, lentils and peas may be purchased in 1, 5, 10, 15, 20, 25, 50 and 100-lb lots.

Low-moisture, dried vegetables are rapidly increasing in use in food facilities. No federal standards have been published for these products. The following is an example of specifications that might be written for dehydrated onions:

Material: The onions used for dehydration shall be clean, sound, mature and of good cooking quality. Varieties that yield a bitter or milk-finished product shall not be used.

Workmanship: The product shall be prepared, processed and packaged under good sanitary conditions in accordance with good commercial practice, in which there are not undue delays between processing steps. Flaked onions shall be cut into slices not less than $\frac{1}{8}$ in. thick and not more than $\frac{1}{4}$ in. thick.

Color: The product shall possess a bright, characteristic color. The color may be off-white or cream but not deep cream or tan.

Aroma: The product shall possess a good typical aroma, free from scorch, musty, moldy or other objectionable odors.

Moisture: The moisture content of the packaged finished product shall not exceed 4% by weight.

All deliveries shall conform in every respect to the provisions of the Food, Drug and Cosmetic Act.

Dehydrated potato granules, flakes, slices or diced units are available. Some potato granules are marketed with dried milk added. Sliced or shredded dried onions are used extensively in food facilities. Green peppers, tomatoes, cabbage, turnips, rutabagas and other vegetables are also being dehydrated. The moisture content of these products should be between 2 to 5%.

Low-moisture vegetables should be examined for color and such defects as blemishes, peel, broken or damaged units and extraneous material. Cooking is recommended to check on quality. Potatoes should be mealy and dry after preparation. The aroma of the product should be natural and typical and possess no moldy, musty or other objectionable off odor. Low-moisture products may be subject to some flavor deterioration in processing or storage, and checks should be made on delivery to see that the products meet acceptable standards.

Recent investigations have indicated that foods which are frozen and then dehydrated to about 2 to 5% of their moisture content retain high quality. This process is called freeze-drying. It should not be confused with dehydro-freezing, a process that leaves around 50% of the moisture in the product and in which the product must be kept frozen. The freeze-dry product requires only ordinary shelf storage.

FIG. 3–14. A large vacu-dryer used for drying low moisture fruits and vegetables. Courtesy USDA.

FIG. 3–15. The dehydrated onions shown in the center are the equivalent of the fresh onions shown on the left. The volume of the dehydrated onions after reconstitution is shown on the right. **Courtesy USDA.**

It is possible to freeze-dry meats, fish and poultry as well as fruits and vegetables. When this type of processing occurs, the product retains original flavor and quality to a much greater degree than with ordinary dehydration. The freezing process is said to keep the food rigid during the dehydration; thus the food does not become toughened and the cellular structure is left expanded and not shrunken. Rehydration is rapid and complete. Drying is done in vacuum chambers where atmospheric pressures are so low that ice crystals vaporize directly into steam without ever becoming liquid. The dried food has the texture of a dry, brittle sponge. Reabsorbtion of moisture takes about 20 minutes. In the future these products will be undoubtedly on the market in much greater quantity, and the use of dehydrated foods in food facilities may materially increase.

SPECIFICATION WRITING FOR PROCESSED FRUITS AND VEGETABLES

A specification for processed food should list either the federal or trade grade desired. Naming the grade removes the need to list the quality factors covered in the grade, providing the grade is commonly accepted on the market. Other quality factors desired other than grade should be listed. The style, type or variety, container size, number of containers in a package, count, net contents, type of packaging, packing medium, drained weight and other factors may have to be included. The specification should also state on what basis quotation of price should be made. Canned items are frequently quoted on the basis of a dozen cans; dried fruits and vegetables by the pound. In some instances it may be necessary to specify the type of lining in cans, such as R-enamel for red fruits and vegetables, and C-enamel for vegetables and meats containing sulfur, such as corn and shellfish.

Specific factors are listed in the material that follows for fruits and vegetables. These should be incorporated into specifications for processed fruits and vegetables. Federal grades are listed in this material only by alphabetical designation and refer to common commercial equivalents. Trade grades are omitted for the most part. Whenever possible the minimum score for the grade is listed. Where minimum scores are not used to calculate grade, as in dried fruits, no score is listed. Buyers should realize that a numerical separation on the basis of score is arbitrary. When buying, select products with a top score for a particular grade or select products that score high in specific quality factors. A short summary is given of the most important quality factors for the grade recommended for usual purchase in institutional feeding. These quality factors and the grade are indicated by an asterisk. Grades below or above the grade recommended will have better or lower quality factors than those listed in this material. Drained weights given should be regarded as minimums. Recommended net can contents for canned items may be obtained by consulting Tables 3-4 and 3-7. For other products, packaging is discussed or has been given elsewhere in this chapter.

Counts or sizes may be determined by referring to specific illustrations listed in this chapter. Tolerances for quality have not been discussed.

Certificates for grade for canned or frozen foods should be issued not less than 3 months prior to delivery. Other more perishable items may require a shorter time. In a number of instances it is recommended that the food be cooked and examined for quality.

Examples of specifications for several of the processed foods follow:

Peaches, yellow cling, halves, canned. U.S. Grade A (Fancy), heavy sirup, 19 to 24° Brix, minimum drained weight 66 oz per No. 10 can. Count per No. 10-30/35. Quote by dozen No. 10 cans. Quantity required, 15 dozen or 30 cases 6/10. Federal inspector certification of grade required.

Corn, cream style, Minnesota grown, golden, canned. U.S. Grade B (Extra-Standard). Green Giant brand acceptable in lieu of government certification for quality. Quote by dozen No. 2 cans. Quantity required, 16 dozen or 8 cases 24/2. Cans must be C-enamel lined. If not Green Giant, federal inspector certification of grade required.

Asparagus, spears or stalks, large, all green, frozen. U.S. Grade B (Extra-Standard). Packed in 2½ lb cartons, 12 cartons per case. Must be delivered at 10° F or below. Quote by pound net. Quantity required 90 lb net or 3 cases. Federal inspector certification of grade required.

Strawberries, whole, medium size, frozen, Marshall variety only acceptable. U.S. Grade B (Choice). Sugar-fruit ratio: 1-4. Should drain out 51% or more. One 30-lb can only. Quote by the pound net.

Tomato Juice, canned, California pack. Be certified as U.S. Grade A (Fancy). Quantity required, 6 cases 12/46 oz cans, lined with acid-resistant enamel, R-type. Quote by dozen cans.

Jam, apricot and pineapple (Type II). Ratio of apricot to pineapple 3:1.
U.S. Grade A (Fancy). Quantity required, 1 case 6/10. Quote by dozen
No. 10 cans.

Raisins, Thompson Seedless. U.S. Grade B (Choice). Extra Fancy color,
size Select, packed in 25-lb carton, polyethylene lined. Soda and oil dipped.
Quantity required, 100 lb. Quote by pound.

Prunes, Italian (tart) type, 30/40 (Extra large trade size). Quantity required,
25 lb packed in 1 carton polyethylene lined. Moisture content must not be more
than 25%. Quote by the pound.

These examples of specifications, along with the material that follows,
may be of assistance to buyers in establishing their specifications for
processed fruits and vegetables. Buyers should not forget that general
purchase specifications precede these item specifications.

Canned Fruits

Apples

Grades: A (85),* C (70).

Type: Some acceptable varieties are Northern Spy, Baldwin, Greening,
Roman Beauty, York Imperial, Grimes Golden, Arkansas Black, Newtown,
Jonathan.

Styles: Sliced.

Recommended drained weight: Solid pack—No. 10, 96 oz; No. 2½, 26 oz; No. 2,
18 oz; No. 303, 14 oz.

*Bright, uniform color, white, creamy, or yellowish depending upon variety,
not gray, pinkish, or brown. Uniform size 1¼ in. in length, thickness vari-
ance not greater than ¼ in. Tender, crisp and crunchy without mushiness,
damaged or broken slices. Whole or practically whole slices. Watch for excessive hardness or softness, excessive carpel tissue, peel, seeds, or other defects. Cook to ascertain quality for specific use. (Quartered or whole baked
apples are also on the market.)

Applesauce

Grades: A (85),* C (70).

Type: Some acceptable varieties are Baldwin, Northern Spy, 20 Ounce,
Gravenstein, Newtown, Transparent, Starr.

*Clear, bright not slightly pink, gray, brown or dull. Consistency—stir and
empty some on dry flat surface; should form moderately mounded mass that
at end of two minutes has no more than slight separation of free liquor.
Good finish, not pasty, "salvy," lumpy; no hard particles but can be granular.
Watch flavor and odor carefully; taste for excessive tartness, blandness,
cooked or scorched flavor. Watch for peel, carpel, seeds, specks and other
extraneous matter.

Apricots

Grades: A (90), B (75),* C (70)

Style: Halves, slices, whole, mixed pieces. May be peeled or unpeeled, pitted
or unpitted.

Sirup density: Extra heavy 25–40°, heavy 19–24°, light 14–19° Brix.

Recommended drained weight: No. 10, 64 oz halves or pieces, 61 oz whole, 70 oz heavy pack, 92 oz solid pack; No. 2½, 17½ oz halves and pieces, 16 oz whole, 25 oz solid pack; No. 2, 12 oz halves and pieces, 11½ oz whole; No. 303, 9¾ oz halves and pieces, 9 oz whole.

*Reasonably bright, typical color, green areas or pale color should not be excessive and little browning evident. Even size and symmetry with no abnormal shape. Worm holes, insect damage, dark bruises or brown spots considered serious defects. Watch for excessive freckling, loose pits, stems, skin, and so forth. Reject overripe, mushy or hard and underripe fruit. Flavor should not be tart or astringent. *Note:* Only U.S. Grade C is usually available in solid pack.

Berries

Grades: A (90), B (80),* C (70).

Sirup density:	Extra heavy	Heavy	Light
Most berries	24–35°	19–24°	14–19° Brix
Red raspberries	28° up	22–28°	14–22° Brix
Black raspberries	27° up	20–27°	14–20° Brix
Blueberries	25–35°	20–25°	15–20° Brix

Recommended drained weight:	No. 10	No. 2½	No. 2	No. 303
Red or purple raspberries	53 oz.	14¼ oz	10 oz	8 oz
Red or purple raspberries, solid pack	60 oz	14½ oz	10¼ oz	8¼ oz
Black raspberries	55 oz	14¼ oz	10 oz	8 oz
Blackberries	62–66 oz[a]		11–12 oz[a]	8½–9¼ oz[a]
Blueberries or Huckleberries	55 oz		10 oz	7½ oz
Other berries	55–60 oz[a]		9½–10 oz[a]	7¾–8½ oz[a]
Other berries, solid pack	70 oz			

[a]Lightest drained weight is for water or light sirup, and heaviest drained weight for extra heavy sirup pack.

*Reasonably bright and typical color of well-ripened berries, uniform size and limited number small berries. Reasonably free of undeveloped berries, cap stems, crushed, broken, mashed or otherwise damaged fruit. Tender texture. Watch for insects, worms or other extraneous matter. Since these fruits are fragile, it may be desirable to specify packs for table use to be extra heavy or heavy sirup packs to preserve shape.

Cherries, Red Sour, Pitted

Grades: A (85),* C (70).
Recommended drained weight: Sirup packs—No. 10, 70¼ oz; No. 2, 12¾ oz; No. 303, 10¼ oz. Water pack—No. 10, 74 oz; No. 2, 13½ oz; No. 303, 11 oz.

*Bright, typical color with little or no prominent brownish or mottled areas. Reasonably free from extraneous material, pits, mutilated or damaged cherries and cherries blemished by scab, hail, discoloration, scar tissue. Tender, soft yet retaining plumpness and shape. Fullness of flavor with tartness. Watch for bird or insect injuries. Mostly heavy or solid packs on market.

Apricot Sizes

Number in Can

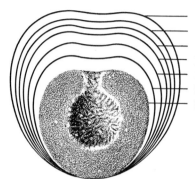

13 or less in No. 2, 18 or less No. 2½, 67 or less No. 10
13 to 15 No. 2, 18 to 20 No. 2½, 67 to 75 No. 10
15 to 17 No. 2, 20 to 23 No. 2½, 75 to 85 No. 10
16 to 18 No. 2, 23 to 36 No. 2½, 85 to 96 No. 10
18 to 23 No. 2, 26 to 33 No. 2½, 96 to 122 No. 10
23 to 27 No. 2, 33 to 39 No. 2½, 122 to 144 No. 10
27 up No. 2, 39 up No. 2½, 144 up No. 10

Cherry Sizes

35 to 40 No. 2, 50 to 60 No. 2½, 210 to 235 No. 10
36 to 39 No. 2, 65 to 70 No. 2½, 240 to 260 No. 10
54 to 64 No. 2, 80 to 90 No. 2½, 290 to 335 No. 10
64 to 75 No. 2, 90 to 103 No. 2½, 335 to 390 No. 10
90 to 95 No. 2, 130 to 135 No. 2½, 480 to 540 No. 10

In between sizes of cherries not shown:

40 to 45 No. 2, 60 to 65 No. 2½, 225 to 240 No. 10
48 to 55 No. 2, 70 to 80 No. 2½, 260 to 290 No. 10
75 to 90 No. 2, 105 to 130 No. 2½, 390 to 480 No. 10

FIG. 3–16.   Apricot and cherry sizes in canned foods.

Cherries, Sweet

Grades: A (90), B (80),* C (70).

Styles: Pitted or unpitted.

Type: Royal Anne is a light-colored, delicately flavored cherry; other sweet cherries are usually dark, such as Bings, Tartarians, Lamberts, and so forth.

Sirup density: Extra heavy 25–35°, heavy 20–25°, light 16–29° Brix.

Recommended drained weight:

	Extra heavy sirup	Heavy sirup	Light sirup or water
No. 10	64½ oz	66½ oz	70 oz
No. 2½	17½	18 oz	18½ oz
No. 2	12 oz	12½ oz	12¾ oz
No. 303	9¾ oz	10 oz	10¼ oz

*Reasonably good color typical of mature cherries, bright not dull. Royal Annes should have no purplish cast or excessive discoloration of the skin. Reasonably absent from such defects as extraneous material, portions of cherry stems, pits, growth or other circular cracks, broken, mashed or otherwise damaged cherries. Good shape and reasonably free from undersize cherries, all reasonably uniform in shape. Full fleshed, tender, no trace of astringency, good flavor.

Figs, Kadota or Other

Grades: A (90), B (80),* C (70).
Styles: Whole, whole and split, split and whole, split or broken.
Sirup density: Extra heavy 26–35°, heavy 21–26°, light 16–21° Brix.
Recommended drained weight: No. 10, 63 oz; No. 2½, 18 oz; No. 2, 12½ oz; No. 303, 10 oz. (For over 71 figs per No. 10, drained weight should be 66 oz or more)

*Reasonably bright uniform color. In Kadota figs light greenish-yellow color. Reasonably uniform in size and symmetry. Reasonably free from scab, scars, bruises, discoloration or other abnormalities. Watch for worm holes, insect damage or other injury. Split or broken figs should conform to style specified; whole and split have less than 50% split or broken and split and whole have over 50% split or broken. Tender, ripe, flesh, full of lush flavor.

Fruit Cocktail

Grades: A (85),* B (70).
Sirup density: Extra heavy 22–35°, heavy 18–22°, light 14–18° Brix.
Recommended drained weight: Federal standards of identity require that drained weight shall be 65% or more of the fill of the container. No. 10, 71 $\frac{1}{10}$ oz; No. 2½, 19⅓ oz; No. 2, 13⅓ oz for Grade A.
Ratio of fruit in mixture: Peaches, diced, 30 to 50%; pears, diced, 25 to 45%; grapes, whole, seedless, 6 to 20%; pineapple, diced or wedge, 6 to 16%; cherries, approximate halves, 2 to 6%. Ratios should be based on drained weight.

*Liquid should be clear, bright in color, with no slight trace of pink or dullness. Small quantity of flocculent pieces of fruit may be present. Fruit should be bright and typical of variety. Diced units should be cleanly cut and even and not more than ¾ in. in greatest dimension. Sectors of pineapple shall be from ⅜ to ¾ in. on outside arc, from $\frac{5}{16}$ to ½ in. thick and from ¾ to 1 in. long. Reasonably free from harmless extraneous material, peels, pits, cap stems, broken or crushed grapes, uneven or broken cherry halves. Texture and tenderness should be firm, with little disintegration.

Fruit for Salad

Grades: A (85),* B (70).
Sirup density: Same as for fruit cocktail above.
Recommended drained weight: No. 10, 64½ oz; No. 2½, 18 oz; No. 2, 12½ oz.
Ratio of fruit in mixture: Peaches, half, quartered or sliced, 24–40%; apricots, peeled or unpeeled half, 18–30%; pears, peeled and cored, half, quartered or sliced, 21–35%; pineapple wedges, 8 to 16%; and cherries or grapes, 3 to 8%.

*Reasonably good color, free from artificial dye stain. Pieces uniform, not broken or crushed or otherwise damaged. Look for defects similar to those described for individual fruit.

Gooseberries

Grades: No federal grades.   Specify Fancy, Choice,* or Standard.

Recommended drained weight: No. 10, 70 oz to 80 oz depending on whether, respectively, water or solid pack.

*Berries reasonably whole with few split, excessively small or immature berries, stems and blossoms.   Reasonably uniform color of pale whitish green and uniform size.   Tender, free from defects, such as scars, scab, insect or worm injury, insects or worms and other extraneous matter.

Grapefruit Sections

Grades: A (90), B (80),* Broken (70).

Sirup density: Recommended 16° Brix cut out.

Drained weight is a part of grade:	No. 3 cylinder	No. 2	No. 303
Grade A	29–30⅔ oz	12 oz	9½–10 oz
Grade B and Broken	27½–28¼ oz	11 oz	9 oz

*Shall be not less than 50% by weight of drained fruit in whole or almost whole segments.   Color reasonably uniform, bright, slightly variable but not off color.   Reasonably free from extraneous material, seeds, membrane, dry cells, "ricey" cells or fibrous material.   Use the broken grade, which conforms to Grade B except for wholeness of segments where segments need not be whole.   Watch for scorched, carmelized, bitter or flat taste.   Soft tender flesh.

Orange and Grapefruit Sections

Grades, drained weight and sirup density as above for grapefruit sections. Quality factors are similar to those for grapefruit sections except color of orange should be typical of that for oranges.   Orange sections to grapefruit sections based on drained weight shall be 37½ to 60% in Grade A and in Grade B and Broken, 32½ to 60%.

Grapes

Grades: A (85),* B (70).

Type: Thompson Seedless.

Sirup density: Extra heavy 24° up, heavy 19–24°, light 14–19° Brix.

Recommended drained weight: No. 10, 62 oz; No. 2½, 17 oz; No. 2, 12 oz.

*Color should be typical for variety.   Grapes should have reasonably uniform color, size, firmness, tenderness and be intact with few broken or crushed grapes.   Bruised grapes, stems, leaves or other defects should be limited.

Peaches

Grades: A (90), B (80),* C (70).

Types: Clingstone or Freestone.

Styles: Quartered, halved, sliced, whole, diced, mixed pieces.

Sirup density: Extra heavy 24–35°, heavy 19–24°, light 14–19° Brix.

Recommended drained weight: (For clingstone peaches only; no recommended drained weights have been established for freestone peaches.)

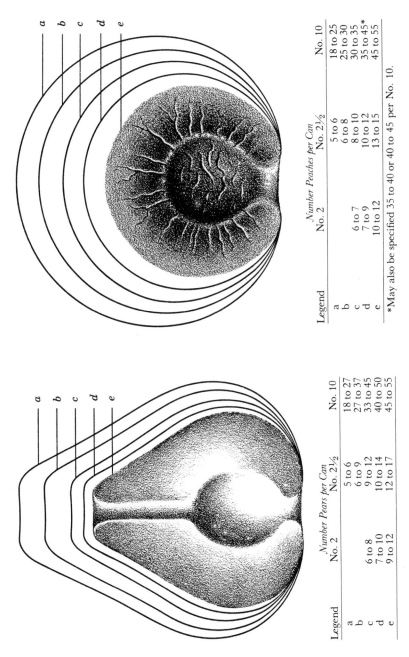

Legend	Number Pears per Can		
	No. 2	No. 2½	No. 10
a		5 to 6	18 to 27
b		6 to 9	27 to 37
c	6 to 8	9 to 12	33 to 45
d	7 to 10	10 to 14	40 to 50
e	9 to 12	12 to 17	45 to 55

Legend	Number Peaches per Can		
	No. 2	No. 2½	No. 10
a		5 to 6	18 to 25
b		6 to 8	25 to 30
c	6 to 7	8 to 10	30 to 35
d	7 to 9	10 to 12	35 to 45*
e	10 to 12	13 to 15	45 to 55

*May also be specified 35 to 40 or 40 to 45 per No. 10.

FIG. 3–17. Pear and peach sizes in canned foods.

			Type Pack			
Can Size	Extra Heavy Sirup	Heavy Sirup	Light Sirup or Water	Diced, Any Packing Medium	Heavy	Solid
No. 10	64 oz	66 oz	68 oz	70 oz	76 oz	92 oz
No. 2½	17 oz	17½ oz	18 oz	18½ oz	20 oz	25½ oz
No. 2	10 oz	10 oz	10 oz	10½ oz		
No. 303	10 oz	10 oz	10 oz	10½ oz		

*Reasonably firm, tender, good texture and color. Clear juice. Reasonably free from defects. Uniform size and symmetry. Reasonable maturity. Note workmanship on inside of peach. Look for pieces of pit, stems, rough ragged pieces, broken or crushed fruit. Only slight amount of green or brown areas permitted. Hardness indicates immaturity. Because of tenderness of the freestone peach, buyers specify heavy sirup packing to give firmness.

Pears

Grades: A (90), B (80),* C (70).
Types: Bartlett, Kieffer.
Styles: Halves, quarters, slices, diced, whole, mixed pieces. (Halves and whole pears may be peeled or unpeeled.)
Sirup density: Extra heavy 22–35°, heavy 18–22°, light 14–22° Brix.
Recommended drained weight:

Halves (*based on number halves in can*)

No. 10   62 oz, 16 to 22 halves; 62½ oz, 23 to 30 halves; 63 oz, 31 halves or over.
No. 2½   16 oz, 3 to 6 halves; 16½ oz, 7 to 9 halves; 17 oz, 10 to 12 halves; 17½ oz, 13 to 15 halves; 18 oz, 16 to 22 halves.
No. 2   11 oz, 3 to 6 halves; 11½ oz, 7 to 9 halves; 11¾ oz, 10 to 12 halves.

Quarters, Slices, Diced, Mixed

No. 10   65 oz; No. 2½, 17¾ oz; No. 2, 12¼ oz.

Solid Pack

No. 10   90 oz; No. 2½, 24 oz.

*Reasonably good color, clear white or creamy white, not pink, tarnished or touched with brown. Not dead or chalky white. Reasonably uniform for style of pack. Few ragged, crushed, damaged or broken pieces. Few halves split. Note workmanship in coring and trimming. Few pieces of extraneous matter, such as peels, seeds, stems and other blemishes. Juice clear. Watch for grainy, tough, hard or mushy fruit.

Pineapple

Grades: A (90), B (80),* C(70).
Styles: Whole slices, half slices, broken slices (arc or slice pieces not uniform), tidbits (small—length of arc ⅜ to ¾ in., length of radius 11/16 to 1¼ in., thickness 5/16 to ½ in.; large—length of arc ¾ to 2 in., length of radius 11/16 to 1¾ in., thickness 5/16 to ½ in.), chunks 9/16 in. wide, 1½ in. long and

Table 3–6
Sizes and Quantities of Fruit in Some Can Sizes

Fruit	Can Size	Amount or Number in Can*	Size Serving or Number Per Serving	Servings per Can
Apples, heavy	No. 10	7 lb 8 oz		Makes 8 pies
Applesauce	No. 10	6 lb 11 oz	½ c	25
Apricot, halves	No. 10	75–85	3 to 4 halves	23–25
Apricot, halves	No. 2½	20/23	3 to 4 halves	6–7
Apricots, whole	No. 10	50	2	25
Apricots, whole	No. 2½	12/16	2	6–8
Blackberries	No. 2	1 lb 4 oz	½ c	5
Blackberries	No. 10	6 lb 10 oz	½ c	25
Blackberries, heavy	No. 10	6 lb 7 oz		Makes 4–5 pies
Cherries, RSP	No. 10	6 lb 14 oz		Makes 5 pies
Cherries, sweet	No. 10	240/260	½ c (8 to 10)	30
Cherries, sweet	No. 2½	65/70	½ c (8 to 10)	7 to 8
Figs, kadota	No. 10	110/120	3	30–40
Figs, kadota	No. 2½	28/32	3	10
Fruit cocktail	No. 10	6 lb 14 oz	½ c	25
Fruit cocktail	No. 2½	1 lb 14 oz	½ c	7
Fruits, salad	No. 10	6 lb 14 oz	½ c	25
Fruits, salad	No. 2½	1 lb 14 oz	½ c	7
Grapefruit	No. 3 cyl	3 lb 2 oz	½ c	11
Grapefruit, broken	No. 10	6 lb 9 oz	½ c	25
Peaches, halves	No. 10	35/40	2	17½–20
Peaches, halves	No. 2½	10/12	2	5–6
Peaches, sliced	No. 10	6 lb 14 oz	½ c	25
Peaches, sliced	No. 2½	1 lb 14 oz	½ c	7
Peaches, solid	No. 10	6 lb 10 oz		Makes 4–5 pies
Pear, halves	No. 10	40/50	2	20–25
Pear, halves	No. 2½	10/14	2	5–7
Pineapple, slice	No. 10	57/64	2	29–32
Pineapple, slice	No. 2½	14/16	2	7–8
Pineapple, crushed solid pack	No. 10	6 lb 14 oz	½ c	25
Pineapple, crushed	No. 2½	1 lb 13 oz	½ c	7
Pineapple, broken or half slice	No. 10	6 lb 11 oz	½ c	25
Pineapple, broken or half slice	No. 2½	1 lb 13 oz	½ c	7
Pineapple chunks	No. 2	48/55 (2½ c)	½ c	5
Pineapple chunks	No. 2½	72/80 (3½ c)	½ c	7
Pineapple chunks	No. 10	232/290 (12–13 c)	½ c	25
Pineapple tidbits	No. 10	6 lb 11 oz (512/960)	½ c	25
Pineapple spears	No. 2	16 spears	3	5
Plums, purple	No. 10	65/90	3	22–30
Plums, gage or egg	No. 10	45/55	2–3	22
Prunes, dried	No. 10	140/170	3–4	50
Prunes, heavy pack, dried	No. 10	210/280	3–4	80

*Numbers given here are good averages for institutional use. Data based on experience in use.

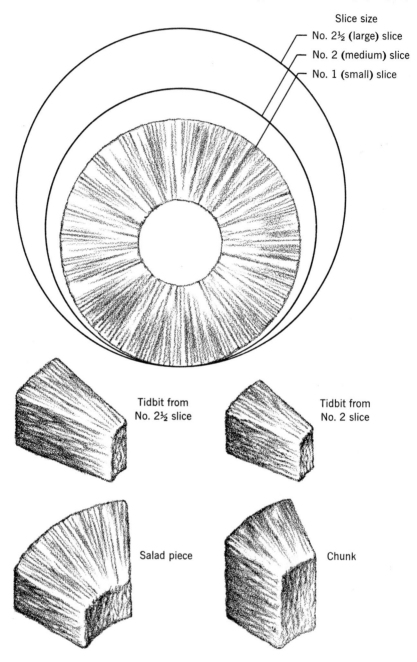

Slice size
— No. 2½ (large) slice
— No. 2 (medium) slice
— No. 1 (small) slice

Tidbit from
No. 2½ slice

Tidbit from
No. 2 slice

Salad piece

Chunk

FIG. 3–18. Pineapple sizes in canned pineapple.

Approximate Sizes of Slices

Slice Size	Number of Slices per No. 10 Can	Slice Size	Diameter, in inches
No. 2½	28	No. 2½	3½ (overall)
No. 2	50		1¼ (center)
No. 1	64	No. 2	2⅞ (overall)
			1⅛ (center)
		No. 1	2⁹⁄₁₆ (overall)
			⅞ (center)

½ in. thick), cubes or diced (not more than $\frac{9}{16}$ in. on any side), spears or fingers (not less than 2½ in. long), crushed (finely shredded or cut—can be called coarse, medium or crisp or fine cut).

Sirup density: Extra heavy 22–35°, heavy 18–22°, light 14–18°.

Recommended drained weight: Canned crushed pineapple other than heavy or solid pack less than 63% of net weight of contents must be labeled "Below Standard in Quality" followed by either "Good Food—Not High Grade" or "Contains Excess Liquid." Heavy pack must be 73 to 78%, and solid must be 78% or more. Drained weights for other packs than crushed are:

	No. 10 Can	No. 2½ Can	No. 2 Can
Slices	61½ oz	18¼ oz	12¾ oz
Half or broken slices	62½ oz	18 oz	12½ oz
Chunks	63¾ oz	18¼ oz	12¾ oz
Cubes	71¼ oz	18¼ oz	12¾ oz
Spears		18¼ oz	12¾ oz
Tidbits	65¾ oz	18¼ oz	12¾ oz

*Relatively few blemishes, such as deep fruit eyes, bruised portions. Not more than 0.4 oz core per lb of fruit. Reasonably uniform size and shape; little mashed or crushed pieces except in crushed; little raggedness of pieces. Reasonably good yellow color; not more than slightly dull; not too deep or too light; some shading and white radiant streaks allowed, providing it does not seriously affect appearance. Tender but not soft; fairly free from porosity. Good, rich, mellow pineapple flavor with some tartness; not bland. Not too tart (not over 1.35 grams anhydrous citric acid per 100 ml of fruit).

Plums or Prunes

Grades: Grade A (90), B (80),* C (70).

Types: Purple—prunes or purple type plums, Green Gage, Yellow Egg, and so forth.

Styles: Half or whole.

Sirup density: Extra heavy 26–35°, heavy 21–26° light 16–21° Brix.

Recommended drained weight: Whole: No. 10, 60 oz; No. 2½, 15½ oz; No. 2, 10½ oz. Half: No. 10, 63 oz; No. 2½, 16¼ oz; No. 2, 12 oz. Water pack: No. 10, 65 oz.

*Reasonably uniform color for variety, with little variation or off color, browning or greenness. Look for loose pits, stems, leaves, burn, scars, worm

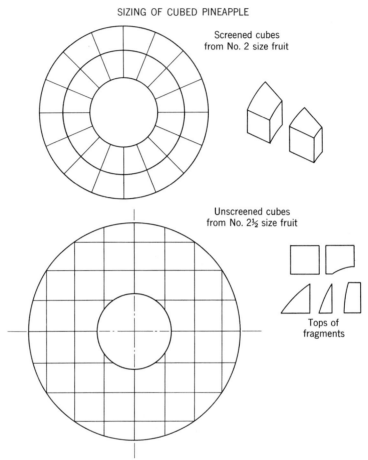

SIZING OF CUBED PINEAPPLE

Screened cubes
from No. 2 size fruit

Unscreened cubes
from No. 2½ size fruit

Tops of
fragments

FIG. 3–19. Cubed pineapple may be either screened or unscreened and cube shapes will vary according to the type cutting used.

holes, scab and so forth. Reasonably uniform in size, few crushed or broken fruit. Reasonably uniform texture, plump, fleshy, firm yet tender. Few shriveled or abnormal fruit. Fruit should be well matured, holding shape. Skin should be tender and not tough. Juice should be clear and not murky, dully or filled with excessively flocculent material.

Prunes, Dried

Grades: A (90), B (80),* C (70).

Types: Sweet—French (Robe), Imperial, Sugar. Tart—Italian.

Sirup density: Extra heavy 30° up, heavy 24–30°, light 18–24° Brix.

Recommended drained weight: No. 10, 70 oz; No. 2½, 19 oz; No. 2, 13 oz. Heavy pack: No. 10, 110 oz; No. 2½, 29 oz.

*Typical black, blue-black or reddish brown color depending upon variety.

Table 3–7
Trade Association Recommendations for Minimum Net Weight of Contents for Canned Fruit

Fruit	Grade	Size Can No. 10	No. 2½	No. 2
Apples				
Slices		90 oz	26 oz	18 oz
Solid pack		96 oz		
Sauce		107 oz		20 oz
Apricots, peaches and plums	A	110 oz	29 oz	20 oz
	B	108 oz	30 oz	21 oz
	C	106 oz	30 oz	20 oz
	D		28 oz	20 oz
Pie		104 oz		
Water		103 oz		
Solid		106 oz		
Berries	A	108 oz	30 oz	20 oz
	B	106 oz	29 oz	20 oz
	C	105 oz	29 oz	20 oz
Water		103 oz	28 oz	19 oz
Cherries, RSP	A	110 oz		20 oz
	C	105 oz		
Water		103 oz		
Cherries, sweet, unpitted	A	110 oz	30 oz	21 oz
	B	108 oz	30 oz	20 oz
	C	106 oz	29 oz	20 oz
Water		104 oz	28 oz	20 oz
Cherries, sweet, pitted	A	110 oz	30 oz	21 oz
	B	107 oz	29 oz	20 oz
	C	105 oz	29 oz	20 oz
Water		103 oz	28 oz	20 oz
Cranberries				19 oz
		117 oz		22 oz
Figs	A	112 oz	30 oz	21 oz
	B	112 oz	30 oz	20 oz
	C	108 oz	29 oz	20 oz
Water		105 oz	29 oz	20 oz
Fruit cocktail and Fruits for salad	A	110 oz	30 oz	21 oz
	B	108 oz	20 oz	20 oz
Grapes (Same as sweet, unpitted cherries)				
Gooseberries		105 oz		20 oz
Peaches (See Apricots)				
Pears	A	108 oz	30 oz	20 oz
	B	106 oz	29 oz	20 oz
	C	105 oz	29 oz	20 oz
Water		104 oz	28 oz	
Pineapple				
Whole, slices and chunks	A	108 oz	30 oz	20 oz
Broken slices	A	107 oz	29 oz	20 oz
Crushed	A	109 oz	30 oz	20½ oz
Water		106 oz	29 oz	20 oz
Crushed		107 oz		
(B and C grades are slightly lighter than those listed for grade A)				
Plums (See Apricots)				
Prunes, dried	A	110 oz	30 oz	20 oz
	B	108 oz	30 oz	20 oz
	C	106 oz	30 oz	20 oz

Reasonably uniform color, with only small amount of dull chocolate or brown color or abnormal flesh darkening. Reasonably uniform size, with largest prune not larger than twice the weight of the smallest. Buyers should state size desired by number of dried prunes per pound as 20/30, 30/40, 40/50, as given in dried fruit. Reasonably free of growth cracks, splits, breaks, insect injury, skin damage, scab, loose pits, stems or other matter. Tough or firm areas caused by thrips damage should be noted. Watch also for evidence of mildew damage, leaf chafing or limb rubs. Reasonably good tender, plump fleshy texture. Skin reasonably tender. No carmelization, cooked or scorched flavor in prunes.

Canned Vegetables

Asparagus

Grades: A (85),* C (70).

Types: Green, green tipped, green tipped and white, and white or bleached.
Styles: Spears or stalks (more than $3\frac{3}{4}$ in. in length), tips ($2\frac{3}{4}$ to $3\frac{3}{4}$ in. in length), points $2\frac{2}{3}$ in. or less in length), cut spears (15% may be $1\frac{1}{4}$ in. or less but 20% must be $1\frac{1}{4}$ in. or over), cuts or bottom cuts (tips removed).
Recommended drained weight: (All weights listed in ounces.)

Spears, Tips and Points

Can Size	Green Tipped and White		Green and Green Tipped		Cut Spears Green Tipped and White	Bottom Cuts Green
	Small Sizes	Large Sizes	Small Sizes	Large Sizes		
No. 303	$10\frac{3}{4}$	$9\frac{3}{4}$	$10\frac{1}{2}$	$9\frac{1}{4}$	$10\frac{1}{4}$	$9\frac{1}{4}$
No. 2	$13\frac{1}{2}$	$12\frac{1}{4}$	$12\frac{3}{4}$	$11\frac{3}{4}$	$12\frac{3}{4}$	$11\frac{3}{4}$
No. 10	$64\frac{1}{2}$	63	$64\frac{1}{2}$	$60\frac{1}{2}$	$64\frac{1}{2}$	$60\frac{1}{4}$

For sizing, see Figure 3–20.

*The liquor should be fairly clear with some cloudiness but not excessive cloudiness. Some accumulation of sediment that is slightly gray or brown, but not seriously objectionable, may be present. Over 25% of the total height of the column of liquid is considered excessive. Color should be good for type 90% or more uniformity. Watch for grit, silt, poorly cut or misshapen pieces. Well-developed, without seedy appearance. Compact heads, tender without toughness or strings. Few soft or mushy pieces, stringy or frayed edges, poor cuts, not smooth or at right angles, or small pieces permitted. Watch for sloughy texture, noticeable bitter or undesirable flavor.

Beans, dried

Grades: A (90), B (80),* C (70).

Types: White, Lima, Red, Black-eye (also called Black-eye Peas).
Styles: Tomato sauce, tomato sauce with pork or meat, brine, sweetened (contains molasses) and sweetened with pork or meat.

*Smooth, even color. No hard, coarse, grainy or lumpy beans, or excessive water, with not more than a slight separation of liquid except in brine pack, which may have a noticeable separation. Presence of one piece of extraneous material allowed for each 20 oz of net weight; few beans with loose

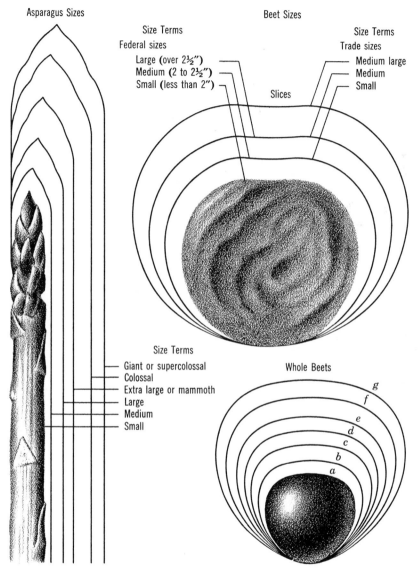

Asparagus Sizes

Beet Sizes

Size Terms
Federal sizes
Large (over 2½")
Medium (2 to 2½")
Small (less than 2")

Slices

Size Terms
Trade sizes
Medium large
Medium
Small

Size Terms
Giant or supercolossal
Colossal
Extra large or mammoth
Large
Medium
Small

Whole Beets

g
f
e
d
c
b
a

Number Whole Beets per Can

Legend	No. 2	No. 2½	No. 10	Legend	No. 2	No. 2½	No. 10
a	60 to 75	80 to 105	300 to 375	e	15 to 24	22 to 34	75 to 124
b	50 to 60	70 to 85	250 to 300	f	10 to 14	15 to 21	50 to 74
c	35 to 49	50 to 70	175 to 250	g	6 to 9	8 to 14	35 to 49
d	25 to 34	35 to 54	125 to 175				

FIG. 3–20. Asparagus and beet sizes in canned vegetables.

Grade A Head Development	Grade C Head Development	Substandard Head Development

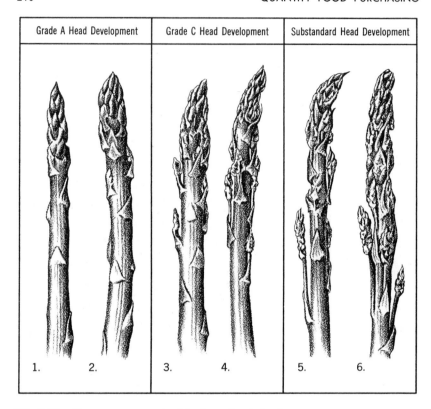

1.   2.   3.   4.   5.   6.

FIG. 3–21. The asparagus to the left shows head development in canned asparagus qualifying for U.S. Grade A. The center asparagus heads will grade C while the ones to the right will be Substandard Grade. **Courtesy USDA.**

skins or broken or mashed or damaged beans.   Even soft texture.   Soft, tender skins.   (See Kidney beans also.)

Beans, Snap

Grades: A (90), B (80),* C (70).

Types: Green or wax.   (Blue Lake is recommended as a variety for green and Kentucky Wonder for wax.)

Styles: Whole (in no arranged position), whole vertical (arranged parallel), whole asparagus (packed parallel with tips and ends cut), French (pods sliced lengthwise), cut or cuts (transversely cut into $\frac{3}{4}$ to $2\frac{3}{4}$ in. pieces), short cut (not less than 75% less than $\frac{3}{4}$ in. but not more than 1% over $1\frac{1}{4}$ in. in length), mixed (any mixture of the above except whole vertical or whole asparagus).

Sieve sizes: See Figure 3–22 and Table 3–8.

Recommended drained weight: No. 10 whole or French 61 oz; whole vertical or

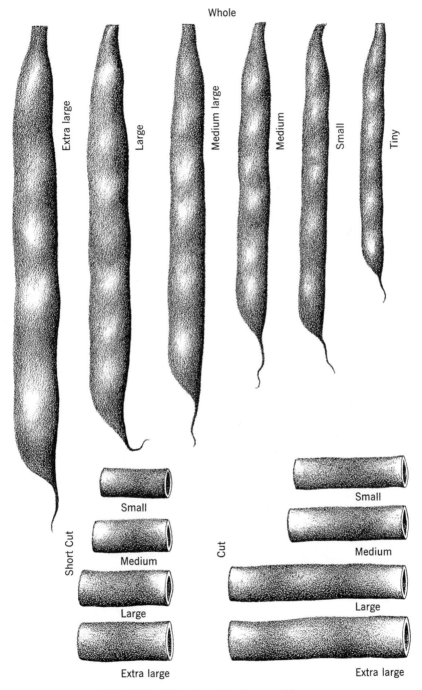

Whole

Extra large

Large

Medium large

Medium

Small

Tiny

Short Cut

Small

Medium

Large

Extra large

Cut

Small

Medium

Large

Extra large

FIG. 3–22. String bean sizes in canned beans.

211

Detached Stems	Stemmed Units	Unstemmed Units
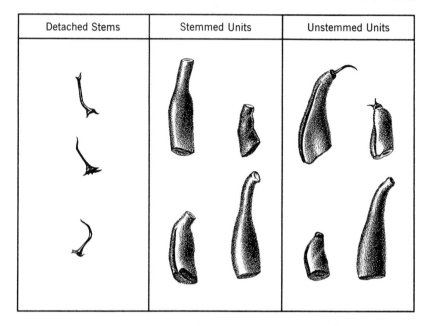		

FIG. 3–23. Some defects buyers should watch for in purchasing canned snap beans. Courtesy USDA.

asparagus 66 oz; cuts and short cuts 63 oz. No. 2 whole or French 11 oz; whole vertical or asparagus 12 oz; cuts or short cuts 11¼ oz.

*Liquid should be reasonably clear, slightly cloudy with a small amount of sediment. The color should be reasonably uniform and typical for variety. Watch for blemishes, leaves, stems, and other extraneous matter, ragged cut or split units, small pieces of pods less than ½ in. long, broken, crushed or damaged pods, free seeds and other defects. There should be few tough strings. Beans should be plump, tender. Note in measuring beans that a straight line is used from end to end and not along length of bean.

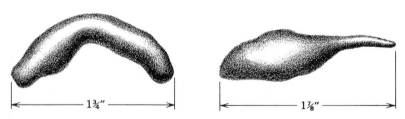

Beans, Kidney
 Grades: A (90), B (80),* C (70).
 Styles: May vary; usually plain pack.
 *Quality factors are similar to those for dried beans. Beans should have (as

FIG. 3–24. USDA inspector matches canned lima beans to color of the color dictionary to ascertain how the samples compare with federal standards. Courtesy USDA.

dried beans) good consistency, with smooth sauce, neither grainy or lumpy, and a product that forms a molded mass when placed on a flat surface, with not more than slight separation of liquid.

Beans, Lima

Grades: Grade A (90), B (80),* C (70).

Types: Thin-seeded (Henderson, Bush, Thorogreen), Thick-seeded (Fordhook or Baby Potato, Evergreen).

Sizes: See Figure 3-25.

Recommended drained weight: No. 303, 11 oz; No. 2, 13½ oz; No. 10, 72 oz.

*Color may be green or white, reasonably uniform, good typical color, not mixed. Liquor reasonably clear. Sieves No. 1, 2 and 3 should not have a

Table 3–8
Sizes of Canned Green and Wax Beans*

Thickness in 64th's Inch	Sieve Number	Round Type†		Flat Type†	
		Size Name		Sieve Number	Size Name
		Whole	Short Cut or Cut		
Less than 14½	1	Tiny	Small	2	Small
14½ to 18½	2	Small	Small	3	Medium
18½ to 21	3	Medium	Small	4	Medium large
21 to 24	4	Medium large	Medium	5	Large
24 to 27	5	Large	Large	6	Extra large
27 or more	6	Extra large	Extra large	6	Extra large

*Sieve sizes and size names are based on federal standards.

†Round-type beans have a width not greater than 1½ times the bean thickness, and flat-type beans have a width greater than 1½ times the bean thickness.

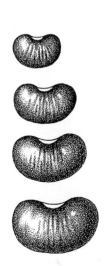

Commercial Sizes			Federal Sizes	
Sieve	Inches*	Trade Name	Inches*	Size Name
No. 1	$\frac{5}{16}$ or less	Tiny		
No. 2	$\frac{5}{16}$ to $\frac{6}{16}$	Small	$\frac{24}{64}$ or less	Midget
No. 3	$\frac{6}{16}$ to $\frac{8}{16}$	Medium	$\frac{28}{64}$ to $\frac{30}{64}$ $\frac{30}{64}$ to $\frac{34}{64}$ $\frac{34}{64}$ to $\frac{38}{64}$	Tiny Small Medium
No. 4	$\frac{8}{16}$ or larger	Large	Larger than $\frac{38}{64}$	Large

*Greatest width through center at right angles to the longitudinal axis.

FIG. 3–25. Lima bean sizes.

viscuous liquid but sieve size No. 4 may have a somewhat viscuous liquid. Look for extraneous matter, broken beans, loose cotyledons and skins, sprouted, or otherwise blemished beans. Reasonably young and tender, not tough or starchy.

Beets

Grades: A (85),* C (70).
Styles: Sliced (not more than ⅜ in. thick), whole, quarters (cut into even quarters), diced (evenly cut cubes), julienne (shoestring or French), cut.
Recommended drained weight:

Can Size	Whole Sizes 1–3†	Sizes 4–6†	Sliced Small	Medium and Large	Diced	Quartered	Julienne
No. 10	69 oz	68 oz	69 oz	68 oz	72 oz	70 oz	68 oz
No. 2	12½ oz	12¼ oz	12½ oz	12 oz	12¾ oz	12½ oz	11½ oz

†Size is measured by obtaining smallest diameter through the center transverse to the longitudinal axis of the beet.
*Uniform, bright, deep red color, not off, brown, oxidized or light pink. Practically uniform in size; evenly cut for cut styles. No woodiness, coarse texture or excessive softness, poor trimming, peel or black spots. Not too many first cuts (slabs), frayed edges, deep knife marks or other injury. Grade A whole beets shall not be over 2¼ in. in diameter; quartered beets shall come from beets of a similar size; sliced beets should have slices not over ⅜ in. thick, with diameters not more than 3½ in.; diced beets should

be in $\frac{3}{8}$ in. cubes or less; julienne not wider than $\frac{3}{16}$ in. and relatively few below $1\frac{1}{2}$ in. in length; cut individual units should not be less than $\frac{1}{4}$ oz and not more than 2 oz in weight. See Figure 3–20 and Table 3–9.

Carrots

Grades: A (85),* C (70).

Styles: Whole slices, quartered, diced, julienne (shoestring or French), cut.

Sizes: Diameter of whole carrots is measured through the center transverse to the longitudinal axis of the carrot, using the largest diameter. Whole carrots are not more than $1\frac{3}{4}$ in. in diameter; quartered carrots are from carrots not larger than $2\frac{1}{2}$ in. in diameter; sliced carrots are not more than $\frac{3}{8}$ in. thick with diameters not more than $2\frac{1}{2}$ in.; diced carrots should be $\frac{1}{2}$ in. cubes or less; julienne should be $\frac{3}{16}$ in. wide and very few less than $\frac{1}{2}$ in. long; cut units should not be less than $\frac{1}{4}$ oz and the weight of the largest unit not more than four times the weight of the second smallest unit.

Recommended drained weight:

Can Sizes	Whole Up to $1\frac{1}{4}''$ Diameter	Over $1\frac{1}{2}''$ Diameter	Sliced To $1\frac{1}{2}''$ Diameter	Over $1\frac{1}{2}''$ Diameter	Diced	Quartered	Julienne
No. 10	69 oz	68 oz	69 oz	68 oz	72 oz	70 oz	68 oz
No. 2	$12\frac{1}{2}$ oz	$12\frac{1}{4}$ oz	$12\frac{1}{2}$ oz	12 oz	$12\frac{3}{4}$ oz	$12\frac{1}{2}$ oz	$11\frac{1}{2}$ oz

*Orange-yellow color, bright and typical, with little or no green. Practically uniform in size and shape. Tender, not mushy or soft. Coarse texture, pronounced fiber and carmelized taste or odor are cause for rejection.

Table 3–9
Sizes of Canned Whole and Sliced Beets

	Trade Sizes		
Size Name	No. 2 Can	No. $2\frac{1}{2}$ Can	No. 10 Can
Midget or Petite	35 or over	55 and over	175 and over
Tiny or Very Small	25 to 34	35 to 54	125 to 174
Baby or Small	15 to 24	22 to 34	74 to 124
Ruby or Medium	10 to 14	15 to 21	50 to 74
Large	6 to 9	8 to 14	35 to 49

	Federal Sizes		
Size Name and Number	No. 2 Can	No. $2\frac{1}{2}$ Can	No. 10 Can
Tiny 1	44 and over	70 and over	250 and over
2	21 to 44	50 to 70	175 to 250
Small 3	22 to 31	35 to 50	125 to 175
4	13 to 22	20 to 35	75 to 125
Medium 5	9 to 13	15 to 20	50 to 75
6	Less than 7	Less than 7	Less than 50

Chili Sauce

Grades: A (85),* C (70).

*Color bright, with tomato red predominant. Heavy bodied, so when emptied on a flat surface it forms moderately mounded mass showing only slight separation of free liquid at mass edges. Finely divided and mixed mass, tender, reasonably firm and crisp ingredients. Practically free from such defects as peel or other items. Good flavor and odor. No scorched flavor.

Corn, Whole Kernel or Whole Grain

Grades: A (90), B (80),* C (70).
Types: White or golden (yellow).
Packs: Brine or vacuum; pack is vacuum when 20% or less of net weight of contents is liquid.
Recommended drained weight:
No. 10 (Grade A) 70 oz, (Grades B and C) 72 oz.
No. 2   (Grade A) 12¾ oz, (Grades B and C) 13¼ oz.

*Reasonably uniform color, typical of tender sweet corn. Reasonably smooth cut surface, uniform and of even depth, with little adhering cob tissue. Reasonably free from defects, such as cob, husk, discolored kernels, silk and other extraneous material. Reasonably tender from kernels in the cream stage of maturity. Firm, not pasty. Few dented kernels. Watch for musty, scorched, salty or mealy tasting corn.

Corn, Cream Style

Grades: A (90), B (80),* C (70).
Types: White or golden (yellow).
*Reasonably uniform color, typical of tender sweet corn of the variety packed. Reasonably good, creamy consistency, with not more than a moderate appearance of curdling, with flow just sufficient to level off to a nearly uniform depth or may be moderately stiff and mounded with some slight separation of liquid after standing 2 minutes on a dry, flat surface. Reasonable absence of silk, cob, husk, off-colored kernels and other extraneous material. Tender kernels taken in the middle to late cream stage. Good characteristic flavor and odor typical of reasonably tender, canned sweet corn.

Hominy

Grades: A (85),* C (70).
Types: White and golden (yellow).
Styles: Whole, grits, and grits in jel (grits, jellied pack).

Recommended drained weight:	No. 2	No. 2½	No. 10
Whole	12 oz	18 oz	72 oz
Grits	14¼ oz	21¼ oz	76 oz

(Grits, jellied pack, are in a mass and have no drained weight)

*White or yellow clear color for type, reasonably free from defects. Whole kernels should have few or no broken pieces, damaged or mutilated parts. Reasonably firm, with little evident softness or mushiness. Tender. Flavor characteristic of sweet, well-processed hominy.

Mustard Greens
Specify Fancy, with applicable factors outlined for spinach.   Minimum
drained weight for No. 10 can is 60 oz.

Mushrooms
Grades: A (85),* C (70).
Styles: Whole, sliced whole, sliced buttons, stems and pieces.
Size: No. 1 (tiny) $\frac{1}{2}$ to $\frac{5}{8}$ in. diameter, No. 2 (small) $\frac{5}{8}$ to $\frac{7}{8}$ in. in
diameter, No. 3 (medium) $\frac{7}{8}$ to $1\frac{1}{8}$ in. in diameter, No. 4 (large) $1\frac{1}{8}$ to
$1\frac{3}{8}$ in. diameter, No. 5 (extra large) $1\frac{3}{8}$ in. or more in diameter.
Recommended drained weight:

Can Size	Drained Weight	Can Size	Drained Weight
2Z	2 oz	No. 1 tall	$9\frac{3}{4}$ oz
6Z	$3\frac{1}{4}$ oz	No. 303	10 oz
8Z tall	$4\frac{3}{4}$ oz	No. 2	12 oz
8Z mushroom	8 oz	Jumbo (307 x 510)	16 oz
No. 300	9 oz	No. 10	68 oz

*Most frequently white or creamy; occasionally, packs may be brown type.
Practically uniform, bright and typical color.   Practically uniform in size
and shape; whole mushrooms not smaller than $\frac{1}{8}$ in.   Sliced whole should
be sliced lengthways, while sliced buttons should be sliced crosswise the
width of the caps.   Stems and pieces may be irregular in size and shape.
Practically free from defects.   Mushrooms should be intact, tender and free
from fibrous or rubbery units, with at least 95% with closed veils.

Onions, Whole
Grade: A (85),* C (70).
Size: Tiny, small and medium.   In a No. 10 can there will be 200 or more of
tiny onions, 100 to 199 small onions, and 80 to 99 medium onions.
Recommended drained weight: No. 10 (tiny) 64 oz, (small), 63 oz, (medium)
60 oz.
*Reasonably bright, characteristic color.   May be touched with slight
greenish area on surface.   Uniform size and shape.   Well trimmed, with few
blemishes, mechanical damage or other defects.   Should retain shape;
reasonably firm and tender, not soft or spongy.

Okra
Grades: A (85),* C (70).
Style: Cut, whole and whole salad (pods $\frac{1}{2}$ to 1 in. long).

Recommended drained weight:	Whole and Whole Salad	Cut
No. 2	12 oz	$12\frac{3}{4}$ oz
No. 2$\frac{1}{2}$	$17\frac{3}{4}$ oz	$18\frac{3}{4}$ oz
No. 10	60 oz	60 oz

*Liquor clear and bright, with thin, gelatinous consistency.   Uniformity
light green color.   Uniform size, with pods not over $3\frac{1}{2}$ in. in length for
whole.   Cut means transverse slices from pods, pieces intact, not shattered
or broken.   Whole pods should be intact, not shattered or broken to an extent detracting from appearance or use.   Tender okra, seeds small and in
earlier stages of development.   Typical characteristic okra flavor.

Peas

Grades: A (90), B (80),* C (70).

Types: Early (Alaska or other smooth skin varieties), Sweet or Sugar (wrinkled varieties).

Sizes: See Figure 3-26.

Recommended drained weight: None established. On refilling original container with peas, the level of peas, 15 seconds after the peas are returned to the can, should completely fill the container.

*Color reasonably bright and uniform, typical of mature canned peas. Reasonably free from defects, such as spotted, discolored peas, harmless extraneous material, pea plant, leaves, pods, stems, thistle buds, nightshade berries and so forth. Relatively few pieces or broken or crushed peas, skins cotyledons and so forth. Shall be reasonably tender and in a brine flotation test the maximum number of peas of all sizes for Grade B, which will sink in 10 seconds, should be: sweet varieties 15% in 13% brine salt solution, 4% in 15% solution; early varieties 30% in 13½% brine solution and 8% in 15% solution. Watch for mealy taste showing maturity. Flavor should be pleasant and sweet.

Peas, Black-eye (See also dried beans.)

Grades: A (85),* C (70).

Federal and Commercial Sizes		
Sieve	Inches*	Size Name
6	$\frac{13}{32}$ to $\frac{14}{32}$	Large
5	$\frac{12}{32}$ to $\frac{13}{32}$	Medium large
4	$\frac{11}{32}$ to $\frac{12}{32}$	Medium
3	$\frac{10}{32}$ to $\frac{11}{32}$	Medium small
2	$\frac{9}{32}$ to $\frac{10}{32}$	Small
1	$\frac{9}{32}$ or less	Tiny

*In diameter; $\frac{14}{32}$ " or larger peas are called No. 7 sieve size.

FIG. 3-26. Pea sizes.

Styles: May be with or without unshelled immature pods (snaps) or pieces of pod (snaps).

Recommended drained weight: No. 2, 13¼ oz; No. 10, 70 oz.

*Typical color of fresh black-eye peas, practically free from loose or pieces of loose skins, loose or pieces of loose cotyledons and other extraneous material, broken, mashed or damaged peas. Texture should be tender of peas fairly early in stages of maturity. Flavor should be good.

Pimientos

Grades: A (85),* C (70).

Styles: Whole, whole and pieces, pieces, pieces sliced, pieces diced.

Recommended drained weight:

Can Size	Whole	Whole and Pieces	Pieces	Diced	Sliced
4Z Pimientos	3¼ oz	3¼ oz	3½ oz	3½ oz	3¼ oz
No. 300	10 oz	10¼ oz	10¼ oz	10¼ oz	10 oz
No. 303	11 oz	11¼ oz	11¼ oz	11¼ oz	11 oz
No. 2	13¼ oz	13½ oz	14 oz	14 oz	13¼ oz
No. 2½	20 oz	20¼ oz	20¼ oz	20¼ oz	20 oz
No. 10	70¾ oz	72¼ oz	74 oz	74¼ oz	71¾ oz

*Color red or reddish yellow according to variety, but uniform and clear. Bright, with relatively few blemishes, spots or off coloring. Practically uniform in size and shape. Practically free from grit, sand or silt, seeds, undeveloped seeds, core and stems, peel, trimmed units or other blemishes. Firm fleshed and tender, with no apparent disintegration.

Potatoes, White

Grades: A (85),* C (70).

Styles: Whole, sliced, diced, shoestring (French or julienne), pieces.

Sizes: Whole, diameter size: tiny, size 1, 1 in. or less; small, size 2, 1 to 1½ in.; medium, size 3, over 1½ in.

*Color should be practically free from oxidation and possess a practically uniform, light creamy color, more on the white side than yellow. Size and shape should be uniform, with no potato over 2 in. in diameter, and the weight of the largest not more than three times the weight of the second smallest. Slices should not be more than ¾ in. thick, with diameters not more than 2 in. Diced potatoes should be cubes not more than ½ in. Pieces should not be less than ½ oz and not more than 2 oz. Practically free from defects, sand, grit and blemishes. Firm, possessing a fine and even grain, with only a small amount of sloughing that does not materially affect the appearance. Good odor and flavor.

Pumpkin or Squash

Grades: A (85),* C (70).

Recommended drained weight: Fill of container shall be 90% of the liquid content of the can.

*Shall be pulp from clean, sound properly matured, golden fleshed, firm shelled, sweet varieties of either pumpkin or squash. Color uniform, bright typical color of well-matured squash or pumpkin. Smooth, even texture, with no hard or grainy particles. Not pasty. Practically free from sand, grit, silt, pieces of seed, fiber and coarse, dark or off-color particles. Not excessively dark orange. No noticeable unpalatable flavor.

Sauerkraut

Grades: A (90), B (80),* C (70).
Styles: Shredded or chopped.
Recommended drained weight: No. 2, 16 oz; No. 2½, 23 oz; No. 10, 80 oz.

*Should possess practically uniform, typical white to light cream general appearance with no pink cast. Cut evenly and uniformly, with no thick, few short or irregular cut pieces. Thickness of shredded type should be about ½₂ in. thick. Practically free from coarse pieces of leaves, large and coarse pieces of core, blemishes, spotted pieces or dark or discolored kraut. Firm, crisp, easy to cut. Characteristic kraut flavor, containing not less than 1.0% lactic acid, with typical lactic acid fermentation and salt flavor of good kraut. Not less than 1½% nor more than 2½% salt. Sometimes purchased in 500-lb barrel where quantity used is large. Specify net weight of barrel contents in this case. Some kraut is purchased in gallons, and in this case specify minimum drained weight of 96 oz. Watch for noticeable lack of crispness, unpalatable flavor with traces of mold, excess salt, staleness or bitterness.

Spinach

Grades: A (85),* C (70).
Recommended drained weight: No. 2, 13 oz; No. 2½, 19 oz; No. 10, 60 oz.

*Typical green color of young, tender canned spinach with little variation in color. Practically free from grit, sand or silt, seed heads, grass and weeds, parts of root stubs or stubs and damaged pieces. Tender. Practically free from coarse or tough portions. Practically free from raggedness, disintegration or shredded leaves.

Squash, Summer

Grades: A (85),* C (70).
Styles: Whole, sliced crosswise, diced, cut.
Recommended drained weight: No. 2, 13 oz; No. 10, 70 oz.

*Bright and typical for young and tender squash. Watch for grit, sand, wilt, poor workmanship, damaged or broken pieces, scars, insect injury and extraneous matter. Full-fleshed texture; tender with seeds that are immature.

Sweet Potatoes

Grades: A (85),* C (70).
Types: Golden (yellow).
Packs: In liquid, vacuum (without packing media), solid (dry pack). Some packs in liquid may be in sirup, in which case extra heavy sirup is 30° Brix or more, heavy 25 to 30° Brix, light 18 to 25° Brix. Most facilities use a water pack or dry pack.
Recommended drained weight for sirup or liquid packs: No. 2, 14 oz; No. 2½ 19 oz; No. 10, 72 oz.

*Color uniform and clear, no dullness or off color. Practically uniform in size and shape. Practically free from particles of peel, secondary rootlets, untrimmed fibrous ends, discolored areas and other defects that do not appreciably mar the appearance. Uniform smooth texture practically free from tough or coarse fibers; soft, yet firm enough to hold original shape and size without material disintegration. Note some soft- or moist-fleshed varieties (yams) may be relatively tender and more sweet than the firmer varieties, which will be more mealy and dry. Sweet potatoes will also be lighter yellow in color than yams.

Tomatoes

Grades: A (90), B (80),* C (70).
Packs: Solid pack (firm, ripe tomatoes with no added liquid), tomatoes with juice (tomato juice added), tomatoes with puree (puree added).
Recommended drained weight: Drained weight is a part of grade. Grade A must drain 66% of the total can contents, Grade B 56% and Grade C 50%. Net can contents should be 90% of the liquid fill of the container.

*Color should vary from uniform, good red typical color for Grade A to fairly good red, typical color for Grade C. Defects should be practically free, reasonably free and fairly free, respectively, for Grades A, B and C tomatoes. Wholeness is a grade factor. Grade A should have 80% of the tomatoes whole or almost whole. Grade B should have 70% whole or almost whole and Grade C less than 70%. About 0.026% calcium chloride may be added to give tomatoes added firmness.

Turnip Greens

Grades: None; specify Fancy.
Use spinach standards as a guide. Minimum drained weight recommended for a No. 10 can is 60 oz.

Tomato Catsup

Grades: A (85),* B (85),* C (70). Grades A and B are similar except the former contains not less than 33% total solids and the latter 29%. Grade C contains not less than 25% solids, but varies also in other quality factors from Grades A and B.

*Color from well-ripened red tomatoes. Consistency such that not more than a slight separation of free liquid shows when the catsup is stirred and poured onto a tray flowing not more than 9 centimeters in 30 seconds at 20° C in the Bostwick consistometer. Watch for defects, such as dark specks or scalelike particles, seeds, core material and so forth. Flavor should be distinct and good. The flavor and odor should be free from scorching or other objectionable flavors.

Tomato Paste

Grades: A (85),* C (70).
Concentrations: Heavy, 33% salt-free solids or more, approximately 1.14 specific gravity; medium, 29 to 33% salt-free solids, approximately 1.11 specific gravity; light, 25 to 29% salt-free solids, approximately 1.09 specific gravity.
Textures: Fine or coarse.

*Color should be red, varying somewhat in degree from Grades A to C. Grade A should be practically free from defects while Grade C should be

Table 3–10
Trade Association Recommendations for Minimum Net Weight of Contents for Canned Vegetables

Vegetable	Can Size No. 10	No. 2½	No. 2	Vegetable	Can Size No. 10	No. 2½	No. 2
Asparagus, tips				Succotash	108 oz		20 oz
and spears			19 oz	Tomatoes	102 oz	28 oz	19 oz
Asparagus, cuts	103 oz	28 oz	19 oz	Tomato catsup			
Beans, dried	110 oz	31 oz	21 oz	Specific gravity			
Beans, snap type	101 oz	28 oz	19 oz	1.11	111 oz	30 oz	21 oz
Beans, lima	105 oz		20 oz	1.15	115 oz	32 oz	22 oz
Beets	104 oz	28 oz	20 oz	Tomato paste			
Carrots	105 oz	28 oz	20 oz	Specific gravity			
Corn	106 oz		20 oz	1.11	111 oz	30 oz	
Mushrooms	103 oz	28 oz		1.14	114 oz	31 oz	
Okra	99 oz	27 oz	19 oz	Tomato puree			
Pimientos	106 oz	28 oz	20 oz	Specific gravity			
Sauerkraut	99 oz	27 oz	19 oz	1.035	104 oz	28 oz	19 oz
Spinach	98 qz	27 oz	18 oz	1.05	105 oz	29 oz	20 oz
Squash	106 oz	29 oz	20 oz				

fairly free. Both should possess a typical, pleasant tomato flavor, free from scorched, bitter green tomato flavors or other objectionable flavors and odors.

Tomato Puree (Pulp)

Grades: A (85),* C (70).

*Tomato puree contains not less than 8.37 to 25% salt-free tomato solids. Heavy puree contains 12 to 25% salt-free tomato solids. Medium contains 10.7 to 12% salt-free tomato solids and light 8.37 to 10.7%. 12% solids will have an approximate specific gravity of 1.05 and 8.37% a specific gravity of 1.035. The puree should possess a good ripe to fairly good ripe, red color, be practically or reasonably free from defects, depending on grade. Watch for off-color, predominantly yellowish red; scorched, bitter, salty or green tomato flavor should be cause for rejection. Watch for excessive presence of dark specks and scalelike particles from seeds, tomato peel or core; poor consistency tending to thinness should lead to rejection.

Tomato Sauce

Grades: A (85),* C (70).

*Concentrated liquid from tomatoes to which salt, spices, sweeteners, vinegar, onion, garlic or other vegetable flavoring ingredients are added to make tomato sauce. The color should be typical of well-ripened red tomatoes, with some variation for Grade C. On a tray, consistency of Grade A should show not more than 18 centimeters flow in 30 seconds at 20° C in the Bostwick consistometer. The sauce should also possess a sufficient fluidity to give some flow. There should be no noticeable separation of free liquid. Dark specks, scalelike particles, seeds, tomato peel, core material and other extraneous matter should be checked. Flavor should be pleasant, with no scorched taste.

Tomatoes and Okra

Grades: A (85),* C (70).
Recommended drained weight: None.

*Mixture shall be at least 50% tomatoes and 12½ to 50% okra; the mixture must be called "Okra and Tomatoes" if the quantity of okra exceeds that of tomatoes and the proportion in this case must be at least 50% okra and 12½ to 50% tomatoes. Check for flavor and odor, color typical of reasonably ripe tomatoes and young tender okra. The product should be reasonably free of dirt, silt, sand and harmless extraneous material. Watch for damaged pods with good wholeness of tomato and tenderness and texture of okra.

Frozen Fruits [1]

Apples

Grades: A (85),* C (70).
Styles: Sliced.
Sugar-fruit ratio recommended: 1:7.
Usual packaging: 25 or 30-lb tins.

*Uniform brightness in internal and external parts. Color characteristic for variety. Uniform, practically whole slices (¾ slice or more is considered a whole slice), 1¼ in. or longer in length, and thickness that does not vary more than ¼ in. Reasonably free from harmless extraneous matter, carpel tissue, peel, seeds, stems, damage and other defects. Texture should be firm, tender and crisp. Watch for discoloration and mushy apples.

Apricots

Grades: A (90), B (75),* C (60).
Styles: Half or whole. Either pitted or unpitted may be obtained in whole.
Sugar-fruit ratio recommened: 1:5.
Usual packaging: 8 lb, 10 lb packs or 25 or 30-lb tins.

*Reasonably uniform, bright typical color of mature apricots, with little green, tarnishing or browning. Some pale areas may be evident around stem end. Only a few misshapen ones. The weight of the largest apricot should not exceed the smallest by more than 75% and no half should be less than ⅖ oz. Reasonably free from blemishes, such as stem pits and worm holes. Uniform, tender texture, thick and fleshy fruit only slightly ragged. Usual drained weight, 64%.

Berries (except Blueberries, Raspberries and Strawberries)

Grades: A (85),* B (70).
Specify type berry: Blackberries, loganberries, dewberries, youngberries and so forth.
Sugar-fruit ratio recommended: 1:4.
Usual packaging: 25 lb or 30 lb tin.

*Color typical for variety, with little variation in intensity or luster of well-ripened berries. Defects such as leaves, stems, caps, undeveloped berries,

[1] Score or judge thawed, not frozen.

blemishes, extraneous matter, insect or pathological damage and other injuries should be limited. Few unripe berries. Juice should be practically free from detached seed cells. There should be little crushing of ripe, plump, tender fruit. Watch for not more than four sepal-like bracts per pound and not more than one leaf or the approximate equivalent of one full cap per four pounds. Not more than 5% of the berries may be damaged. Usual drained weight, depending upon variety, 50 to 65%.

Blueberries

Grades: A (90), B (80),* C (70).
Types: Wild or cultivated.
Sugar-fruit ratio: 1 : 4 (Sometimes local supplies frozen without sugar.)
Usual packaging: 20, 25, 30 lb tins or packs.

*Reasonably uniform in color, possessing a red-purple color, with few green berries. Few berries in clusters. No dull or off color. Reasonably few defects, such as cap stems, undeveloped berries. May be lacking in firmness and fleshy texture, but only reasonably so. Berries should be reasonably whole, with little crushing, splitting or broken berries evident.

Cherries, Red, Sour, Pitted (RSP)

Grades: A (85),* C (70).
Sugar-fruit ratio recommended: 1 : 4 or 1 : 5.
Usual packaging: 30-lb tins.

*Good flavor and odor; reasonably red color of well-matured cherries without market discoloration from oxidation, improper processing or under coloring in fruit. Few pits, pieces of pits, damaged or multilated or blemished berries. Usual drained weight, 55%.

Cherries, Sweet

Grades: A (85),* C (70).
Sugar-fruit ratio recommended: 1 : 7.
Usual packaging: 25 or 30 lb tins.
Types: Light (Royal Anne or Napoleon), Dark (Bing, Schmidt, Black Republican, Lambert, Tartarian).
Styles: Pitted and unpitted.

*Practically uniform typical color. Minimum weight of single, unpitted cherry should average about $\frac{1}{10}$ oz, and the variation in size of diameter of largest over smallest should be not more than $\frac{1}{4}$ in. Cherries should be 90% or more free from pits or pieces of pits, unseparable doubles, bruised, checked, cracked or damaged cherries. Watch for oxidation and browning. Cherries should be thick fleshed, firm and well ripened. There should be few split or crushed cherries. Usual drained weight is 56%.

Grapefruit

Grades: A (90), B (80),* Broken (70). (Broken is same grade as B in all other respects except for wholeness of pieces.)

*At least 50% whole but not more than 75% whole or almost whole segments. (Above 75% whole is a requirement of Grade A.) Reasonably good clear color, not dull. Reasonably good characteristics, with fairly firm, plump flesh, with but few ricey segments. Color bright, with only a small amount of color variability.

Peaches

Grades: A (90), B (75),* C (60).
Types: Yellow clings, yellow freestones, white freestones.
Sugar-fruit ratio recommended: 1 : 4.
Usual packaging: In containers not less than 6½ lb net; usually 25 or 30 lb tins.
Styles: Half or slices. (Some quartered fruit available.)
*Reasonably uniform, bright, typical color, which is yellow-orange or creamy white, depending on type. Size and symmetry uniform, with few misshapen pieces. Watch for split, broken, crushed or otherwise mutilated sections. There should be limited raggedness. No half should weigh less than ⅗ oz and no quarter less than ³/₁₀ oz. Slices should be reasonably full, with few broken ones. Reasonably free from defects, with limited slight browning from oxidation. Uniform tender texture, which may be slightly soft to slightly firm. Usual drained weight, 64%.

Pineapple

Grades: A (90), B (80),* C (70).
Variety: Hawaiian or Philippine are best varieties.
Sugar: Specify sirup density 20 or 25° Brix, which is fairly heavy.
Usual packaging: 25-lb containers.
Styles: Whole slices, half slices (two pieces should approximately equal one whole slice), broken slices (should be approximately the same thickness and diameter), chunks (must not exceed 1½ in. in any dimension), crushed (may be shredded or crushed), tidbits or wedges.
*Reasonably uniform in yellowish color, no gray cast or dull color. Reasonably uniform shape and symmetry, with little crushed or broken fruit, or raggedness unless crushed. Reasonably uniform ripeness, compact structure and porosity. Taste for fullness of flavor.

Plums

Grades: A (85),* B (70).
Varieties: Red (Satsuma or Santa Rosa), Yellow-green (Yellow Egg, Jefferson and Reine Claude), Purple or Blue (Prunes, Damson plum).
Styles: Halved or whole. Whole may be pitted or unpitted.
Sugar-fruit ratio recommended: 1 : 5.
Usual packaging: 25-lb containers.
*Reasonably uniform, bright, typical color, with reasonable freedom from browning. Reasonably uniform in size and symmetry, with the weight of the largest unit not more than twice the weight of the smallest one. Reasonably free from defects, harmless extraneous matter, crushed and broken units, pits and other materials. Reasonably good texture of plump, well-ripened, tender fruit. Usual drained weight, 65%.

Raspberries

Grades: A (85),* B (70).
Varieties: Red or Black; latter may sometimes be called black caps.
Sugar-fruit ratio recommended: 1 : 4.
Usual packaging: 25 or 30 lb tins.
*Practically uniform, typical color, with marked intensity and luster of well-ripened berries, with no darkening from overmaturity or oxidation. Practi-

cally free from harmless extraneous material, sepal-like bracts, caps, stems, undeveloped, hard or damaged berries. Mature, well-developed, fleshy, tender character. The liquor should be practically free from detached seed cells. Usual drained weight, 50%.

Rhubarb

Grades: A (85),* B (70).
Varieties: Crimson or Green; Crimson may be called red, strawberry or hothouse.
Sugar-fruit ratio recommended: 1:3 or 1:4.
Usual packaging: Containers 25-lb or 30-lb net.

*Judge after thawing for color, glossy, bright, typical clear, not dull or gray. Practically free from defects, extraneous material, leaves, root ends, growth cracks, and other defects. Reasonably good tenderness and texture means that not more than 5% of the units may be tough, spongy or stringy. Cook and judge for color, flavor, tenderness and texture; use 5 oz water to 12 oz rhubarb and sugar. Sweeten if rhubarb is unsugared in freezing. Judge after 6 minutes of boiling.

Strawberries

Grades: A (90), B (80),* C (70).
Styles: Whole or sliced; sliced means two or more slices per strawberry.
Sugar-fruit ratio recommended: 1:4.
Usual packaging: 6½ lb, 8 lb, 10 lb, 15 lb, 20 lb and 30 lb containers.

*Color reasonably uniform, characteristic pink to red, not materially affected by dull, gray or reddish brown. Specify Marshall variety, which, when sliced, will not show a white core but all solid red meat. Good color should appear on ⅘ of the berry. Reasonably free from grit, sand, caps, stems and damage. Firm, plump, tender, soft berries, with only a reasonable amount of crushing or mushiness. Strawberries may be specified in sizes as:

Small	Diameter* less than ⅝ in.
Medium	Diameter* ⅝ to 1¼ in.
Large	Diameter* over 1¼ in.

*Diameter measured at right angles to a straight line running from stem to apex. (To meet U.S. Grade A, whole berries may not contain more than 5% by count of strawberries that fall into small classification.) Usual drained weight, 51%.

Frozen Vegetables[2]

Asparagus

Grades: A (85),* B (70).
Styles: Spears or stalks (head and adjoining portion of shoot 3 in. or more in length), tips (head and adjoining portion of shoot less than 3 in. in length), cut spears or cuts and tips (head and portions of the shoot cut transversely into units 2 in. or less but not less than ½ in.), center cuts or cuts (portions of shoots that are cut transversely into units 2 in. or less, but not less than ½ in.).

[2] Do not judge frozen. Cook and judge.

Sizes: Small (No. 1) less than $\frac{3}{8}$ in., medium (No. 2) $\frac{3}{8}$ to $\frac{5}{8}$ in., large (No. 3) $\frac{5}{8}$ in., extra large (No. 4), $\frac{7}{8}$ in. or larger.

Color: All green, green, green-white.

*Asparagus should possess good characteristic color, typical of well-developed and tender asparagus, with all green, or green having little or no white color, evident. Uniformity of size and length should be good. Defects such as grit, silt, loose material, shattered heads, misshapen units, poorly cut units or otherwise damaged, discolored or broken units should be noted. Heads should be compact and well-developed, not shriveled. The entire product should be tender and the texture good, with few tough fibers.

Beans, Snap, Green or Wax

Grades: A (90), B (80),* C (70).

Styles: Whole (pods not less than $2\frac{3}{4}$ in. in length or transversely cut pods not less than $2\frac{3}{4}$ in. in length); julienne—French, shoestring or sliced lengthwise (cut into thin strips lengthwise); cut (pods cut transversely into pieces $\frac{3}{4}$ to $2\frac{3}{4}$ in. in length; short cut ($\frac{3}{4}$ to $1\frac{1}{4}$ in. transverse cuts); mixed (any mixture of above).

Types: Round or flat; the former has a width not greater than $1\frac{1}{2}$ times the thickness, and the latter a width greater than $1\frac{1}{2}$ times the thickness.

*Reasonably good, uniform color, bright and typical of young and tender beans. Reasonable amount only of extraneous matter, small pieces or other blemishes. Stems, free beans, damaged pods and other defects should be noted. Reasonably good maturity but not late maturity. Units should not be materially affected by sloughing; be tender, with reasonably good plumpness and fleshy structure. Determine flavor and odor after boiling 15 minutes.

Beans, Lima

Grades: A (90), B (80),* C (70).

Types: Thin-seeded (Henderson Bush, Thorogreen), thick-seeded (Baby Potato, Baby Fordhook and Evergreen).

*Reasonably good color for type, possessing a typical color and a uniform color in the thin-seeded types of 65% green and 35% white, and in the thick-seeded varieties, 60% green and 40% white, with white defined as lighter in color than the typical pale green of fresh, frozen lima beans. Reasonably free from defects, such as free pieces of flesh, skins, shriveled or hard beans, sprouted beans and extraneous matter. Check flavor and odor after cooking 18 minutes in boiling salted water.

Broccoli

Grades: A (85),* B (70).

Styles: Spears of stalks (not less than 3 in. and not more than 6 in. in length), short spears or florets (not less than 1 in. nor more 3 in.), cuts (spears or stalks cut into $\frac{3}{4}$ to 2 in. piece containing not less than 25% head material and not more than 25% leaf material), chopped (units less than $\frac{3}{4}$ in. in size containing not less than 25% head material and not more than 25% leaf material), pieces (units not in excess of 2 in. in length, which may or may not contain head or leaf material).

*Good, bright green color of young tender broccoli; no yellowing of head

FIG. 3–27.   Leaves, leaf spurs and small shoots are neatly trimmed on the frozen broccoli sample on the left.   This illustrates a well-trimmed unit.   The center spear has slightly
ragged appearance from short, small leaf spurs and small side shoots.   Ragged appearance of sample on left is caused by large, coarse leaf spurs.   This sample illustrates a
poorly trimmed unit.   Courtesy USDA.

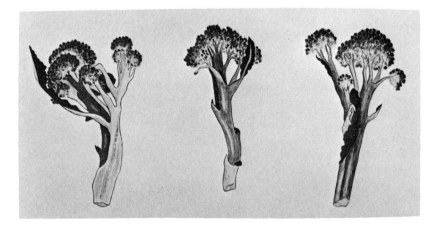

FIG. 3–28.   Degrees of "well-developed" stalks, of which at least 80% are required in
Grade A or Fancy frozen broccoli, in addition to other requirements of color, uniformity of
size, defects and tenderness.   The practically compact heads, buds closed and no elongation of individual bud stems illustrates near top quality for well-developed frozen broccoli.
Courtesy USDA.

material. Uniform size; free from grit, silt, sand, harmless extraneous vegetable material, such as weeds or grass. Reasonably free from loose leaves, detached fragments and showing good workmanship in trimming. Few damaged, broken or damaged pieces. Well-developed bud clusters, compact and well closed, not showing more than slight elongation. Tender and free from tough fiber. Cook to ascertain characteristics.

Brussels Sprouts

Grades: A (90), B (80),* C (70).

*Reasonably good color, with more than 5% but not more than 25% yellowish and the remainder yellow-green or more green in color. Reasonably free from grit, silt, harmless extraneous material, loose leaves and loose small pieces. Look for poorly trimmed cuts and damaged pieces. Should be well developed, compact, well formed and reasonably firm. Only 10% allowed in loose structured, spongy or soft heads. Cook for flavor, texture and color evaluation.

Carrots, Diced

Grades: A (85),* B (70).

*Bright, typical orange-yellow color, with only slight evidence of any green. Uniform size of cubes from $\frac{1}{4}$ to $\frac{1}{2}$ in. Practically free from damaged, unpeeled units or otherwise blemished units. Cook to ascertain flavor. Carrots should have tender texture, not fibrous or tough. Flavor should be sweet and characteristic of sweet, young carrots.

Cauliflower

Grades: A (85),* B (70).

*White to light cream color, which may be slightly variable, with a slight green color or blue color on the branching parts and a greenish yellow to light green or modified green on the bracts. Reasonably free from poorly trimmed clusters and small clusters, damaged clusters, from pieces and detached fragments and other defects. Reasonably free from "ricey" or fuzzy units. Cook for flavor, texture and color evaluation.

Corn on the Cob

Grades: A (85),* B (70).

Types: Yellow or golden; white.

*Bright, uniform, typical color of young and tender corn. Practically free from loose material, poorly trimmed ears, damaged kernels or other defects. Tender kernels that are in the milk or early cream stage of maturity. Evenly filled cobs, with no worm damage or excessive trimming. Free of silk, husks and other extraneous material.

Corn, Whole Kernel or Whole Grain

Grades: A (90), B (80),* C (70).

Types: Yellow or golden; white.

*Reasonably good yellow color or creamy white of tender young corn. Reasonably bright and free from "off-variety" kernels. Reasonably free from defects, such as damaged kernels, cob, husk, silk, ragged or crushed kernels, extraneous vegetable matter and loose skins. Check flavor and odor after cooking. Kernels should be reasonably tender and in the cream stage.

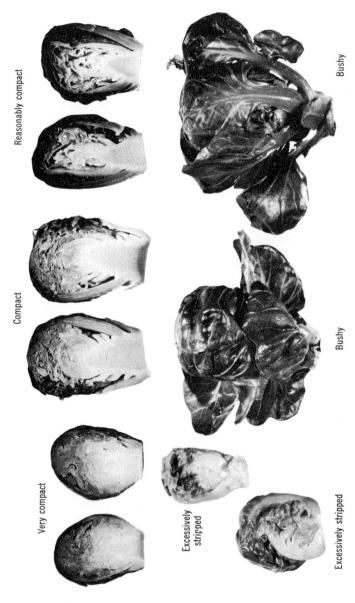

Reasonably compact

Compact

Very compact

Bushy

Bushy

Excessively stripped

Excessively stripped

FIG. 3–29.   Degrees of compactness, stripping and bushiness considered in the grading of frozen brussels sprouts.   Courtesy USDA.

Greens (other than Spinach)

Grades: A (85),* B (70).
Types: Beet, Collards, Dandelion, Endive, Kale, Mustard, Swiss chard, Turnip.
Styles: Whole leave, sliced leaves, cut or chopped.

*Sound, succulent, clean leaves from fresh leafy greens, washed, trimmed, sorted, blanched and frozen. Practically a uniform color, bright for variety. Reasonably free from grit, sand and silt, damaged or yellow or brown leaves, extraneous matter. Reasonably tender, without coarse or tough leaves or stems.

Mixed Vegetables

Grades: A (90), B (80),* C (70).

*Mixture should be composed of snap beans, green or wax varieties, cut into transverse pieces $\frac{1}{2}$ to $1\frac{1}{2}$ in. in length, diced carrots in $\frac{3}{8}$ to $\frac{1}{2}$ in. cubes, sweet, whole kernel corn and peas of the early or sweet type. If the mixture consists of three vegetables, no vegetable can be in excess of 40%. If of four vegetables, none may be less than 8% nor more than 35%, and if of five vegetables, none may be less than 8% nor more than 30%. Color should be bright and good for each vegetable. Practically free from defects or extraneous material. All units should be tender, full and plump for variety and type.

Okra

Grades: A (85),* B (70).
Styles: Whole, cut; in latter pods are cut transversely into pieces; specify that pieces shall not be less than $\frac{1}{2}$ in. in length for cut. Size is measured from stem end to end of tip.

*Practically uniform bright, young and tender okra. Practically free from extraneous vegetable matter, sand, silt, grit, poorly trimmed units, small pieces of $\frac{1}{4}$ in. or less, damaged units, misshapen units and blemishes. Few broken or crushed pieces. Seeds tender and white, not developed toward maturity. Desirable length in pods (whole) is $3\frac{1}{2}$ in.

Onion Rings, Breaded

Grades: A (85),* B (70).

*May be deep fried or uncooked. When cooked should be free of rancid or bitter flavor, or any carmelized or oily flavors. Color should be golden brown. Color of uncooked should be creamy white. Should not possess excess breading in either type. Both should be reasonably free from broken or imperfect rings, blemishes, extraneous matter, black specks or other deformities or defects.

Peas

Grades: A (90), B (80),* C (70).
Types: Early or sweet. (Best freezing variety, Telephone pea.)

*Reasonably uniform, typical green color. Few spotted or off-color brown, gray, creamy or yellow-white peas. Reasonably free from harmless extraneous vegetable material and other defects; few crushed or broken peas; few

FIG. 3–30. A USDA inspector
determines the relative specific
gravity of frozen peas by brine
flotation test. This test gives an
index to maturity, an important
quality factor for this item. Courtesy USDA.

peas without skins; few loose skins. Tenderness and maturity of young,
tender peas. Not more than 12% after removing skins should sink within 10
seconds in a 15% salt brine solution.

Peas and Carrots

Grades: A (90), B (80),* C (70).
Proportions: Peas, not less than 50% by weight of early or sweet type; carrots
not less than 25% by weight of diced carrots predominantly ¼ to ⅜ in.
cubes.

*Reasonably good color, bright and typical of reasonably young, tender peas
and carrots. Reasonably uniform color. Reasonably free from leaves, stems,
pods, thistle buds, night-shade berries or damaged units. Few broken,
mashed, loose cotyledons, loose skins, spotted or off-colored units. From
reasonably mature, plump, full-fleshed peas or carrots.

Peas, Black-eyed or Field

Grades: A (85),* B (70).
*Good typical color of reasonably young field peas or black-eye peas.
Reasonably free from extraneous vegetable matter, such as loose skins, pieces
of skins, loose cotyledons, broken units or otherwise damaged units. Tender
and in a reasonably young stage of maturity.

Peppers, Sweet

Grades: A (85),* B (70).

Types: Green, red or mixed red and green.

Styles: Whole stemmed or whole unstemmed (shall be 2½ in. in length and 2½ in. in diameter as measured at widest part), halves from whole peppers, sliced (at least 1¼ in. in length) and diced (½ in. square approximately).

*Good characteristic bright color for type. When appearance of the product is seriously affected by a mixture of red and green, it shall be considered mixed. Practically free from grit, sand, silt, excessive trimming and damaged units. Cut styles should be fairly free from seeds and extraneous matter. Uniform in size and shape. Reasonably full fleshed, firm, full and plump.

Spinach

Grades: A (85),* B (70).

Styles: Whole, whole leaf, cut or chopped.

*Practically uniform, bright, characteristic green color; practically free from grit, sand or silt, seed heads, grass and weeds, crowns of root stubs and other blemishes or defects. Watch for brown or yellow leaves, stems, coarse or tough stems or leaves, or insect injury. The leaves should not be ragged or torn.

Squash, Summer

Grades: A (85),* B (70).

Styles: Sliced (transverse cuts), cut (in pieces).

*Fresh, sound, immature product from summer squash varieties. Color should be bright and typical of young, tender squash. Practically free from sand, grit and silt, poorly cut units, damaged units, discolored, scarred or other defects. Fleshy, full, plump units. Texture should be tender not tough. The seeds should be soft and undeveloped, as in immature young summer squash.

Squash, Winter (Cooked)

Grades: A (85),* B (70).

*The squash, after warming and mixing on a flat, dry surface, should form a well-rounded mass, which, after two minutes, has only a slight separation of liquor at the edges. The color should be practically uniform, bright and typical, free from discoloration from oxidation or other causes. The texture should be even and may be granular, but not lumpy, pasty, and the particles should not be hard. Practically free from sand, grit and silt, pieces of seed, fiber and dark or off-colored particles.

Succotash

Grades: A (90), B (80),* C (70).

Recommended proportions by weight:	Not more than	Not less than
Corn, white or golden	75%	50%
Lima beans, fresh not dried	50%	25%
Soybeans, vegetable	50%	25%
Green or wax beans	50%	25%

The lima beans may be thin or thick-seeded varieties. Green or wax snap beans may be cut or short-cut style.

*Colors of vegetables should be bright and typical of young, tender products. Practically free from pieces of pod, leaves, stems, pieces of cob, husk, silk, damaged units or other defects. Tender, young, immature, full, plump vegetables.

Fruit Spreads

Apple Butter

Grades: A (85),* C (70).

*Uniform, polished, dark-chocolate brown color, which may possess a reddish shade. Practically free from defects, with not more than a slight amount of black specks, particles of seed, stem, peel, calyx or other particles. Stir and place on a flat surface so a prominently mounded mass is formed, but one not so stiff that it cannot be spread readily. At the end of 2 minutes there should be no more than a slight separation of free liquor. The texture should be fine-grained, evenly divided and smooth. Flavor should be free from any traces of bitter, scorched, caramelized, molasses-like or noticeable brown sugar flavor.

Cranberry Sauce

Grades: A (85),* C (70).
Styles: Whole, jellied or strained.

*Product should possess a dark red color, typical of canned red cranberries. The jel should be tender and in whole style, uniformly spread throughout. Reject stiff or rubbery jellied products. There may be some slight separation of liquor evident. In whole, look for defective crown stems. Both styles should possess good flavor and odor.

Fruit Jelly

Grades: A (85),* B (70).
Types: Type I made from a single fruit; Type II made from two up to five fruits.

*Bright typical color for fruit variety, sparkling luster, not more than slightly cloudy, and free from any dullness. Tender to slightly firm, retaining compact shape, with little or no syneresis (weeping). Not tough or rubbery. Distinct and normal flavor characteristic of the fruit ingredient or ingredients. Free from any caramelized or objectionable flavor. In jellies of two or more fruits, the weight of each fruit used must not be less than 20% of the total used. If the jelly is made of two to five fruit juices, the name "jelly" used is preceded or followed by the words "mixed fruit" or by the names of the fruits used.

Fruit Preserves or Jams

Grades: A (85),* B (70).
Types: Type I made from a single fruit; Type II made from two up to five fruits.

*Color bright, practically uniform throughout and characteristic of the variety or varieties of fruits used; free from dullness. Fruit particles should be dispersed uniformly throughout the jellied product. The jel should be tender, not stiff or rubbery. There may be a small tendency to flow, and preserves will be somewhat less viscuous than jams. Wholeness of fruit should be evident in preserves, and wholeness should be specified if desired. In jams or preserves made from two to five fruits, the weight of each fruit must be not less than 20% of the total. If the jam or fruit is a mixture of two or more fruits, the name "jam" or "preserve" is preceded or followed by the words "mixed fruit" or by the names of the fruits used.

Orange Marmalade

Grades: A (85),* B (70).

Varieties: Sweet—made from Navel or Valencia oranges or other sweet oranges; bitter—made from Seville or sour oranges; sweet and bitter—made from equal porportions of sweet and sour oranges.

Styles: Slices or thin strips, chopped or small pieces either irregular or diced.

Types: Type I is a clear jellied product with peel suspended in the translucent semi-solid mass, whole type II is a peel suspended in a cloudy opaque jel.

*Color uniform, bright and sparkling. Little or no dullness. Practically free from green-colored peel. Firm but tender. Jel possess a very slight tendency to flow. Jel should contain a substantial amount of peel evenly distributed but not excessive amount. The peel should be tender and if sliced into strips, the strips should be $\frac{1}{32}$ to $\frac{1}{16}$ in. wide. In chopped types, the peel should be reasonably uniform in size. Practically free from harmless extraneous material, seeds or parts of seeds, blemished peel, specks and other particles. Flavor and odor characteristic of the type orange used. The flavor should be neither excessively tart nor excessively sweet and should be free from caramelized flavor or other objectionable flavors or odors.

Dried Fruits[3]

Apples, Dry

Grades: A, B,* C.

Styles: Slices or rings (circular portions of cored apples), wedges (sectors cut longitudinally and radially from cored apples), pie pieces (irregular sectors), cuts (irregular shapes).

Size: Size is a grade requirement.

	Grade A	Grade B	Grade C
Pie pieces			
Approximate thickness	$\frac{1}{16}$ to $\frac{1}{4}$ in.	$\frac{1}{16}$ to $\frac{1}{4}$ in.	$\frac{1}{16}$ to $\frac{5}{16}$ in.
Length, 1 in. or more (minimum)	85 percent	60 percent	40 percent
Pass through $\frac{5}{16}$ in. square			
(maximum)	2 percent	6 percent	10 percent
Slices (or rings)			
Approximate thickness (maximum)	$\frac{1}{4}$ in.	$\frac{1}{4}$ in.	$\frac{5}{16}$ in.
Whole and practically whole rings			
(minimum)	75 percent	60 percent	40 percent
Length, $1\frac{1}{4}$ in., or more (minimum)	75 percent	60 percent	40 percent
Wedges			
Variation in thickness (maximum)	$\frac{1}{4}$ in.	$\frac{1}{4}$ in.	$\frac{5}{16}$ in.
Length, $1\frac{1}{4}$ in., or more (minimum)	90 percent	75 percent	50 percent

[3]Cook for best quality evaluation.

*Not more than 24% moisture.   Normal flavor and odor; reasonably uniform in size and shape.   Reasonably free from defects.   Good, clear, bright color. Watch for discoloration, blemishes, seeds, stems, peel or other defects.   Cook and note flavor, odor, texture and color.

Apples, Low Moisture or Dehydrated

Grades: A (85),* B (70).

Styles: Flakes (parallel cut, irregular shaped pieces around ³/₁₆ in. or less thick and ¾ in. or more long), wedges (fairly thick sectors not over ⅝ in. thick), small pieces or nuggets (about the size of unpopped corn or smaller), fine cut (pass through ⅜ in. square opening).

*Moisture content 2½% or less.   Product should possess normal flavor and odor, good texture and color, be reasonably uniform in size and practically free from defects.   Watch for discoloration, seeds, stems, blemishes and other defects.

Apricots, Dry

Grades: A, B,* C.

Types: Loose or slab.

*Reasonably uniform, bright, typical color characteristic of well-matured apricots, but some may possess a pale yellow area around the stem, not more than 25% of the outside surface.   Defects of immaturity, pits or pieces of pits, damage from discoloration, hail, sunburn, scab, disease, insects, mold, decay, dirt, foreign material and others should be watched.   Inspect for insect infestation.   For loose type, B Grade, not more than 15% can be in slabs. Apricots may be sulfured to prevent discoloration.   Moisture should not be more than 26% for sizes No. 1 and No. 3 and slabs, and not more than 25% for larger sizes.

Apricots, Low Moisture or Dehydrated

Grades: A (85),* B (70).

Styles: Nugget (foamlike, evenly sized pieces that will pass through a ⅝ in. square hole), pieces (irregular pieces that will pass through a ⅝ in. square hole, diced (cube shaped units), slices (predominantly parallel-cut strips of irregular shape and thickness).

*Moisture limits are: nuggets 3½%, pieces 3½%, diced 5%, sliced 5%. Should be made from clean, sound, ripe apricots.   May be sulfured to preserve color.   Flavor and odor should be good, with no objectionable flavors or odors, scorched flavors and so forth.   Should be practically free from defects and seriously damaged units.   Look for such defects as those listed above for dry apricots.

Currants

Grades: A,* B.

Varieties: Black Corinth or White Corinth.

Types: I Zante (domestic) unseeded or seeded; II, other than Zante, such as Amalias, Patras, Vostizza.

*Not more than 18% moisture.   Good typical color, flavor from well-matured berries.   Watch for defects, such as stems, grit, sand or dirt or foreign material, cap stems, sugared currants, damaged berries, poor develop-

Table 3–11
Yields of Dried Fruit

One Pound Dried Fruit	Cooked Yield	Portion	Number Portions per Pound
Apples	4 lb 8 oz	½ c	17
Apricots	2 lb 15 oz	4 halves	10
Figs	2 lb 7 oz	3 figs	10
Peaches	2 lb 10 oz	3 halves	11
Pears	2 lb 10 oz	2 halves	14
Prunes	2 lb 3 oz	5 prunes	12
Raisins	3 lb 4 oz	⅓ c	17

ment, mold, decay and seeds in unseeded. Stem in raisins and currants means portion of main stem. Cap stem means small body stems not more than ⅛ in. in length.

Dates

Grades: A (90), B (80),* C (70) for fresh; B (80),* C (70) for dry.

Styles: Whole—pitted or unpitted, pieces (cut or sliced pitted dates), macerated (ground, chopped, mashed or broken pitted dates), slab (whole or pieces in slab not loose form).

*Good color, free from defects. Watch discoloration, checking, deformities, puffiness, mashed or broken dates. Severe checking, in which flesh becomes dark, crusty and dry, may occur. Side spot damage is a dark area in the flesh, which may indicate mold. Best grades of dates are light in color, turning darker as the grade lowers. Watch for pits, stems, caps and extraneous matter. Dry dates are only to be purchased by those operations using large quantities of dates for large quantity processing. If dates are to be broken up or chopped, purchase macerated or slab dates.

Figs

Grades: A, B,* C.

Color types: Adriatic—white to dark brown (Adriatic, Calimyrna, Kadota), Black—black to dark purple (Mission).

Styles: I-whole, loose, pulled or flattened—may be slightly split; layer or slab usually in staggered arrangement. II-sliced (cut into slices ¼ in. thick).

*Not over 23% in moisture except for white, whole types, which may be 24% in moisture content. Even, clear, uniform color of well matured figs. Reasonably uniform in size. Watch for mold, decay, scars, blemishes, sunburn, mechanical injury, damaged, broken or crushed fruit. Look for visible sugaring. Cook to ascertain flavor and odor. Size is not a factor of grade.

Peaches, Dry

Grades: A, B,* C.

Varieties: Freestone (Muir, Lovell, Elberta and others), Clingstone (Midsummer, Phillips and others).

*Shall not be over 25% moisture by weight. Use factors discussed above for dried apricots for judging quality. Size is not a part of federal grade.

Peaches, Low-moisture or Dehydrated

Grades: A (85),* B (70).

Styles: Same as for low-moisture apricots above.

*Moisture content: nugget 3%, pieces 3%, diced 5%, sliced 5%. Use factors discussed above for low-moisture apricots for judging quality.

Pears, Dry

Grades: A, B,* C.

*Moisture content not over 26%. Use factors discussed above for judging quality of dried apples. Size is not a factor of federal grade.

Prunes

Grades: A, B,* C.

Size and Type: Type I—French or Robe (sweet); sizes per pound, 30/40, 40/50, 50/60, 60/70, 70/80, 80/90, 90/100, 100/120, 120 and over. Type II—Italian (tart); sizes per pound, 25/35, 35/45, 30/40, 40/50, 50/60, 60/70, 70/80, 90/100. Type III—Imperial or Sugar (sweet); sizes per pound, 15/20, 18/24, 20/30, 30/40, 40/50, 50/60, 60/70. Type IV—mixtures of the above.

Trade nomenclature for size: Extra large, average 43 per lb. Large, average 53 per lb. Medium, average 67 per lb. Small or Breakfast, average 85 per lb.

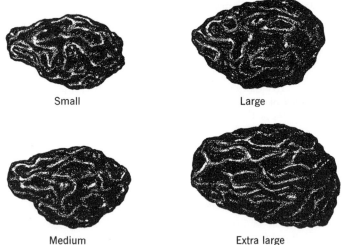

Small   Large

Medium   Extra large

*Moisture content: 60 or less per pound, 25%; 61 or more per pound, 64%. Look for good color, black or blue-black. Tough, dry, rubbery prunes should be rejected. Watch for end cracks, skin or flesh damage. Smell for fermentation, and examine for scars, insect infestation or injury, heat damage, mold, dirt, foreign material, decay.

Raisins

Grades: A, B,* C for Thompson Seedless, A,* B for Muscat and Sultana.

Types: Type I—Thompson Seedless, unbleached or natural, sulfur bleached

Table 3–12
Yields in Prunes

Size Prune	Pits per Pound	Size Portion	Number Portions per Pound Dried Prunes
Extra large	$2\frac{1}{2}$ oz	4 prunes (3 oz)	11
Large	$2\frac{1}{2}$ oz	5 prunes ($3\frac{1}{4}$ oz)	$10\frac{1}{2}$
Medium	$2\frac{3}{4}$ oz	6 prunes (3 oz)	11
Small	$3\frac{5}{8}$ oz	7 prunes ($2\frac{4}{5}$ oz)	12

or golden seedless, soda dipped; Type II—Muscat, seeded, unseeded cap stemmed (loose), unseeded uncap stemmed (loose), layer or cluster; Type III —Sultana; Type IV—Mixed (any mixture of above).

Size: Size is not a factor for grade in any except Type II, Muscat layer or cluster. Buyers may specify size as follows for raisins in diameter sizes:

Thompson Seedless: Small or midget, $\frac{5}{16}$ in., select-$\frac{3}{8}$ in.

Muscat, seeded: Small or midget, $\frac{11}{32}$ in., select-$\frac{17}{32}$ in.

Muscat, unseeded: 1 crown, smaller than $\frac{3}{8}$ in.; 2 crown, $\frac{3}{8}$ in.; 3 crown, $\frac{17}{32}$ in.; 4 crown, $\frac{21}{32}$ in. (Three crown is the smallest that cluster Muscat raisins can be and meet grade B.)

Sultana: No size classifications.

(Mixed may mean a mixture not meeting any specific size.)

Approximate Sizes in Raisins

Thompson Seedless	Muscat, Seeded	Muscat, Unseeded
Small or midget	Small or midget	2-crown (1-crown any size smaller)
Select	Select	3-crown
		4-crown

*Moisture content may vary 18 to 23%, depending on type of raisin. Look for stems and cap stems. A stem is a portion of the main stem, and a cap stem is a small woody stem not more than ⅛ in. attached to the raisin. Watch for poorly developed, damaged, sugared, moldy, fermented or decayed berries. Inspect for insect infestation. Examine for dirt, foreign material, decay, grit, sand or silt, shattered or damaged berries.

Color is not a factor for grade, but the best quality is indicated by the lighter more uniform grades for type. Thompson Seedless may be specified as Extra Fancy (well bleached color); Fancy (reasonably well bleached color, predominantly yellow or golden to greenish yellow or light amber); Extra Choice (greenish yellow to light greenish amber); Choice (bleached or yellowish green to dark amber or dark greenish amber); Standard (definitely dark or dark amber in color). Higher tolerances for darkness of color are allowed for the golden type as against the sulfur bleached type.

Soda-dipped raisins are used by bakers for decorating the tops of bakery
*Soda-dipped raisins are used by bakers for decorating the tops of bakery products. The soda causes the raisin to swell or puff and the skin to check. These raisins may be oil dipped to give them a higher gloss.

Table 3–13
In Cooking
Increase by Weight in Some Dried Vegetables

Dried Vegetable	Increase in Cooking
Beans, all types	2½ times
Peas, split	2½ times
Peas, black-eyed	2⅔ times
Cabbage, low-moisture	5⅓ times
Carrots, low-moisture	6 times
Celery, low-moisture	7 times
Onions, low-moisture	4½ times
Potatoes, diced, low-moisture	4½ times
Tomatoes, low-moisture	4½ times

Table 3–14
Cooking Chart for Vacuum-Dry, Low-moisture Fruits

Vacuum-Dry Low-moisture Fruit	Pounds of Fruit	Water Lb	Water Qt	Minutes Cooking Time	Sugar* Lb	Sugar* Cup	Approximate Yield Cooked
Apple sauce nuggets —small cut (sauce)	1	10	5	15	½	1	1¼ gal
Apple pie slices (stewed)	1	9¼	4⅝	20	½	1	1 gal
Apricot slices (stewed)	1	5	2½	15–20	½	1	2¾ qt
Peach slices (stewed)	1	5	2½	15–20	½	1	2¾ qt
Whole pitted prunes (stewed)	1	4	2	†	½	1	2½ qt
Fruit mix—large cut (stewed)	1	6	3	10–15	½	1	3⅓ qt
Fruit cocktail mix (stewed)	1	5½	2¾	5	½	1	3¼ qt

*Sugar may be varied to taste. Add sugar during the last 5 minutes of cooking for all fruits except prunes and figs. Add sugar to prunes and figs at the beginning of cooking. *DO NOT OVERCOOK.*
†Bring to boil, only.

4 Dairy Products

MILK AND CREAM

The importance of dairy products as human food, their high perishability, their ease of adulteration and their susceptibility to contamination from bacteria, undesirable flavors and odors have made it necessary to provide government controls for their processing. Most states and incorporated communities have regulatory provisions for the production and marketing of dairy products. The U.S. Public Health Service's Milk Ordinance and Code is used as a model for most of these state and local codes. This code requires high standards of health in dairy herds and sanitation in the production of raw milk and its subsequent handling. The milk must receive rapid transportation under refrigeration. Upon receipt at the dairy it is examined for temperature, flavor, quality and butterfat. It is then pasteurized by subjecting it to 143° F for 30 minutes or 160° F for 15 seconds. The latter is called *flash* pasteurization. Cream is usually pasteurized at slightly higher levels. Rapid cooling to 50° F or below is then accomplished. Pasteurization destroys almost all pathogenic bacteria and most of the common bacteria found in milk.

A large part of our fluid milk is homogenized. This is a process in which the milk is forced under pressures of 2500 psi or more through tiny orifices. This divides the fat globules so that they remain as a permanent emulsion in the milk. Vitamin D may be added to the milk or the milk may be irradiated by ultra-violet light to give added vitamin D. Cream is made from non-homogenized milk. Separation of cream and non-fat milk is accomplished by centrifuging the heavier non-fat milk to the outer areas and the lighter cream into the center where each can be drawn off.

242

Because bacterial flora is largely destroyed in pasteurization, desirable bacteria may be added to milks for processing into buttermilk, cheese or other products.

Fresh Fluid Milk and Cream

The quantity of milk solids, especially butterfat, in the product is one of the main factors establishing identity of many dairy products. Federal standards state that milk shall be "fresh, clean, cow's milk free from objectionable odors and flavors produced under local, state or federal code containing not less than $8\frac{1}{4}\%$ non-fat milk solids and not less than $3\frac{1}{4}\%$ milk fat. It should contain no added water, preservatives, neutralizers or other foreign substances except that vitamin D may be added in accordance with good commercial practices. It should have a specific gravity at 60° F of 1.028. At no time after pasteurization shall it be above 50° F." The quality of the milk or cream is based on flavor, odor and the quantity of solids present. Bacterial counts are also a part of grade.

There are a number of types of fresh fluid milk on the market. Certified raw milk is unpasteurized milk with less than 10,000 bacterial count per cubic centimeter (cc). This also meets the requirements of the American Association of Medical Milk Commission for purity. The herds and farms producing this milk must meet the highest standards of sanitation. Certified pasteurized milk must not have more than 10,000 bacterial count. Grade A raw milk may not have an average bacterial count exceeding 50,000 per cc. Grade A pasteurized milk cannot have a bacterial count which exceeds 30,000 per cc after pasteurization. Grade B pasteurized milk may not have more than 50,000 per cc after pasteurization. Some codes state that the raw milk from which pasteurized Grade A or Grade B are made must be within certain limits in bacterial count before pasteurization. Other codes state that Grade A or Grade B pasteurized milk after pasteurization may have no coliform bacterial count or can only have coliform counts within prescribed limits. If milk is delivered in capped bottles, the capping for Grade A milk must meet certain requirements. Skim or non-fat milk must meet all of the above requirements for whole milk to meet the grades except that it may have less than $3\frac{1}{4}\%$ butterfat. Fat-free or defatted milk must contain not more than 0.1% butterfat.

Buttermilk is a fluid resulting from the churning of milk or cream. It must contain not less than $8\frac{1}{4}\%$ non-fat milk solids. Most buttermilks today are cultured buttermilks, which are made from pasteurized non-fat milk to which a lactic acid producing bacteria has been added to sour and thicken the milk. *L. Acidolphilus* is a special bacteria added to milk to give a buttermilk that some claim has therapeutic value. Fortified milk has added vitamins and minerals. The amounts and kinds of added nutrients must be approved. A flavored milk is one to which sirup or flavorings have been added. If the word *drink* instead of milk is used, the product need not meet the standards of identity established for milk. Flavored drinks made from non-fat milk are included in this group. Reconstituted or recombined milk is made from milk concentrates and water.

Any product containing less than 18% butterfat cannot be called cream. Cream must also be pasteurized. Coffee or table cream contains 18 to 20% butterfat but it may go as high as 30%. Whipping cream must contain more than 30% butterfat. If below 36% butterfat, it is *light* whipping cream and above 36% it is *heavy*. Whipping cream should be ripened 3 days after being made. Half and half is a combination of milk and cream having not less than $11\frac{1}{2}$% butterfat content. Sour cream must have 18% or more milk fat with, more than 0.2% acidity expressed as lactic acid. The maximum allowable limits for bacteria in pasteurized sweet cream should be 60,000 per ml and not more than 20 coliform per ml.

Products resembling cream may be made, using non-milk fats and milk solids. A mixture of this type containing sugar and flavoring is frequently dispensed in a container having a gas that whips or aerates the product as it is forced from the container. This gives it the appearance of whipped cream. These products may also be purchased as powders, pastes or liquids.

Concentrated Fluid Milks

Concentrated fluid milks are made from milk that meets standards established under the federal milk ordinance and code for processing. Evaporated milk has had moisture removed until it has not less than 7.9% butterfat and the 25.9% total milk solid content. Cream may be extracted or added to give this proper ratio. It may be homogenized. If the label states that vitamin D is added, the milk must contain not less than 25 U.S. Pharmaceutical Units per fluid ounce. Extraction of the moisture is accomplished by creating a vacuum so that rapid boiling occurs around 130 to 140° F. The product is usually processed in 6 oz, $14\frac{1}{2}$ oz, No. 10 and 1-gal cans. After placing in cans and sealing, it is sterilized by subjecting it to 240° F to 245° F for 15 minutes. A $14\frac{1}{2}$-oz can with water added makes the equivalent of 1 qt of fresh, whole milk. If evaporated milk is left too long in storage without turning, crystals will settle to the bottom and this graininess will be evident in the milk when used.

Sweetened condensed milk has moisture evaporated off similar to the method used for removing moisture in making evaporated milk. It contains not less than 28% total milk solids, 8½% fat and 45% sugar. The sugar content is the equivalent of 19 to 20 lb to every 100 lb of fresh milk. It is marketed in cans similar in size to those used for evaporated milk. Some sweetened concentrated milk is sold in bulk. It contains less sugar than the canned, sweetened condensed milk.

Dried Milk Products

The moisture of milk may be removed so that only 2 to 5% remains. If properly packaged, this milk will keep for a long time without deterioration. Manufacture is either by spray or by roller-drum drying. Spray-dried milk is usually of better quality and far exceeds drum-dried milk in supply on the market.

Spray drying is accomplished by slightly concentrating the milk and then spraying it through atomizers into warm-air chambers. Here the

FIG. 4–1. The lower portion of a spray dryer for milk. About one half to three fourths of the moisture is extracted in condensers. The remaining moisture is extracted in this cone-shaped drier. Forced under a pressure of 7,000 psi through a small hole in a special nozzle, the milk enters the top as a fine spray. Filtered, heated air removes the moisture and the milk particles fall to the bottom where they are drawn off through suction pipes. Courtesy USDA.

FIG. 4-2. A can of non-fat dry milk with the USDA grade stamp on it. Courtesy USDA.

moisture is extracted by evaporation, and the milk solids fall to the bottom of the chamber as fine powder.   Drum drying may be either atmospheric or vacuum.   In the former, drums are heated by steam.   The bottom of this drum projects down into a vat of milk.   As the drum turns and reaches the open air, the heat of the steam dries the milk and scrappers remove it before the drum rolls around again into the vat of milk.   If this same process is accomplished under vacuum, a process called vacuum-drum drying, the milk is of better quality.

Dried milk, processed so that it goes into solution quickly, is called instant dry milk.   Whole dried milk should contain not less than 26% milk fat, and have a moisture content not above $2\frac{1}{4}\%$.   Non-fat dried milk solids should contain not more than $1\frac{1}{4}\%$ fat and 3 to 4% moisture.   Staleness, oxidation or tallowiness, caramelization and other flavors should be watched in purchasing dried milks.   Whole milk may become rancid.   Pasteurization of the milk before processing is a requirement.

Grades established by the federal grovernment for non-fat dry milk solids are U.S. Extra and U.S. Standard.   The former is preferable for food facility use.   Spray process should be specified.   The flavor and odor of this product should be sweet, with not more than a slight cooked flavor and odor.   It should be white or light cream in color, free from lumps that fail to break up under slight pressure and practically free from brown and scorched particles. The bacterial count should not be more than 50,000 per gram. The bacterial content of U.S. Standard should not be more than 100,000 per gram.

Whole dry milk has three federal grades: U.S. Premium, U.S. Extra and U.S. Standard. The first and second grades are usually specified for food service use. Grade is established on the basis of flavor, odor, physical appearance, bacterial and coliform count, butterfat content, oxygen content and other objective factors. The top grade should have a sweet flavor, with not more than a slight cooked flavor and odor. It should be white or light cream in color; be free from lumps that fail to break up under slight pressure and be practically free from brown and scorched particles. The bacterial estimate should not be more than 30,000 per gram and the coliform count not more than 90 per gram. Butterfat content should be not less than 26%. Oxygen content should be not more than 2%. Some standards also state that bacterial counts upon reconstitution of skim and whole dried milk must be within certain limits.

Dry buttermilk may be made by the spray or roller process. It must be pasteurized at a temperature of 143° F for 30 minutes before drying. Grades are U.S. Extra and U.S. Standard. The first grade is preferred for institutional use. Spray process should be specified. The flavor and odor should be free from non-buttermilk flavors and odors; the color should be cream. It should be free from lumps that fail to break up under slight pressure and practically free from scorched particles. It should have not more than 50,000 bacteria per gram. The moisture content should not be more than 4%. The butterfat content should not be less than 4½%. The acidity should be not less than 0.1% nor more than 0.18%, expressed as lactic acid.

The American Dry Milk Institute, 221 N. LaSalle Street, Chicago 1, will grade milk samples sent to it. It will submit a full report of analysis and examination, including grade of sample.

Dry milks should receive good storage. When exposed to air they will absorb moisture rapidly, especially the instant types. If moisture absorption is sufficient, deterioration will take place. High moisture absorption is indicated by lumping. Above 5% moisture content, staling, discoloration and other deteriorative processes start. Good storage conditions include a moderately cool temperature, a dry place, minimum exposure to air and location away from products having objectionable odors.

Malted milk is a dried milk having approximately 3½% moisture, 7½% butterfat, and remaining solids based on a fluid mixture before drying of 40 to 45% whole milk and 55 to 60% malt extract. Each pound of malted milk contains the solids of approximately 2.2 lb of whole milk. Double malted milk means that twice as much malt is used as in regular malted milk; that is, the milk-malt ratio is approximately 1:3 rather than the 1:$\frac{1}{2}$ as in the regular product.

ICE CREAM AND FROZEN DESSERTS

Minimum butterfat content for vanilla ice cream should be 12%, and 10% for ice cream that contains chocolate, cocoa, fruit and nuts for extra flavoring. Pasteurizing at 155° F 30 min. is required before adding flavors, fruits and nuts. A maximum of 50,000 bacteria per gram is permitted after freezing. Milk solids in ice cream should be between 9 to 12$\frac{1}{2}$% and sugar, 14%. Stabilizers, such as gelatin, approved vegetable stabilizers or mixtures of monoglyceride and gelatin, are permitted if not in excess of $\frac{1}{2}$%. All percentages should be based on weight. Overrun permitted may go as high as 100% and should not be below 80%. Excess or lack of overrun harms flavor. The weight of a gallon of ice cream should not be less than 4$\frac{1}{2}$ lb. Ice cream to meet standards should contain 1.6 lb of solid food per gallon. Frozen cream or unsalted, sweet cream butter may be used to give required butterfat content. It is recommended that specifications state that non-fat milk solids shall be 80% of fat solids and the total non-fat and butterfat solids should not exceed 22% of the total weight. This may be waived when specialty ice creams are specified, such as a French ice cream or ice creams high in butterfat. Some ice creams may contain 18 to 20% butterfat, and some ice creams may contain 17 to 18% sugar. Corn sugar may be used to replace only 25 to 30% of the total sugar. Liquid ice cream mixes may be obtained from creameries for use in freezing ice cream in one's own operation. Ice cream powders and pastes are also available. The prepared mixes from these items should meet the above standards.

Sherbet is a frozen dessert made from pasteurized milk flavored with fruit juices and other natural or approved artificial flavors. It may contain egg white and a stabilizer. Usually gelatin is not used alone because it gives too frothy a sherbet. It also lacks body. Alginates, pectins or equal parts gelatin and agar, or approved vegetable stabilizers, may be used. Percent of stabilizer should be $\frac{1}{2}$%. An overrun not over 35% may be allowed, based on weight before freezing. The milk solid content by weight should not be less than 4%. The acid content expressed as lactic acid should not be less than 0.35%. Bacterial count after mixing should not be greater than 50,000 per gram. An ice is made from water and sugar flavored with fruit juices or other flavors.

Permitted maximum overrun based on weight before freezing should not be over 30%. The product should contain not less than 0.35% acid, expressed as lactic acid. Pasteurization before flavoring is added should be not less than 155° F for 30 minutes. The bacterial count after freezing should not be greater than 10,000 per gram of frozen mixture.

There is much confusion on the market regarding names of frozen desserts. General accepted definitions are:

French ice cream: contains eggs in the amount of 1.4% of the weight of the finished product if vanilla, and 1.12% if other than vanilla; may be flavored with ground vanilla bean.

Philadelphia ice cream: Plain frozen mixture of milk, cream, sweetener and flavoring; stabilizers may be added.

Frappe: a water-ice mixture frozen to a mush, possessing a coarse, granular texture.

Bisque ice cream: 16 to 20% milk fat and some baked product or confection added, such as macaroon, bread, cake or marshmallows.

Low-fat ice cream: not less than 5% but not more than 9.99% milk fat, and not less than 15% total milk solids, and not less than 1.5 lb of food solids per gallon.

Parfait ice cream: richer than ice cream; may have fruits and nuts added.

Au fait ice cream: layered ice cream in bricks.

Frozen pudding: lower than regular ice cream in milk fat; eggs, nuts and fruits added.

New York (Neapolitan): usually means an au fait brick consisting of chocolate, vanilla and strawberry layers.

Molded ice cream: ice cream molded and then removed from the molds. They may be plain or decorated.

Ice cream should be stored at temperatures below 0° F but at 10 to 15° F for dishing.

Ice cream and frozen desserts have no federal quality standards established for them; that is, there are no grades, only standards of identity given above. Scores are assigned at times on the basis of: flavor, 35 points; texture, 20 points; body 20 points; appearance, 15 points; and packaging, 10 points. Flavor is largely influenced by the quality of the dairy products and the flavoring used. Metallic, old cream and rancid, bitter, stale or cooked flavors lower the score. Proper acidity and sweetness are a part of flavor. Excess or insufficiency of flavoring or flavorings of inferior quality cause loss in flavor score. Body and texture may be considered as one quality. Both may also affect flavor evaluations. The structure of the frozen mass, the smoothness of the melted mix and the aftertaste in the mouth make up body. Texture has to do with the grain fineness, creaminess and firmness. A grain not too open, yet sufficient so as to give lightness, is sought. Texture defects may be described as fluffy, weak, crumbly, watery, icy, soggy and gummy. Poor quality ingredients, inferior methods of processing or freezing and excessive or under overrun will contribute to poor body and texture. Appearance may be partly based on naturalness, proper amount and evenness of color. The grain may affect appearance. The product should have a bright, smooth sheen. Those products with the least milk solids, such as ices, should have the most brilliance.

Specifications for Dairy Products

Buyers should ascertain what the local and state codes are before establishing their specifications for dairy products, for these may differ, depending on state and local regulations. Reference to the provisions of the U.S. Public Health Service Milk Ordinance and Code will be helpful in establishing many criteria. Specifications should state that all dairy products shall be produced and handled in accordance with the best sanitary practices and manufacturing and processing plants shall meet the highest standards of sanitation. Employees and equipment must similarly meet the provisions that will assure clean, sound and sanitary products. Many factors mentioned in the foregoing material should be incorporated into specifications.

CHEESE

Cheese is a food of world importance. It is eaten by many national groups. It is an economical source of complete proteins and other essential nutrients. The flavor and texture of cheese make it of value for combining with other foods. Most food services fail to merchandise cheese well. The many kinds available and the number of ways they can be served make it possible to create high menu interest when cheese is featured. To purchase cheese properly, a buyer should know the kinds available, their use and the factors that make for quality in each. To know quality a buyer must understand how cheese is made.

Cheese Manufacture

The federal government has established standards for the manufacture of cheese. Whole, partially defatted or non-fat milk may be used, depending upon the type of cheese to be made. The milk must be of good quality. Annatto or other colorings approved by the Food and Drug Administration may be added without noting it on the label. Cheese must be made from pasteurized milk or, if made from raw milk, must be held not less than 60 days in curing during which time pathogenic bacteria are destroyed. Standards of identity established by the federal government control the quantity of moisture and fat allowed in cheese as well as the processing methods.

Milk curd is the basic ingredient of most cheese. It may be obtained by coagulating milk, either by rennet or by lactic acid bacteria. Some cheese may be made from the serum or whey that separates from the curd in processing. Some bacterial growth is necessary in the early processing and, since pasteurization destroys bacteria, bacterial cultures must be added. These are called *starters* and usually consist of lactic acid producing bacteria. These increase milk acidity. Rennet will not set a proper curd, and the curd will not condition properly if the milk is not at a desired acidity. Bacteria may be added also to secure proper curing. *Penicillium roqueforti* are added to develop the mold and flavor in bleu-type cheeses. *Propionibacterium shermanii* develop the eyes in Swiss cheese. *Penicillium camemberti* give the rich flavor and soft texture from their growth in Camembert. The quantity of cheese obtained from 100 lb of non-fat or whole milk will be $7\frac{3}{4}$ and $9\frac{1}{2}$ lb, respectively. The fat of the milk will be found chiefly in the curd, while most of the sugar will be in the whey.

At one time it was necessary to import many of the varieties of cheese eaten in this country but this is no longer necessary because American cheese manufacturers can now duplicate almost any cheese of a foreign nation. Cow's milk is used almost exclusively in cheese making in this country in contrast to milk from cattle, ewes, nannies, mares and cow buffalo, all of which may be the basis of the curd in imported cheese. Usually domestic cheese will be milder in flavor than its foreign counterpart.

The Cheddar Process

The cheddar process is extensively used to make cheese. For American cheddar, the milk is pasteurized, then cooled to around 70° F. A lactic acid starter is added and when the acidity reaches a desired point, the temperature is raised to 86° F. Rennet is added in the amount of $0.2\frac{1}{2}$ to 0.4%. In about 3 hours the rennet sets the milk into a firm, glossy mass. It is then cut with curd knives or wires. This divides the solidi-fied jellylike curd into small cubes and allows the waterlike whey to separate. The casein, fat and some of the other milk constituents remain in the curd. The whey is drained off and the curd mixed. During this mixing the temperature is raised to around 98° F to cook the curd. The curd is now set in piles against the side of the trough to drain, to set and form into a solidified rubbery mass. This process is called "ditch-ing." After a time the mass is cut into strips about 8 in. wide. The strips are then piled about three or four deep and left to drain. They

Table 4-1
Origin, Characteristics, and Mode of Serving Commonly Used Cheeses*

Cheese	Characteristics	Mode of Serving	Place of Origin
American	Hard; smooth; light yellow to orange; mild. Made of cow's milk (whole). Cheddar type.	As such; in sandwiches; in cooked foods.	United States
Apple	Hard; sharp flavor; apple-shaped. Made of cow's milk (whole). Smoked.	As such.	Italy
Asiago	Hard; granular texture; piquant flavor (sharp in old cheese). Made of cow's milk (whole).	As such; as seasoning (grated) when old.	Italy
Blue	Semi-hard; white with blue mold; flavor similar to Roquefort. Made of cow's milk (whole).	As such (dessert); on crackers; in cooked foods; in salads.	France and Italy
Brick	Semi-hard; smooth; flavor between Limburger and Cheddar. Made of cow's milk (whole).	As such; in sandwiches; with salads.	United States
Brie	Soft; flavor resembles Camembert. Made of cow's milk (whole).	As such (dessert).	Paris, France
Caciocavallo	Hard; sharp flavor; ten-pin shape. Made of cow's milk (whole or partly defatted). Smoked.	As such; as seasoning (grated).	Southern Italy
Camembert	Soft; full flavor, often ammoniacal. Made of cow's milk (whole).	As such (dessert).	Camembert, France
Cheddar	Hard; smooth; light yellow to orange; mild. Made of cow's milk (whole or partly defatted).	As such; in sandwiches; in cooked foods.	Cheddar, England
Cottage	Soft; white; mildly sour flavor. Unripened; usually made of cow's milk (defatted). Cream may be added to finished product.	As such; in salads; in cooked foods.	Uncertain
Cream	Soft; smooth; buttery; mild, slightly sour flavor. Unripened; made of cream and cow's milk (whole).	As such; in sandwiches; with salads; on crackers.	Uncertain
Edam	Hard; rubbery; Cheddar flavor, but nut-like; "cannon-ball" shape. Made of cow's milk (partly defatted).	As such; on crackers.	Northern Holland
Gammelost	Hard; golden brown; strong flavor; pungent. Made of cow's milk (defatted, soured).	As such.	Norway

Gorgonzola	Semi-hard; marbled with blue mold; spicy flavor. Made of cow's milk (whole).	As such (dessert); with salads.	Gorgonzola, Italy
Gouda	Semi-hard; flavor like Edam. Made of partly defatted milk.	As such; on crackers.	Southern Holland
Gruyere	Hard with gas holes; nut-like, salty flavor. Made of cow's milk (usually partly defatted).	As such (dessert).	Gruyere, Switzerland
Jack	Semi-hard; smooth; mild; made of cow's milk (whole).	As such; in sandwiches.	United States
Limburger	Soft; full flavor; highly aromatic. Made of cow's milk (whole or partly defatted).	In sandwiches; on crackers.	Limburg, Belgium
Muenster	Semi-hard; flavor between brick and Limburger. Usually made of a mixture of cow's and goat's milk (whole).	As such; in sandwiches.	Muenster, Germany
Neufchatel	Soft; creamy; white; mild flavor. Unripened. Made of cow's milk (whole).	As such; in sandwiches; on crackers; in salads.	Seine Inferieure, France
Parmesan	Hard; granular texture; sharp flavor. Made of cow's milk (partly defatted).	As such; as seasoning.	Parma and Lodi, Italy
Port du Salut (Oka)	Semi-hard; rubbery texture; flavor between Limburger and Cheddar. Made of whole, slightly acid cow's milk.	As such (dessert).	Trappist Monasteries, France and Canada
Primost	Soft; light brown; mild flavor. Unripened; made from whey.	As such.	Norway
Provolone	Hard; sharp flavor; usually pear-shaped. Made of cow's milk (whole). Smoked.	As such.	Italy
Roquefort	Semi-hard; white with blue mold; sweet, piquant flavor. Made of sheep's milk (whole).	As such (dessert); on crackers; with salads.	Roquefort, France
Sapsago	Hard; green color; flavored with clover leaves; small; cone-shaped. Made of cow's milk (defatted and soured), buttermilk, and whey.	As such; as seasoning (grated).	Glarus, Switzerland
Stilton	Semi-hard; white with blue mold; spicy flavor. Made of cow's milk (whole with added cream).	As such (dessert); in cooked foods; with salads.	Stilton, England
Swiss	Hard with gas holes; nut-like, sweet flavor. Made of cow's milk (partly defatted).	As such; in sandwiches; with salads.	Emme Valley, Switzerland

*Courtesy National Dairy Council.

FIG. 4–3.   When milk is at the proper acidity and temperature, the rennet is added.   This sets the milk into a soft curd.   After the curd forms, workers on opposite sides of the vat cut the curd into small particles with fine wire knives.   Courtesy USDA.

are frequently alternated from middle, top and bottom to give even pressure.   This piling and alternating of strips is called *cheddaring*.   During all this handling, additional whey is lost and the curd now has reached an acidity of 0.45 to 0.60%, expressed as lactic acid.   After the curd is properly cheddared, it is cut into cubes of uniform size, a process called *milling*.   Salt is added in the ratio of about 1 to 3%.   The green cheese is piled into hoops, wrapped in a cloth or metal foil and then put into a press for 1 to 2 days.   Afterward it is dried for several days, then dipped into warm paraffin, if cloth wrapped, and moved into curing rooms.

Curing

Favorable action will occur in storage to change the texture of the cheese from a rubberiness to a soft, pasty, waxy consistency and the flavor to a more pungent, biting, higher flavor.   Temperature, humidity and salting are used to give proper curing control.   Some cheese may be salt-rubbed while others may be brine dipped to reduce unfavorable reactions.   When well ripened, a plug drawn from good quality cheddar cheese should be solid, compact, translucent and have a close grain with few but small openings caused by gas or yeast development.   These holes

DAIRY PRODUCTS   255

FIG. 4–4. The ditched cheese is cut into blocks and turned for the first time. This turning and resting are known as cheddaring. Courtesy USDA.

FIG. 4–5. Here the 8 in. strips are piled to cheddar. Courtesy USDA.

FIG. 4–6. Milling the curd. Courtesy USDA.

are called "sweet" or "Swiss" holes. Flecks of white will be evident in well-ripened cheese. By exerting proper control it is now possible to cure cheese without developing a rind.

Curing can be shortened or given what is termed "forced cure." This is done by increasing temperatures and relative humidity. Cheese aged at a temperature of 45 to 55° F at 80% humidity will age in 90 days as much as it will age in 12 to 18 months at 32 to 34° at 70% relative humidity or 8 to 10 months at 38 to 40° F at 70% relative humidity. The loss from improper curing reactions will be higher, however. Cheese must be checked frequently to detect cheese failing to take a proper cure. Cheese of highest quality going into storage may be expected to have about 10% failures, while cheese of lesser quality may have 30 to 40% failures.

Different curing procedures will be used for different types of cheese. Some cheese receives little or no curing. Acid coagulated cheese, such as cottage, cream and Neufchatel, is not aged at all.

Cheddar-Process Cheeses

Cheddar cheeses. Some market sizes of the commonly used American cheddar cheeses appear in Table 4–3. Boxes containing cheddar cheese will be marked only in full pounds on the wholesale market. If a box contains 60¾ lb, the box will be marked 60-lb.

Federal quality standards for American cheddar cheese are U.S. Grade AA, A, B and C. All grades must contain not more than 39% moisture. The cheese solids should contain not less than 50% milk fat; this makes cheddar around 30% fat. Cheddar cheese is graded on the basis of body, texture, flavor, aroma, color and general appearance. The requirements for cheddar cheese for U.S. Grade A, the grade frequently specified for purchase by food services, are given in Table 4–4.

Cheddar may be manufactured in different forms and may be given special seasoning. A pineapple-shaped cheese that originated in Connecticut is made similar to cheddar cheese except that the curd is cooked to a higher temperature. The net in which the cheese is hung after pressing gives this cheese its shape. The oil rubbed onto the surface during curing accounts for the bright-yellow, glossy exterior. Curing is

FIG. 4–7. From the press the young Swiss cheese goes into a brine tank to float in salt for several days. This treatment adds salt to the cheese. It also controls undesirable curing reactions. During the curing process some dry salt may be rubbed into the cheese to control undesirable reactions. Courtesy USDA.

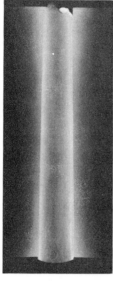

X-ray

X-ray

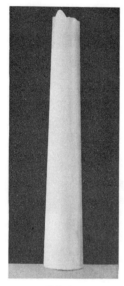

Exterior

Exterior

FIG. 4–8. Pictures on left page show a good grade of cheese with fine holes. Pictures on the right page show excessive development of holes during curing. The holes result from gas, which forms during the curing process. These holes are called sweet or Swiss holes.

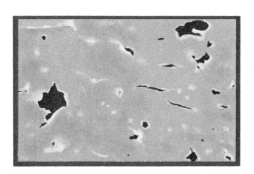

X-ray

X-ray

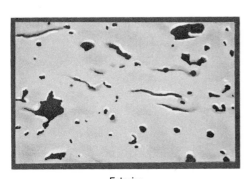

Exterior

Exterior

Table 4-2
Classification of Cheese on the Basis of Hardness or Softness*

Hard			Semi-hard		Soft		
Bacteria Ripened 12–16 months	Bacteria Ripened 3–12 months	Bacteria Ripened 2–3 months	Bacteria Ripened 1–8 months	Mold Ripened 2–12 months	Bacteria Ripened 1–2 months	Mold Ripened 2–5 months	Unripened
Cheshire	American	Appetitost	Bel Paese	Bleu	Hand	Brie	Cottage
Parmesan	Apple	Nokkelost	Brick	Blue	Limburger	Camembert	Cream
Reggiano	Asiago	Kumminost	Fontina	Gorgonzola		Livarot	Neufchatel
Romano	Cheddar		Gammelost	Roquefort		Pont l'Eveque	Primost
Sardo	Edam		Gouda	Stilton			Ricotta
	Gjetost		Jack				
	Gruyere		Muenster				
	Provolone		Port du Salut				
	Sapsago						
	Sbrinz						
	Swiss						

*Courtesy National Dairy Council.

FIG. 4–9. A good quality Swiss cheese that has cured for 3 months. Eyes start to form 2 or 3 weeks after the cheese goes into the curing room. As curing progresses, the eyes grow in size. Note shiny eyes, large in size, indicating quality. Excessive eye development is undesirable. Courtesy USDA.

Table 4–3
Common Market Sizes of Cheddar Cheese

Market Name	Shape	Number in Box	Weight of Each Piece
Cheddar	Cylindrical	1	60 to 65 lb
Twin or flats	Cylindrical	1 or 2*	30 to 33 lb
Daisy	Cylindrical	1 to 3†	19 to 21 lb
Longhorn	Cylindrical	4	$11\frac{1}{2}$ to 13 lb
Picnic	Cylindrical	Varies	1 to 2 lb
Square	Rectangular	Varies	10 lb
Print	Rectangular	Varies	10 lb

*Two flats in a box are called "twins."
†Called single, double or triple daisies, depending upon number in box.

Table 4–4
Quality Factors in U.S. Grade A Cheddar Cheese

Quality Factor	All Cures	Fresh or Current	Medium Cured	Cured or Aged
			Type Cures†	
Flavor	Free from objectionable flavors and odors but may have slight regional or seasonal feed flavors.	Practically no flavor development.	Mild characteristic cheese flavor; may have some slight acid flavor.	Well-developed characteristic cheese flavor; may be slightly acid.
Body and texture	Practically solid, compact and close, although it may have a few mechanical openings, but these are not large and connecting; may not have more than 2 sweet or Swiss holes per trier sample; should be free from yeast holes and other gas holes; is translucent.	Firm, smooth and curdy or may be partially broken down if the cheese is over 3 weeks old.	Reasonably firm, smooth and waxy; may be slightly curdy or not entirely broken down or slightly short, mealy or weak.	Reasonably firm, smooth and waxy; may be slightly short or mealy, or slightly weak and pasty.
Color	May be uncolored or medium colored* and slightly seamy.	Same as given for all cures.	Same as given for all cures.	May have tiny white specks in addition to color factors listed for current make.

*In the South and other areas a deeper colored cheddar is preferred, and graders may allow additional coloring, even to yellow orange, in cheese evaluated for that area.

†Current, under 30 days cure; medium, 30 to 150 days; cured or aged, over 150 days.

4 to 6 months. English Daisy is a cheddar cooked to an even higher temperature than Pineapple cheese. Because of this, it is a harder cheese and is used largely for grating. Sage may be added to cheddar when the curd is placed in the hoops for pressing and wrapping. Other flavor ingredients may be similarly used, and the resulting color and flavor of the cheese will be modified according to the ingredients used.

Cheddars of higher moisture content than regular cheddar are Colby (40% moisture), Washed Curd (42% moisture) and Stirred Curd (42% moisture). They are cured at temperatures of 38 to 40° F for approximately 30 days and will lack the flavor development of a more aged cheese. The texture is more tough and rubbery than regularly ripened cheddar. Purchase should be made only in small quantities, since these cheeses mold easily. Federal regulations require that these cheeses be made from pasteurized milk.

When well-ripened cheddar is ground free of lumps and pressed into a loaflike shape or packed in jars, the product is called *club* or *cold pack* cheese. It is frequently pasteurized, and sometimes about 10% butter may be blended in. The term "milled" cheese is sometimes used to indicate an unpasteurized club. Flavorings, wines and other ingredients may be added.

Monterey Jack or just Jack or Monterey is a California cheese resembling brick cheese in texture and light creamy-white color but it is slightly more compact. Small holes should be evident in good quality Monterey, like apertures between layers of rock. The surface should be slightly dull, not glazed. Good Monterey should have a springy, spongy texture but lack rubberiness. When a small piece is pulled from the mass, the cheese should tear rather than crumble. This tearing should not be with a stretchy pull. The poorer grades have large, splotchy holes caused by excessive gas development. The flavor will also be bitter and off. Regular Monterey should contain not more than 44% moisture. Milk fat should be 50% of total solids. A high moisture Monterey is on the market containing more than 44% moisture. It does not keep well. Dry Monterey is made by drying the cheese in a warm place for a year or more. Previous to drying it is coated with a mixture of pepper, oil and baryta earth (clay). It is a hard, crumbly and dry cheese and is usually grated like the hard Italian-type cheeses.

Foreign cheddars. Cheshire is an English import made in much the same fashion as American cheddar. It is a hard cheese made from cow's milk. The color may be a rich yellow or natural white and the texture is loose, flaky and crumbly.

Edam and Gouda are cheeses from Holland, but domestic types have largely taken over the market in this country. Both are lower in fat content than cheddar. The color of Edam is similar to cheddar. The flavor is sweeter and somewhat resembles the flavor of medium-cure cheddar. The grain is firm and compact. The texture is usually more rubbery than well-ripened cheddar. Both Edam and Gouda are marketed in small, round balls dipped in red wax or plastic. Gouda is sometimes colored with saffron. This gives it a reddish cast and a special flavor. If not saffron flavored, it resembles Edam very much in color, but the texture is somewhat softer and the flavor milder. Some describe the flavor as nutlike. Edam should contain not more than 45% moisture and its solids not less than 40% milk fat.

A number of Italian cheeses are made by the cheddar process, although they are very much unalike in the final product because of subsequent treatment. Parmesan cheese is one of the most common. It has a hard, black rind composed of oil, pepper and baryta earth. The color of the cheese is whitish yellow. It is hard and must be grated. The flavor is rich, tart and somewhat sharp, with a touch of mellowness. It is usually made in copper kettles, and the processing and cooking temperatures (125° F) will be higher than those used for regular cheddar cheese. The curd will be cut into pieces the size of a wheat kernel to express as much whey as possible. Federal standards state that Parmesan cheese must be cured 14 months or longer. Romano is another hard, granular, yellow-white cheese, with a piquant flavor. If cow's milk is used, the flavor will be milder than if goat's or sheep's milk are used. A Sardo Romano is another cheese of this group made from cow's milk. Grana and Reggiano are two hard cheeses similar to Parmesan and Romano. Provolone or Provolona is a moderately soft cheese. It has a smoky flavor. After milling, the curd is dipped into whey at 160° F and pulled like taffy. It is then salted, formed into a bottlelike shape and smoked. It should have not more than a 45% moisture content and at least a 45% butterfat content in the solids. Caciocavallo is similar to Provolone but it is lighter in color. It is shaped like an Indian club and weighs 3 to 6 lb. Mazzorella is a soft Italian cheese. It has little curing. It is rubbery or stretchy in texture, delicate in flavor. When heated it has a stringy texture. Scarmorze is a small, hard, sweetish cheese made in Italy from the milk of buffaloes. The domestic type is made from cow's milk. It has a high moisture content, is sweet and mild in flavor and is usually sold when less than 10 days old. Mazzorella and Scarmorze are used for making Pizza. Both do not keep well and mold easily.

Swiss or Gruyere. Swiss cheese is a highly popular cheese. ·The process of making it is very similar to that of regular cheddar. Gruyere, Emmenthal and Schweizer cheese are similar to Swiss cheese. All are made from partially defatted milk. Swiss imports are usually made from goat or sheep's milk but domestic Swiss is made from cow's milk. The milk is frequently processed in large kettles. A special curd knife called the "Swiss harp" is used to cut the curd. Stirring and ditching are more vigorous than for cheddar, and more fat is lost because of this. Cooking temperatures are 128 to 135° F. The cheese is innoculated in the press with special bacteria. This develops the eyes or holes.

After pressing, the cheese is held at 50 to 55° F for about 7 to 10 days to dry. It is then moved into curing rooms at 70° F and held 2 to 3 weeks until the fermentation gases develop the eyes. Mold must be inhibited during this time. Salt may be rubbed onto the cheese or the cheese may be given brine dips to control the mold. Curing next takes place at around 60° F, at a relative humidity of 80 to 85%. The cheese must be checked carefully during this time for improper curing. Excess humidity will favor mold development, while too low a humidity will cause rind checks. Imported Swiss is usually cured longer than domestic. It is whiter in color, slightly drier and has more flavor.

Swiss cheese for food service use may be purchased in blocks, drums or rounds. The blocks will frequently have smaller eyes. A round weighs approximately 20 to 30 lb. Large rounds may be 50 to 60 lb.

Federal standards for Swiss cheese are U.S. Grade A, Grade B, Grade C and Grade D. Quality is determined on the basis of flavor, body, eyes and texture, finish and appearance, salt and color. As in cheddar, different standards apply, depending on the age of the cheese. A current make and a cured Swiss will be judged on different standards. Current-make Swiss is not more than 60 days old, while cured is more than 6 months old. Medium cured would fall between these two groups.

The flavor of cured Swiss should be characteristic and have a full, nutty flavor. The body should be firm, smooth and flexible, resisting bite but having a texture that will mold between the fingers like solidifying wax. It should be free from pinholes and over-developed eyes or holes but may have picks and checks within 1 in. of the surface. The eyes should not be close together and should be round or slightly oval, evenly distributed and at least $\frac{1}{2}$ in. in diameter. The size of the eyes will affect the grade. Grade B Swiss need only have eyes about $\frac{5}{16}$ in. in diameter. The walls of the holes should be glossy, with few dull or dead eyes. Watch for sticky, dry or crumbly texture, or horizontal cracks that appear like a piece of fractured glass (called glassiness). Sometimes Swiss cheese will be found having small holes like brick cheese. These are called "nizzlers" and are cause for grading down the cheese. "Blinds" are cheeses having no eyes. Good Swiss should be well shaped, with a clean, sound, dry rind free from mold. Salting should be uniform, and salt flavor should be neither under or over for good taste. The color should be creamy in young Swiss, with an increasing whiteness developed as it ages. Appenzell, Samsoe (Danish), Conte (French) and Sbrinz are other Swiss or Gruyere-type cheese. Sbrinz lacks the characteristic Swiss eyes and is a better keeping cheese. Lapland is a rare cheese made from the milk of reindeer, which in taste and texture resembles Swiss but it is softer. The shapes of these cheese resembling Swiss may be odd, round or flat or so formed that a cross section resembles a dumbbell with angular instead of round ends.

Bleu-type cheeses. Bleu cheeses are made by the basic cheddar process but will be distinguished by their creamy white color. They have a greenish, black-gray mold in the open areas. The texture is semi-hard, crumbly. It should feel slightly sticky to touch. The mold should be spread evenly throughout. Straight lines may be evident where needle-like instruments are inserted to make a path for the mold to spread evenly and to bring oxygen to the interior so that the mold can grow. The flavor should be sharp, clean, lingering, not dull, as evident in dry, splotchy cheese.

Mold growth is encouraged by a special inoculation after milling. As the curd is placed in the form for pressing, the interior is innoculated with mold cultures, which develop the typical appearance, flavor and texture. Aging should be at least 3 months at 45 to 48° F and 75% relative humidity. Aging after 6 months does little to increase quality. The cheese is usually molded into 5 to 10 lb rounds but may also be purchased in 3 oz, 1¼ oz and ¾-oz packs.

Roquefort cheese has been called the "cheese of kings." It is a blue-veined, creamy white, semi-hard cheese made from the raw whole milk of ewes. The cheddar process is used, and the cheese is aged in the caves of Roquefort, France. Only this cheese can bear the name of Roquefort. Imitations must be called "bleu," "domestic Roquefort" or "Roquefort type." Only true Roquefort cheese bears the red seal with the word "Roquefort" over a ewe in the center and the words "Garanti Veritable" under. Modern technology has made it possible to duplicate conditions of the Roquefort caves; and caves in Minnesota, around St. Paul, a bleu-cheese center, duplicate closely the conditions of the caves of Roquefort, France. Domestic bleu cheese is made from cow's milk. It has also been found possible to produce the typical flavor without developing the typical bluish or greenish mold growth.

There are many other fine imports of bleu-type cheese besides Roquefort. Danish Bleu, Stilton (English), Gorgonzola (Italian), Septmosell (French), and Gex (French) are some. It is difficult to tell these cheeses apart. Gorgonzola is not as salty as Roquefort and is firmer, with a blue rather than greenish mold. It is marketed in 15 to 20-lb rounds. Stilton has a slightly more biting flavor than Roquefort. The surface rind is brown and crinkled. It has a high fat content due to the cream added to the cow's milk from which it is made.

Camembert-type cheeses. There are many cheddar-type cheeses that after pressing, are set into curing chambers to ripen from the surface in. Bacterial innoculations are used to induce this type of ripening and most often this is done by spray. Camembert, a French cheese, is one of the best known of this group. Mold and bacteria during the curing may form a heavy, well-developed rind. Cheese enthusiasts will insist that the rind be eaten as well as the cheese for full flavor. Salt rubbing or brine dips are used to control the development of bacteria and molds during curing. Camembert is difficult to cure for it must be dried as well as cured. Curing takes 4 to 5 weeks. The cheese loses quality rapidly after curing.

Camembert should have a creamy, soft consistency throughout and a rich, piquant flavor, slightly astringent or ammonical but pleasantly so. The color is creamy yellow. Camembert is cured at 53 to 59° F, at 90% relative humidity. Proper curing can be ascertained by pressing gently in the middle and close to the outside of the disc where it should give gently to pressure. All cheese of this type should be sufficiently soft to almost flow. They are not properly ripened or of acceptable top quality if they do not.

Bel Paese is an Italian cheese that resembles Camembert but it is more firm and delicate in flavor. Brie could never be said to resemble any cheese other than itself. It is slightly firmer than Camembert and has a distinctive richness and mellowness of flavor. The rind frequently has a reddish coloration developed by the bacteria in ripening. Only small quantities of domestic Brie are made; most is imported. Other cheeses resembling Camembert are Meaux, Coulommiers and Melun. They are made from cow's milk. The size of the disc will usually be larger than that of Camembert. Port du Salut and Oka are Trappist cheeses; they are yellow or orange colored and ripened much like the Camembert types. They are not as strong as their relatives, Limburger and Brick. Chantelle and Trappist cheeses are cured much like Camembert.

Limburger is another cheese ripened from the outside in. When well-ripened, it is soft and pasty. The odor and flavor are strong and ammonical but sweet and pleasing. It is made from partially defatted milk and must be cured at least a month. It is improved if cured 55 to 70 days. The curing process changes the color from a white to a reddish, creamy yellow. Curing is at 60 to 65°, at a relative humidity 95%. Limburger is considered by cheese makers to be one of the most difficult to cure. It is available in 6 oz, 8 oz, 1 lb or 2-lb bricks.

Brick cheese originated in this country and took its name from its shape. It is cured at 60 to 65° F and 90% relative humidity. It is milder than Limburger. Imported brick is apt to have a pungent flavor, with some sharpness. It has a lower acidity than cheddar and a moisture content of 44%. It may have fine gas holes but not as large as Swiss. The texture is somewhat elastic in body. Leyden, a cheese resembling brick, is made from partly skimmed cow's milk. It has a dark brown surface and is frequently spiced with cumin, cloves or caraway. Red coloring may be applied on the rind. Leyden cheese may also be called Delft or Hobbe cheese. Noekkelost is a semi-hard cheese similar to Leyden but differing in the proportion of spices used for its flavor. Muenster is a cheese that also closely resembles brick. A similar French cheese is called Gerome. Domestic Muenster must only be made from pasteurized milk. It is blander and milder in flavor than the imports because of its shorter curing period.

Gammelost is a semi-hard Norwegian cheese made of skimmed sour milk. It is golden brown in color. The strong flavor is caused largely by a mold growth on the cheese, which is developed during curing under wet straw. Holstein cheese may be made from sour skim milk or from skim milk to which buttermilk has been added. The former comes in molded pieces about a half pound in size, while the latter is marketed in sizes of 12 to 14 pounds.

Processed Cheese

Processed cheese is a mixture of natural cheddar cheeses. For years cheese makers sought means whereby cheese quality could be held at desired levels without continuing to cure. Processed cheese was the answer. Curing is stopped by pasteurization at 145° F for 30 minutes or 160° F for 1 minute. The cheese is also re-emulsified. Maximum permitted emulsifying agent is 3%. Either sodium phosphate or sodium citrate is used as an emulsifier. Because of this emulsifier, processed cheese melts and mixes easier into sauces and other cooked items. Total fat content must be not less than 50% dry solids, and the moisture content of most processed cheese must not be over 40%, but a 1% variation over the established moisture content for the cheeses used is allowed.

By careful selection and blending, cheese manufacturers can consistently make the mildest or the most strongly flavored cheese. The product will be consistent in quality and flavor also. Cheeses that fail in curing are taken and used for making processed cheese. Other

FIG. 4-10. USDA inspector takes sample of process cheese from the assembly line. He grades the samples of natural cheese as it comes into the plant, checks on sanitation and the processes used in the plant. He also supervises the plant quality control laboratory. Courtesy USDA.

cheeses that may have developed desirable flavors for blending may be used also.

The body and texture of processed cheese should be homogeneous and free from openings or sweet holes except those caused by trapped air. The cheese should be medium firm, resilient and not grainy to touch. It should slice without breaking or sticking to the knife. The cheese should not oil-off when melted and should be free from lumps or grit from crystallized salt. Aged or sharp, mild or medium-flavored processed cheese should resemble the flavor of regular cheese cured to these stages. The aged processed cheese may show a slight stickiness and a bit of graininess when cut. Processed cheese should show no mold, cracks or other surface defects. Packaging should be in sound, new, clean units. The cheese is usually plastic wrapped. It may be purchased in 1, 2, 3, 5 and 10-lb bricks. The most common processed cheeses are cheddar and Swiss.

Cheese foods are similar in appearance to processed cheese. They cannot be called cheese because they do not come up to the standards of identity established for cheese by the Food and Drug Administration. Some cheese is used, and milk solids, evaporated whey and other ingredients may be added. They will usually contain around 40% moisture and 20 to 23% butterfat; the latter based on total weight rather than dry solids.

A "filled" cheese is a cheese made from milk, as are other cheeses, but all or a part of its fat is not milk fat. At one time cheese imports were noted for their "filling," but standards of identity now make it impossible for this type of cheese to be shipped into this country.

Acid-Coagulated Cheeses

Latic acid bacteria, rather than rennet, may be used to develop sufficient acidity in milk to set the curd.[1] There are a number of cheeses made by this processes. They are not cured.

Cottage or Farmer's cheese is the soft, uncured curd from pasteurized milk. It may also be made from reconstituted, concentrated, dried or raw milk. If made from non-fat or raw milk, it cannot enter interstate commerce because it fails to meet federal identity regulations. If cream is added after manufacture so that the total butterfat content is 4% or more, the product may be called "creamed." The moisture content of cottage cheese should be not more than 80%.

To make cottage cheese the milk is soured by adding bacteria. After souring, the clabbered milk is heated to 90° F. The curd is cut and the whey separated. Heating is continued for 15 minutes, after which the whey is drained off, the curd washed and salt added, usually in the amount of 1% by weight. The size of the curd is regulated by the size of the curd knife used, and different types of cottage cheese are available on the market. A pot cottage cheese is an uncreamed, freshly made mass that has large curds about the size of popped corn. Baker's cheese is an uncreamed cheese with finer curds. It is usually coagulated with the aid of rennet. A flake-type curd cheese may also be obtained. Dry curd cheese is specified by food services for salads and other uses. It should have a moisture content around 70%. If too dry, the curd is harsh and has a hard, sawdust-like texture. The coliform count of cottage and creamed cheese should be under 50 per gram and the combined yeast and mold estimate not over 100 per gram. In some states calcium chloride, in the amount of 0.02% may be added to improve the firmness of the curd. Gelatin may be added in the amount of $\frac{1}{2}$ to 1%; this is illegal in most states. Cottage cheese is usually packed for food facilities in 5, 10 or 25-lb containers. Defects consist of off-color, excess acid, off flavor, which may be yeasty, fruity, feed, mold and so forth. Excess moisture, hard curd or excessively dry, grainy or gritty cheese will lack required quality standards. Look for broken, messy curd. The flavor should be sweet, slightly acid and mild. Ricotta is an Italian cheese that resembles cottage cheese, but it is slightly drier than the regular cottage cheese.

[1] A combination of setting by lactic acid development and rennet is used in some dairies where these cheeses are made.

Cream cheese is another lactic acid-type precipitated cheese. It has a smooth, fine texture, creamy and mild to taste. It should not have less than a 33% milk fat content. Federal standards of identity state that the fat content of the water-free solids should be not less than 65% milk fat. Sweet cream cheese should be acid free. Sour cream cheese may have a mild acidity. Neufchâtel cheese is a French origin, cream-type cheese. It has a higher moisture content and a lower fat content (20%) than cream cheese. It may, like cream cheese, be flavored with pimientos, olives or other ingredients and be used as a spread.

Whey-Made Cheeses

A number of cheeses are made from whey. Myost, also called Primost, is a light brown cheese, buttery in texture, with a mild, rather sweet taste. The whey is evaporated by heat while stirred, until it reaches the consistency of thickened milk. It is then poured into wooden troughs and stirred until cool. This stirring prevents the formation of the sugar lactose crystals. The cheese is molded into different forms. Imported Myost is usually made from goat's milk. Gjetost is another whey-base Scandinavian cheese. Gjetost is a hard cheese, golden brown in color, sweet in flavor. It too is made from goat's milk. Sapsago is a hard cheese made from cow's milk. It is a hard, small, cone-shaped cheese. It has a greenish color because it is flavored with Alpen Krauter clover. The true Sapsago is made from sour whey to which hot buttermilk is added. The curd is milled, the clover and salt added and the cheese dried.

5 Cereal Products

Products made from wheat, rice, corn, rye, oats, barley and buckwheat are widely eaten by man. Wheat far outstrips the others in quantity used in food preparation. Purchase specifications should be written for these products with care so that the correct items are obtained for the food production need. The type and quality of cereal product purchased will materially affect the quality of the foods made from them.

WHEAT

Wheat may be classified: (1) according to its time of planting; winter wheat is planted in the fall, winters as a grass and is harvested in mid-summer; spring wheat is planted in the spring and is harvested later than winter wheat; (2) by its density as hard, semi-hard or soft; (3) by its use as a flour for breads, pastry, cake or macaroni; (4) by its color as white, amber or red wheat; or (5) by its protein strength, as making a strong, moderate or weak flour. Strength of flour in bread or hard flours refers to a strong gluten that will give strong structural support to a baked product. Strength in a cake or soft wheat flour means that it has the ability to carry high ratios of sugar, fat and other ingredients in pastry making. Hard wheat flour used mainly for breads is planted in the spring in the northern central states and Canada. The hard durum wheats, amber in color, are also planted in the spring. They contain high amounts of gluten or protein and are used for making macaroni products. Durum wheat grows in the same general area as hard wheat. Soft wheat is grown largely south of the hard wheat area. Much of this is red wheat and its starch content is higher than hard or durum wheat and its gluten or protein content lower. This wheat may

272

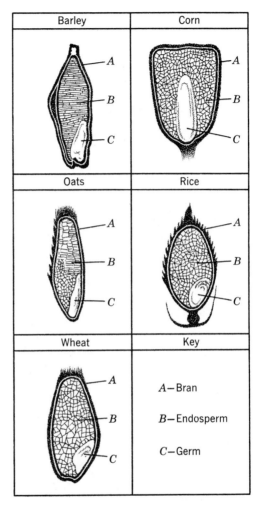

FIG. 5–1. The structure of various grains. The interior of the grain contains the endosperm from which farina, semolina, hominy and other products are derived depending on the grain.

also have a protein that is not as elastic or strong as the other two wheats. The flour made from winter wheat is soft to touch and not grainy like flour from hard or durum wheat. If the soft wheat flour is pressed in the hand, it will hold its shape and not crumble the way hard wheat or durum flour will. Flour made from soft wheat is whiter in color and lacks a creaminess seen in flour from hard wheat or in macaroni products made from the durum wheats. The finest soft wheats are used to make the delicate, low-protein and high-starch flour required for cakes and pastry.

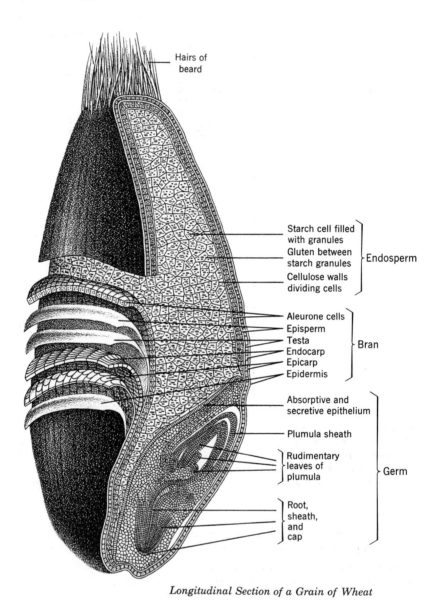

Hairs of
beard

Starch cell filled
with granules
Gluten between
starch granules
Cellulose walls
dividing cells
} Endosperm

Aleurone cells
Episperm
Testa
Endocarp
Epicarp
Epidermis
} Bran

Absorptive and
secretive epithelium
Plumula sheath
Rudimentary
leaves of
plumula
Root,
sheath,
and
cap
} Germ

Longitudinal Section of a Grain of Wheat

FIG. 5–2.   The major component parts of the cereal grains.   Courtesy Wheat Flour
Institute.

Essential qualities for proper flour performance may be obtained by blending several flours or wheats. A wheat high in ash or mineral content will not make a good flour, and other wheats may have to be blended with it to reduce this mineral content. Flour made from good wheat will have approximately 13% moisture, less than $\frac{1}{2}$% mineral or ash, 11% protein, slightly over 1% fat and 75% starch. Percentages of starch and protein will vary according to whether the flour is hard or soft. Cake flours may have only 7 to 8% protein compared with 14% in a good bread flour. The starch ratios vary inversely with the protein. Flour may be enriched with thiamin, riboflavin, niacin and iron to replace nutrients lost in processing. All cereal products should be specified enriched except for oats and a few others, which are never enriched.

Poor flours may be distinguished by a gray, dull color. This lack of vivacity in appearance may be readily seen if an ounce of flour is patted onto a flat surface, dipped quickly into water and placed in a moderate oven for about 30 to 45 seconds. The gray cast will be apparent. Good hard wheat flour should absorb about 65% of its weight in water and still form a pliable non-sticky ball. Good pastry flour will absorb slightly less moisture. Good stability in a cake or pastry flour is indicated when the flour can carry a high quantity of moisture, sugar, eggs, fat and other ingredients.

Bakers frequently take bread flour and work it for five or more minutes into a stiff dough. They carefully wash out the starch, take the remaining yellow ball of gluten and bake it to see how this protein factor of the flour performs.

To make flour, wheat is ground between rollers and then sifted through fine sieves. The dustlike particles that sift through are flour. Grinding and sifting will continue until all the flour is extracted. The remaining portion, called "red dog," is used for animal feed. Each grinding and sifting is called a "break" or "stream." Wheat flour may be made from as many as three to nine streams. Sifting is also called "bolting," and at one time silk cloth was used as the sieve material.

The best flour comes from the first streams. This is called "patent" flour. It is higher in protein and lower in ash than the later streams. The "clears" come from the last streams.

About 72% of the wheat kernel is made into flour. (See Figure 5–4.) This entire 72% is called "straight" or "100%" flour. Only 40 to 60% of straight flour is used for the best patent flours. Fancy or extra short patents are taken from the first streams. "Medium" patents are about 90% straight flour. "Long" or "family" patents are about 95% straight flour. A patent containing 90% of the straight flour is also called a "baker's" or "standard" patent. If a fancy patent is taken (60%), the

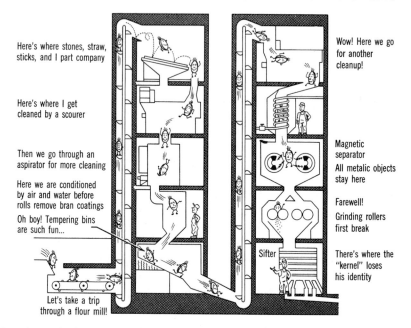

Here's where stones, straw, sticks, and I part company

Here's where I get cleaned by a scourer

Then we go through an aspirator for more cleaning

Here we are conditioned by air and water before rolls remove bran coatings

Oh boy! Tempering bins are such fun...

Let's take a trip through a flour mill!

Wow! Here we go for another cleanup!

Magnetic separator
All metalic objects stay here

Farewell!
Grinding rollers first break

Sifter

There's where the "kernel" loses his identity

FIG. 5–3.   In the first step in milling, the wheat is cleaned.   Next, it is cracked by passing it between steel rollers running in opposite directions at high speed.   This is called the first break.   The broken grain is then sifted or bolted to separate the fine flour particles

remaining 35% may be called a "fancy clear" flour.   This leaves 5% for a poor type clear.

A "filled" flour has more clears in it than one would normally find in straight flour.   Whole wheat flour is not only straight flour but also includes the bran.   "Light" whole wheat flour contains only part of the bran.   Sometimes whole wheat flour is also called "graham" flour.   Unbolted whole wheat flour contains the wheat germ in addition to the bran.   Wheat germ has poor keeping qualities.

Federal regulations require that labels state if flour is bleached.   Flour must be aged 8 to 10 weeks or chemically treated to give the same properties obtained by aging.   Unaged flour will lack pliable qualities.   Products made from it are apt to be "bucky" and hump in baking.   The products will be tough and poor in quality.   Such flour is frequently called "green" flour.

Flour for food facilities will usually be purchased from a wholesaler or jobber, but larger users may go directly to the millers for their supply.   Jobbers generally take a 13 to 18% markup on cereal products.

Flour is sold by the barrel, which is two 98-lb sacks or 196 lb.   Half-

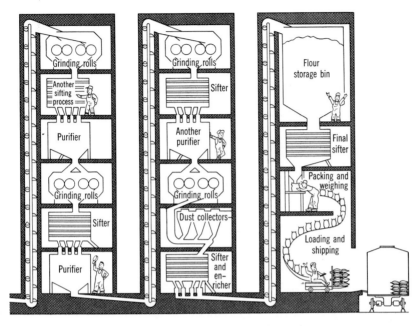

from the kernel. A purifier is used to remove some bran. The kernel portions pass through successive breaks or rollings and boltings. Not all the bran can be removed and the clears or last breaks of flour may be tinted by it. Courtesy Wheat Flour Institute.

barrel quantities are always 98 lb, but fourths or eights of a barrel may be 48 or 49 lb and 24 or 24½ lb respectively. Some specialty flours, such as cake flours, are sold in 100-lb sacks. Buyers should note whether prices are for 100 or 98 lb. Market prices for flour are usually stable and it is unwise to purchase more than several months' supply.

Storage should be off the floor, with sacks crisscrossed for good ventilation. Because flour can absorb odors, the storage area should be dry and free from odors. Mice, insects and flooding are dangers to stored flour.

Most food facilities use the cheaper pastry flour for dusting foods, thickening gravies and other general work. Three types of flour should be purchased for the average institution: bread, pastry and cake.

Breakfast Wheat Cereals

Cracked wheat, farina and malted wheat are wheat cereals that require cooking. Quick cooking types should cook in 5 minutes after coming to a boil. For 100 portions, about 7 lb of uncooked cereal are required.

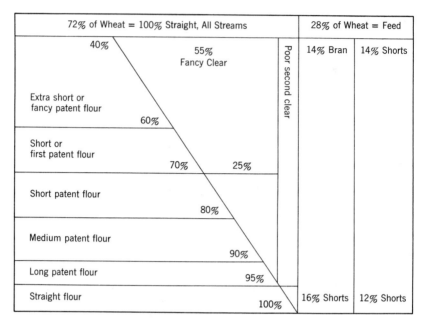

FIG. 5–4. The quantity of different flours derived from wheat. Courtesy C. O. Swanson, *Wheat and Flour Quality,* **Burgess Printing Co., Minneapolis, Minn., 1951.**

Cracked wheat is wheat that is cleaned and washed. A part of ·the bran is removed and the wheat is cracked into fine kernels. Some steaming may occur before cracking, and some malt or other products may be added for flavoring. The cracked wheat may also be rolled or flaked.

Farina, a meal, is the inner portion of the wheat kernel, the endosperm. When whole wheat farina is made, some or all of the bran is left on. Some whole wheat farinas may also contain the germ.

Malted cereals are largely farina flavored with malts and other flavoring ingredients.

Prepared cereals from wheat are shredded wheat, wheat flakes, bran flakes, puffed wheat, bran and malted cereals. They should be prepared from clean, sound wheat. Usually the bran is not removed.

Shredded wheat is made from a high grade soft wheat. Seasonings and flour are formed into a paste and cooked, and the product is sent through a shredding machine. The shreds are formed into a loose biscuit and baked. Baking should be even and the color golden brown. Large biscuits should be not less than ½ oz each or more than 1 oz each. Small biscuits should weigh 28 to 70 to the ounce. The biscuits should be crisp, porous and friable. They should contain no hard particles except, perhaps, at the seam edge. Some biscuits may be in circular shape. Biscuits made from pressed flakes may also be obtained.

Wheat flakes are made from soft white or red winter wheat. A heavy paste is made, flavored, cooked, partially dried, then flaked and toasted. Toasting should be even and the color a golden brown. Malted wheat flakes are flavored with malt.

Bran flakes are manufactured in a manner similar to wheat flakes but contain 25 to 40% bran. If they contain raisins, the raisins should be of the seedless type, pliable, meaty, well developed, of good color and reasonably uniform size. A paste of wheat bran and flour from soft white or red winter wheat is extruded through plates in making bran. It is then toasted.

Puffed wheat is processed in the same way as puffed rice. (See rice.) The grains should be individual, porous and uniform. Expansion should be eight times normal kernel size.

Malted cereal granules are made from wheat flour flavored heavily with malt and shaped into loaves, which are given a slight fermentation. The loaf is baked until toasted. After cooling, the loaf is ground into granule form.

Crackers

A flour paste containing salt, shortening, leavening, malt and a small quantity of sugar is formed into cracker shape and baked to make crackers. Richness of sugar and shortening may be a significant factor in deciding the type of cracker. Some crackers may contain whey, milk solids or other added products. Wide variety is found in crackers. They may have additional cereal products, such as potato flour, whole wheat and rye flour, or they may contain cheese, caraway seed or other products.

Macaroni Products

The European name for macaroni products is *alimentary pastes*, a term that may also be encountered in this country for these products.

Macaroni products are shaped and dried doughs. Government standards of identity permit the addition of $\frac{1}{2}$ to 2% egg white, salt, onions, celery, bay leaf, in addition to water and flour. Maximum moisture content allowed is 13%.

Durum flour from hard amber durum wheat, strong in gluten, is required to make a macaroni product that, when boiled, will retain shape and not be soggy, pasty and break or crack easily. Too much salt weakens the paste and some buyers specify the product without salt. Maximum quantity should be 1 to 2%. Disodium phosphate may be

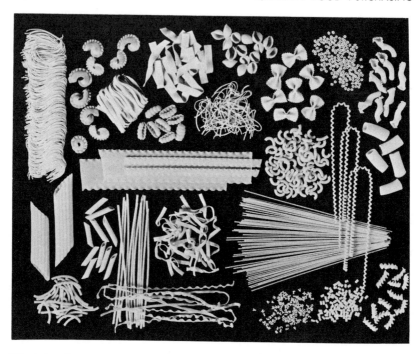

FIG. 5–5.   There are many shapes used in forming macaroni products.   Here are a few.
Starting at the upper left and reading across are: folded fine egg noodles, create di gallo,
wide egg noodles, shell macaroni, egg noodle bow ties, stelline riccini, mezzani, folded
medium egg noodles, cavatelli, fine egg noodles, curly-edged lasagne with malfalde on
top of it, elbow macaroni, fusilli, rigatoni, manicotti rigati, mostaccioli, long macaroni,
medium egg noodles, spaghetti, maccaroncelli, margherite, egg alphabets, tubettini, and
corkscrew macaroni.   Courtesy National Macaroni Institute.

added as a dough conditioner.   If claims are made for added milk, the
product must contain not less than 3.8% milk solids.   Protein content
from wheat should be 13%.   Egg noodles must contain not less than
$5\frac{1}{2}\%$ whole egg solids or egg yolk.   No yellow coloring may be added
to macaroni products.   If a product claims to have egg added, it may not
be wrapped in yellow transparent paper to make it appear more yellow
than it is.

Unlike flour made for baking purposes, the durum flour used for
macaroni products is taken only from the middlings or middle streams.
About 20% of the kernel is removed.   The next 50% is a product called
semolina, which is high in protein.   The color is creamy yellow, and
products made from good quality semolina are yellowish in color.   The
remaining 30% is bran and feed products.   Semolina for macaroni

products is ground into larger sized particles than for ordinary flour. It is made into a paste. The paste is then shaped and dried.

Farina, also a middling or middle stream from non-durum type flours, may be combined with semolina flour or used alone for macaroni products. If of high quality, farina will not make an inferior product, but it will lack the typical yellow color of semolina. When soft wheat farinas are used, the products have a dull gray color and a weak structure when cooked.

Vegetables, such as spinach or tomatoes, may be added to macaroni products. The label must state the addition, and the product must contain not less than 3% or more than 5% of the added product. Whole wheat macaroni products are also on the market.

Many shapes are used. Round, solid, rod types, such as vermicelli or spaghetti, are solid. Macaroni and larger round types are tubular. Only 12 out of sixty or more shapes are in common usage in the United States. Styles of macaroni products may sometimes be known as Naples, Genova or Bologna styles. Table 5–1 lists trade and federal sizes for macaroni products.

Quality in macaroni products is indicated by color and a hard brittle-

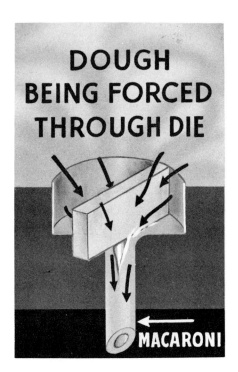

FIG. 5–6. How the hole is made in macaroni. The macaroni dough, when pushed against the die, is split by the wings and then pressed together around the lower end of the pin to form a solid tube. As it comes from the bottom of the die, the macaroni is cut to proper length.

Table 5–1
Classification of Macaroni Products

Type	Name	Sizes Trade	Sizes Federal Standards
Solid round rods	Vermicelli	$\frac{1}{32}''$ diameter	not more than 0.06″ in diameter
	Spaghettini	$\frac{1}{16}''$ diameter	
	Spaghetti	$\frac{3}{32}''$ diameter	0.06–0.11″ in diameter
Hollow tubes, plain	Foratini or Maccaroncelli	$\frac{3}{32}''$ diameter	
	Forati or perc-catelli	$\frac{1}{8}''$ diameter	
	Mezzarrelli or Mezzani	$\frac{5}{32}''$ diameter	
	Macaroni or Mezzani	$\frac{1}{4}''$ diameter	0.11–0.27″ in diameter
	Zitoni	$\frac{1}{2}''$ diameter	
Hollow tubes, corrugated	Mezzani regati	$\frac{1}{4}''$ diameter	
	Zitoni rigati	$\frac{1}{2}''$ diameter	
Noodles, flat ribbons	Broad	$\frac{1}{4}''$ wide, 0.030″ thick	
	Medium	$\frac{1}{8}''$ wide, 0.033″ thick	
	Fine	$\frac{1}{16}''$ wide, 0.035″ thick	
Sheets, scalloped	Lasagne (the widest)		
	Reginette and Margherite		
Elbows, hollow, small, smooth	Tuchetti	$\frac{1}{8}$ to $\frac{5}{32}''$ diameter	
Elbows, hollow, large, smooth	Ditali lisci	$\frac{1}{4}$ to $\frac{7}{16}''$ diameter	
Elbows, hollow, corrugated, very large	Rigatoni	$\frac{9}{16}''$ diameter	
Elbows, hollow, hexagonal	Bonballati	$\frac{3}{8}''$ diameter	
Bunches, curled	Vermicelli rella (morella)		
	Spaghetti rella		
Fancy small pastes	Alfabeto		
	Puntette		
	Stelletta		
	Crowns, and so forth		

ness or flinty quality. The product should be semi-translucent and break squarely across with a clean, glassy fracture. While the rod type products may show some springiness, they should make little more than a broad arc before snapping. Poor macaroni products break unevenly. A reddish cast indicates red durum or soybean flour. A grayish white cast indicates manufacture from a low grade farina. The finished products should be reasonably smooth and reasonably free from broken, misshapen or checked pieces. They should have good taste and odor. Cook to ascertain quality.

Macaroni products are packed in 10-lb, 15-lb, 20-lb and 40-lb containers. Purchase in 300-lb barrel size is not recommended unless the quantity used is large. Some facilities purchase in 100-lb bags. Quantities required for approximately one month only should be purchased because these products may become infested with weevils or other insects. Broken macaroni products are sold at a discount and may be purchased for economy meals. It takes about 8 lb for one hundred portions. One pound on cooking will yield about $2\frac{1}{2}$ qt.

RICE

In this country rice is grown commercially in Louisiana, Texas and Arkansas. California grows some rice under irrigation.

After harvest, rice is hulled and polished, leaving a white kernel. Whiteness may be enhanced by coating the kernels with glucose and talc. If the rice is not polished, it is called brown rice. All or most of the bran is still on brown rice. It has a richer flavor than polished rice but does not keep as well.

Under-milled rice is a semi-polished rice with part of the bran on. Converted polished rice has been steamed; nutrients have been added for fortification and the product has been redried. Instant-type rice is a precooked rice that needs only rehydration with boiling water to have the texture of cooked rice. It is usually fortified. The converted and instant rices are less subject to insect infestation. Brown and under-milled rice are easily infected.

Purchase of rice for institutional use is usually in 100-lb bags.

Wild rice is not a grain but a grass seed gathered from the swamp areas of northern Minnesota, Wisconsin and Michigan.

Varieties of rice should never be mixed, for each variety has a different cooking time; for instance, Rexoro will take 16 minutes, Fortuna 21 minutes, Blue Rose 22 minutes, Caloro 20 minutes, Edith 22 minutes, Lady Wright 23 minutes and Early Prolific 24 minutes to cook.

Some rice will cook light and dry, with the grains separate; other

Table 5-2
Common Rice Varieties

Long Grain	Medium Grain	Short Grain	Pearl (round)
Rexoro, Edith, Fortuna, Lady Wright, Blue Bonnet, Nira	Blue Rose, Early Prolific	Calrose, Magnolia, Zenith	American Pearl, California Pearl

types will not. In general, Fortuna, Edith, Lady Wright, Blue Rose or California Pearl cook up well.

Trade and federal grades exist for polished rice. Trade grades are Extra Fancy, Fancy, Extra Choice, Choice, Medium and Sample Grade. Federal grades are U.S. No. 1, No. 2, No. 3, No. 4, No. 5 and Sample Grade. Grades are governed by cleanliness, wholeness, quality of milling, white or creamy color according to variety, freedom from foreign matter and mixture of varieties.

Broken rice, milling second-head rice and similar lower qualities are used by manufacturers of rice flour, brewers or others.

Brown rice has four trade grades; Extra Fancy, Fancy, Choice and Sample Grade. U.S. No. 1, 2, 3 and 4 are similar grades. The Fancy or Extra Choice grades (U.S. No. 2 or 3) are recommended for purchase by institutions. It takes 6 to 8 lb of rice to yield one hundred portions.

Rice Breakfast Cereals

Puffed rice is a prepared breakfast cereal from cleaned and polished rice. It is first cooked; then it is placed into a chamber under heavy pressure and heated. The pressure is suddenly released by a process called "gun-puffing." This sudden release of pressure forces out the cellular walls, puffing up the rice. Puffing should be eight times the original grain size. The rice used should be sound, clean, whole rice. The finished product should have a good color, a light, porous texture and a good flavor. Rice flakes and shredded rice biscuits are also found on the market.

Rice flour is used commercially as an inexpensive dusting flour. It also has limited use in some quantity food preparation.

CORN

The endosperm of corn is called hominy. Like farina or semolina from wheat, it is the middling or hard, flinty, inner part of the kernel. Hominy may be prepared by soaking whole kernels of corn in lye to remove the outer bran portion. It is then dried. This product is frequently boiled and canned. Most hominy products are, however, just cracked endosperm of the corn.

Pearled hominy, a dry meal coarser than corn meal, is used extensively for the manufacture of cornflakes and other corn products. Pearled hominy may also be called coarse hominy or samp. It may be cooked in milk or water and served as a vegetable. Table grits are finer than pearled hominy. Grits are also called granulated hominy and may be obtained in three sizes: coarse, medium and fine. When grits are ground smaller than fine, the product is called cream or pearl corn meal.

Hominy flakes are made from thinly pressed paste. Flaking permits more rapid cooking.

Hominy should have a good characteristic color, possess a natural ground taste and odor, and be free from rancid, bitter, nasty or other undesirable tastes or odors.

Regular corn meal is made from the degermed endosperm of corn. It contains more of the corn kernel than hominy. It may be purchased either coarse or fine.

If the old-process method or stone grinding is used, the bran and germ may remain. This corn meal is also called old-fashioned or water-ground corn meal. Old-process corn meal will not keep as long as other types of corn meal because the germ is perishable. It is said to have a better flavor than other corn meals. Bolted corn meals have more bran than those not labeled so. The color of corn meal may be white or yellow. Corn flour is finely ground and sifted corn meal.

Corn Breakfast Cereals

Cornflakes are made from pearled hominy of commercial screen size 4 or 5. A cooked paste that is flavored with malt, sugar, salt and other seasonings is made. It is partially dried, made into flakes and toasted. Corn is used for many other breakfast cereals. It may be combined with soya to make shredded corn with soya.

Cornstarch

The starch in corn may be removed, refined and finely pulverized to make cornstarch. The product should be pure, unmodified, pulverized cornstarch prepared from clean, sound corn. Cornstarch is almost pure carbohydrate. It should be uniformly white and free from any foreign taste or odor. There should be no lumps or hard or gritty particles. The product is used extensively in food production as a thickening agent. Its opacity in cornstarch puddings and its ability to form, upon cooling, a firm structure that shears or breaks sharply makes it desirable for puddings or cream-pie fillings.

The waxy maize starch, however, is replacing cornstarch or flour for use in berry pies and for thickening sauces and products that must be frozen. This new type of starch has the advantage of giving greater clarity, softness and pliability to thickened mixtures. The starch is as thick when hot as cold. These same maize starches have also been utilized to develop instant puddings, meringue stabilizers, cream-puff mixtures, marshmallow toppings and others. Manufacturers are now able to modify cornstarch to give it some of these properties. The thickening power of the waxy maize starch is greater than that of corn-starch. About 14⅓ oz of cornstarch will be required to give the same thickening power to a gallon of pie filling as 10¼ oz of waxy maize starch.

OATS

Oats are mainly used as a cooked breakfast cereal. About 6 to 7 lb of the longer cooking type and about 8 lb of the quick cooking type are required for one hundred portions.

After removing the outer husk, the kernel or endosperm called the groat remains. Scotch or regular, long-time cooking oatmeal is made by steaming the groat. It is next cut into smaller pieces and then passed through rollers, which press it flat. The meal is then dried. Extra steam treatment, plus finer division, is used to make quick-cooking oat-meal. This product should cook in boiling water to doneness in 5 minutes.

The product should have a bright, uniform, creamy color. The flavor should be the natural flavor of the oat and free from rancid, bitter, musty or other undesirable flavors or odors.

Stone grinding of oatmeal gives a product called "old-fashioned" or "stone" or "buhr" ground. "Old-fashioned" may also be used to indi-cate the longer cooking type. Some breakfast oats are "steel cut," which is a term given groats cut by steel cutters so as to resemble cracked wheat.

Oatmeal may be used for breads, cookies, cakes, wafers, muffins and other baked goods, besides its use as a breakfast cereal. Oat puffs are a processed cereal made largely of paste from the endosperm of the oat kernel. Some oat flour is used in quantity food production.

BARLEY

Barley is used more to make malt than as a cereal. Malt is made from sprouted barley. In sprouting, much of the starch is changed to maltose. This is a sugar that, besides sweetness, has desirable flavor qualities. Malted barley may also be used for malted-milk beverages, coffee substitutes and other purposes.

Pearled barley is used in soups or it may be boiled and served buttered as a starch vegetable. Pearling is done by removing the outer husks, leaving the endosperm. It is then polished. Some abrasion may occur to give the barley a rounder shape. The product should come from clean, sound barley and should not possess rancid, musty, sour or other undesirable tastes or odors.

Pearled barley is graded into first and second grades. First-grade barley should have no bran showing at the crease of the barley endosperm. It should be light in color, uniform in size, and there should be few broken pieces. Second grade may be darker in color, have more bran, be less uniform and contain more broken pieces.

Barley may be white or brown. The brown type has most of the bran remaining on it. Sizes in the white type may be large, medium or small. Brown types are all large. Commercial sizes for grade are:

Grade	Sieve Size, in Inches
Large	0.101 by 0.750
Medium	0.090 by 0.750
Small	0.086 by 0.750

Barley flour lacks gluten and, if used for breads, wheat flour must be added to it to give the required gluten structure to the bread.

RYE

Rye is mainly used as flour in food preparation. Because it lacks gluten, wheat flour must be added to it. Three types of rye flour are available: light, medium and dark. The amount of bran remaining decides which shade it shall be.

Pumpernickel flour is a coarsely ground, whole rye flour. It may also be called rye meal or rye graham. Rye flour is used for pancake mixes, crackers and other products.

BUCKWHEAT

Buckwheat is a herbaceous plant. Because the seed can be ground into a meal or flour, it is classified as a grain. The lighter buckwheat flours have most of the bran removed. Fine buckwheat flours made of the inner endosperm are almost as white as wheat flour. The darker flours containing more bran have stronger flavors. Wheat flour is generally used with buckwheat to give it gluten strength. Buckwheat is used largely in making griddle cakes. It performs well in yeast-leavened griddle cakes. These may also be called "sour-dough" or "old-fashioned" griddle cakes.

SOY

Soy is another product that is not a true cereal but because it grinds into a flourlike product, it is classed with cereals. Because of its high protein content, soy flour is used in making high-protein content breads. Dietary value is increased. Soy gives a yellowish cast to the bread, which detracts somewhat from its desirability. It can also be used to make pie crust, for it gives some flavor enhancement and tenderness to the crust. Soy meal or flour is also used in making several breakfast cereals. If the product contains much oil, it will become rancid quickly.

MISCELLANEOUS CEREAL PRODUCTS

A number of starches are made from plants. These plants are not all cereals but, again, they are classified with the cereal group because of the nature of the product.

Tapioca is made from the root of the cassava plant, which is grown in the West Indies, South America and Java. The roots are washed, grated and reduced to a pulp. The starch is then extracted, after which it is mixed into a dough, made into various forms and baked. Very little tapioca starch or flour is used on the market. *Pearl* tapioca is made by passing the dough through sieves. The size of the pellet will depend on the size of the sieve used. The dough may also be spread out in thin sheets and then baked, after which it is ground into small pieces. Unlike the pearl tapioca pellets, these pieces require no soaking before cooking. Cooking is also much more rapid. The ground pieces are frequently called "minute" tapioca.

Potato starch is used in making breads, crackers and several other items. It lacks gluten and is combined with high quality bread flour. It gives a delicate white color to the product.

Sago is a product of the pith palm. It is quite similar to tapioca in appearance and may be similarly used in food production. As a rule, it is sold in small, pearl form.

Arrowroot is obtained from the arrow plant grown in the tropics. It is a very finely divided starch, easily digested but more expensive than other starches. It makes a fine quality blancmange and other thickened puddings. It may also be used to thicken sauces and gravies. Arrow-root cookies and other pastries are considered high quality items be-cause of the tender, delicate quality given them by the addition of arrowroot starch.

SPECIFICATIONS

Very few federal standards for quality exist for cereals. Buyers should, therefore, attempt to write their own. All cereal products should be made from fully matured, sound grains of the latest crop, in accordance with the best commercial practices. The resulting product should have sound, good, bright color; be dry, clean and free from adulteration. Fortification is desirable. Immediately upon receipt of cereals, ascertain quality by use.

BREAD AND YEAST ROLLS

Many food facilities purchase their own bread and rolls. Standards should be established for these products as well as for other items pur-chased. Bread and rolls should be specified as having crusts that are uniform in color and thickness. The shape should be even, with a gently rounded top. There may be a slight break or shred on the side of loaves, but not a significant one. The color of the crust should be golden brown. The interior crumb should be clear white or slightly creamy. A grayish cast denotes inferior flour or poor processing. The crumb should have a soft sheen, and when a slice is held up to the light, it should be semi-translucent. The texture of the grain should be soft and velvety, with no large holes; and the consistency of the grain should be soft and delicate, not crumbly or doughy. The ingredients used should be flour, shortening, water, milk or buttermilk, sugar, salt and yeast. The type of flour and the proportions will vary according to the variety of bread.

When purchasing, as much variety as possible should be sought in bread. Avoid monotony and increase consumption by displaying differ-ent types of bread. If the bread is made from milk or buttermilk, the ratio by weight of milk solids to flour should be 8.2 parts milk solids to every 100 parts of flour used. This will yield a bread containing the same amount of milk solids as if liquid milk were used. If bread is made from whole wheat, only whole wheat flour should be used; not a combination of whole wheat and white flour. Calcium or sodium pro-pionate, used to give softness and keeping qualities to bread, should be not more than 0.32 parts for each 100 parts of flour used for white bread and 0.38 parts for each 100 parts of flour used for whole wheat, rye or other varieties of bread. Raisin breads or breads containing fruit or nuts should be specified as having not less than 50 parts seeded raisins, fruits or nuts for each 100 parts of flour used.

The bread should come wrapped. Standard slices are $\frac{3}{8}$ in. thick, but slices may be varied upward to $\frac{5}{8}$ in. thick if desired. Sandwich slices should be approximately $4\frac{1}{2}$ by $4\frac{1}{2}$ by $\frac{1}{4}$ in. to $\frac{1}{2}$ in. thick.

Breads of many shapes may be obtained. Different shapes on a bread tray promote interest. Such loaves as round top, split top, twin and twists are available as pan loaves. Hearth-type loaves (non-panned) are available as Italian hard loaves, Vienna, French, braided and cottage or round baked loaves. Vienna and Italian bread and rolls are sometimes called hard breads because they are baked in ovens in which steam is introduced during baking to form a hard, crispy crust on the bread. Sour-dough breads are those having a small portion of over-fermented bread dough added to a normal dough. Sour dough is frequently used for making rye and Italian hard breads. Pumpernickel may be a sour dough. There are also many roll shapes, such as pan, parkerhouse (also called pocketbook), finger rolls, napkin rolls and twists.

Sweet dough, containing eggs and higher quantities of sugar and fat than regular dough, is used to make cinnamon rolls, raisin buns, butterhorns or snails, butterfly buns, bear claws, coffee cakes, pecan rolls and a host of other products. When a sweet dough is rolled out, spread with butter, folded and rolled a number of times, a rolled-in dough called a *Danish* is made. Danish pastries come from this. Salt-rising bread is an overfermented bread having a cheesy flavor, which results from adding a yeast culture developed in milk, salt and corn meal. Cheese bread has approximately 20 parts of cheese to 100 parts of flour.

Boston brown bread is a steamed mixture of wheat flour, corn meal and rye flour combined with molasses, milk and salt. Soda and baking powder are the leavening agents. Raisins may be added. It may be purchased canned.

Matzoth is an unleavened bread made from flour and water. It resembles crackers but is thinner. It is eaten by the Jewish people during their Passover period. Zwieback is a toasted, sweetened bread. Both matzoth and zwieback are crumbled and used in some food preparations.

6 Fats and Oils

PROPERTIES OF FATS

Buyers should select fats and oils to meet specific production needs. There is no single all-purpose fat or oil. Manufacturers today process oils and fats to meet specific needs in cooking and baking. Buyers should understand some of the basic properties that fats possess to be able to select the fats required for these particular needs.

Chemical Makeup of Fats and Oils

Fats and oils are much the same compounds. Both are made up of fatty acids and glycerine. The fatty acids are straight chains of carbon atoms attached to each other in the following manner: $-\overset{|}{\underset{|}{C}}-\overset{|}{\underset{|}{C}}-\overset{|}{\underset{|}{C}}-\overset{|}{\underset{|}{C}}-$ The open prongs or bonds at the top, bottom and ends indicate areas where hydrogen, oxygen or other atoms or compounds may attach themselves. An example of a long-chain or a short-chain fatty acid would be:

$$H-\overset{H}{\underset{H}{C}}-\overset{H}{\underset{H}{C}}-\overset{H}{\underset{H}{C}}-\overset{H}{\underset{H}{C}}-\overset{H}{\underset{H}{C}}-\overset{H}{\underset{H}{C}}-\overset{H}{\underset{H}{C}}-\overset{H}{\underset{H}{C}}-\overset{H}{\underset{H}{C}}-\overset{H}{\underset{H}{C}}-\overset{H}{\underset{H}{C}}-\overset{H}{\underset{H}{C}}-\overset{H}{\underset{H}{C}}-\overset{H}{\underset{H}{C}}-\overset{H}{\underset{H}{C}}-\underset{\underset{H}{O}}{C}=O$$

(Palmitic acid, a long chain fatty acid)

$$
\begin{array}{ccccc}
 & H & H & H & \\
 & | & | & | & \\
H= & C- & C- & C- & C=O \quad \text{(Butyric acid, a short chain fatty acid)}\\
 & | & | & | & | \\
 & H & H & H & O \\
 & & & & | \\
 & & & & H
\end{array}
$$

Three fatty acids are joined together with glycerine to form a tri-glyceride. This is the chemical name for a fat or oil. The glycerine and the three fatty acids are joined as follows:

$$
\begin{array}{l}
H \\
| \\
H-C-\text{Fatty acid} \\
| \\
H-C-\text{Fatty acid} \\
| \\
H-C-\text{Fatty acid} \\
| \\
H
\end{array}
$$

A fatty acid is called *saturated* when all the top, bottom or end bonds are joined with hydrogen, oxygen or another atom or compound. The palmitic acid and butyric acid above are saturated fats for all bonds are filled. When the fatty acid has two carbon atoms that join together in double bonds as $-C-C=C-C-$, there will no longer be two bonds open on these two middle carbons joined by the double bond but only one bond open. This double bond is called an "unsaturated bond." The carbon chain is weak at this point and the fatty acid is much more easily split here than at any other point. A long-chain fatty acid that has several unsaturated bonds may therefore break into several short-chain fatty acids. It is desirable in fats and oils used for cooking or baking to prevent attachment of other atoms or compounds at these weak points or to prevent the fat or oil from splitting up at the weak points.

Since fatty acids may be of different lengths and different degrees of unsaturation, the possibilities for many different types of fats are evident. Fat manufacturers make use of these possibilities to develop different kinds of fats to meet specific production needs in food preparation.

Shortening Power

To make a pie dough, puff paste dough or similar product, a plastic fat is required. A hard fat will not spread well, while a soft fat will blend too thoroughly with the flour. Oils spread too much to make a good pie crust. Suet and tallow fats are too hard for good pastry work. Lard and hydrogenated fats are excellent for pie crusts because both are plastic and have good shortening power.

Fats or oils can be given a desired solidity or plasticity by a process called hydrogenation. If hydrogen gas is bubbled under pressure through heated oil containing finely ground nickel to act as a catalyst, the unsaturated bonds of a fat or oil will add on hydrogen. This will make the fat or oil saturated and when it cools it will become more solid. The reaction can be controlled so that a solid fat of exactly the correct plasticity is obtained. Fats that have too much solidity can be made more plastic by a reverse process in which hydrogen atoms are removed to make unsaturated fats or oils.

Greater shortening power may also be achieved by adding plasticizers or emulsifiers to a fat. This causes the fat to spread more easily. These emulsifiers are usually monoglycerides or diglycerides, compounds closely associated with the triglyceride or fat. These compounds are also added to fats to be used in making cakes or other pastries.

Fats and oils must also possess good shortening power to give proper tenderness to bakery products. Some fats are given greater shortening power by the addition of free fatty acids. Animal fats usually contain more free fatty acids than vegetable oils or fats do. That is why lard has such excellent shortening power in pie crusts. Removal of free fatty acids is accomplished to reduce shortening power.

Frying Properties

Fats for deep-fat frying or frying must have high stability. The fats should not break down easily at high temperatures. A fat or oil that has too many unsaturated bonds may break down in frying or grill work. If a fat has a high amount of free fatty acids, it will break down more quickly in frying. Frying fats that have a low fatty acid content should be selected. Animal fats do not perform well for fry work because of their high fatty acid content. Cottonseed or corn oils perform well in deep-frying and grill work, but specially developed fats have largely replaced these in quantity food work. These special fats contain large quantities of long-chain, saturated fats. Special stabilizers such as silicons are added to reduce the chance of fat breakdown at high temperatures.

When fats break down from the action of heat or use, they may divide themselves into short-chain fats, or take on oxygen, or increase their free fatty acid content. One, two or three of these may occur at the same time. The first two reactions develop undesirable flavors, while the last speeds further breakdown. Continued breakdown will cause the fat to turn into water, glycerol and acrolein. The last compound is a volatile substance that causes the eyes to smart and water.

One of the criterias used to judge the desirability of fat for frying is to ascertain its smoking point. If a fat or oil has a smoking point above 425° F when fresh, it is usually considered acceptable for frying purposes. It also should be stable for a long period of use at high temperatures.

Creaming Properties

Fats for cakes and other bakery items must cream well. To do this they must possess a plastic, waxy consistency at room temperature. These fats must also form a stable emulsion in a batter. Fats used by bake shops may be texturated or precreamed in addition to being plasticized. This texturating is a process in which very fine gas bubbles are incorporated into the fat, giving it a creamed texture. As a result, the time needed for creaming in cake making and other bakery work is reduced.

Flavor

Fats and oils used for general baking and cooking purposes should be neutral in flavor and colorless. At other times flavor may be desirable, and a fat or oil may be selected because of its flavor properties. Butter or margarine used as a spread must have fine flavor. Olive oil, peanut oil, bacon fat, soy oil and others are frequently used for their flavor contribution to foods. Salad oils, at times, must possess distinctive flavors. Flavorings that give a butter taste to fats are sometimes added to fats used in the bake shop to give a butter flavor to the products. The flavors in fats come either from impurities, as in bacon fat or olive oil, or from flavor esters incorporated in the fat, as in corn or peanut oil.

Fats may develop undesirable flavors also. If the fatty acid is less than ten carbon atoms in length, it will have a disagreeable flavor. Rancid butter derives a great deal of its flavor from butyric acid, a four carbon fatty acid. Caprylic acid and caproic acid, with eight and six carbons respectively, are highly distasteful. When long-chain fats split into short-chain fats, as they will in deterioration in storage or use in frying, the short-chain fats developed give off-flavors to the products cooked with or in this fat. Items such as salt and copper may cause fats to break down faster in use. These compounds are carefully removed in processing fats.

Off-flavor may also develop from rancidity. This is the addition of oxygen, usually at the weak, unsaturated bond. Compounds can be added to fats and oils to retard rancidity development. The most common of these are propyl gallate or butylated hydroxy anisole. Rancidity development is favored by high temperatures and light. Contact with the air is another favoring factor. Fats or oils should be stored in airtight containers in cool, dark areas.

Some fats may undergo a reaction exactly opposite to oxidation rancidity, and this develops off-flavors because of oxygen loss. The flavor developed is called fishy or beany. Reversion or oxygen loss in fats was at one time a serious deteriorating factor in soy oil products, but better processing methods have stabilized these products so that it is now rare in foods containing soy oil.

PURCHASE FACTORS

Labeling

The Pure Food and Drug Administration makes it mandatory for fats and oils, as in other foods, to bear labels that identify the product by its common name. If the fat or oil is a mixture, the label must name the oils and fats used. There are few federal standards for quality in fats and oils. The substances used for anti-oxidants, emulsifiers and stabilizers must be approved by the food and drug authorities.

Fats and oils may be classified as to whether they are vegetable or animal in origin. Butter is an animal fat, while margarine today is largely processed from vegetable fats. Because of their very similar use as spreads, they are discussed separately from vegetable and animal fats.

Margarine and Butter

Margarine. The standards of identity of the federal government state that margarine is a "food, plastic in form, which consists of one or more of the various approved animal or vegetable fats mixed with cream." Optional ingredients are vitamins A and D, butter, salt, flavoring, emulsifying agents, artificial color and preservatives. The type and amount that may be added is controlled, and labels must state their use and, in some instances, the actual quantities used. Most margarines contain 15,000 International Units of vitamin A per pound. Finely ground soy beans may be used to replace up to 10% of the moisture content. The product must be labeled margarine or oleomargarine. Coloring is common, but some states prohibit its use. Many states require that margarine sold in individual pats must be triangular in shape rather than square like butter. The number of pats per pound to specify is the same as for butter.

Margarine must be 80% fat. At one time margarine was processed largely from olein fats from beef. This is the origin of the term *oleo* margarine. Today soy oil exceeds all fats used. Some cottonseed and other vegetable oils are used. A number of margarines on the market are blends of animal and vegetable fats. Some states require the use of at least some animal fat in margarine. Manufacture must be under government inspection for sanitary processing and operate under sanitary conditions. All products used must be sound, clean and fit for food. Improved margarines that are more plastic and better flavored are now on the market.

A specification of a food facility for purchase of margarine might read: "Good grade product, sweet, fresh, clean with firm and uniform body, not sticky or mottled. The color should be a delicate straw color and coloring matter should not cover inferior merchandise. The product should contain not less than 1% milk solids and 9000 International Units of vitamin A per pound. It must contain 80% or more of approved fats and not more than 15% moisture and 4% salt." The specification should also state packaging and whether the margarine is to be in pats, quarter-pound cubes, in pound prints, 5-lb prints, 30-lb containers or in barrels. Margarine may be obtained in 24-lb or 32-lb cubes also.

Margarine may be graded much as butter is graded. Packaging is considered. Coloring should be natural straw color and uniform. The body and texture should be that of good butter. Margarine made from coconut oils has a definite break and a lower melting point. The flavor of margarine should be pleasing, clean, sweet and free from taint or foreign odor. Off-flavors or odors can be detected if the margarine is warmed slightly. When heated, margarine melts with little browning and sputtering, while butter tends to foam. Lecithin may be used as an emulsifier in margarine and, if added, this will aid in browning. The keeping quality of margarine is about equal to butter, but it is less likely to absorb flavors. Storage of margarine should be the same as for butter.

Butter. Butter manufacture is no longer a farm industry local in nature. The process is carefully controlled, and manufacture is in large creameries. Manufacturing grades for cream have been established by the federal government, and butter manufacturers purchase their cream by grade. Cream used for butter must be pasteurized at not less than 165° F for at least 30 minutes.

Federal standards state that butter must contain not less than 80%

milk fat; it may or may not contain added salt or coloring matter. Butter used by the Jewish trade, and occasionally elsewhere, is unsalted. The usual composition of butter found on the market is 81.3% milk fat, 1% milk solids or curd, 2.3% salt and 15.3% moisture. If cream used for butter is below 33% milk fat, a butter of better texture and body will be obtained. About 100 lb of milk fat will make 120 to 125 lb of butter.

After pasteurization, a lactic acid bacteria starter is added to the cream to ripen it and to give it desirable flavor and an acidity around 0.18%, expressed as lactic acid. Cream above this acidity is neutralized by chemicals. Coloring may be added to butter, and it is not necessary

Table 6–1
Allowed Flavor Deviations in the Various Butter Grades

Identified Flavors*	AA†–93 Score	A‡–92 Score	B–90 Score	C–89 Score
Feed	Slight	Definite		
Cooked (fine)	Definite			
Aged		Slight		
Bitter		Slight	Definite	
Coarse acid		Slight	Definite	
Flat		Slight	Definite	
Smothered		Slight		
Storage		Slight	Definite	
Cooked (coarse)		Definite	Definite	
Musty				
Neutralizer			Slight	Definite
Scorched			Slight	Definite
Utensil			Slight	Definite
Weed			Slight	Definite
Whey			Slight	Definite
Woody			Slight	Definite
Old cream			Slight	Definite
Barny			Definite	
Cheesy				Slight
Fruity				Slight
Metallic				Slight
Oily				Slight
Sour				Slight
Wild onion or garlic				Slight
Yeasty				Slight
Stale				Definite

*If more than one flavor is evident, the flavor should be based on the flavor that carries the lowest classification.
†Shall be fine, highly pleasing.
‡Shall be pleasing and desirable.

to note this on the label. After the product is churned, it is washed, salted and worked. Working is very important to the quality to give a waxy, compact, tenuous body. Overworking will give a loose, leaky body, which may be gritty from undissolved salt. Overworking may also produce a greasy butter.

Butter may be made into 64-lb cubes or packed into eastern boxes of 50 lb. Most is processed into one-fourth or one-pound prints. The pound prints are usually packed 30 lb to the box. Pats may be purchased in 5-lb cartons. The number of pats should be 72 to 90 for institutional use.

Federal standards for butter are Grade AA (93 score), Grade A (92 score), Grade B (90 score), Grade C (89 score), Grade CG (cooking grade, below 89 score) and No Grade. Grade or quality is established on the basis of flavor, body, salt, color and packaging. The aroma of butter is a large part of its flavor. Body is partly appearance and partly texture. Graininess, raggedness, crumbliness or streaked color or color specks are defects. The butter should show a rough, irregular edge when broken, stand up well under warm temperature and have no visible moisture. Color should be even and clear, not mottled, wavy or streaked. The package should be clean, dry, sound and properly filled. Graders are highly trained and must possess an acute sense of smell and

Table 6–2
Classification and Score Loss for Defects Other Than for Flavor

Body	Score Loss in Points	Body	Score Loss in Points	Color	Score Loss in Points
Slight crumbly	½	Definite spongy		Definite color	
Slight bumpy	½	or weak	1	specks	2
Slight leaky	½	Definite sticky	1	Definite mottled	2
Slight mealy	½	Definite ragged		Definite	
Slight short	½	boring	2	streaked	2
Slight spongy		Definite grainy	2		
or weak	½				
Slight stick	½	Color		Salt	
Slight ragged		Slight wavy	½	Slight sharp	
boring	1	Slight mottled	1	salt	½
Slight grainy	1	Slight streaked	1	Slight gritty	
Definite crumbly	1	Slight color specks	1	salt	1
Definite leaky	1	Definite high color	1	Definite sharp salt	1
Definite mealy	1	Definite wavy	1	Definite gritty salt	2

Table 6–3
Total Defects Allowed within Butter Grades

Flavor	Defects Body	Defects Color	Defects Salt	Total Defects	Permitted Total	Excess of Permitted Total	Grade
AA	½	0	0	½	½	0	AA or 93
AA	0	1	0	1	½	½	A or 92
AA	1	0	½	1½	½	1	B or 90
AA	1	1	0	2	½	1½	B or 90
AA	1	1	½	2½	½	2	B or 90
A	½	0	0	½	½	0	A or 92
A	0	1	0	1	½	½	B or 90
A	1	0	½	1½	½	1	B or 90
A	1	1	0	2	½	1½	C or 89
A	1	1	½	2½	½	2	C or 89
B	½	0	0	½	½	0	B or 90
B	0	1	0	1	½	½	C or 89
B	1	0	½	1½	½	1	C or 89
C	1	0	0	1	½	0	C or 89
C	1	½	0	1½	½	0	C or 89

taste. Triers are inserted into blocks of butter, twisting out a long cylindrical plug. This is examined for flavor, odor, texture, body, salt and other factors. Scores are given to each specific quality and the score totaled. The total score indicates the grade.

The federal classification for scoring defects is given in Tables 6–1 and 6–2.

Table 6–3 indicates how flavor and defects are combined to establish grade.

Vegetable Oils

Most vegetable oils come from the seeds of plants, but there are exceptions, such as olive oil, which comes from the meat of the olive. Separation of the oil is obtained by crushing and grinding, steam treatment and then pressing. Cold extraction gives better oil. The methods of extraction may be by centrifugal expellers or hydraulic press. Some oils are obtained by solvent extraction, after which the solvent is distilled from the oil and reused. Most vegetable oils for food are deodorized, decolored and clarified, but one or more of these processes may be omitted for specific oils.

Vegetable oils may deteriorate by discoloring or developing rancid flavors. Light, air and moisture may be cause of rancidity. Air should be excluded by sealing in airtight containers. Light should

also be excluded. High-storage temperatures will assist in the breakdown of fats or oil. Storage should not be above 70° and should be in
a dry place.

Olive oil. Probably the oldest vegetable oil used as food is olive oil.
Today in this country, California and Arizona produce significant
quantities of olive oil. Much is also imported. The oil content of the
olive varies between 14 and 40%. Its flavor will depend upon growing
conditions, soil and extraction methods. The Lucca district of Italy
produces some of the finest oils, but adulteration is so common and
so many areas outside of Lucca have claimed their oil comes from that
district that it is difficult to obtain the true oil.

After about 10 days of drying, ripe olives are crushed and pressed to
obtain the oil. If the pits are removed before crushing, the oil is of
better quality. Olives must be pressed immediately after crushing
or the oil will deteriorate. The first oil is known as *virgin* or *sub-
lime* oil. It is of highest quality. Olive oils are not heat treated,
deodorized or decolored, but may be clarified. Refined oils are later
pressings. Some of these may be obtained by heat extraction. Oils
from the third and fourth pressings are seldom used for food; instead
they are used for soap and lubricant manufacture. Refined oils are not
recommended for food facility use.

Because adulteration of olive oil is difficult to detect, only reliable
brands should be purchased. The Olive Oil Association of America is
attempting to enforce association standards and to obtain labeling
in this country that will indicate origin, extent of adulteration with
other oils, quality and other factors of interest to buyers. Provisions
of the Food and Drug Act prohibit adulteration. Adulterated oils
cannot be called olive oil. All imported olive oil is inspected by the
Food and Drug Administration and its purity determined before entry
is allowed. Most adulteration is encountered in imported oils.

A good olive oil should have a light-greenish to yellow color. The
flavor and odor should be pleasing, typical of olive oil, free from strong,
green olive odors and flavors, musty, moldy, butyric, zapateria, rancid
or other off-odors or flavors. Low grade or old oils will have these
off-odors or flavors. Buyers should taste olive oil before buying. A
good quality oil will have 0.5 to 2½% free fatty acids. U.S. Grade A
oil may not have more than 1.4% free fatty acids, Grade B not more
than 2½% and Grade C 3%. In total quality score, Grade A is 90 or
above, Grade B 80 or above and Grade C 70 or above. To meet
standards of identity, the iodine number of olive oil must be between
79 and 90 Hanus and have a refractive index of 1.4668 to 1.483 at
25° C.

Cottonseed oil. The cotton plant furnishes a seed that produces the cottonseed oil. Large quantities are grown in this country, India, China, Egypt and South America. The average oil content of the seed is 18 to 25%. Conditions of soil, season, fertilizer and variety will affect the flavor and the quantity of oil in the seed.

After hulling and extraction of oil by expellers, the oil is refined. The cottonseed meal is used as animal feed. Good cottonseed oil should be 100% oil, slightly amber in color and of good clarity and odor. A high fatty acid content indicates an oil of low quality. Dark color indicates low quality and poor refining methods. Cottonseed oil is used frequently for hydrogenating. The smoking temperature of cottonseed oil is high.

Coconut oil. The coconut palm produces the coconut from which oil is extracted from the dried meat known as copra. Fresh coconut meat contains 30 to 40% oil and 50% moisture. Dried copra usually contains less than 8% moisture and 60 to 65% oil. If the moisture content of copra is held below 8%, it will not mold, and the oil will not deteriorate.

The oil of the coconut was extensively used in tropical countries where palms grow. After crushing the copra, the natives boiled it in water and skimmed the oil as it floated to the top. This was a superior oil called *cochin* oil. Today the name "cochin" refers to the best of coconut oils. Cold pressing of copra produces the best oil. After the oil is extracted the remaining copra is ground into meal and used as animal feed. After refining, coconut oil is practically odorless and tasteless. Its use as an edible oil, especially for margarine, was once much more extensive than it is today. However, it still has wide commercial uses in industry.

Corn oil. Corn oil comes from Indian corn or maize, which contains between 3 and 6½% oil. Corn oil is a by-product from the manufacture of glucose and starch or from the manufacture of corn meal, corn-flour or hominy. Most of the corn oil manufactured in this country is used for salad and cooking oils. It has a high smoking temperature. It is frequently hydrogenated to make plastic fats for cooking and baking. Refined corn oil has a light amber color. When quite fresh it has a distinctive corn-meal flavor.

Corn oil should stand after manufacture to allow heavy fats to settle and drain off. If this is not done, the corn oil will solidify when cold in salad dressings. This process is called *winterizing*. Winterized oil may also be obtained by centrifuging the oil to throw out the heavy particles. Unwinterized oils may be cloudy at room temperature.

Peanut oil. From 38 to 50% of the peanut may be oil. The variety of peanut and the conditions of growth, in addition to the processing method, are important for flavor and quality of the oil. Peanut oil is expressed either by hydraulic or expeller process. After refining, the oil has a nutty, pleasing flavor and should be amber in color, like corn oil. Some peanut oils of good quality may be slightly darker than cottonseed or corn oils. Color will depend upon the peanuts from which extracted.

Soybean oil. The oil from soy is used in greater quantity for margarine manufacture than any other oil or fat. The oil content of the seed varies from 11 to 25%, but plants cultivated for oil production usually produce seeds containing 16 to 19% oil. The condition of the soil, seasonal and climatic conditions, and processing have a definite effect on the quantity and quality of oil obtained. After crushing, the seeds are cooked and the oil expressed from them. Soybean meal has a high protein content and makes good animal feed. While soybeans will produce hogs with soft fat, the meal will not.

Unless soybean oil is carefully refined and deodorized, a characteristic fishy or bean flavor develops from reversion. Stabilizers now may be added to retard this reaction. More careful refining methods have also decreased the tendency of this oil to revert. The oil is a yellowish color after refining.

Cacao butter. Cacao butter is made from the oil of the cacao bean. It is used mostly in the manufacture of confections or for pharmaceutical preparations. Cacao butter is discussed further under cocoa.

Miscellaneous vegetable oils. Oils may also be made from sesame seed, poppy seed, rape seed, sunflower seed and mustard seed. These are not used in any large quantity in food preparation, however. Unless sold for special dietary purposes, foods may not contain mineral oil. The Food and Drug Administration has interpreted the use of mineral oil as adulteration of vegetable or animal oils unless for medical purposes.

Animal Fats

Lard. The federal definition for lard is "fat rendered from fresh, clean, sound, fatty tissues of hogs in good health at the time of slaughter." Pure leaf lard comes from leaf fat, the fat surrounding the kidney and abdominal walls. It is the highest quality lard. Lard may not be processed from bones, heads, ears and other low-cost meats and tissues. If pork fat comes from other sources than fatty tissues, it must be labeled "rendered pork *fat*" not lard.

The best process for lard extraction is moisture rendering. This is usually done in large steam kettles. The product is called "kettle-rendered" lard. There are three ways to obtain this type lard: (1) by drip rendering, (2) by dry rendering and (3) by neutral-lard rendering. Drip rendering is a method of introducing steam around the fat and allowing it to drip down and run free as it separates from the fatty tissues. In this manner the lard is subjected to a minimum of heat. Dry rendering is the drawing off of fat as it accumulates in a steam kettle, the kettle heated by steam in its outside chamber. Open kettles are used for neutral rendering, but the kettles are heated by hot water, not by steam. The temperatures are kept lower than when steam is used. Neutral lard is used for oleomargarine and for medicinal purposes.

Other types of lard on the market are "prime steam," which means a lard rendered in a closed tank using direct steam. This lard lacks the quality of the kettle-rendered lards because the fat is subjected to heat for a longer period of time. Natural lard is obtained from slowly heated back fat and leaf lard. It is very white in color and lacks a definite flavor.

Lard may be hydrogenated to improve its quality and raise its melting point. The shortening power of lard and its plasticity make it good for pie crusts. It has a lower smoking temperature than vegetable oils and is seldom used for frying purposes.

Lard may be graded according to the color, texture and flavor of the product. The color of the lard can be best observed when melted. It should not be turbid and should have a light, golden color. Smell and taste the lard when it is melted.

Lard when chilled should be snow white. The solidified lard should be firm and moderately resistant to pressure of the finger. It should have no graininess. Lard may have strong flavors resulting from too high a temperature in rendering or too long a rendering period. Rancidity easily develops in lard unless anti-oxidants are added. A good quality lard should contain not more than $\frac{1}{2}\%$ free fatty acids.

Beef suet. Most beef fats sold on the market are for use by industrial users rather than food services. The trade name for beef fat or suet is *oleo* or *oleo stearin*. Stearin is a long-chain fatty acid, and much beef suet is composed of fats made from this long-chain compound. Suet may be used in food services for deep-fat frying and general cooking, although it has serious limitations, such as a lack in plasticity and high free fatty acid content unless refined. It may, however, be plasticized, emulsified and made into a usable fat.

Fats that come from the abdominal cavities of cattle are of the highest quality. Trimmed fats from carcasses are next in quality. Lowest in quality are those called "shop fats," which are fats accumulated in meat cutting. The rendering of suet is much like that used for lard. Although at one time a considerable quantity of suet fats were used in the manufacture of oleomargarine, this use has dropped off. Oleo is sought by the baking and cracker industries.

Beverages

COFFEE

Coffee Selection

Coffee is the berry of an evergreen shrub grown in a tropical or semi-tropical climate. The most common variety of coffee grown is the Arabica, which originated in Mocha on the Red Sea but was found adaptable to many climates. Most coffee plantations in Brazil, Colombia, Venezuela, Mexico and Central America have Arabica bushes. In other areas of the world the Robusta, Liberacia and Stenophylla varieties are grown. Some species within varieties may be so common as to be considered almost a variety in themselves, such as the widely grown Arabica called Maragopipe.

Climate and soil are more important, however, than variety of plant in deciding coffee quality. The coffee quality of one variety of plant will change materially, depending upon conditions of temperature, rainfall, soil and especially altitude. Plateaus or mountain areas 2,000 feet or higher above sea level produce the best coffee. Bushes grown at or near sea level produce a large, soft and flabby bean which has a grassy, pungent, undesirable cup flavor. The bushes must also have shade and for this reason are usually found growing under taller trees. Coffee quality will also be affected by weather during harvest season. In a wet harvest the beans overmature and this causes them to become too soft and to lack cup quality. Too hot or dry weather during the growing season causes the coffee cherries or fruit to dry on the bushes, and the resultant seeds or beans are hard, flinty and gnarled. Some may be immature, shriveled and blighted. Misshapen beans are an indication of lack of quality and the flavor of the coffee becomes harsh,

FIG. 7–1. Planting coffee beans for new growths. Much care must be taken in culti-
vating and transplanting the young plants. In 5 to 6 years they bear fruit. Courtesy
the Coffee Brewing Institute.

lacking the desirable mellow, delicate flavor of top quality coffee.
Coffee grown at low altitudes is called "rio" or "river" coffee, and
the term "rio" is used to indicate a cup of coffee harsh in flavor and
lacking in other good, essential quality factors.

    After picking, the cherries are brought to the plantation headquarters
where the pulp is removed either by an enzymatic (washed) or fermentation (unwashed) method. Washed coffee is usually considered higher
in quality, and buyers may find that an unwashed coffee may have a
darker colored bean with a somewhat sour cup flavor. After the pulp is
removed, the beans are dried and hulled. The green bean is now ready
for market. It is hard, semi-translucent and bluish-green to tan in color.

FIG. 7–2.   Good shade must be provided the coffee bush.   In Arabia the fogs off the Red
Sea act as a shade much of the day.   Here tall trees provide it.   Courtesy the Coffee
Brewing Institute.

FIG. 7–3.   The coffee flower and
the green cherries.   Courtesy the
Coffee Brewing Institute.

FIG. 7-4. Mature green cherries. The dark ones in the center are red in ripeness. Courtesy the Coffee Brewing Institute.

FIG. 7-5. Picking the ripe red cherries. Courtesy the Coffee Brewing Institute.

FIG. 7–6. **Removing pulp residue and washing.** **Courtesy the Coffee Brewing Institute.**

The shape may vary from a small round bean to an extra-long, elongated flat bean.

Green beans from different growing areas are blended to give desirable cup quality. A coffee from one area may be mild, with good flavor, but lack acidity, astringency and body. Other coffees may be blended with this to give the missing qualities. Coffee tasters, expert in judging coffee, develop the blend. Since the flavor of a coffee will differ each season, blends must be established each year.

Buyers are frequently confused by the many terms used to describe coffees. Bourbon coffee has long been known for its high quality. It is an Arabica grown at high altitude in Brazil. Coffees may be classified according to the area in which they are grown, such as Mocha (Moca), Java and Medellin (Colombia). Coffee flavor plus area of growth may be another means of classification, such as Brazils, good coffee grown only in Brazil, and Milds, good coffee grown outside of Brazil, or rio, poor coffee grown anywhere. It is usually necessary, in order to obtain a cup of coffee suited to our tastes, to blend Brazils with Milds. Coffee may be named after a seaport from which shipped, for example, Santos from Brazil. Santos make up about 60% of the total world coffee crop. Bourbon Santos are acid and mild in flavor and are used extensively in the best urn blends. "Old Crop" Santos are mildest in flavor and acidity. Not all Brazilian coffees called Santos are good coffees. The

Victoria, an Arabica of Brazil, has a poor reputation. A coffee termed "soft" is said to possess a fine flavor readily extracted from the bean when the coffee is made. In the trade, the term "soft" is the opposite of harsh or rio. If the term "strictly soft, fine cup" is used in a specification, a top quality coffee is indicated.

Mexico produces three main types of coffee: the Coatepecs, the Oxacas and the Rios. The Coatepecs are usually excellent in flavor and have a relatively heavy body. Coatepecs stand up well in urn blends and may be 20% of the total blend in many good coffees. Oxacas lack the quality of the Coatepecs, but they have good flavor and life and are used largely in blending. The Rio coffees of Mexico are what their name implies, a harsh and pungent coffee, but these may be used in blends in small quantities to give astringency and acid.

Salvador, Guatemala and Costa Rica produce coffees which are sharply acid but have fine body. They are sought for blends. They cannot take a heavy roast, however, since they become bitter with it. The superb, mild Alta Verapaz Coban, an Arabica coffee grown in Guatemala, is one of the finest coffees.

Venezuela is noted for its Marcaibo coffees which are mild, rich and flavorful but unsuited to urn blends since they do not hold up well after brewing. Most Colombia coffees are called Excelsos, of which some of the best are Medellin, Armenia, Seville, Manizales and Giradot, all excellent in flavor and sought for blending. Colombian coffees may be also referred to as Bogatas.

Jamaica produces the high quality Blue Mountain coffee, which is shipped largely to England. Porto Rico produces a coffee prized for its flavor by the Spanish, who take almost the entire crop each year.

Java produces a coffee of that name which is rich, mild, mellow and flavorful, resembling the Brazilian Santos in that respect. Coffee was first grown in the high plateaus overlooking the Red Sea in Arabia. Here the famed Mochas, bathed by heavy morning fogs rising off the Red Sea and the bright sunshine of the afternoon on the high plateaus, obtain favorable growing conditions for their growth. Mochas have good vitality and holding quality in urn blends. Sumatra produces the sweet delicate Ankola and Mandhelling coffees, known over the world for their fine quality.

Africa produces a coffee grown from the Robusta bush. The coffee is usually strong and harsh or almost neutral in flavor, and buyers should avoid it in specifying blends. Much cheap coffee in this country has a high amount of this coffee. Liberica varieties of bushes are found in plantations grown in or around Liberia. This coffee is also harsh in flavor; sometimes it may have a flavor associated with scorched leather, but the Asia Minor coffee drinkers favor this coffee in their heavy blends.

If a coffee buyer in this country wanted to obtain a good blend of coffee, he might state: "Roasted coffee shall be produced from green coffee of the following description and blend:

20% Santos, grading 3's or 4's,[1] Bourbon, medium to good bean shape, strictly soft, solid bean, good greenish color and good cup quality.

40% Colombian of usual good cup, quality; may be Excelsos of the following growths: Medellin, Armenia, Sevilla, Manizales, Giradot.

40% high grown washed Central American coffee from Salvador, Costa Rica, Guatemala or Genuine Coatepecs of Mexico." The buyer should add the type of grind and type of roast desired to complete the specification.

Coffee shipped to this country must meet certain standards which have been established by the New York Coffee and Sugar Exchange. The Food and Drug Administration prohibits the sale of coffees under trade names which do not belong to them and will not allow the importation of coffee below No. 8 grade or artificially colored (sweated) coffee. These coffee grades as established by this exchange have little to do with coffee quality other than to indicate such extraneous matter as sticks and stones. The grades of coffee established by the exchange are shown below.

Range of Defects Allowed in Grade	Grade
1–9	No. 1
10–21	No. 2
22–45	No. 3
46–90	No. 4
91–170	No. 5
171–348	No. 6
349–450	No. 7

Good coffee should be judged on its appearance, quality and character. *Appearance* has to do with the size, shape, color, uniformity of size and defects of the beans. Extraneous matter, defects such as shriveled beans, broken beans, lack of plumpness and unevenness of size and roast, should be noted. The beans should be brittle and crisp. *Quality* indicates the taste and odor as determined by cup testing. Good cup quality may be described by a taster as "desirable" or "undesirable." Criteria for this factor are richness, excellence, fineness, smoothness, mellowness, goodness, heaviness in body or good body. Undesirable qualities may be described as winy, bitter, fermented, medicated and poorly processed or

[1]This is a New York Coffee and Sugar Exchange grade. See material that follows.

FIG. 7–7. **Careful sorting of the split green beans improves grade.** **Courtesy the Coffee Brewing Institute.**

poorly handled. Age deterioration gives a "woody" flavor. Coffee may absorb flavors and should not be stored with oils, paints, chemicals, hides, leather or other items from which it can get off-flavors. *Character* is described by taste. It may be described as acid, sweet, neutral or bitter. Acid is desirable in coffee, although too much acid is undesirable, and blending may be required to remove an excess. All coffee should be bitter or astringent but not objectionably so. The amount of sweetness desired will depend upon its combination with other flavors and on its aroma. Ankola and Mandheling coffees from Sumatra are prized coffees, heavy with sweetness, but Brazil Rios, with as much sweetness, are high undesirable. They would be improved if the flavor were not so sweet. A neutral coffee is neither acid nor bitter nor sweet to any noticeable degree. A coffee described as "thin" is neutral and lacks quality.

Roasting

Green coffee has little or no flavor. Roasting is necessary to develop flavor. The bean also changes color from a tan or greenish cast to chestnut or dark brown, depending upon the degree of roast. A light roast is a light brown or pale chestnut color; medium roast is coffee roasted until dark brown, while a heavy, dark or high roast is coffee roasted until the coffee is dark chocolate in color. Heavy roasts are preferred by many foreign groups. These roasts may be called "French" or "Italian." The coffee used for *café expresso* is a high roast.

The coffee bean swells about 50% also in roasting. The development of flavor is caused by the caramelization of carbohydrates and the formation of volatile esters, furfuryl derivates and several other aromatic substances. Coffee contains from 0.75% to 2% caffein, which is a mild stimulant in these proportions. In roasting, the cell walls of the bean are ruptured, which makes the flavoring and coloring substances in the coffee readily available to extraction in water of about 212° F. Roasting temperatures range from 385 to 500° F. There is about a 15% loss in weight because of moisture loss.

The roasted coffee may be water or "dry" finished. Finishing by water should not be allowed using over one gallon of water to 100 lb of coffee. "Dry finish" means no water is used. Finishing is done just as the coffee reaches the proper color in roasting. Water is added to the very hot beans. Steam is developed, which produces a more uniformly colored and better appearing bean. Coffee sold in the bean is sometimes glazed with eggs, starch, gelatin, sugar or other compounds to improve appearance, to protect flavors from oxidation and to assist in clarification according to some roasters, but it is doubtful if it has any other effect except to add 5 to 10% in weight and to improve the appearance. Buyers are advised to specify coffee without glaze.

Coffee may be adulterated with parched wheat, peas, beans or chicory. Chicory is desired by some for the added color and the bitter flavor it gives the brew. If used, the label on the container must state the fact. If gound coffee contains chicory, it will stick together when pressed firmly in the hand and will quickly color a clear glass of water brownish red. It will also quickly sink to the bottom of the glass, while real coffee colors the liquid slowly and sinks only after some time. A further test is to add a few drops of iodine to the stained water. If it turns blue, starch is present. Starch is a compound found in chicory but not in pure coffee. Artificially colored coffee beans can be detected by cutting through the bean with a sharp knife and noting the localization of color on the surface of the bean.

Coffee Freshness

The flavor and aroma developed in freshly roasted coffee can be rapidly lost because of the high volatility of the flavor esters, even at room temperatures. Ground coffee loses its freshness much more rapidly than bean coffee. For this reason many food facilities grind their own coffee from the bean as required. Buyers are also better able to inspect and recognize the quality of the coffee when it is in the bean rather than when it is ground and has lost its identity. Ground coffee held at room temperature loses 20% of its freshness in 24 hours. At the end of 20 days it will have lost 50% of its flavor.

Coffee not only loses freshness rapidly, but also develops staleness rapidly. The volatile oils or flavors are easily oxidized. This oxidation gives a stale, rancid, soapy flavor that is undesirable. The development of staleness in conjunction with the flavor loss may, in 8 days at room temperature, give a cup quality labeled *poor* by expert tasters and only *fair* at the end of 5 days. Chilling coffee, or, better yet, freezing coffee, retards the loss of flavor of the volatile oils and the development of staleness. Coffee oils left in coffee equipment will rapidly develop rancidity and cause fresh brews to develop off-flavors.

To preserve coffee flavors, coffee manufacturers pack coffee in vacuum so that oxygen in the air is not present to develop staleness. Coffee

FIG. 7–8. An expert coffee taster samples blends. The coffee is not swallowed. Only the taste and aroma are sampled. The coffee is then spit out. Courtesy the Coffee Brewing Institute.

packed in vacuum will soon fill the vacuum with carbon dioxide, which it gives off after roasting. This increased pressure within the can will decrease volatile flavor ester loss. Coffee packed in vacuum will, therefore, retain freshness for a long time. Vacuum pack coffee will express carbon dioxide when opened and sometimes cans will swell or bulge from the pressures developed by the freeing of this gas when the can is opened. Coffee cannot be packed in too large cans under vacuum because of the pressures developed.

Grinding

Coffee usually is ground into three degrees of fineness. Steel cut is a coarse grind passing through a 6/64″ screen. Medium grind will find 50% passing through a screen having 16 meshes to the inch. Fine grind will all pass through a screen having 24 meshes to the inch. Quite frequently urn coffee will be specified as coarse or medium grind. Fine grinds are used for silex or rapid extraction methods where the water is in contact with the coffee for only a short time and only once in extraction. Boiled coffee should be made from a steel cut or coarse grind. Turkish coffee and Coffee Expresso may be made from grinds which are powdery. Ground coffee should have a distinctly pleasant aroma and should show little chaff or extraneous matter.

Quantities to Use

One pound of coffee will make from 2 to 2½ gallons of coffee or approximately 40 to 50 6-oz cups. Since the cost differential between good and poor coffee is only a few cents a pound, the cost per cup will not be in comparison with the higher quality obtained. Procedures for making coffee as recommended by the Coffee Brewing Institute should be followed.

Coffee Products

Pure soluble coffee is the dry, powdered, water-soluble solids extracted from coffee brews percolated under vacuum. Some carbohydrates may be added. These products have the flavor of freshly brewed coffee but lack aroma. Some soluble coffee products have added aromatic agents and with continued research it is expected that they may have as much aroma as regular coffee. The use of this product is increasing. The best soluble coffees are made from Santos coffee.

Some coffee sirups are used. These are concentrated coffee flavors containing liquid and high amounts of sugar. Decaffeinated coffee will

FIG. 7–9.   The young tea bushes in the nursery are being tended before transplanting to the main garden.   Courtesy the Tea Council of U.S.A.

FIG. 7–10.   Two leaves and a bud, the standard pluck.   Courtesy the Tea Council of U.S.A.

have from 85% to 87% of the caffein extracted by processing the green beans under steam in vacuum. This does not materially alter flavor.

Cereal beverages are wheat, molasses and wheat or bran given a dark roast; the solids are extracted by moisture, dried and ground.

TEA

Tea comes from a tropical evergreen bush or tree. When growing wild it will grow 15 to 30 ft high, but under cultivation it is pruned back to around 2 ft. This makes it easy to pick top leaves. The plant matures in about 8 years. An acre of tea will produce up to 1000 lb of finished tea per year, depending upon the soil and elevation. Plucking occurs every 7 to 10 days; in some countries plucking continues throughout the year, in others it is limited to an 8 to 9 month season. The terminal bud and the next two leaves are the standard pluck. The best quality comes from the terminal bud and perhaps the first leaf. A pluck

FIG. 7–11.   The first stage of manufacture is known as withering.   The leaves are spread evening and thinly on specially prepared racks and allowed to remain there until they turn into a flaccid condition.   Courtesy the Tea Council of U.S.A.

FIG. 7–12. The rolling machines process the withered green leaves, which are twisted or rolled. This breaks open the cells, which contain the stimulating flavored juice of the tea. Courtesy the Tea Council of U.S.A.

of three or four leaves with the terminal bud gives a larger leaf and poorer flavor. Delicacy of flavor and body start with the terminal bud. Pungency and heavier flavor come with leaf progression. Tea, like coffee, must be grown at high elevations to be of fine quality. Normally, sea level to 7000 feet elevation are used, but the finest tea grows at or about 6000 feet.

After plucking, most tea is withered, rolled and fired. Oolong tea is semi-fermented. Green tea is unfermented. Black tea is fully fermented between its rolling and firing. Fermentation causes the tea to oxidize, develop flavor and turn a coppery color. Withering makes the leaves flaccid and removes some of the moisture so that they can be rolled without too much breaking. The rolling is done by machine. Rolling ruptures the tiny cell walls releasing flavor and enzymes so that their fermentation process can take place. Fermenting occurs on glass or

FIG. 7–13.   After withering and rolling, the leaves are spread out in a cool, humid place to absorb oxygen from the air, a process known as fermentation.   Courtesy the Tea Council of U.S.A.

cement tables and takes from $1\frac{1}{2}$ to 4 hours.   The firing stops the oxidizing process.   It is now done in a machine into which the tea is fed onto moving trays at a temperature of 210 to 235° F.   This is called pan-firing.   When this process is complete, all but about 5% of the moisture is removed.   The essential oils are dried into the leaves, ready to be released when boiling water is poured over them.   Basket-fired tea

FIG. 7–14.   The process of firing heats the fermented and damp leaves to a high temperature imparting the familiar black appearance of tea to the fermented leaves.   Courtesy the Tea Council of U.S.A.

FIG. 7–15. The finished tea leaves are sorted according to their sizes and quality. Courtesy the Tea Council of U.S.A.

is tea that is dried or fired in baskets. Native women hold the tea in baskets over fire and carefully lift and turn the tea until it is dried. It is high in price and only a small amount comes onto the market.

The main tea producing regions are India, Pakistan, Ceylon, Indonesia and Africa. Over 90% of our tea comes from India, Ceylon, Indonesia and Africa. China at one time supplied a bulk of the world's tea, but Chinese teas are of little importance today on world markets. Some teas are imported from Japan and Formosa, but the quantity on the world market compared with that from other areas is small. Transcaucasia in the Union of Soviet Socialist Republics (U.S.S.R.) produces some tea.

Grades

The grade of a tea indicates the size of the leaf. The quality depends on (1) locality and elevations where grown, (2) soil, especially mineral content, (3) climate and (4) processing. Black teas, to which we are accustomed, may be graded for size as shown in Table 7–1.

Tea leaves may be deliberately broken or cut to give proper size. The use of tea in bags has hidden the tea so that leaf size is no longer as important, and, since the modern trend is towards rapid extraction, the broken grades have become more popular. Most tea stems are removed in processing, but some are still found in tea, which may reduce the quality if too prevalent.

The term orange pekoe, or pekoe, or any other term for size does not mean that the tea will necessarily have quality. It only states that the tea is of a certain size. While size does have something to do with quality, all gardens, both low and high grown, can produce all leaf sizes.

To maintain a uniform blend, teas from various countries must be mixed together. It is seldom that one garden can maintain the necessary flavor, strength and color at all times, and good blending is required.

Table 7–1
Black Tea Grades

Trade Size Term	Trade Abbreviation for Grade	Description of Grade
Leaf grades*		
Orange Pekoe	O.P.	Thin long wiry leaves that sometimes contain tip leaf. Tea liquor is light or pale.
Pekoe	P.E.K.	The leaves are shorter and not so wiry and the liquors have more color.
Souchong	SOU.	A bold and open leaf; makes a pale liquor.
Broken-leaf grades†		
Broken Orange Pekoe	B.O.P.	Best grade generally; much smaller than leaf grades; contains tip; tea liquor has good color and strength.
Broken Pekoe	B.P.	Slightly larger than B.O.P. with less color. Used as a filler in blends.
Broken Pekoe Souchong	B.P.S.	A little larger and bolder than B.P. giving a lighter color; also used as a filler in blends.
Fannings	E.N.G.S.	One of the top grades today because of tea bag use; smaller than B.O.P.; gives a good flavored brew with good color; more quickly made because of finer size
Dust	D.	Smallest grade; useful for quick brewing of a good strong cup of tea; used in blends with larger sizes.

*About 10% of the crop.
†About 90% of the crop.

Blending, like coffee, is a job for an expert who must know how to blend to obtain the desired body, strength and flavor. A blend may easily consist of four or five Indian teas, a similar number of Ceylons or other growths. Frequently, to produce a desired flavor, a single tea bag may contain as many as ten to thirty teas from different gardens.

As stated previously, quality will vary with each tea, depending on the area where grown, the soil, elevation, climate, and processing. In low elevations where hot, moist conditions exist, growth is lush and the tea is lacking in flavor but has useful color and body. Even at high elevations, if the season is exceptionally wet, the teas are thin and uninteresting. They are called "weathery." A general description of teas grown in some of the various districts follows:

India

ASSAM—Extremely useful for all purposes; having good appearance, strong, pungent flavor, with good color; ideal for blends. Early teas from this area may have a fine, golden-tippy appearance and bring high prices.

DARJEELING—The high elevation of this area is conducive to good tea with fine quality and a distinctive, delicate flavor. Sometimes these teas are called "blackcurrant" or "muscatel" because of their fruity, distinctive flavor. They are used in special blends to give distinctive flavor.

DOOARS—Good blending teas, with smooth, mellow, full-bodied liquor and good color. Used as a binder of flavors in blends. Teas produced in this area and in the other two areas above in India attain a distinct flavor and strength, which is called "autumnal," for they are produced in the fall of the year.

CACHAR—Not as good quality as from the above districts. Useful as a filler, but plain and thin in flavor.

SOUTHERN INDIA—Much tea is produced at all elevations up to 6000 feet, with the high elevation of Travancore and Nilgiri Hills in this region producing the best teas. Other teas from this district are used for blends because of their ability to give a moderate flavor, bright colored liquor, but are not as pungent as North India tea. They have a Ceylon character and are used in place of this growth at times.

Pakistan

Sylhet is the main producing region, giving teas very similar to Cachar teas.

Ceylon

Up country are the high elevations and the teas from here are bright, aromatic in flavor and sought for blending. Distinct flavor is indicated by the area of production, such as Nuwara Eliya, Dimbula and Uva. Seasonal variations also will vary the character of the tea from these areas. Mid-country teas have full, rich liquor and an aromatic flavor that makes them suitable for blending. Low-country tea has a black leaf and gives a highly colored liquor. It lacks distinctive flavor and is used as a filler in blends.

Indonesia

Teas from this area come from Java and Sumatra, but there are fewer distinct production areas, as found in India and Ceylon. Because of the more consistent seasonal conditions, the quality of teas produced here will be found to vary less. The teas have good appearance, giving a good color brew and flavor. They are used largely for blending. The teas from the high elevations of Pengelengen have distinctive flavor, such as that found in southern India or Ceylon teas from corresponding elevations.

African

Nyasaland, Kenya, Uganda, Tanganyika, Mozambique and the Belgian Congo are fast developing their tea-growing regions and quantities of teas of very useful quality are increasing. In 1959, this continent produced more tea than Indonesia.

Green Tea

Green tea is produced in Japan and Formosa, but only Japan manu-factures pan-fired and basket-fired green teas. These grades have a bold, flat leaf, with a delicate, greenish character and pale liquors. They make a delicate brew. Only about 1½ million pounds, or 1% of the total, are imported annually. Both Japan and Formosa have copied some of the China grades and produce small quantities of the following: (1) Gunpowder, delicate in flavor with small round leaf, (2) Young Hyson, a more open leaf with similar quality to gunpowder, (3) Hyson, a bolder tea not seen on this market in any quantity and (4) Imperial, large bolder leaves, stems may be apparent; flavor is not so delicate. Less than 5% of the world's tea is manufactured into green tea.

FIG. 7–16. Each year the seven-man board of tea experts meets to establish tea stand-ards for the year. High standards are maintained even though growing and processing conditions vary, for the standard can be adjusted each year by changing blends. Courtesy the Tea Council of U.S.A.

FIG. 7–17. A government inspector takes a sample to see that it meets the standard established by the tea board. Courtesy the Tea Council of U.S.A.

The Tea Act

A number of years ago the Tea Act was passed in this country to regulate the import of teas. This act established standards of purity and quality. Government tea inspectors are appointed through this act to taste samplings of teas. Each year six men are chosen from the trade and one from the government to meet and establish standards for that year. The date of the meeting is usually the first five days in February and the standards established go into effect on May 1st. Teas that do not meet the established standards may not be imported. Appeals against the decisions of the tea examiners may be taken to a board of appeals consisting of three members who call in tea trade experts who may review the tea examiners' decision. Their finding is final.

COCOA

Cocoa comes from the theobroma cacao tree. It is indigenous to Central and South America, but plantations are now found on the west coast of Africa and in the West Indies. The fruit is a pod 4 to 7 in. in diameter. It has a hard, thick, leathery rind containing twenty-five to seventy-five seeds inside in five rows. The seeds are imbedded in a soft white or pinkish pulp.

The trees may grow 30 to 40 ft in height, but for ease in harvesting and to permit a greater number of trees per acre, the trees are pruned to about 20 ft. From 150 to 200 lb of cleaned cacao beans are produced per acre. The quality of the bean depends on the variety, climate, soil and processing. Some varieties are mild; others are more aromatic. The beans will vary in the character of the chocolate, its pungency, acidity, mildness, bitterness and fragrance. Like coffee beans, cacao beans are frequently blended to give desirable flavor characteristics.

After picking, the cacao pods are cut open and fermented. The beans are then cut out and cleaned. Fermenting reduces bitterness. The beans are roasted, which develops flavor. After cracking into small pieces or nibs and removing chaff, the nibs are ground or milled into chocolate liquor. This liquor is then subjected to hydraulic pressure, which removes a part of the fat or cacao butter. Total fat content of the nib is 45 to 55%. The remaining pulp is then ground into a fine powder known as cocoa. The amount of fat or cacao butter left in the cocoa is a significant factor in deciding the quality of the cocoa. The highest quality cocoas may contain as much as 35% cacao butter.

Government standards of identity state that cocoa must contain 22% cacao butter before it can be called "breakfast cocoa." For baking or other purposes, cocoas of 10 to 12% cacao fat may be used. Buyers should watch for scorched or bitter flavor, a bright, good chocolaty color and fine texture in cocoas purchased. If the quantity of cocoa needed is sufficiently large, cocoas used for beverages and for bakery purposes should be differentiated on the basis of cacao butter. Breakfast cocoas should be mild and rich in flavor.

The color of cocoa will depend upon the degree of roast given the beans and on their processing treatment. To give a darker color, a finer flavor and to improve the solubility of the cocoa, cacao beans are treated with an alkali. This also breaks down some of the fiber or cellulose structure of the bean. Some claims of added digestibility are made for cocoa processed by this alkaline treatment. This process is called the "Dutch process" because it was first discovered by C. J. Van Houten, a Dutch cocoa manufacturer.

8 Miscellaneous Groceries

Food buyers sometimes forget that a significant amount of the food dollar may be spent on miscellaneous items. In food services approximately 52% of the food bill will be for meat, 17% for fruits and vegetables, 13% for dairy products, 5% for cereals, 4% for eggs, 4% for miscellaneous groceries, 3% for beverages and 2% for fats and oils.

Even if the costs were of little importance, many items purchased under the miscellaneous grocery classification would be of great importance because of their effect on food quality and flavor. The cost of a teaspoon of spice or flavoring may vary only a few cents for a high or lower quality product, but the flavor contribution of the higher quality may make a vast difference in eating quality. It takes only one poor product to ruin a number of good ones in a batch. Unfortunately, only a few reliable quality standards exist for miscellaneous grocery products. Buyers will have to compile much of their own purchase specifications for these foods.

PICKLED PRODUCTS

Pickling is a preservation process in which spoilage is retarded by salt, fermentation acids developed in the pickling process and temperature. Elevated temperatures during or after pickling, without other preservation media, may cause spoilage. Texture, appearance and flavor change during pickling. A retention of crispness or firmness is necessary to retain good eating quality.

Cool temperatures around 45°F and a salt brine of 2 to 10% are usually sufficient to develop favorable pickling action on a food and retard unfavorable ones. Sugar, alum, calcium chloride or other ingredients may be added to develop firmness of texture. Sugar, spices or aromatic compounds may be added for flavor. After pickling, heat sufficient to sterilize in sealed containers or higher acidity or salinity may be required to give proper shelf life to the product.

Olives, pickles and sauerkraut are the three main products preserved by pickling.

Olives

Fresh olives may be processed into ripe, green, Sicilian-style green or salt-cured, oil-coated olives. Green olives may also be called Queen or Spanish olives and salt-cured, oil-coated olives may be called Greek, Greek-style or oil-cured olives.

Ripe olives. The ripe olive process originated in this country. There are almost no imports. The variety of olive used to make this olive comes largely from the Mission olive tree which originated from seeds brought from Mexico into California by missionaries. The new olive was firm in texture, rich in oil and when allowed to ripen to a greater degree than that possible for processing green olives would yield still a firm, rich luscious olive. It is a small olive, seldom running over extra-large in size. For this reason, larger riper olives must be made from olive varieties usually used for green olives. These cannot be ripened as

Table 8–1
Characteristics of Leading California Olives*

Variety	Shape	Characteristics
Mission	Smallest variety; oval in shape.	Originated in California. Rich in oil; has mellow, firm flesh when ripe. Cures well.
Manzanillo	Round, cherry shaped; moderate size.	Spanish variety maturing earlier than the Mission and used where frosts endanger late-maturing olives.
Sevillano	Oblong shape, very large.	Spanish variety rivaling Manzanillo in production. Requires mild cure because of tendency to shrivel from salt osmosis. Cures into a desirable Queen or Green olive.
Ascolano	Resembles Sevillano in size and shape.	Italian olive; also tends to shrivel in processing. Highly popular for Queen or Green olives.
Barouni		Coarse, woody and difficult to cure; it is frequently used for Sicilian green olives.

*Ranked in order of greatest to least quantity produced in this country.

Table 8–2
Standard Sizes of Ripe Olives

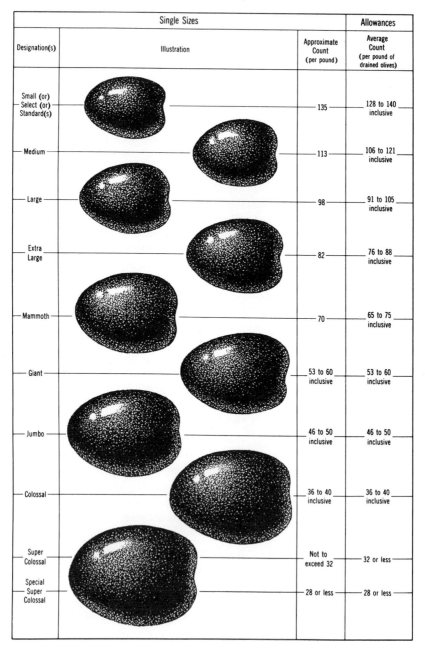

Single Sizes			Allowances
Designation(s)	Illustration	Approximate Count (per pound)	Average Count (per pound of drained olives)
Small (or) Select (or) Standard(s)		135	128 to 140 inclusive
Medium		113	106 to 121 inclusive
Large		98	91 to 105 inclusive
Extra Large		82	76 to 88 inclusive
Mammoth		70	65 to 75 inclusive
Giant		53 to 60 inclusive	53 to 60 inclusive
Jumbo		46 to 50 inclusive	46 to 50 inclusive
Colossal		36 to 40 inclusive	36 to 40 inclusive
Super Colossal		Not to exceed 32	32 or less
Special Super Colossal		28 or less	28 or less

much as the Mission and for this reason the quality of larger olives is usually not as good as that of the smaller olives which come from the Mission olive. Ripe olives from Mission olives will be almost black in color, while the others will be brownish-black.

There are two types of ripe olives, the black and the green-ripe. Only the Mission can be processed into the green-ripe. The reason is that the olive must be allowed to ripen to a good blush of pink. The degree of ripeness is important to the olive quality. Sufficient sugar must be allowed to develop in olives to encourage fermentation; ripeness must not be allowed to progress to the extent that a poor texture results. Green olives are allowed to ripen only to the soft green stage, black to the yellowish green stage and green-ripe to the pink stage. All olives then continue to ripen into the cherry red and black stages, a ripeness too great for good processed olives. The color of the processed green-ripe olive may vary from a yellowish-green to a light brown. A mottled surface may be evident. It is softer than the dark ripe Mission because of its greater ripeness. A green-ripe olive retains its greenness of color because in pickling it is not allowed to come in contact with air. Green olives are green because of the same processing technique. Black olives become dark because they are exposed to the air for 2 to 3 days after the pickling process. Both black and green ripe olives are packed in enamel-lined cans, covered with salt brine and heat-treated to preserve them.

Green (Queen or Spanish) olives. Sevillano, Manzanillo, Ascolana and Mission olives are preferred in that order for making green olives.

Table 8–3
Trade Designations of Blended Sizes in Ripe Olives

Blended Sizes		Average Count (per pound of drained olives)
Designation	Composition of Blend	
Family	Medium, Large, and Extra Large and no more than 15 percent, by count, of Standard(s).	91 to 105 inclusive
King	Giant, Jumbo, and the smaller half of Colossal and no more than 15 percent, by count, of Mammoth.	45 to 53 inclusive
Royal	Large half of Colossal; and Super Colossal or Special Super Colossal.	Not to exceed 34
Other blends	Two or three adjacent sizes, as in Table I, and no more than 15 percent, by count, of smaller size(s).	Not applicable

Table 8-4
U.S. Trade Sizes for Green Olives

Size No.	Trade Term	Federal Count per Pound	Spanish Equivalent per Kilo	Approximate Size of Olive
00	Peewee	181/220		
0	Midget	141/180		
1	Small	128/140	280/300	
2	Medium	106/127	240/200	
3	Large	91/105	200/220	
4	Extra Large	76/90	170/190	
5	Mammoth	65/75	150/160	
6	Giant	53/64	120/130	
7	Jumbo	42/52	100/110	
8	Colossal	33/41	80/90	
9	Super Colossal	32 or under	70/80	

Barouni olives may be used, but the texture of this olive is poor and its use is limited. Large quantities of green olives are imported into this country. Spain and Italy are the largest suppliers in that order. Green olives are firmer in texture and more bitter in flavor than the ripe olive. Immediately after harvest both green and ripe olives are soaked in lye. This removes a bitter glucoside. Green olives are soaked a shorter time than ripe olives and are, therefore, slightly more bitter than ripe olives. The lye is removed by washing. Fermentation then follows. As noted, after fermentation black olives are exposed to the air but green or green-ripe olives are carefully held under liquid to prevent them from darkening. Because of the variety and because of the lesser ripeness green olives will be firmer in texture than ripe olives. After pickling is completed, the green olives are packed in glass because of the corrosive action of green olives on metal. Pattern or place packing, also called "stick packing," is more expensive than thrown or jumble packing and since institutions use these out of the jar there is little or no need to purchase the higher price item. After packaging, a salt brine is poured over the green olives to keep them moist and to preserve them. Government standards state that the acidity of green olives shall not be more than 4.00 pH and the salt content not less than 7%.

Sicilian green olives. If green or Queen olives are not lye soaked, they are called Sicilian-style green olives. They resemble the Queen olive in appearance but are bitter in flavor. They may be plain or spiced.

Salt-cured, oil-coated olives. The Greeks process an olive by giving it a moderate lye soak. After fermentation, it is preserved in dry salt. Oxidation in this process causes the olive to darken. Osmosis from the salt cure causes the olives to shrivel. They are dipped in oil and packed without brine. Their oil coating gives them a high sheen.

Quality. Uniformity of size and color, flavor, texture and defects decide the grade or quality of olives. Ripe olives showing light meat under the skin are graded higher than olives showing dark meat. Bitterness in olives indicates a failure to reduce glucosides completely or other processing failures. A soapy taste indicates failure to remove lye completely in washings after treating with lye. A musty or moldy flavor develops when olives are held too long in processing or, in the case of ripe olives, are held too long in storage before processing. Butyric or zapateria odor and taste indicate decomposition.

Pickles

Cucumbers are the most common item pickled, but green tomatoes, mangoes, onions, cauliflower, cabbage, corn, beans, green and ripe (red) peppers, carrots, watermelon rind, peaches, pears, walnuts, corn and other fruits and vegetables may be pickled. The pickling process may be a natural cure or with hot vinegar, sugar, salt and spices. In the latter process, the product is canned to further preserve it.

Special varieties of cucumbers are used for pickling purposes. The cucumber is picked immature and sent to salting stations for inspecting, washing and grading for size. The cucumbers are placed in a salt brine and allowed to proceed through fermentation until sufficient lactic acid is formed to stop the pickling action.

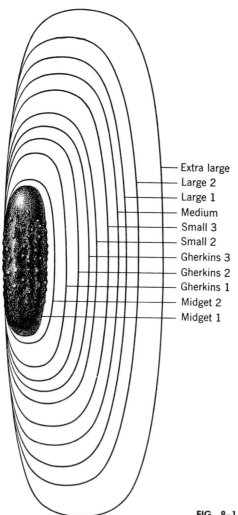

Extra large
Large 2
Large 1
Medium
Small 3
Small 2
Gherkins 3
Gherkins 2
Gherkins 1
Midget 2
Midget 1

FIG. 8–1.   Standard pickle sizes.

Pickles used for salt stocks are fermented in a high-salt brine containing 8 to 10% salt. Pickles to be cured naturally (also called "genuine" pickles) are fermented in a brine containing approximately 5% salt. Flavoring ingredients, such as dill, dill emulsion and vinegar, may be added to genuine pickles while processing is going on. Calcium chloride or alum may be used to obtain crispness. The color of the cucumber will change in pickling to a dark olive green. The white flesh will change to a light creamy white, which is slightly translucent. Tumeric is added by some processors to remove the dead white, outside areas and change them to a light, whitish yellow. The green areas and flavor are not affected to any degree by the tumeric. During fermentation, especially with the lower-salt brines, good temperature control must be maintained to avoid undesirable bacterial actions that soften the pickle. Mushy or soft pickles lack desirable texture qualities. "Floaters" are pickles that have developed hollow areas in pickling, either because of too rapid fermentation or undesirable bacterial action. Black, ropy or slimy pickles are usually the result of undesirable bacterial actions. These may be caused by too high a temperature during fermentation.

Naturally fermented or genuine pickles are processed in the low-salt (5%) brines. These are usually cured 4 weeks, with desired seasonings added at the start of processing. This cure will hold the pickles up to 6 months, providing the pickles are kept in a cool place. After natural pickling, the pickles may be placed in sealed containers under brine and pasteurized, but some of the quality is lost. Pickles that must be kept for extended periods are usually made from salt stocks.

Size		Approximate Count per Gallon	Recommended Maximum and Minimum Length (inches)
Word Designation	Number Designation		
Midgets	1	445–545	1½ and less.
Midgets	2	330–444	Over 1½ but not over 2.
Gherkins	1	225–329	Over 2 but not over 2¼.
Gherkins	2	135–224	Over 2¼ but not over 2½.
Gherkins	3	100–134	Over 2½ but not over 2¾.
Small	1	80–99	Over 2¾ but not over 3.
Small	2	66–79	Over 3 but not over 3¼.
Small	3	52–65	Over 3¼ but not over 3½.
Medium	–	40–51	Over 3½ but not over 4.
Large	1	26–39	Over 4 but not over 4¼.
Large	2	22–25	Over 4¼ but not over 4¾.
Extra large	–	16–21	Over 4¾ but not over 5¼.

FIG. 8–1. (continued)

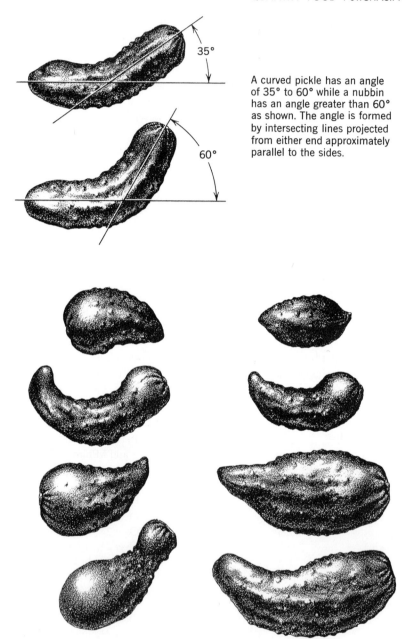

A curved pickle has an angle of 35° to 60° while a nubbin has an angle greater than 60° as shown. The angle is formed by intersecting lines projected from either end approximately parallel to the sides.

Nubbins or badly misshaped pickles   Slightly misshaped pickles

FIG. 8–2. Standards for curved, slightly misshapen and badly misshapen pickles.

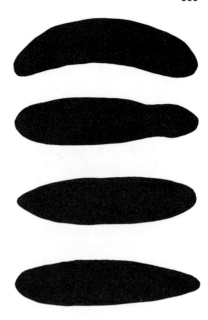

FIG. 8–3. Minimum shapes recommended for Grade A dills.

Salt-stock pickles are fermented in stronger brines. After fermenting, the pickles are washed and then barreled in strong salt brines and stored in cool warehouses. Each fall large quantities of cucumbers are moved into salt stocks and held for demand by pickle processors. Salt stocks are a regular commodity on the market. Pickle processors purchase these, soak them to extract the salt and make them into many types of pickles. Salt-stock pickles are available throughout the year, while naturally fermented products may not be available after April unless non-seasonal cucumbers or other items are used.

Many terms are used to describe specific types of processing in pickles. *Kosher* may indicate natural or processed dills which have garlic, onions and peppers (the two latter products being optional) added. Natural or genuine dills containing onions, garlic and red peppers may be called *Polish* or *Hungarian* dills. *Pasteurized* pickles are heat treated to preserve them. *Sweet* dills are dills just slightly less sweet than sweet pickles. *Iceberg* or *quartered* dills are dill pickles sliced in quarters. When dill pickles are cut into smaller sizes than quarters, they are called *dill sticks*. *Sour* pickles have added vinegar, while *sweet* pickles have added sweetening and vinegar. Spices may or may not be added. A *chow chow* may be either a sour or sweet-type pickle seasoned with prepared mustard. Sour-mixed, sweet-mixed, sour-chow chow or sweet-chow chow pickles must contain: cucumbers 60 to 80%, cauliflower 10 to 30% and onions (not over $1\frac{1}{4}$ in. in diameter) 5 to 12%. Red peppers or pimientos are optional. The cucumbers in these mixtures must be cut into pieces of $\frac{1}{2}$ to $\frac{3}{4}$ in. Sour or sweet *pickle relish* is a finely chopped mixture composed of: cucumber 60 to 100%, cauliflower (optional) 10 to 30%, onions (optional) 5 to 12%, green tomatoes (optional) not to exceed 10% when used in lieu of equal quantities of cauliflower, red peppers or pimientos (optional). The peppers used are the sweet type. If the term "hot" appears on the label, red pepper capsicums have been added. *Chutney* is a tart, sweet Indian relish. The real chutney is made from mangoes, green ginger, mustard seed, raisins, East Indian tamarind, chili peppers, black pepper, butter and various spices. *American chutney* is made from vinegar, green tomatoes, orange marmalade, raisins, lemon peel, dates, lime juice, onion, flour and spices. *Mixed* chutney may be American chutney or contain cut pickles, cauliflower and other vegetables in imitation of real chutney. *Bread and butter* or *country-style* pickles are thinly sliced cucumber pickles cured for a time in strong salt solution (or they may be made from salt stocks) and then packed in heavily spiced, sweet sirup containing celery seed. *Capers* are pickled buds from the caper shrub, which grows in southern Europe. The buds are shipped as dried products. Processors place them in a sweetened solution of 6 to 7% distilled vinegar. They are about the size of small peas.

Quality. Federal grading exists for some pickles. Top quality pickles should be uniform in shape, almost cylindrical, with well-rounded ends, smooth and uniform color, and few defects that are obvious or objectionable. Curved or misshapen pickles are considered defects. Sweet pickles will have color intensified and a firmer texture because of the effect of sugar on the cellulose of the pickle. The texture of pickles should be firm and crisp. They should break clean with a snap. They should not be soft, slippery or contain hollow, spongy centers. The interior flesh should be uniform in color and translucent. There should not be any white or opaque flesh or badly shriveled pickles outside tolerance allowances. As the quality drops, defects increase. Flavor characteristics for grades are well defined, and the amount of acidity, density of packing medium and salt are all a part of grade. Table 8–5 shows examples of the allowed acidity, salt and density of packing medium between a top quality (Grade A) and a reasonably good flavored pickle (Grade B). Pickles should be tasted for flavor.

Sizing

The smallest pickles bring the highest prices, but size is not a quality factor. Federal standards recognize size in grading only as a factor in

Table 8–5

Type Pickle	Acid,* Grams per 100 ml Grade		Packing Density Salometer Grade		Packing Medium (maximum) per Grams NaCl per 100 ml Grade	
	A	B	A	B	A	B
Dill†	0.6	0.5	10–12°	8–21°	3	3½
Sweet, Sweet Mixed, Sweet Relish	1.7–2.7	1.3–3.0	18°	15°	3	3½
Sour chow chow	1.7–2.7	1.3–3.0			3	3½
Sweet chow chow	1.7–2.7	1.3–3.0	over 15½°	over 12½°	3	3½

*Calculated as acetic acid for all pickles except natural dills, which are calculated as lactic.

†Natural or processed.

uniformity. Whole pickles may be divided into size groups as follows: 2¾ in. or less may have no length variation greater than ¾ in., 2¾ to 4 in. may have no greater variation in length than ¾ in., and over 4 in. may have no greater variation than 1½ in. Parts of pickles less than whole must also conform to certain size requirements. These are dis-

Table 8–6
Sizes and Counts per Gallon of Pickles

Size Term	Size Number	Approximate Count per Gallon	Length in Inches
Midgets	1 Midget	445/545	1½ or less
Midgets	2 Midget	330/444	1½ to 2
Gherkins	1 Gherkin	225/329	2 to 2¼
Gherkins	2 Gherkin	135/224	2 to 2½
Gherkins	3 Gherkin	100/134	2½ to 2¾
Small	1 Small	80/99	2¾ to 3
Small	2 Small	66/79	3 to 3¼
Small	3 Small	52/65	3¼ to 3½
Medium		40/51	3½ to 4
Large	1 Large	26/39	4 to 4¼
Large	2 Large	22/25	4¼ to 4¾
Extra Large		16/21	4¾ to 5¼

Note: A special type of gherkin, called the Burr Gherkin, is a West Indian fruit, not a true cucumber. It is used for small, sweet cucumber pickles. It is pale green and covered with prickly spines. Some of the smallest midgets and gherkins are made from this product.

cussed in grading factors for pickles on page 339. Table 8–6 gives federal recommended sizes and trade nomenclatures for pickles.

Packaging

For quantity use, pickles are usually packed in gallon glass jars, 4-gal to the case. No. 10 can or $3\frac{1}{4}$-qt packs are also common, packed six cans to the case.

Standards

Federal standards for quality have been developed for ripe and green olives and some pickles. The asterisks indicate quality usually recommended for institutional use.

Ripe Olives
Grades: A (90), B (80),* C (70).
Type: Ripe, green-ripe.
Styles: Whole, whole pitted, halved, sliced, chopped or minced, broken, pitted.
Recommended drained weight: No. 10—Mammoth size or smaller 66 oz; Giant or larger 64 oz, blends of large sizes 64 oz, blends of small sizes 66 oz, halves 50 oz, chopped or minced 100 oz, sliced 50 oz, broken pitted 55 oz.
*Color for ripe should be almost black or blackish brown. Color should be uniform or nearly so between olives. Normal color for green-ripe is yellow green, green yellow or other greenish casts and some mottling may be evident. Should be uniform in size. Whole olives should not vary in standard counts more than $\frac{3}{16}$ in. in diameter. Cutting on cut styles shall be even with little or no raggedness evident. Fairly free from defects such as blemishes, wrinkles, mutilated olives, pits or pit fragments, stems, injuries or damaged units. Free from harmless extraneous material. The flesh should be reasonably firm.

Green Olives
Grades: A (90), B (80),* C (70).
Styles: Unpitted, pitted without stuffing, pitted stuffed with pimiento, onion, almond, celery, other.
Packs: Thrown or jumble, place or stick packed.
Recommended drained weight:

Container size	$\frac{1}{2}$ pt	pt	qt	gallon
Drained weight	5 oz	10 oz	21 oz	88 oz

Flavorings added: Plain, spiced with dill, anise, garlic, pepper. (Buyers should ascertain flavoring in olives called Bordelaise, French, Kosher or Italian. Cuban usually means tomato paste has been added.)
*Reasonably uniform typical color, which is yellow-green to green color typical of variety. If olives are stuffed, the stuffing shall possess a good characteristic color for the stuffing used. Packing brine shall be clear and not cloudy. There should be few broken pieces. Workmanship should be reasonably good. Texture should be reasonably uniform, reasonably good

with a moderately firm and crisp flesh only slightly tough, which must be characteristic of variety. Reasonably free from slip skins, extraneous material, pits or pit fragments and other defects.

Note: Sicilian-style green olives have only one grade, No. 1. These are olives of similar varietal characteristics, which are green or straw in color, clean, firm, and fairly well formed; are free from damage caused by discoloration, shriveling, hail, wind, frost or other means; and possess the normal flavor of Sicilian-style olives.

Cucumber Pickles

Grades: A (85),* B (70).

Styles: Whole, cross cut (sliced crosswise into uniform thicknesses not more than 2 in. in diameter and $\frac{1}{8}$ to $\frac{3}{8}$ in. thick); sliced lengthwise (cut longitudinally into units with parallel surfaces with no length differences over 1 in. and thicknesses between $\frac{1}{8}$ and $\frac{3}{8}$ in.; cut (units not uniform; the weight of the largest cut unit should not be more than four times the weight of the smallest); finely cut (uniform finely cut or chopped as in pickle relish).

Recommended drained weight:

Whole Pickles

Container	Count	Whole Sour or Dill	Whole Sweet
No. 10 can or 3¼-qt jar	29 or less	66 oz	
	30–39	66½ oz	72 oz
	40–74	68 oz	72½ oz
	75–99	69 oz	74 oz
	100 or over	70 oz	76 oz
No. 12 can or gallon jar	39 or less	82 oz	
	40–51	84 oz	90 oz
	52–99	85 oz	91 oz
	100–134	86½ oz	92½ oz
	135 or over	88 oz	94 oz

Whole in Small Containers or Other than Whole

Container	Whole Sour and Dill	Whole Sweet	Other than Whole or Relish Sour	Other than Whole or Relish Sweet	Relish Sour	Relish Sweet
Pint jar	11 oz	12 oz	10 oz	12 oz	12½ oz	14 oz
Quart jar	21 oz	22 oz	22 oz	24 oz	25¾ oz	28 oz
No. 303 can or jar	10¾ oz	11½ oz	10 oz	11 oz	13½ oz	15 oz
No. 2½ can or jar	19 oz	20½ oz	19½ oz	21 oz	25¾ oz	28 oz
No. 10 can or jar			72 oz	78 oz	91¾ oz	100 oz
Gallon or No. 12 can			90 oz	95 oz	114¼ oz	125 oz

*The pickles should be free from any objectionable flavors and should possess the characteristic normal flavor for the type of pickle. They should meet standards for acidity, sugar and salt content. Color should be typical, practically uniform and practically free from bleached areas. Uniformity in size within reasonable limits is a requirement. Check for damaged units, blemishes, improper processing, soft units, nubbins, curved or misshapen units. Check workmanship on cut styles. There should be no extraneous matter and few stems or other material.

Sauerkraut

Sauerkraut is a pickled product made by shredding or cutting cabbage finely. Salt is added to the fresh, shredded cabbage in the ratio of $2\frac{1}{2}:100$ lb. The mixture is packed tighlty into vats, barrels or containers and heavy weights placed on top. A juice soon forms to cover the cabbage and fermentation begins. To retain quality, the kraut after pickling is packed into enamel-lined cans and given heat treatment. It may be purchased untreated, however, in barrels or containers. This naturally cured sauerkraut will keep in a cool place for 4 to 6 months. (For more information, see Chapter 3.)

SPICES

Approximately 200 million pounds of spices are used each year in this country. In the food facility the amount spent for spices is 0.6% of the food dollar. Spices are aromatic substances used for flavoring food. These substances may be either a spice or an herb from parts of plants, such as flowers, fruits, buds, bark, roots, leaves or seed.

Spices may be divided into *aromatic* types, such as anise, caraway, cardamon, cinnamon, cloves, cumin; *stimulant* types, such as mustard, pepper and tumeric; *sweet herb* types, such as basil, majoram, oregano and sage; and *pot herb* types, such as onions, garlic, parsley and celery. About 60% of the flavor in a normal spice is aroma, and the essential oil or flavoring compound may vary from $\frac{1}{2}$ to 4%, depending upon the quality of the spice. These volatile flavors may be rapidly lost; only about a month's supply should be purchased at one time. Spices lose flavor rapidly in open or paper containers or in storage areas where heat and moisture are excessive. Select spices on the basis of strength and quality of flavor. Watch for imitations or weak or poorly flavored products. Purchase from reliable spice dealers. Spices may be purchased in 1 oz, 4 oz, 1 lb, 6 lb and 10-lb containers. There are no federal standards established for quality, but standards of identity of the Food and Drug Administration do much to control purity and eliminate undesirable imitations. One-fourth teaspoon of a good quality spice is sufficient to give adequate flavor to one pound or one pint of food on the average. Fresh, good quality spice should possess a soft, earthy freshness of color. It should not be dull. The aroma should be fresh and pungent. Check quality of grind, wholeness, extraneous material, broken, shriveled or damaged units.

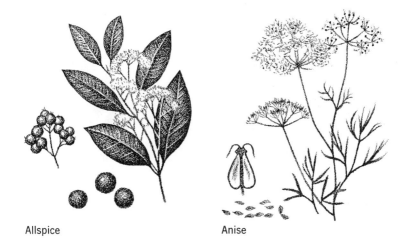

Allspice   Anise

Allspice

The nearly ripe, dried berry of an evergreen tree that grows mainly on the island of Jamaica, but also in Mexico, Guatemala, Honduras, Brazil and the Leeward Islands, is called allspice. It has a flavor blend of cinnamon, nutmeg and cloves. This gives it its name. The spice is usually purchased ground, and a small quantity is sufficient to give strong flavor. Do not purchase in large quantity.

Anise

The seed of anise comes from a small plant of the parsley family, grown mainly in Spain and Mexico. It is greenish brown, small, oval in shape like caraway. Possessing a licorice flavor, it is sprinkled over coffee cake, sweet rolls, cookies and candies, in bakery goods or in sweet pickles. Anisette and other liquors are flavored with it. Use is normally small. Star anise is grown in China and is similar in flavor to the true anise.

Basil

Sweet basil, a native of India and Persia, is now grown commercially in the north Mediterranean. It is a member of the mint family, with bright green leaves that turn brown when dry. It has a sweet and warm flavor, with a pungent undertone. It is used to season tomato products, salads and other food dishes.

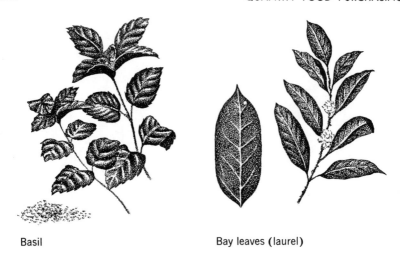

Basil   Bay leaves (laurel)

Bay Leaf

The dried leaves of the evergreen laurel tree, Sweet Bay, grown in Turkey, Greece, Yugoslavia and Portugal, are used for bay. In drying, the color turns from a shiny green to a yellowish-olive green. The leaves may be 3 in. in length. The flavor is distinctively pungent. Bay leaf is used for meats, stews, soups, sauces, fish and as a salad flavoring. It may be purchased whole or cracked (crushed). Use is moderate and a pound goes a long way.

Caraway

This is a brown, hard seed about $\frac{3}{16}$ in. long; curved and tapered at the ends. A plant related to parsley gives us caraway seed. The Netherlands furnish most of this spice. The flavor is pleasant, slightly sharp, with a sweet undertone. It is used whole in rye bread, rolls, biscuits and cakes, mixed into cheese, sauerkraut, cabbage, soups, meats and stews. It is a part of mixed pickling spice. It is also the main flavoring ingredient of Kummel cordial. May be used in moderate quantity in the bake shop, if the food facility bakes its own breads.

Cardamon

Guatemala ships us most of our cardamon but some also comes from India and Ceylon. The seeds are creamy white, irregularly round and about $\frac{3}{32}$ in. long. It is a seed of the ginger family. The flavor is aromatic and pungent. It is frequently combined with coffee flavors. Ground cardamon is used to flavor Danish pastry, buns, breads, coffee

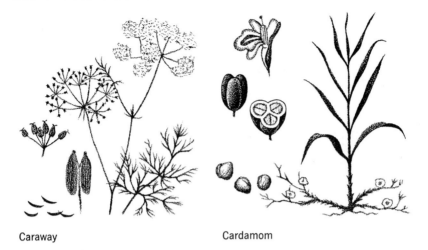

Caraway   Cardamom

cakes and to improve the flavor of grape jelly. It is used in curry and in sausage spices. Sometimes it is dropped as a seed into demitasse coffee. Use will normally be small.

Cassia

Cassia buds have a flavor similar to cinnamon but more pungent. They are dried ripe or immature fruits of the cassia plant growing in semi-tropical areas. Cassia is used for spicing fruits, pickles and other products. Use will be small.

Cayenne

A pepper grown commercially in Louisiana, California and other world areas furnishes our cayenne. The capsicum is small, having an orange-red to bright deep-red color. It is usually ground. It has a hot, pungent flavor. Only a small amount is required to give flavor. Do not buy in large quantities.

Celery Seed

A plant related to the parsley family produces celery seed. France and India send most of our requirements. The seed is a small, round pellet, light brown or tan in color. The taste is similar to the flavor of celery. It is used in sauces, salads, bread and butter pickles, pickling spices, soups, vegetables and other dishes. It is not used in quantity. Celery salt is made by combining the ground seeds with salt.

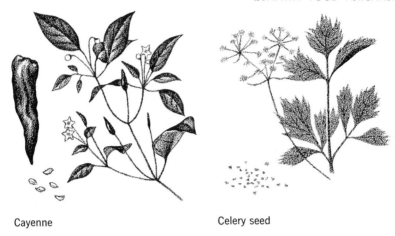

Cayenne   Celery seed

Chervil

The leaves of chervil have the flavor of mild parsley. They are used in soups, salads, egg dishes, French dressing and butter sauce for chicken. Chervil may be sprinkled over fish before broiling.

Chili Powder

A blend of spices usually consisting of chili pepper, red pepper, ground cumin seed, ground oregano and garlic powder, with perhaps ground cloves, ground allspice and powdered onion, is called chili powder. Cumin is the predominating flavor. The powder may not always be hot. Different brands will have different flavors. Chili powder is used as a barbecue spice, in Mexican dishes, in flavoring for eggs, omelets,

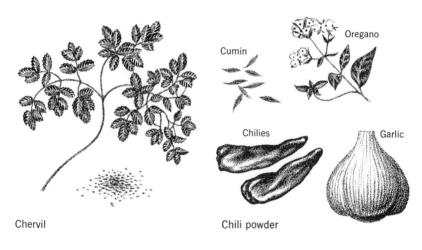

Cumin

Oregano

Chilies

Garlic

Chervil   Chili powder

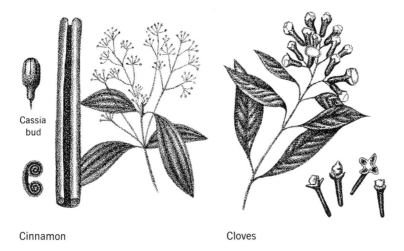

Cassia
bud

Cinnamon   Cloves

cottage cheese, shellfish and oyster cocktail sauces, gravy, stews and as
a subtle seasoning for such vegetables as corn.   In some food facilities
the quantity used is large; in others the use is small.

Cinnamon

The cinnamon used in this country is not true cinnamon but is the
bark of the Cassia tree.   It is dark brown in color, and the flavor is
sweet, slightly pungent, milder, but similar to the flavor of cloves.   It
may be ground into powder for use in baking pies, breads, rolls, cakes
and other pastries.   The sticks may be used for flavoring beverages,
pickling and other seasoning purposes.   Ceylon cinnamon tree bark is
true cinnamon but is seldom used in this country.   Its flavor is milder
than the bark of the Cassia tree and the color is lighter.   Most countries
use this true cinnamon.   Substantial quantities of cinnamon from the
Cassia tree are used in food facilities in this country.

Cloves

The French word "clou," meaning nail, is the source of the word
clove.   Cloves are the dried, unopened buds of an evergreen tree grown
commercially on the islands of Zanzibar and Madagascar.   The flavor
is strong, pungent and sweet.   The color should be rich brown.   A
small quantity gives high flavor; use is small.

Coriander

A plant related to the parsley family and grown in Yugoslavia and
Morocco produces coriander seed.   The seed is small and may range in

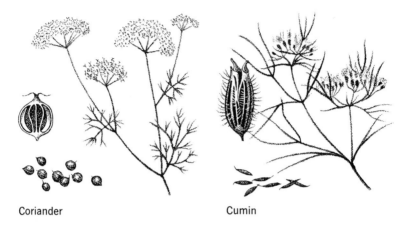

Coriander   Cumin

color from white through orange to a yellowish brown. The seeds have alternating straight and wavy edges. The spice has a mild, distinctive, fragrant odor and a pleasant, aromatic taste that one associates with lavender or a "lemon peel with sage" flavor. Coriander is used whole or ground. It is used in sausage meats, pickling spice and curry powder. In ground form it may be used to flavor rolls, pastry, cookies and cakes.

Cumin (Comino or Cummin) Seed

A plant of the parsley family grown in Iran and Morocco produces cumin seed. The seed is yellow-brown in color; it is oval and thin in shape and $\frac{1}{8}$ to $\frac{1}{4}$ in. in length. It has a strong pungent taste, somewhat sweet. It is the basis of curry and chili powder and is also used commercially in preparing meats, pickles, cheese, sausages and chutney. It is used for seasoning soups, stews and for flavoring variety breads and rice dishes.

Curry Powder

A blend of ground spices having no established formula is called curry powder. The main spices used are fenugreek, cayenne, tumeric, coriander and cumin. Buyers should select a curry that has a sweet, mild flavor, not harsh, and one that gives foods a bright, deep-yellow color, not a dirty tan. If many curry dishes are served, the quantity of the spice used may be substantial. Rice, veal, chicken, shrimp, eggs, vegetables and other foods are enhanced by curry flavor. It may be used as a subtle contrast in French dressing, tomato soup, meat dishes and other products. Fish dishes are frequently improved in flavor by just the delicate suggestion of curry.

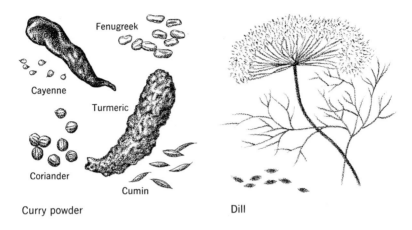

Fenugreek

Cayenne

Turmeric

Coriander

Cumin

Curry powder

Dill

Dill

Much of our dill seed is imported from India and Europe, although a small quantity is grown domestically. The plant belongs to the parsley family. The seed is a small, ovular, crescent-shaped, hard, brownish product, with a mellow, sweet tang faintly reminiscent of caraway. Some describe the flavor as "weedy." It is used ground or whole for making dill pickles, soups, salads, sauces, meats and fish. Many sausage meats are flavored with it. It may be used to produce subtle flavor with cole slaw, potato salad, cooked macaroni or cooked sauerkraut. It may have substantial use in making specialty-type foods in some operations and little use in others.

Fennel

A plant of the parsley family growing in India and Rumania furnishes our fennel seed. The shape of the seed is long and oval. The color is yellowish-brown. It has an agreeable odor and an aromatic, sweet taste resembling anise. It is used both ground and whole. Many Italian-type breads and rolls are topped with it before baking. It may be used to flavor sweet pickles, soups, fish dishes and sauces. It is not used in any great amount in normal food production.

Fenugreek (Foenugreek)

The seed of the fenugreek is small, with an irregular, oval shape produced in a plant belonging to the pea family grown in India, France, Lebanon and Argentina. The color of the seed is yellowish-brown. The flavor is distinctive, pleasant, slightly bitter like burnt sugar. It is

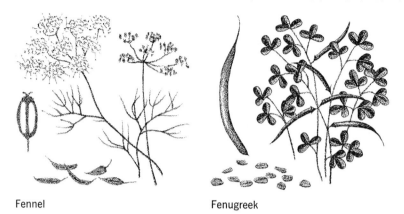

Fennel   Fenugreek

used both whole and ground. It is used in seasoning chutney, in making maple extract and with blends of other spices. It may be used in curry. Little is used under normal conditions.

Garlic Powder

Dehydrated ground garlic has many commercial uses in flavoring sausages, meats and other foods. Food services find it economical to use when fresh garlic is hard to obtain or labor is expensive. *Garlic* salt is salt and garlic powder combined. It is preferable to purchase only the powder and make one's own salt.

Ginger

The root or rhizome of a tropical tuberous plant produces ginger. The flavor is aromatic, sweet, spicy and pungent. The color of ground

Ginger

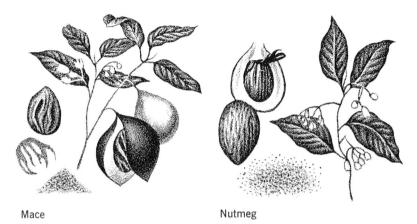

Mace   Nutmeg

ginger is light buff. Whole dried ginger may be peeled or unpeeled. Fresh green ginger is used in Chinese dishes, ginger marmalade, preserves and confections. Ginger is used to make gingerale and as a spice in gingerbread, snaps and baked goods, including pies, cookies, cakes and biscuits. It is one of the spices used in pickling spice. A touch of ginger can give a subtle flavor to meat.

Mace and Nutmeg

The two spices, mace and nutmeg, come from the same plant. Mace is the skin of the seed of the nutmeg tree, a tropical evergreen having a peachlike fruit. The spice, mace, forms a lacy network around the shell in which the nutmeg seed is found. Mace is milder and less pungent than nutmeg. The flavor of nutmeg is sweet, with a warm, spicy undertone. Nutmeg may be purchased whole in balls up to 1 in. in diameter or ground as a coarse salt. Mace and nutmeg are excellent in baked pastries, sweet roll doughs, puddings, sauces, vegetables, eggnogs and spiced drinks. They may give heightened flavor to a cream sauce, meats or meat sauces. Mace may be used in pound cakes, fish dishes and meat stuffings. More nutmeg will be used in food facilities than mace.

Marjoram

The leaves of a plant related to the mint plant, grown in France, Chile and Peru, furnish our marjoram. The leaves are grey-green, with a distinctly aromatic flavor and a slightly bitter undertone. Marjoram may be whole or ground. It is used to flavor lamb or mutton dishes, stews, soups, sausage and poultry stuffings. Many processed sausage items, such as liverwurst, bologna and head cheese, are flavored with marjoram. It may be used to give a subtle flavor to lima beans, peas or

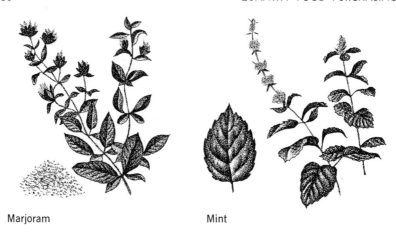

Marjoram   Mint

string beans. A small quantity should last a long time in the ordinary food facility.

Mint

The flavor of mint has long been associated with lamb. The leaves have a strong, sweet, tangy, cool flavor. They are dried and crushed. The supply usually comes from domestic sources.

Mixed Pickling Spice

A number of whole spices may be mixed together to make a pickling spice. In most operations this spice mixture will have moderate use, and a pound will generally last longer than 3 months in the medium-sized units.

Mustard

The seeds of mustard may come from two varieties of plants, the black or brown seed and the white or yellow seed varieties. The former is smaller. Both are small, round pellets. We produce a large part of our own requirements. The seed has a hot, sharp, pungent bite, which is slightly sweet. Mustard may be purchased as seeds for use as garnishes for salads, flavoring for pickles, beets, cabbage or sauerkraut. Ground mustard is used to flavor many meat and fish dishes. Sometimes food facilities like to serve ground mustard made into a paste with vinegar for meats, such as tongue, corned beef, ham and beef. It is hot and is usually called "English-type" mustard to differentiate it from our mild, prepared mustard, which contains mostly tumeric and not mustard.

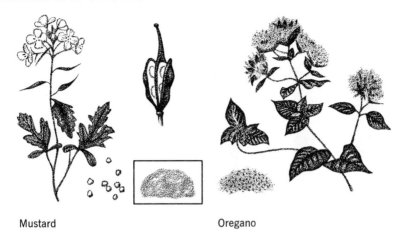

Mustard   Oregano

Chinese foods are frequently served with a hot mustard. Depending upon the type of service, the use in a facility can be large or small.

Onion Powder

Onions may be dried and ground to produce a powder that has many uses commercially in food production and in food services. *Onion salt* is a combination of onion powder and common salt.

Oregano

Oregano may also be called oreganum, Mexican oregano or sage, or origan. It is the dried leaves of a plant related to the mint family. The herb when dried is light green in color. The flavor is strong and aromatic, with an assertive, pleasantly bitter undertone. The flavor resembles that of marjoram and bay combined. It is used crushed or ground. It is one of the major spices used in chili powder and finds much use in Mexican and Italian dishes. It has a subtle flavor in lamb dishes. Its use is rather limited in most food facilities.

Paprika

A mild pepper belonging to the capsicum family produces our paprika. Hungarian-grown paprika is darker in color than Spanish-grown paprika. It also has less flavor and is cheaper. The richer red color and bouquet of the Spanish pakrika make it more desirable for use in foods. Some paprika is grown in California and resembles the Hungarian-grown type. Paprika has a mild, pleasant, delicately sweet flavor. It is usually ground and used as a garnish or to contribute color to sauces or cooked dishes.

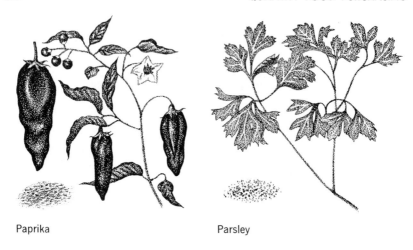

Paprika   Parsley

Because of its frequent use as a garnish, the quantities used in some food facilities may be substantial.

Parsley

The dried leaves of parsley make an excellent seasoning. It has extensive use as a delicate flavoring for soups, salads, meat, fish, sauces and vegetable dishes. It may also be sprinkled over foods as a garnish.

Pepper

Many different varieties of pepper are used in the ordinary food facility. The very hot peppers come from the capsicum family. These are related to the mild, sweet bell pepper group.

Red pepper is redder than cayenne but the flavor is not so hot. It comes from subtropical America—California, Louisiana, Carolinas— and Turkey. It is used largely in ground or crushed form. Crushed red pepper may also be called *pepperoni rosso*, *pizza pepper*, *coarse crushed red pepper* or *red pepper, crushed*. Because of the small quantity required to give full flavor, quantities used are generally small in most food facilities.

Whole chili peppers are whole red pepper capsicums. They are found in pickling spice, are used whole for seasoning foods and have other limited uses. Most whole chili peppers are red but some green hot peppers are pickled. A vinegar sauce may be used on some and this sauce is used for seasoning rather than the peppers. Tabasco sauce is made from tabasco peppers, a type of red pepper.

True pepper, the black and white varieties commonly used for flavoring foods, is not related to the capsicum family. Both black and white

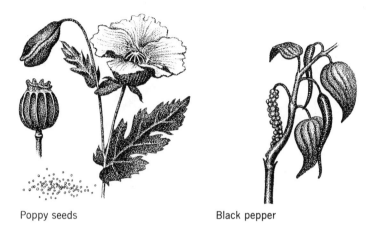

Poppy seeds   Black pepper

pepper come from a climbing vine that produces a small, red berry. When dried, the berry is dark brown. Of all spices it is the one used, perhaps, in greatest quantity. Most imports come from India, Indonesia and British Malaya. Black pepper is picked before the berry is fully ripe; dried, cleaned and shipped. Ground black pepper shows both light and dark portions of the berry. White pepper is allowed to ripen fully so that the interior meat separates from the outer shell. This shell is removed and the small white peppercorn is dried. White pepper should have no trace of outer shell in it. It is hotter but somewhat more mild in other flavors than black pepper. Black pepper will have a more penetrating odor and a more pungent taste. White or black peppercorns may be purchased whole or gound.

Poppy Seeds

Most of the poppy seeds used in food are grown in Holland. The seeds are round, tiny and may be tan or darker in color. They are used to top breads, rolls; used in cakes, cookies and other items. They may be used both as a flavoring and garnish over cooked noodles or over salads. They are mixed with honey or other items for use as fillings in pastries.

Poultry Seasoning

A ground blend of sage, thyme, marjoram and savory may be used as a poultry seasoning. Rosemary and other spices may also be added. In addition to flavoring poultry, the product may be used as sage or marjoram are used to flavor other foods.

Rosemary   Saffron

Pumpkin Pie Spice

Another blend of ground spices, usually composed of cinamon, cloves, ginger and nutmeg or mace, may be used to flavor pies. Most operations prefer to make their own blends, however.

Rosemary

An evergreen shrub, related to the mint family and grown in France, Spain and Portugal, produces a curved crescent-shaped leaf resembling a pine needle. It has a fresh, distinctive, sweet flavor. The seed may be over 1 in. in length. It is excellent for flavoring lamb dishes, soups, stews and for adding to salads.

Saffron

A crocuslike flower grown in Spain produces saffron, one of our most expensive spices. Only the three stigmas are used, and it takes 225,000 stigmas or 75,000 blossoms to make one pound of saffron. It has a pleasantly bitter, mildly distinctive flavor. It combines well with seafood. Saffron gives a rich, yellow or orange color to foods. It is used to season bread, rolls, Spanish or Creole dishes. Many rice dishes are flavored with it. A small quantity will go a long way. Since use is restricted to a relatively few dishes, only a very small amount should be purchased at one time.

Sage

Sage is the dried leaf of an herb belonging to the mint family. It is grown commercially in Dalmatia and has a mild, delicate flavor that

Sage   Savory

may be somewhat astringent or bitter. Many varieties grown in other areas, including our domestic sage, lack the fine flavor of Dalmatian sage. These others may give a bitter, terpentinelike flavor to products. Sage may be purchased whole, rubbed, crushed or ground. It is used extensively to flavor dressings for poultry or pork, or to flavor meat dishes, baked fish, salad dressings or chowder. It heightens the flavor of some tossed salads. It is generally used in considerable quantity in most operations, but since it may lose flavor rapidly, it should be purchased only in quantities required for a month.

Savory

Summer savory is the dried leaf of a plant belonging to the mint family. Most of our imports come from France and Spain. The leaves are small, brown-green in color and have a distinctively warm, aromatic, slightly resinous flavor. It is used whole or ground, but in most food operations it will have limited use. It is a good flavoring for meats, meat dressings, chicken, soups, salads, sauces or scrambled eggs.

Sesame

The seed of an annual plant grown in Nicaragua, Salvador, Egypt and Brazil is the source of our sesame or benne (bene) seed. Texas produces some of this seed, but mostly for the production of sesame seed oil. The seed has a rich, toasted-nut flavor. It is used for topping rolls, breads and some pastry products. It is available hulled or unhulled and is seldom ground. It is a basic ingredient of the Jewish candy, Halvah. The Chinese use the oil as a flavoring ingredient. If used in bake shop production, the quantity required can be substantial.

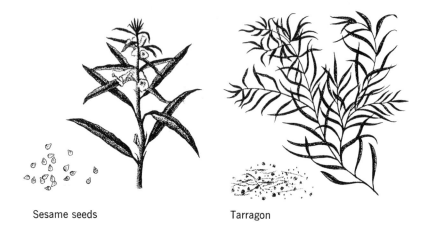

Sesame seeds   Tarragon

Tarragon

The leaves and flowering tops of an herb grown in Europe and in this
country are used to flavor vinegar, pickles, sauces, salads, chicken,
meats, eggs and tomato dishes. This is tarragon. It has a delicate
flavor resembling anise. When used subtly, it can give many interesting
flavor contrasts. The use is generally small.

Thyme

The leaves of another member of the mint family are used as a seasoning. This is thyme, which grows in France, Spain and the United States.
The leaves are brown-green, and the flavor is distinctively warm, aro-

Thyme   Turmeric

matic and pungent.   It rivals sage in use in clam chowder, clam juice, meat, fish sauces and other products.   The use is usually moderate.

Tumeric

Like ginger, tumeric comes from the roots or rhizomes of a plant. The plant is related to the ginger family.   It is grown in India, Haiti, Jamaica and Peru.   The flavor is distinctive, differing from ginger in that it is mild, sweet and highly aromatic.   It is available whole or ground.   It has a distinctive, bright yellow color and is the main ingredient in prepared mustard.   It is also one of the major spices used in making curry powder, contributing to curry's bright yellow color.   It may be used to replace saffron in some dishes; it lacks the flavor contribution of saffron, however.   Saffron usually has a more reddish-yellow color.

FLAVORINGS

Flavorings are aromatic esters used to flavor food.   They are usually dissolved in some type solvent, such as water or alcohol.   Some flavorings, may, however, be in powder or tablet form.   These esters are obtained by extraction from the roots, bark, fruit, sap, leaves or other portions of a plant.   Imitation flavorings are those that do not come from a plant but are artificially produced.   Even though the imitation compound is identical in chemical structure and taste to the natural product, if it is not from the natural product, the law requires it be labeled *imitation.*   Sometimes in the trade, "artificial" is used to indicate flavors that are similar to but not quite like the natural flavoring, while the word "imitation" is used to indicate a flavoring identical to the pure product but not coming from the natural product.   Some flavorings are best when derived from the natural product.   Others, such as banana, maple, raspberry, brandy, rum, black walnut, cherry, pineapple and strawberry are best in the imitation or artificial.

Vanilla

Vanilla can be purchased either as pure or imitation extract.   Pure vanilla comes from the vanilla bean which is related to the tropical orchid parasitic plant.   The vanilla plant is native to Mexico but has been transplanted to other parts of the world.   The world's largest producing area is Madagascar and its surrounding islands.   At one time these were called the Bourbon Islands and because of the special process used to cure the vanilla beans, a hot water soak before drying, the vanilla is called Bourbon vanilla.   Mexican beans are cured by drying in

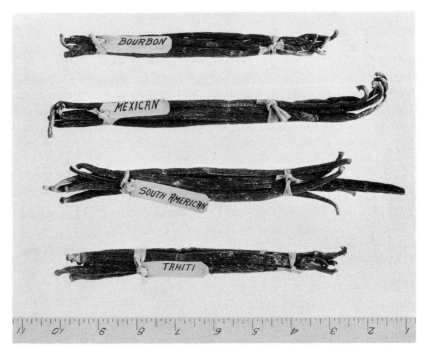

FIG. 8–4. Vanilla beans. The buyer should specify that true vanilla extract shall come from high quality Mexican or Bourbon beans. Courtesy USDA.

the sun after picking. Mexican and Bourbon vanilla are considered best in quality while South American, Java and Tahiti vanilla are usually considered lower in quality.

A new method of curing and extraction has been developed which lowers cost and improves the product. The bean is ground after picking without drying, cured in a curing tank and then dehydrated and shipped. In this country the product is percolated in alcohol.

Government identity standards state that 100 cc of extract shall contain the soluble matter from not less than 10 grams of vanilla beans, or 1 gal of vanilla extract shall contain the extractives from $13\frac{1}{3}$ oz of vanilla beans.

Quality is best determined by aroma and flavor in use. To test for flavor, add 1 teaspoon of vanilla to 8 oz room-temperature milk and smell and taste. This test is especially valuable when comparing two or more vanillas. Pure vanilla concentrates are available on the market, but are not generally used in ordinary food production.

Imitation vanilla extracts are made from a compound called vanillin.

This is a colorless crystalline compound with a sharp, pleasant flavor and aroma similar to that of pure vanilla. Vanillin is obtained from certain types of wood or heavy oil of cloves. The latter, called eugenol, can be changed chemically to produce vanillin. While natural and imitation vanilla may not be distinguished when used separately, comparative tests in use generally will show the pure extract to be superior.

Lemon

Extracted volatile oils of lemon, held in alcohol, give lemon extract. The pure flavor should contain not less than 5% oil of lemon and not less than 80% ethyl alcohol. Natural lemon esters have 90% terpenes and 4 to 6% each of aldehyde esters and alcohol esters. Imitation lemon extract is made from a compound called *oily terpenic aldehyde*, which imparts the flavor and aroma of lemon. It is relatively unstable and stabilizers must also be added to it. Some lemon powders are found on the market and are used for lemonades. They usually contain a high amount of citric acid, plus some of the imitation or pure flavoring compound.

Other Flavorings

Other pure extracts on the market are mint, clove, cinnamon, tonka, spearmint, peppermint, anise, wintergreen, almond and orange. Usually the ratio of natural oil to solvent is 5 or 8:100. Imitation extacts are also available. Fruit flavorings are on the market. Most are imitations. They are usually called essences rather than flavors. Beverage bases of many types are manufactured. They are combinations of fruit essences, color and citric acid. Sugar may be an added ingredient.

Food colorings purchased for food facility use should be U.S. Certified.

Sunlight, temperature and air can cause deterioration of flavorings. Unless a large quantity is used, flavorings should be purchased in small amounts. Flavorings required for 3 months only should be purchased.

CONDIMENTS

A condiment is "an agent used to give relish to foods and to gratify taste." A blend of spices, flavoring ingredients from cereals or other foods, vinegar, tomato or others may be combined to accompany foods.

Tomato catsup is a commonly used condiment. It is the strained tomato pulp to which vinegar, sugar and spices have been added. Chili sauce also contains tomato pulp but seeds are allowed to pass through the pulpers. Vinegar, sugar and spices are added to complete this condiment. Tomato and chili standards are discussed under canned vegetables.

Worcestershire sauce is prepared from a base of vinegar and soy sauce. Other ingredients, such as East India tamarinds, capsicums, cloves, garlic, onions, anchovies, black pepper, mushrooms, lemons or limes, may be added. The resultant product is usually aged at least 2 months, then bottled and marketed.

Chop suey sauces were at one time made by boiling soy beans with equal quantities of roasted wheat or barley. This mash was fermented and the sauce drained off. The federal government now forbids shipment of this type of sauce into the country. Present sauces are hydrolyzed proteins from soy beans, wheat, corn, yeast and other products. Imitation soy sauces may be made from dark molasses and salt dissolved in water.

Pepper sauces may be of two varieties. One is the original pepper sauce from New Orleans, made by filling a bottle with whole red pepper or chili pods and pouring vinegar over them. The other is tabasco or hot sauce, made by concentrating an extraction from the long-podded tabasco peppers.

Mustard sauces are made by grinding ripe mustard seeds with vinegar. Our common table mustard is largely a product flavored with tumeric and contains only a small quantity of mustard.

Prepared mustard must be of the best quality, prepared in accordance with the finest commercial practices, under strict sanitary conditions, and it should be free from preservatives and impurities. USDA inspection and grading certificate may be specified, with the quality of the mustard complying with Federal Specifications EE-M-821b. Mustard may be purchased twenty-four 8-oz jars per case, in gallon jars, French style, four 1-gal per case or in barrels, 50 gal to the barrel.

Fruit sauces are used as relishes or accompaniments. Perhaps the most common are cranberry and applesauce. Standards for these are discussed under processed products. Chutney has been discussed previously under pickles in this chapter.

Condiments keep well but unopened products should always be used before a year after processing. Tomato products may show some darkening at the end of $3\frac{1}{2}$ months' storage, especially if held at somewhat elevated temperatures.

Sugars and Sirups

Sugars. There is little difference in cooking between cane and beet sugar. Both are almost pure sucrose. Different sizes in sugar crystals, however, are important. White refined sugars will run from coarse to very fine. Sugar that is finer than very fine is ground sugar and not composed of crystals; this ground sugar is designated by an "X." Coarse sugar will be required by bakeries, for sugar work, hard candies and fondants. Sanding sugars will be needed for glaced fruits and pan-coated goods and these also must be somewhat coarse. Common sugar may be used for ordinary cooking or for table use. The sugar used for cakes, cookies and other pastries should be finely crystallized so it will go into solution rapidly in batters and doughs. Berry or fruit sugar is frequently used for this purpose in the bake shop. Berry or fruit sugar is also preferred for common table use, especially for fruits and cereals at breakfast. It may, for this reason, be called "breakfast sugar." Extra fine sugar may be required for the bake shop for foam-type cakes and for use at the bar for mixed drinks. Coating sugar is the finest of the crystallized sugars. It is used as a coating sugar for pan goods, doughnuts, cookies, sweet dough products and so forth. A special type of crystalline granulated sugar, called "transformed" sugar, is now on the market. This sugar has crystals composed of tiny clusters, which have rough edges that assist in incorporating more air during creaming. The crystals also go into solution more rapidly.

Sugars below coating size are ground sugars and not crystallized sugars. The size of the particle is indicated by an "X." XX sugar is called standard powdered sugar. Four X (XXXX) is confectioner's sugar, which is commonly used for icing. Six X is also used for icing and bake shop purposes. About the finest sugar is 10X.

Brown sugar is available in various grades. The color is used as an indicator of quality. Brown sugar is usually made from cane sugars, but some brown sugar made from beets is appearing on the market. Brown sugar gets its color from molasses, ash or minerals and other impurities that white sugar does not contain. Brown sugar has hydroscopic or moisture drawing properties. It is about 85 to 92% pure sucrose (the percentage depending upon grade), 4% moisture and the remainder invert sugars. Grades may be numbered from 1 to 15 on the commercial market. The lowest number grades are the lightest in color and the highest number grades darkest in color. Trade designations may also be light, medium and dark.

At one time corn sugar was not recognized by the federal government as a legal sweetening agent in food products, but today it is accepted within certain limits. This limit is usually stated in ratio or percent to sucrose in the food product. Corn sugar is made by changing cornstarch to invert sugars. It has practical use in food services when sweetening agents are used in quantity. Its price and its high sweetening power make it desirable from the standpoint of both economy and utility. More buyers should investigate this product as a substitute for the more frequently used, higher-priced sugars.

Maple sugar has limited use in food-service work. It is crystallized from the concentrated sap of the maple. A buyer may purchase what is called "maple sugar concrete" on the market for making into desired food items. The quantity used should be large for purchase in this form. Quality grades may be ascertained in much the same way as those established for maple sirup below.

Sirups. There are a number of liquid sweeteners used in quantity food production. Perhaps the most commonly used is molasses. This sweetener is separated by federal standards into grades: A (Fancy), B (Choice), Standard (C) and Substandard. Grades A and B should be specified for food use. The grade chosen will depend upon the use. Grade A may contain not less than 79% total solids, not less than 63½% sucrose or other sugars and not more than 5% ash. The color should be light. Grade B molasses should contain not less than 79% total solids, 61½% sugars and not more than 7% ash. Color should be medium. Cloudiness, sediment or extraneous matter are causes for loss in grade. Lower grades of molasses may be excessively dark in color, bitter and unsuitable for use in normal food production. Buyers should taste brands and decide on flavor qualities. Use to judge quality.

Federal standards for grades have been established for table maple sirup. The quality for all grades is the same except for color and opacity or clouding. The weight of all grades shall be not less than 11 lb per gallon. The flavor shall be characteristic of maple and "shall be clean, free from fermentation and free from damage caused by scorching or other objectionable flavors." The federal grades are AA (Fancy), A and B, and the color shall be light amber, medium amber and dark amber, according to color standards established by the federal government. Highest grades are clear and brilliant.

Maple sirup contains approximately 35% moisture. It is extracted from the maple in the early spring as the sap starts to flow and is then concentrated by boiling. Much of the quality of the sirup is established in this boiling. Recent developments of boiling under vacuum have changed the traditional methods of maple sirup production, and light grades are now more common. The distinctive flavor comes from impurities and ash. Grade A will usually be satisfactory for food use.

Sorghum is made from the sorghum plant. It is similar in many ways to sugar cane sirup, but it has a more distinctive flavor and may be slightly bitter and acid. It contains a fairly high amount of iron. This, plus other impurities, gives it a dark amber color. It is not as sweet as cane sirup, for it contains less sucrose and more glucose. It has a 30% moisture content and about $2\frac{1}{2}$ ash content. Trade names of corn sirup may vary. It is also known as glucose, dextrose, confectioner's glucose or unmixed glucose. It may be made by the action of acid or enzymes changing cornstarch to glucose. Enzymatic action makes a sweeter sirup. The finished sirup should have approximately 5% ash and be composed of roughly 30% dextrin, 35% glucose, 20% maltose and 15% moisture. Some prepared corn sirups for retail use may be higher in glucose content and higher in moisture and ash than the figures given here.

Sugar and maple sirup is a blend of granulated sugar and maple sirups. Specifications should state that it contain not less than 25% maple sirup. This sirup may be processed from granulated sugar and maple sugar concrete.

Maltose may be purchased in sugar or sirup form, but because of its high hydroscopic properties it is usually purchased as a sirup. It is used in the bake shop for making bread, rolls and other yeast products. It is amber in color and has a distinctive flavor, which limits its use for some bakery products, such as cakes and cookies. It has a moisture content of about 20% and is composed of about 65% maltose or malt sugar; the remainder being inverted sugars.

Honey is the concentrated nectar of flowers. Bees gather the nectar and bring it to the hives for concentration by evaporation. Enzymes from the bees' bodies assist in its change from nectar into honey. Honey should have not more than 25% moisture, $\frac{1}{2}$% ash and 8% sucrose. The sweetening agents should be divided evenly between fructose and glucose. Honey should be quite sweet in flavor and slightly acid. The color and flavor will be governed by the flowers from which the bees select their nectar. Fireweed, orange and clover are considered desirable sources.

Federal standards differ for extracted and comb honey. Extracted honey is obtained by breaking the seal on the comb and centrifuging the honey. The liquid should be free from crystallization and comb. Federal grades are U.S. Grade A, B and C. Grade B is usually satisfactory for cooking. The flavor should be reasonably good, free from smoke, scorching, fermentation or other objectionable flavors. It should be reasonably free from defects and contain no matter affecting edibility. Colors in honey may be described as "water white," "extra white," "white," "extra light amber," "light amber," "amber" and "dark amber." Federal grades for comb honey are U.S. Fancy, No. 1 and No. 2. Comb honey may be purchased as comb section, section frame comb honey, wrapped cut-comb honey and chunk or bulk-comb honey packed in tin or glaze.   Specific standards exist for each type within the three grades.

NUTS

Nuts are perishable and may easily become rancid or infested with insects.   Buyers should specify that purchases come from the current year's crop and be sweet and full flavored, with no trace of rancidity or other objectionable flavors.   Quantities for a month's supply only should be purchased if in non-airtight seal.   Careful inspection should be given upon delivery.   Purchase for the specific use intended.   There is little need to purchase expensive whole grades when the items are to be chopped or broken in use.

Federal standards exist for almonds, filberts, walnuts and peanuts in the shell.   Because of labor cost, few food facilities purchase in the shell.   Table 8–7 briefly summarizes some of the most pertinent information on quality of nuts in the shell.

Shelled almonds may be purchased graded U.S. Fancy, U.S. Extra No. 1, U.S. No. 1, U.S. Select Sheller Run and U.S. Standard Sheller Run. U.S. No. 1 is acceptable for general use, but the higher grades may be required for specialty purposes.   The quality of the kernel for each grade is very similar and should be whole, clean, well dried, free from decay, rancidity, insect injury, foreign matter, doubles, split and broken kernels. The term "mixed" means that 1% bitter almond varieties may be included in the sweet almonds.   Whole almonds with broken pieces may be graded U.S. No. 1 Whole and Broken or U.S. No. 1 Pieces.   In the first grade, 30% or more shall be whole kernels, with doubles counted as whole, but only 35% of the total may be doubles.   Pieces shall be almond kernel meats not less than ⅛ in. in diameter.   Shelled almonds may also be purchased skinned, whole slices or pieces.   There are no federal grades for these.

Buyers may specify sizes of whole almonds by number per ounce, which run inclusively: 16 to 18, 18 to 20, 20 to 22, 22 to 24, 23 to 25, 24 to 26, 26 to 28, 27 to 30, 30 to 34, 36 to 40, 40 to 50, 50 and smaller.

There are no federal grades for shelled filberts.   Quality factors applicable to other shelled nuts may be used to establish a specification for these products.   Besides whole, they may be obtained chopped, sliced or ground.   The chopped and ground products should be very fresh and free from any trace of rancidity.   Taste and smell the product for good flavor.

Shelled, Virginia-type peanuts are graded U.S. Extra Large Virginia, U.S. Medium Virginia, U.S. No. 1 Virginia, U.S. Virginia Splits and U.S. No. 2 Virginia.   A split is a separated half of a peanut.   Sheller Runner-type shelled peanuts are graded U.S. No. 1 Runner, U.S. Run-

Table 8–7
Federal Grades and Quality Standards for Nuts in the Shell

Type Nut	Federal Grades	Quality Factors
Almonds	U.S. No. 1* U.S. No. 2	If the term "mixed" is used after the grade, up to 1% bitter almond varieties may be in the batch. No. 1 should be clean, fairly bright and uniform in color; free from loose hulls, pieces of shells, chaff and foreign matter. The kernels should be well dried; free from decay, rancidity, insect injury, mold, gum, shriveling, brown spots or other defects. Unless otherwise specified, the thickness should not be less than $\frac{7}{16}$ in.
Filberts	U.S. No. 1*	The nuts shall be of similar type, well formed, dry, clean and bright; free from blanks, broken or split shells and damage, such as stain, adhering husks and other defects. The kernels should be reasonably well developed, not badly misshapen; free from rancidity, decay, mold, insect injury and from damage caused by shriveling, discoloration or other means. Sizes are Jumbo, Large, Medium, Small.
Peanuts	U.S. Jumbo Hand Picked* U.S. Fancy Hand Picked*	The quality of the two grades is the same except that Jumbos shall not pass through a hole $\frac{37}{64}$ by 3 in. and shall not average more than 176 per lb. Fancy shall not pass through a hole $\frac{1}{2}$ by 3 in. and not average more than 225 per lb. The nuts shall be clean, mature, fairly free from dry parts of shell and loose nuts, dirt or other foreign material, pops (fully developed shells containing practically no kernels), paper ends (soft or very thin ends), and free from damage caused by cracked or broken shells, discoloration or other means. The kernels should be free from damage.
Pecans	U.S. No. 1* Commercial	Shells fairly uniform in color, fairly well-shaped and free from damage caused by stains or adhering hulls, split or broken shells, loose hulls or other foreign material. The kernels should be well cured, free from rancidity, mold, decay, insect injury, shriveling, leanness, hollowness, discoloration or other damage. Sizes are Oversize— not more than 52 per lb, Extra size—not more than 60 per lb, Large—61 to 73 per lb, Medium—74 to 90 per lb, Small—91 to 115 per lb.
Walnuts	U.S. No. 1* U.S. No. 2 U.S. No. 3	Shells shall be bright colored and fairly uniform in color. All grades shall have shells that are dry, practically clean; free from splits, injury by discoloration and from damage caused by broken shells, perforated shells, adhering shells and other means. The kernels shall be well dried, free from decay, dark discoloration, rancidity, insects or insect damage; free from damage caused by mold, shriveling and other means. Splits are walnuts with shell halves separated at the suture but held together by the kernel. The color of the nut should be light or better, with only a few going down to light amber.

*Grade recommended for food facility use. The quality factors cited apply mainly to this grade. Tolerances apply in many cases, but they have been omitted from discussion in quality factors.

ner Splits and U.S. No. 2 Runner. They are not used as extensively as the Virginia variety in food services.

Buyers should watch for such defects as other varieties, split or broken nuts, foreign material or damaged or unshelled peanuts. They may be ordered sized $\frac{5}{8}$ in., running about 512 to the lb; $\frac{9}{32}$ in., running 640 to the lb; $\frac{15}{64}$ in., 800 per lb. In the $\frac{5}{8}$ in. size, not more than 10% by weight shall be splits; in the others, not more than 25% by weight shall be splits.

Peanut butter is ground, roasted peanut kernels, which may or may not be emulsified or stabilized and seasoned. Grinds may be specified fine (fine smooth texture), medium (grainy texture) and coarse or chunky (having a coarse or chunky texture and in some types may be chunks combined with fine). Colors of roast may be specified as light or heavy. Grades are U.S. Grade A or B. Off-grade may be called U.S. Grade C or Standard. Food services should specify Grade A. This grade should have a good, bright, typical color for the roast, be free from inorganic residue, fairly free from particles of brown to black seed coat and scorched or discolored peanut tissue. The flavor and odor should be that of freshly roasted peanuts free from staleness, rancidity or objectionable flavor or odor of any kind.

Shelled pecans are graded U.S. No. 1 and U.S. Commercial for halves, and similar grades are applied to pieces. U.S. No. 1 halves should be well dried, clean, free from pieces of shell and center wall, foreign material, chipped halves, broken kernels, particles and dust, noticeable shriveling, rancidity, mold, decay and insect injury, and from damage caused by leanness, hollowness, discoloration or other means. The pecan halves should be fairly uniform in size and color. The Commercial Grade has nearly the same requirements except for chipped halves and not as high a requirement on uniformity of size and color. Sizes for halves may be:

Trade Size	Number per Pound	Trade Size	Number per Pound
Mammoth	200–250	Medium	551–650
Junior Mammoth	251–300	Topper	551–750
Jumbo	301–350	Large amber*	400 or less
Extra Large	351–450		
Large	451–550	Regular amber*	more than 400

*Used only for Commercial Grade.

Pecan pieces have the same quality factors as halves except there are no restrictions in regard to proportion of broken pecan halves that may be included. Size of pieces shall not be less than $\frac{1}{8}$ in. in diameter.

Federal grades for shelled English walnuts are U.S. No. 1 and U.S. Commercial. U.S. No. 1 kernels shall be well dried, clean, free from shell, foreign matter, insect injury, decay, rancidity and from damage caused by shriveling, mold, discoloration of the meat or other means. The color should be specified as extra light, light, light amber or amber, which are, respectively, tan cream, tan, light brown and dark brown in color. Sizes may be specified as halves consisting of 85% or more of half kernels and the remaining 15%, $\frac{3}{4}$ kernels, $\frac{1}{2}$ kernels or pieces.

Prepared coconut should be of high quality, sweet and fresh. The nuts are picked from the palm and carefully dried. Sugar is used as a sweetener, and stabilizers and hydroscopic agents may be added, such as sorbitol and propylene glycol. It may be purchased shredded in long, medium or short form. An extremely short shred form, sometimes called *grated*, is used for dipping purposes. Since coconut may dry out or become rancid, it should not be purchased in large quantities but only that required for 1 or 2 months.

MISCELLANEOUS PRODUCTS

Chocolate

Federal standards that establish identity of chocolate state that it shall be chocolate liquor made by finely ground cacao nibs. It may also be called baking chocolate, bitter chocolate, cooking chocolate, chocolate coating or bitter chocolate coating. It must contain 50 to 58% cacao fat. It may contain optional ingredients, such as ground, spices, vanilla, butter, milk fat and malt cereal, but for food facilities plain chocolate is usually specified. Emulsifying agents, such as lecithin or mono or diglycerides, may be added, not more than $\frac{1}{2}$% by weight.

Sweet chocolate, or sweet coating chocolate as it may be called, is the solid or semi-plastic food prepared from finely ground chocolate liquor, with or without the addition of cacao fat, sweetened by an approved sweetening agent. Like bitter chocolate, it may also contain optional ingredients. It must contain not less than 15% by weight of chocolate liquor. If a chocolate is called bittersweet or semi-sweet, it must contain 35% chocolate liquor. Milk chocolate or sweet milk chocolate (also called milk chocolate coating or sweet milk chocolate coating) must contain not less than $3\frac{2}{3}$% by weight of milk fat, not less than 12% milk solids and not less than 10% by weight chocolate liquor. It is sweetened like sweet chocolate. Skim milk chocolate or sweet skim milk chocolate is similar to milk chocolate except that it contains less than $3\frac{2}{3}$% milk fat and over 12% milk solids. Buttermilk chocolate is usually sweetened. It contains less than $3\frac{2}{3}$% milk fat, but not less than 12% milk solids, which are derived from buttermilk.

Gelatin and Gelatin Desserts

Gelatin is made by changing the connective tissue collagen in animal tissues to gelatin. Gelatin has the ability to imbibe large quantities of water and swell. If the water is warm, the gelatin will melt or disperse into solution. When the solution is cooled, its viscosity increases and a gelatinous mass develops. It may be purchased in granular or pulverized form. Most food services purchase it in finely ground form. Some gelatins are acidulated, usually with citric acid, but most are plain. Gelatin may vary in its behavior because of the method of manufacturing and processing. Buyers should specify a good quality of plain gelatin, flavorless and odorless, with no objectionable flavors evident from manufacturing, fermentation, bacterial action or other causes. Time of setting, quality of the gel formed and the quality of the finished product should be that of the highest quality gelatin and should display no weakness of gel, no wateriness, little or no opacity. The color may be a very delicate light buff. Poorer grades of gelatin will be darker in color. Bacterial count should be low and highest standards of sanitation should be observed in its manufacture. Bloom is an important factor in gelatin. This quality has to do with the appearance, the sheen and feeling of softness in texture that is evident.

Gelatin desserts or mixes include sugar, acid, coloring, preserving stabilizer, salt and flavoring substances. Inferior gelatin desserts are found on the market. It is difficult in writing specifications to eliminate these products from the best. Good quality gelatin desserts should be made from high quality gelatin. Only approved coloring matter and flavoring ingredients may be used. Flavor is usually one of the main factors affecting gelatin dessert quality outside of gelatin, and this factor is most difficult to define. Natural flavors may be specified as acceptable for some; yet these may be poor and artificial flavors may be good. Brands should be specified if possible. Purchase is best on the basis of traditional satisfaction and high standards of production.

Vinegar

Vinegar is a dilute solution of acetic acid. Its flavor also comes from esters in the materials from which it is made. Apple vinegar must be from fermented apple juice or cider. After fermentation, bacterial action is continued. The alcohols are changed into acetic acid. Vinegar may be made by fermenting products such as wood chips. Except for flavor esters, the resulting vinegar is the same. Vinegar strength is specified by the grain or percent acid. Regular pickling or table strength is 50 grain vinegar and contains 5% acetic acid. Vinegar may be purchased in quantity in gallons, 4 gal to the case, or in barrels. White or amber vinegars are available. Color does not affect quality.

Cake and Other Bakery Mixes

Cake and other bakery mixes have rapidly gained in popularity in food services. Studies have indicated that, while material costs are higher, the labor savings are such that costs of cakes or products made in the institution from a standard recipe and from the mix are about the same. Quality control, production standardization and management control are cited as factors that give advantage to the mix. Wide variety in cakes, muffins, yeast products, cookies and other products are now found in mixes.

Mixes are blends of flour, sugar, shortening emulsified with mono or diglycerides, dried eggs, salt, leavening agent, milk solids and flavoring. Ratios of ingredients are varied according to the product, and some of the foregoing ingredients may be omitted or others added, depending upon what type of product is desired. Loss of leavening power and some loss of flavor may result in mixes stored more than 6 months. Quantities required should be limited to a shorter period. Mixes may be purchased in 5, 10, 25, 50 and 100-lb sacks. Sponge and angel cake mixes are best prepared in small quantities. Brand purchase is recommended.

Yeast

Compressed yeast is the most common form used in food services. It is usually purchased weekly in pound bricks. Storage should be in a refrigerated area. Yeast will mold and deteriorate if held too long. Fresh compressed yeast should be a creamy white or light-tan color, with a slight gray evident. The product should be moist, not slimy, and should crumble easily. The odor should be that of fresh yeast. Stale or old yeast will become slimy, brown in color and develop strong flavors. Dry yeast that reacts as quickly in use as compressed yeast may be obtained. It is dried in fine granular form and marketed in sealed containers packed with nitrogen gas. It will store for much longer periods of time than fresh, compressed yeast. Cans should be dated to indicate time of processing. It does not require refrigeration but, if kept under refrigeration in closed cans, it will retain strength longer.

Compressed yeast may be frozen, but it will lose strength slowly during frozen storage and may, at the end of several months, lose much of its potency. It should be thawed out under refrigerated conditions. Dry, active yeast may be frozen without much damage to the yeast.

Soup Bases

Monosodium glutamate, also called MSG for short, gives a "meaty" flavor to many foods. It is possible, by blending MSG with hydrolyzed protein, beef extract, beef fat, caramel coloring, salt and other compounds, to make a product that gives the flavor of meat to a broth, although it may contain none. A number of soup bases can be made in this manner. Some may be given the flavor of chicken broth, others bouillon, consomme, onion soup and so forth. They are not only used in food services as soup bases but may be used for flavoring gravies, sauces, and prepared entrees. There are few objective criteria for the purchase of these items, and buyers should attempt to select these products by brand and the reliability of the manufacturer. There are many inferior products on the market in this line.

Salad Dressings

Mayonnaise may also be called mayonnaise dressing or mayonnaise salad dressing. It has been defined by government identity standards as "the semi-solid emulsion of edible vegetable oil, egg yolk or whole egg, vinegar and/or lemon juice, with one or more of the following: salt, other seasoning used in preparation of the mayonnaise and/or dextrose." The finished product must contain not less than 50% edible vegetable oil.

A salad dressing is similar to mayonnaise in appearance and consistency, but differs in flavor, oil content and cost. Water and fillers, rather than eggs, are used to extend the oil and to make the emulsion required. It may contain less than 50% oil. Items must be marked salad dressing on the label when so made.

French dressing is a mixture of oil and vinegar or lemon juice and seasoning. French dressing must contain not less than 35% oil to meet government standards of identity. Emulsifiers may be added to give a permanent emulsion. Some French dressings may have thickening agents in them, such as starch or flour pastes.

9 Poultry and Eggs

POULTRY

There are many advantages in featuring poultry on a menu. A popular item, it competes well with steaks, chops, roasts and sea food. It is usually lower or equal in cost to these items. Wide variety is possible not only because of the many different kinds of poultry but also because they can be prepared in a number of different ways.

Poultry consumption has been increasing more rapidly than meat or fish. In 1930 the per capita consumption of poultry was about 17 lb per year. In 1956 it was nearly 29 lb, an increase of 71%. Meats in the same period increased 25% per capita, while fish hardly increased at all. A part of this increased consumption has undoubtedly resulted from improved production and marketing procedures and the low cost of poultry compared with other flesh foods.

Poultry is no longer a casual farm crop. Huge poultry farms where the sole crop is one class of poultry now exist. Shipments of market-ready birds may be made almost every week of the year. Poultry production is losing its seasonal aspect and a stable supply is now usually available. Year around supply has a steadying effect on prices. Although October is the peak month and March and April the low months for hens and cocks, the variation is much less today than in former years. Chicken and turkey fryers and broilers have little if any peak or low production cycles during the year. Freezing of stocks has given stability also to the market. Of the total crop, 12% of the broilers and fryers, 45% of the mature chickens, 66% of the ducks and geese, and 82% of the turkeys are frozen. Buyers seeking fresh supplies of ducklings will find them most plentiful from July through September and turkeys and

FIG. 9–1. This stamp must appear on all poultry shipped interstate; it indicates wholesomeness of product. Courtesy USDA.

geese in November and December. The quality of the frozen product is so high, however, that the market no longer discriminates as much against it in price as formerly.

Improved breeding, feeding and care have improved poultry on our markets. Carefully controlled processing and marketing methods aid in retaining this improved quality. Inspection for wholesomeness and grading has increased consumer confidence.

To obtain highest quality in frozen poultry, buyers should specify that poultry should be chilled to 40° F immediately after slaughter. Freezing should be within 48 hours, with storage temperatures from chilling to freezing at 36° F. Individually packaged poultry need not be prechilled to 40° F if it is packaged and frozen rapidly within 2 hours of slaughter. All poultry should be frozen by rapid freezing methods.

Inspection for Wholesomeness

Federal regulations require that all poultry products shipped interstate must receive ante and post-mortem inspection. Approval of wholesomeness is indicated by the stamp shown in Figure 9–1. This approval requires that the poultry not only be fit for consumption but also that it be handled in a sanitary manner in processing. The slaughter house, the employees and other factors must meet established standards. The approval stamp may appear on the wing as a metal tag; be stuck to the bird as a paper tag or be printed on a paper or plastic wrap. The circle approval stamp should not be confused with the grade shield stamp.

Food and Drug Administration regulations also control certain production and marketing procedures. Only approved compounds may be included in the diet of the birds. Only the antibiotics, chlortetracycline or oxytetracycline, may be used in the chilling water into which freshly killed poultry is plunged after slaughter. The use of these two compounds reduces bacteria on the poultry.

State and local laws are very important in marketing poultry. Buyers should learn local regulations for the area in which they purchase poultry.

Kinds and Classes

Poultry is separated into kinds on the market: chickens, turkeys, ducks, geese, guineas and pigeons. Cornish fowl and some cross breeds are also on the market. Cornish fowl are classified as chickens. Peafowl, swans, quail, wild ducks or geese, pheasants, chukkars, snipes and others are called game birds.

These poultry kinds are further separated into classes. A class is a division within a kind that reflects physical characteristics as influenced by age and sex. Federal descriptions for poultry, according to kind and class, are listed in Table 9–1. Factors helpful in identifying age and sex appear in Tables 9–2 and 9–3.

Styles

Specifications for poultry should state the style or state in which poultry is to be delivered. This may be *live, dressed* (formerly called New

FIG. 9–2. Sex can be distinguished by the larger wattles and helmet of the male guinea on the left. Courtesy USDA.

Table 9-1
Classes of Poultry*

Chickens

Rock Cornish game hen or Cornish game hen

A Rock Cornish game hen or Cornish game hen is a young immature chicken (usually 5 to 7 weeks of age) weighing not more than 2 pounds ready-to-cook weight, which was prepared from a Cornish chicken or the progeny of a Cornish chicken crossed with another breed of chicken.

Broiler or fryer

A broiler or fryer is a young chicken (usually 9 to 12 weeks of age), of either sex, that is tender-meated with soft, pliable, smooth-textured skin and flexible breastbone cartilage.

Roaster

A roaster is a young chicken (usually 3 to 5 months of age), of either sex, that is tender-meated with soft, pliable, smooth-textured skin and breastbone cartilage that may be somewhat less flexible than that of a broiler or fryer.

Capon

A capon is a surgically unsexed male chicken (usually under 8 months of age) that is tender-meated with soft, pliable, smooth-textured skin.

Stag

A stag is a male chicken (usually under 10 months of age) with coarse skin, somewhat toughened and darkened flesh, and considerable hardening of the breastbone cartilage. Stags show a condition of fleshing and a degree of maturity intermediate between that of a roaster and a cock or old rooster.

Hen or stewing chicken or fowl

A hen or stewing chicken or fowl is a mature female chicken (usually more than 10 months old) with meat less tender than that of a roaster, and nonflexible breastbone.

Cock or old rooster

A cock or old rooster is a mature male chicken with coarse skin, toughened and darkened meat, and hardened breastbone.

Turkeys

Fryer-roaster turkey

A fryer-roaster turkey is a young immature turkey (usually under 16 weeks of age), of either sex, that is tender-meated with soft, pliable, smooth-textured skin, and flexible breastbone cartilage.

Young hen turkey

A young hen turkey is a young female turkey (usually 5 to 7 months of age) that is tender-meated with soft, pliable, smooth-textured skin, and breastbone cartilage that is somewhat less flexible than in a fryer-roaster turkey.

Young tom turkey

A young tom turkey is a young male turkey (usually 5 to 7 months of age) that is tender-meated with soft, pliable, smooth-textured skin, and breastbone cartilage that is somewhat less flexible than in a fryer-roaster turkey.

Yearling hen turkey

A yearling hen turkey is a fully matured female turkey (usually under 15 months of age) that is reasonably tender-meated and with reasonably smooth-textured skin.

Table 9–1 (Continued)
Classes of Poultry*

Yearling tom turkey
A yearling tom turkey is a fully matured male turkey (usually under 15 months of age) that is reasonably tender-meated and with reasonably smooth-textured skin.
Mature turkey or old turkey (hen or tom)
A mature or old turkey is an old turkey of either sex (usually in excess of 15 months of age) with coarse skin and toughened flesh.
For labeling purposes, the designation of sex within the class name is optional and the three classes of young turkeys may be grouped and designated as "young turkeys."

Ducks
Broiler duckling or fryer duckling
A broiler duckling or fryer duckling is a young duck (usually under 8 weeks of age), of either sex, that is tender-meated and has a soft bill and soft windpipe.
Roaster duckling
A roaster duckling is a young duck (usually under 16 weeks of age), of either sex, that is tender-meated and has a bill that is not completely hardened and a windpipe that is easily dented.
Mature duck or old duck
A mature duck or an old duck is a duck (usually over 6 months of age), of either sex, with toughened flesh, hardened bill, and hardened windpipe.

Geese
Young goose
A young goose may be of either sex, is tender-meated, and has a windpipe that is easily dented.
Mature goose or old goose
A mature goose or old goose may be of either sex and has toughened flesh and hardened windpipe.

Guineas
Young guinea
A young guinea may be of either sex and is tender-meated.
Mature guinea or old guinea
A mature guinea or an old guinea may be of either sex and has toughened flesh.

Pigeons
Squab
A squab is a young, immature pigeon of either sex, and is extra tender-meated.
Pigeon
A pigeon is a mature pigeon of either sex, with coarse skin and toughened flesh.

*Table prepared from USDA's "Grading and Inspection of Poultry and Edible Products Thereof; and United States Classes, Standards, and Grades with Respect Thereto," July 1, 1960.

Table 9–2
Age Factors Identifiable in Live, Dressed or Ready-to-Cook Poultry*

Factor to Note	Young Bird	Mature Bird
Comb on chickens	Pliable, resilient, not wrinkled with sharp points.	Wrinkled, coarser, thicker points with more roundness.
Bill on ducks	Pliable, not completely hardened.	Hardened.
Plumage	Fresh, glossy appearance.	Faded and worn except on birds that have recently molted.
Fat	Smooth layers; not lumpy over heavy feather areas.	Generally darker and inclined to lump over heavy feathered areas.
Breastbone	Cartilage pliable and soft.	End of keel hardened and bony.
Pinbones	Pliable.	Not pliable.
Shanks	Scales on shanks, smooth and small.	Scales, larger, rougher and slightly raised.
Feet	Soft and pliable, fresh appearing; light in color in chickens, ducks, geese, guineas, etc., but dark or black on young turkeys.	Hard and horny; darker in color on chickens, ducks, geese, guineas, etc. but grow lighter and pinker on older turkeys.
Oil sac	Small, soft.	Enlarged, often hardened.
Spurs on chickens and turkeys	Small, undeveloped, cornlike on males.	Increase in length with age becoming somewhat curved and sharper on males. Hens may have a fine smaller sharp spur after the first year.
Windpipe on ducks and geese	Easily dented.	Hardened, almost bony-like to touch.
Flesh	Tender-meated, soft, translucent appearing; fine texture.	Coarser texture, darker, hardened muscle fibers.
Drumsticks	Lacking in development. Muscles easily dented.	Generally rounded, full, firm.
Dewbill on turkey (fleshy appendage over beak)	Small on males; almost lacking on females.	Enlarged on older males and well developed on older females.
Beard on turkeys (hairy growth on breast)	Starts at about $2\frac{1}{2}$ months on young male turkeys and at the end of a year is 3 to 5 inches long.	Well developed on older males. Hen turkeys start a beard at about a year but it is small compared with that of toms.

*Adapted from USDA *Handbook No. 31.*

Table 9–3
Factors that May Indicate Sex in Poultry*

Factor	Males	Females
Head	Usually larger, with larger and longer attachments such as comb and wattles; coarser than that of females in appearance.	Smaller, rather fine and delicate in appearance compared with males. Hen turkeys have hair on center line of head.
Plumage	Feathers usually long and pointed at the ends. Tail feathers in chickens long and curved. Parti-colored varieties have more brilliant colors than females. Most male ducks have a curl in tail feathers.	Feathers inclined to be shorter and more blunt than those of the male. Tail feathers short and straight in comparison. Modest colors in parti-colored varieties.
Body	Larger and more angular. Depth from keel to back greater on same weight birds. Bones, including shanks, are longer, larger and coarser.	Finer boned, body more rounded. Usually deeper, broader, with more slender wings, shanks and thighs.
Skin	Slightly coarser, particularly in the older birds. Feather follicles larger. Less fat under skin between heavy feathered areas and over back.	Smoother, generally a better distribution of fat between feather areas. Feather areas narrower but carry more fat.
Keel	Longer with fleshing tending to taper at the base.	Shorter, with more rounded appearance over the breast.
Legs	Drumstick and thigh relatively long, with flesh tending to show less fullness until maturity is reached.	Drumstick and thigh relatively shorter, with drumstick more inclined to roundness; increasingly so with age.

*Note: Sex is not a factor in the quality of young poultry but as age increases, it may become so.

York dressed), and *ready-to-cook*. Most poultry on the market today is ready-to-cook, and buyers may specify it whole carcass, split, quartered or cut-up. Cut-up may be in parts proportional to the carcass or as selected parts. Increased quantities of selected parts of poultry are being purchased. Stuffed chicken legs and breasts and other poultry parts with much built-in labor are also appearing on the market. Buyers should determine portion size available on the market of parts and these other products.

Little poultry is marketed alive today. However, some foreign-born and Jewish population groups may purchase live poultry on the consumer market. Dressed poultry is killed by bleeding. It is then picked clean and cooled rapidly. The crop should be free of feed and the intestinal tract free of fecal matter. The head is left on and is usually wrapped. The feet are on and some wing feathers may remain. The bird is not eviscerated. Ready-to-cook means that the carcass comes from dressed poultry and, in addition, the exterior is singed and pin-feathers and vestigial feathers removed. The head, shanks at the back joint, crop, windpipe, esophagus, entrails, gall bladder, lungs and oil sac are removed. The giblets, consisting of heart, liver and gizzard, are adequately cleaned, drained and wrapped in non-absorbent paper and placed in the body cavity. On large birds the neck may be removed and wrapped in non-absorbent paper and placed in the body cavity.

Buyers should know shrinkage losses that occur in preparing poultry into the various styles. Table 9–4 lists some of the preparation losses found in preparing poultry for market.

Table 9–4
Shrinkage Losses in Preparing Ready-to-cook Poultry from Live Poultry

Type Poultry	Percent Loss	Type Poultry	Percent Loss
Chickens, all types	27.8	Geese	22.5
Broilers and fryers	28.0	Turkeys, all types	20.3
Roasters	27.6	Fryers	24.0
Fowl	27.8	Heavy hens	20.4
Ducks	27.0	Heavy toms	20.3

Chicken parts are defined by the United States Department of Agriculture as follows:

(1) "Breasts" shall be separated from the back at the shoulder joint and by a cut running backward and downward from that point along the junction of the vertebral and sternal ribs. The ribs may be removed from the breasts, and the breasts may be cut along the breastbone to make two approximately equal halves; or the wishbone portion, as described in subparagraph (3) of this paragraph, may be removed before cutting the remainder along the breastbone to make three parts. Pieces cut in this manner may be substituted for lighter or heavier pieces for exact weight-making purposes and the package may contain two or more of such parts without affecting the appropriateness of the labeling as "chicken breasts." Neck skin shall not be included.

(2) "Breasts with ribs" shall be separated from the back at the junction of the vertebral ribs and back. Breasts with ribs may be cut along the breast-bone to make approximately two halves; or the wishbone portion, as described in subparagraph (3) of this paragraph, may be removed before cutting the re-mainder along the breastbone to make three parts. Pieces cut in this manner may be substituted for lighter or heavier pieces for exact weight-making pur-poses and the package may contain two or more of such parts without affecting the appropriateness of the labeling as "breasts with ribs." Neck skin shall not be included.

(3) "Wishbones" (Pulley Bones), with covering muscle and skin tissue, shall be severed from the breast approximately halfway between the end of the wish-bone (hypocledium) and front point of the breastbone (cranial process of the sternal crest) to a point where the wishbone joins the shoulder. Neck skin shall not be included.

(4) "Drumsticks" shall be separated from the thigh by a cut through the knee joint (femorotibial and patellar joint) and from the hock joint (tarsal joint).

(5) "Thighs" shall be disjointed at the hip joint and may include the pelvic meat but shall not include the pelvic bones. Back skin shall not be included.

(6) "Legs" shall include the whole leg, i.e., the thigh and the drumstick, whether jointed or disjointed. Back skin shall not be included.

(7) "Wings" shall include the entire wing with all muscle and skin tissue intact, except that the wing tip may be removed.

(8) "Backs" shall include the pelvic bones and all the vertebrae posterior to the shoulder joint. The meat shall not be peeled from the pelvic bones. The vertebral ribs and/or scapula may be removed or included. Skin shall be substantially intact.

(9) "Halves" shall be prepared by making a full-length back and breast split of the carcass so as to produce approximately equal right and left sides.

(10) "Quarters" shall be prepared by splitting the carcass as specified in sub-paragraph (9) of this paragraph and the resulting halves shall be cut crosswise at almost right angles to the backbone so as to form quarters.

Type

Type poultry indicates whether the poultry is fresh chilled or frozen. Specifications should state type. Fresh-chilled poultry may be held at 40° F for only 3 days. The following definitions are usually accepted in channels of trade for types of poultry:

Fresh: Killed and cooled immediately; not held longer than 3 days under refrigeration. Fresh-chilled poultry may be dry or iced upon delivery. Around 20 lb of ice are used per 80 lb poultry. Check net weight of iced poultry carefully. Should be 40° F on delivery.
Storage: Similar to fresh but held over 3 days.
Frozen: Cooled rapidly by rapid freezing at −25 to −60° F until frozen. May also be frozen by packaging in plastic wrap and dropped into extremely cold propylene-glycol.
Hard chilled: Poultry held in frozen storage up to 60 days.
Frozen storage: Frozen poultry held over 60 days but not over 100 days.

Buyers should specify that frozen poultry should be hard frozen upon delivery.

Plucking

Specifications may state the type of plucking desired. At one time great care was taken in processing poultry to dry pluck it in order to retain a desirable softness or appearance called bloom. Because of newly discovered techniques, the use of automatic pluckers, better packaging to preserve bloom and economy in processing, dry plucking has largely been discontinued except where feathers are desired as down. A semi-scald method is now generally used. In dry picking, the bird is picked at body heat as it is being bled.

To semi-scald, the poultry is bled and then immediately plunged into water around 138° F for about 30 to 45 seconds. This slightly loosens the feathers from the skin. The poultry is next sent through automatic pluckers and plunged into ice cold water to cool. This gives a satisfactory pluck and a fairly good bloom. The use of plastic wraps prevents tarnishing and skin blemishes that detract from the appearance of poultry; factors that would otherwise develop if the poultry were to remain exposed to the air.

Heavy scalding at 170° F for 20 to 30 seconds may be used in some cases for plucking. This is called scald plucking.

Wax plucking may be specified. This is a combination type pluck where most of the surface feathers are removed by dry, semi-scald or scald method. The poultry is then dipped into wax and the remaining feathers removed. The resulting appearance is very satisfactory. Some premium packs of poultry may be wax plucked.

Size

The size of the poultry purchased should receive careful consideration. Portions must be correct, and birds must be purchased to yield the desired portion size. A 1½ lb ready-to-cook broiler may be a desirable size for two portions if the bird is split lengthwise, while a 2½ lb ready-to-cook broiler may only be desirable for cut-up portions. If a duckling is to be cut into fourths for portions, a 3 to 3½ lb bird may be desirable. A larger sized duckling would not be economical. Turkeys over 20 lb give a higher yield per skeleton than those under 20 lb.

Hens (chicken) over 4½ to 5 lb will usually be found wasteful because of excessive abdominal fat. Turkeys over 20 lb will have a greater proportion of meat to skeletal structure. While tom turkeys are larger boned than the female, the proportion of flesh to bone is greater giving more servings per pound of purchase weight than hen turkeys.

After roasting, a 24-lb dressed turkey yields about 3½ lb dark meat slices and 4 lb white meat slices, plus giblets, wings and picked meat. The total yield in cooked meat will be around 12 to 13 lb. The following information has been obtained in cooking turkeys:

Table 9–5

Average Dressed Weight	Ready-to-Cook Weight as a Percent of Dressed Weight	From Dressed Weight	
		Final Roasted Weight	Edible Meat
32 lb	90.0%	63.1%	52.2%
16	84.4	58.8	41.2
8	82.5	51.3	37.5

A 5 lb ready-to-cook roasting chicken (6⅓ lb dressed weight) will give 48.8% roasted weight and 29.3% edible meat. The edible yield on ducks and geese is low when sliced. More adequate yields are obtained from these birds if the meat is portioned bone-in. A 3½ lb duckling, if split in half and then divided again so a quarter is obtained, gives a much more satisfactory portion than if sliced and served.

Average quantities of ready-to-cook poultry required per portion are:

Chicken		
	Broiler	¾ to 1 lb
	Fryer or roaster	¾ to 1 lb
	Stewing	¼ to 1 lb
Turkey		
	Roasting	½ to 1 lb
Duck or goose		
	Roasting	¾ to 1 lb

Specifications should state the poultry weight desired. Geese and turkeys may be specified by individual weight. Many smaller birds are specified in weights per dozen, with minimum and maximum limits allowed per bird. Buyers should select carefully to obtain the most economical buys and favorable portion sizes.

Packaging for birds of the size of chickens may be 12 to 24 per case. Large birds may be packed singly or 4 per case. Containers should be plainly marked to show net weight, kind, class, style and grade of poultry in the container. Some trade names used on the market follow:

Squab broilers: Chickens that weigh 1¼ lb or less dressed.
Spring chickens: Fryers around 2½ to 3½ lb each.
Exports: Fryers 3½ lb or over.
Fancy large: Good quality birds selling at a premium price.
Heavy: Heavier birds than desired offered at a lower price when lighter birds are specified.
Rocks: Chickens from the Plymouth Rock strain, which are a good meat bird.
Black: Dark-colored varieties of chickens that are usually meaty and heavy but may have dark pinfeathers.
Colored: The meaty heavy type birds as in contrast to the light or white varieties, which are used for egg laying purposes; white or light-colored chickens of good conformation are preferred for the market because the pinfeathers are less evident.
White: Leghorns or other light birds grown for egg laying purposes. Most of these chickens no longer find their way into institutional markets but are purchased for processing into cooked chicken products.

Breed

The breed of poultry purchased is important. The yield of meat and the flavor are influenced by the breed.

At one time young cocks from egg-laying strains were force fed and rapidly moved to market as broilers. Hens from egg-laying strains, after completing their productive laying cycles, were culled from flocks and moved onto the market. However, few are found on the general market today. The young cocks are destroyed as soon as they can be identified from the pullets. The fowl or hens now mostly find their way into processed chicken products.

Meat breeds of chickens will yield good-sized, compactly built birds. These are the birds frequently called colored. (See above definitions.) Some general purpose breeds may be on the market. These are raised for both table meat and eggs. Most turkeys on the market today are the broad-breasted Beltsville breed, which have broad breasts, thick, short, plump legs and which give a high yield of meat to bone. The meat breeds of ducks are Peking, Aylesbury, Moscovy, Rouen, Cayuga, Buff and Swedish. Only one laying-type duck is found in this country, Indian Runner, which is raised for both eggs and meat. The Peking duck by far outranks all other breeds marketed. It is raised in large numbers on duck farms on Long Island and in the Midwest. The most common breeds of geese marketed are the Toulouse and Embden. The Toulouse is a gray bird weighing 20 to 26 lb at maturity. Its appearance is somewhat dark when plucked. The Embden is preferred because it is white and has a better appearance than the Toulouse after plucking. Quality is not affected by the darker appearance and since the Toulouse is a larger bird giving a higher yield of meat to bone, it is usually preferred for institutional use. Homer and Carneaux pigeons are the most commonly raised breeds for the market.

Grading

Federal grades for dressed or ready-to-cook poultry are U.S. Grades A, B or C. At the consumer level, all poultry in a lot must meet the grade requirements for the grade. At the wholesale level, a lot may be designated U.S. Extra if not less than 90% by count is A quality and the remainder B quality. The lot may be wholesale grade U.S. Standard if not less than 90% by count is B quality and the remainder C quality. U.S. Trade Grade in the wholesale market is poultry not less than C quality. "No Grade" is a term applied to poultry with dirty or bloody head or carcass, dirty feet or vent, fan feathers, neck feathers, garter feathers or feed in the crop. Inspection certificates should show the percentage of qualities in the "No Grade" lot, including those that cause the "No Grade" designation. The condition of the "No Grade" birds should be described.

Governmental or other agencies will sometimes purchase lots on the basis of procurement grades. Procurement Grade I has 90% or more of

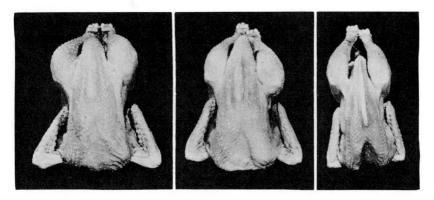

FIG. 9–3.   Young chicken carcasses: (left to right) A Quality, B Quality and C Quality.
Courtesy USDA.

the carcasses Grade A, except that fat covering may be that for B
quality. Trimming of skin and flesh to remove defects is allowed if not
more than one quarter of the flesh is exposed on any part and the meat
yield is not materially affected. The wings may be severed at a joint
and the tail at the base. The remaining 10% must meet the same requirements except that it can have only a moderate covering of flesh.
If a lot fails to meet Procurement Grade I it may be designated Procurement Grade II, providing the trimming of flesh from any part does not
exceed 10% of the meat; and portions of a carcass weighing not less
than one-half the whole carcass may be included if the portion approxi-
mates in percentage the meat to bone yield of the whole carcass.

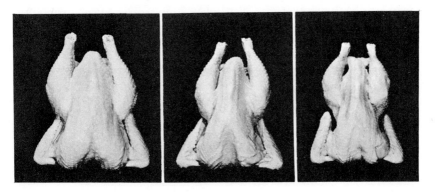

FIG. 9–4.   Hen, stewing chicken or fowl: (left to right) A Quality, B Quality and C
Quality.   Courtesy USDA.

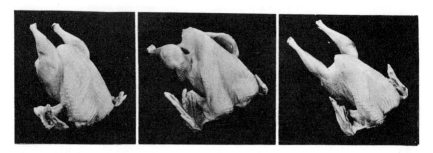

FIG. 9–5. Young hen carcasses: (left to right) A Quality, B Quality and C Quality. Courtesy USDA.

No poultry may be graded that has not passed inspection for wholesomeness. Inspection certificates should state, in addition to grade, the class of poultry, quantity in the lot, condition and edible parts covered.

Buyers should watch grading factors and select from the grades most suitable for the purpose intended. Poultry that is to be steamed or simmered and picked for clear meat need not have all high grade characteristics. A breast defect that might interfere with slicing may not be important if the meat is to be picked from the bones. A skin tear or discoloration that drops an otherwise good bird into a lower quality may be used to good advantage for many quantity cooking purposes.

Factors considered in establishing U.S. Grades A, B and C for ready-to-cook poultry are: (1) conformation, (2) fleshing, (3) fat, (4) freedom from pinfeathers and vestigial feathers (that is, hair or down), (5) degree of freedom from tears and cuts, (6) degree of freedom from disjointed or broken bones, (7) degree of freedom from blemishes and bruises of the skin and flesh and (8) degree of freedom from freezer burn. Table 9–6 summarizes quality factors for U.S. Grades A and B. Poultry that does

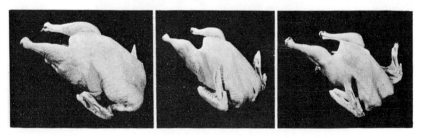

FIG. 9–6. Young tom turkey carcasses: (left to right) A Quality, B Quality and C Quality. Courtesy USDA.

Grade Marks

Metal Wing Clips

Wing Tags

FIG. 9–7.   Some of the grade stamps used to indicate poultry grades.   All poultry bearing federal grades must first be approved for wholesomeness.   Poultry for food facilities may bear individual grade stamps or a grade may be indicated on a bulk package. Federal-state grading may be indicated and means that the federal and state governments are jointly engaging in the inspection program.   The grade tags on the middle and bottom rows may be tags, wing tags or appear on the wrapper.   Courtesy USDA.

Table 9–6
Quality Factors Determining U.S. Grades A and B in
Dressed and Ready-to-Cook Poultry

A QUALITY

Conformation

The carcass or part is free of deformities that detract from its appearance or that affect the normal distribution of flesh. Slight deformities such as slightly curved or dented breastbones and slightly curved backs may be present.

Fleshing

The carcass or part has a well-developed covering of flesh. The breast is moderately long and deep and has sufficient flesh to give it a rounded appearance with the flesh carrying well up to the crest of the breastbone along its entire length.

Fat covering

The carcass or part, considering the kind, class and part, has a well-developed layer of fat in the skin. The fact is well distributed so that there is a noticeable amount of fat in the skin in the areas between the heavy feather tracts.

Defeathering

The carcass or part has a clean appearance, especially on the breast. The carcass or part is free of pinfeathers, diminutive feathers, and hair which are visible to the inspector or grader.

Cuts, tears and missing skin

Parts are free of cuts, tears and missing skin (other than slight trimming on the edge). The carcass is free of these defects on the breast and legs. Elsewhere the carcass may have slight cuts, tears, or missing skin areas providing the aggregate of the areas of flesh exposed thereby does not exceed the area of a circle of the following diameter, respectively: (1) on chickens, ducks, guineas and pigeons, $1\frac{1}{2}$ inches; (2) on turkeys and geese, 2 inches.

Disjointed and broken bones and missing parts

Parts are free of broken bones. The carcass is free of broken bones and has not more than one disjointed bone. The wing tips may be removed at the joint and the tail may be removed at the base. Cartilage separated from the breastbone is not considered as a disjointed or broken bone.

Discolorations of the skin and flesh

The carcass or part is practically free of such defects. Discoloration due to bruising shall be free of clots (discernible clumps of red or dark cells). Evidence of incomplete bleeding, such as more than an occasional slightly reddened feather follicle, is not permitted. Flesh bruises and discolorations of the skin such as "blue back" are not permitted on the breast or legs of the carcass or on these individual parts and only lightly shaded discolorations are permitted elsewhere. The total area affected by flesh bruises, skin bruises and discolorations such as "blue back" singly or in combination shall not exceed one-half of the total aggregate area of permitted discoloration. The aggregate area of all discolorations on a part shall not exceed that of a circle $\frac{1}{4}$ inch in diameter. The aggregate area of all discolorations on the breast and legs of a carcass shall not exceed the area of a circle 1 inch in diameter for chickens, ducks, guineas and pigeons and 2 inches for turkeys and geese. Elsewhere on the carcass the aggregate area of all discolorations shall not exceed that of a circle having a diameter of 2 and 3 inches respectively.

Table 9–6 (Continued)
Quality Factors Determining U.S. Grades A and B in
Dressed and Ready-to-Cook Poultry

Freezer burn

The carcass or part may have an occasional pockmark due to drying of the inner layer of skin (derma), provided that none exceed the area of a circle ⅛ inch in diameter on chickens, guineas, ducks and pigeons, or ¼ inch on turkeys and geese.

B QUALITY

Conformation

The carcass or part may have slight abnormalities, such as a dented, curved or crooked breast, crooked back, or misshapen legs or wings which do not materially affect the distribution of flesh or the appearance of the carcass or part.

Fleshing

The carcass or part has a moderate covering of flesh considering the kind, class and part of the bird. The breast has a substantial covering of flesh with the flesh carrying up to the crest of the breastbone sufficiently to prevent a thin appearance.

Fat covering

The carcass or part has sufficient fat in the skin to prevent a distinct appearance of the flesh through the skin, especially on the breast and legs.

Defeathering

The carcass or part may have a few nonprotruding pinfeathers or vestigial feathers which are scattered sufficiently so as not to appear numerous. Not more than an occasional protruding pinfeather or diminutive feather shall be in evidence under a careful examination.

Cuts, tears and missing skin

Parts may have cuts, tears and missing skin, provided that not more than a moderate amount of the flesh normally covered by the skin is exposed. The carcass may have cuts, tears and missing skin, provided that the aggregate of the areas of flesh exposed thereby on the breast and legs does not exceed the area of a circle of the following diameters, respectively: (1) on chickens, ducks, guineas and pigeons, 1½ inches; (2) on turkeys and geese, 3 inches. Elsewhere on the carcass the aggregate area of flesh exposed shall not be greater than the area of a circle having the following diameters respectively: (i) on chickens, ducks, guineas, and pigeons, 3 inches; (ii) on turkeys and geese, 6 inches.

Disjointed and broken bones and missing parts

Parts may be disjointed but are free of broken bones. The carcass may have two disjointed bones or one disjointed bone and one nonprotruding broken bone. Parts of the wing beyond the second joint may be removed at a joint. The tail may be removed at the base.

Discolorations of the skin and flesh

The carcass or part is free of serious defects. Discoloration due to bruising shall be free of clots (discernible clumps of red or dark cells). Evidence of incomplete bleeding shall be no more than very slight. Moderate areas of discoloration due to bruises in the skin or flesh and moderately shaded discoloration of the skin such as "blue back" are permitted, but the total areas affected by such discolorations singly or in any combination may not exceed one-half of the total aggregate area of permitted discoloration. The aggregate area of all discolorations on a part shall not exceed the area of a circle having a diameter of 1 inch for chickens, ducks, guineas and pigeons and 1½ inches for turkeys and geese. The aggregate area of all discolorations on the breast and legs of a carcass shall not exceed that of a circle having a diameter of 2 inches on chickens, ducks, guineas and pigeons and 3 inches on turkeys and geese. Elsewhere on the carcass the aggregate area of all discolorations shall not exceed that of a circle having a diameter of 4 inches and 6 inches respectively.

Freezer burn

The carcass or part may have a few pockmarks due to drying of the inner layer of skin (derma), provided that no single area exceeds that of a circle ½ inch in diameter.

Courtesy USDA.

not meet the requirements for A or B quality may be of C quality if the flesh is substantially intact. Both wings may be trimmed in C quality. Trimming of the breast and legs is also permitted but not to such an extent that the normal meat yield is materially affected. In any grade, if ready-to-cook poultry is to be disjointed and packed as parts, a defective portion may be removed without loss of grade. Ready-to-cook carcasses in Grades A or B may only have wing tips removed.

Figure 9–7 shows the type of grade stamp that may appear on federally graded poultry.

Rabbits

Although rabbits are not poultry, their grading and handling are very similar to that of poultry. Inspection and grading by federal government are offered.

Fryers are young domestic rabbit carcasses weighing not less than 1½ lb and rarely more than 3½ lb. They are less than 12 weeks old. A roaster is a mature or old domestic rabbit of any weight, usually, however, it is over 4 lb and over 12 weeks old. Most average around 8 months old.

Grades for rabbits are A, B and C. In the A quality, conformation is short, thick, well rounded and full fleshed, with a broad back, broad hips and broad, deep-fleshed shoulders and firm, tender muscle texture. Strips of fat should appear over the loins, shoulders and back, and be plentiful in the interior. Many of the characteristics that indicate quality in chickens or other poultry indicate quality in rabbits.

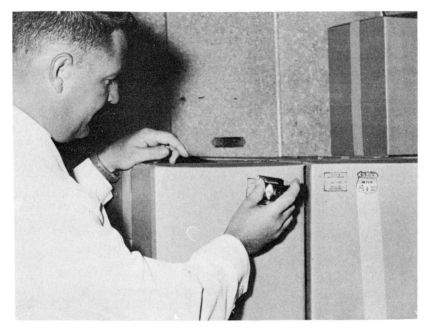

FIG. 9-8.   A federal inspector affixing the acceptance inspection stamp on a case of eggs. Note that, to the right of the stamp, the federal shield with the grade appears, indicating that the eggs meet federal standards in addition.   Courtesy USDA.

Specifications for Poultry

The kind, class, grade, style, weight classification, state upon delivery, breeds and other factors should be well defined in poultry specifications for the institution.   The poultry should be inspected and passed for wholesomeness.   An example of acceptable specifications is shown in Chapter 1.

Buyers may make arrangements for federal inspection of poultry based on the specifications of the buyer.   This is an arrangement of inspection similar to that given by the government for other foods and is called acceptance inspection.   To obtain this service federal inspectors are given the buyer's specifications.   Purveyors are told before bidding that inspection and certification by federal inspectors are required.   Arrangements for this service are made through the USDA Poultry Division, Agricultural Marketing Service, regional or national offices.

Usually this type of service can be given when lots of over 500 lb are purchased and federal inspectors are available.   The purveyor pays for the inspection and certification service.   Upon inspection each package of poultry and the invoice are stamped to indicate the poultry meets the buyer's standards.   An example of an inspection stamp would be:

> U. S. D. A.
>
> Officially Sampled
>
> * (D a t e) *
>
> Accepted for (establishment)

Certification should also verify kind, class, weight, quality and other factors.   Inspection and certification should be within 1 to 2 days of delivery.

EGGS

Food facilities may purchase their egg requirments in several forms. Shell eggs will be required for many cooking purposes.   Frozen and dried eggs may be used in the bake shop or for specialty use.   The use, convenience and economy of purchase should dictate the type for purchase.   Freeze-dry eggs, a dehydrated product dried under high vacuum

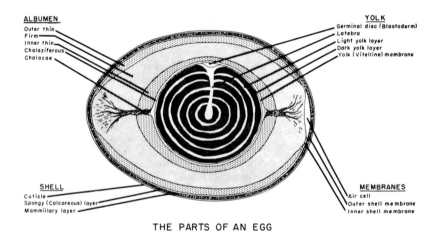

THE PARTS OF AN EGG

FIG. 9-9. The parts of an egg. The yolk is suspended in the center of the white by the chalazae. As the egg ages, the firm white decreases and turns either into thin outer or inner portions; the air cell increases in size and the chalazae weaken, allowing the yolk to lose its center position. Courtesy USDA.

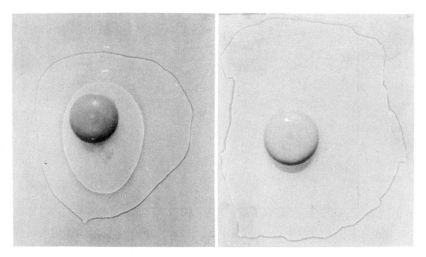

FIG. 9–10. Condition of albumen and yolk in the Grade A egg on the left contrasts noticeably with these factors in the Grade B on the right. Courtesy USDA.

while frozen, are on the market but as yet are not used extensively in quantity preparation.

The total weight of an egg is made up of 58% albumen or white, 31% yolk and 11% shell. Dry solids in eggs are whole egg 34%, yolk 52% and albumen 20%.

Shell Eggs

Judgment of the quality of shell eggs is based upon interior and exterior factors. The condition of the yolk and albumen and the size and condition of the air cell are noted in evaluating interior quality. The shell soundness, cleanliness, shape and texture are judged for exterior factors. Flavor is not evaluated but certain of these quality characteristics may indicate flavor.

Candling is extensively used to determine egg quality. Holding an egg before a strong light shows the position of the yolk, the size of the air cell, blood spots on the yolk, a bloody white and other defects. Cracked shells or other shell defects are also generally evident. From time to time candlers may break an egg from the shell onto a plate and check quality by noting visually the condition of the white and yolk.

A good quality egg has an albumen that holds closely to the yolk. The thick portion of white and yolk stand high. The albumen is firm and gelatinous and there is only a small quantity of watery material. A newly laid egg may have a cloudy or whitish opaque albumen, which

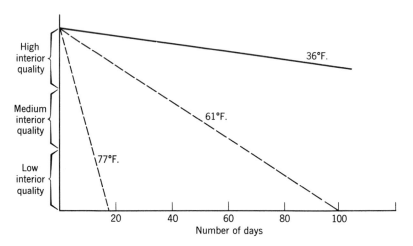

FIG. 9–11.   Egg quality loss is rapid when the eggs are held at high temperature.   Courtesy of Poultry Processing and Marketing Magazine.

will disappear in about 3 days.   The yolk should have good shape and color and should not break when the egg is shelled.   It should be suspended in midcenter of the egg.   The yolk is held in place by two chalazae, which extend from the two ends of the egg.   The membrane wall enclosing the yolk should be strong.   The air cell should be small.

Freshly laid eggs are apt to have shells that are rough and dull in appearance.   Storage eggs may appear smoother and shinier, but this is not an absolute criteria.   Oil-treated eggs may appear shiny; yet these may only be several days old.

The candler will also note the shape of the egg and the condition of the shell.   Sound eggs, when clicked together, will give a bell-like tone, while a checked egg (slightly cracked) will give a flat tone.   Cleanliness of shell will also be noted.

As an egg ages there is a loss of carbon dioxide and moisture through the shell.   The air cell will increase in size.   Albumen consistency becomes more liquid and watery, and the firm, high part surrounding the yolk begins to vanish.   The chalazae weaken and the yolk loses its central position.   The yolk may even come to rest against the shell.   When hard boiled, this off-center yolk plainly shows.   The membrane enclosing the yolk weakens, and the yolk may break when the egg is removed from its shell.

An egg is at highest quality when newly laid.   It deteriorates rapidly after laying, if not given proper care.   An egg at room temperature quickly loses quality.   Depending upon the care given the egg, age may

FIG. 9–12. A Haugh meter used for measuring the height of albumen. This is one of the objective tests in determining quality in Fresh Fancy Quality eggs. Courtesy USDA.

have little or much to do with its quality. Eggs stored for extended periods under optimum conditions may come out of storage at better quality than freshly laid eggs. Flocks in poor physical condition, after long laying, during molting or in winter months may lay poor quality eggs. These may be lower in quality than storage eggs. Eggs are

FIG. 9–13. Two labels that may be used on eggs which meet quality standards under the federal-state quality control program. Courtesy USDA.

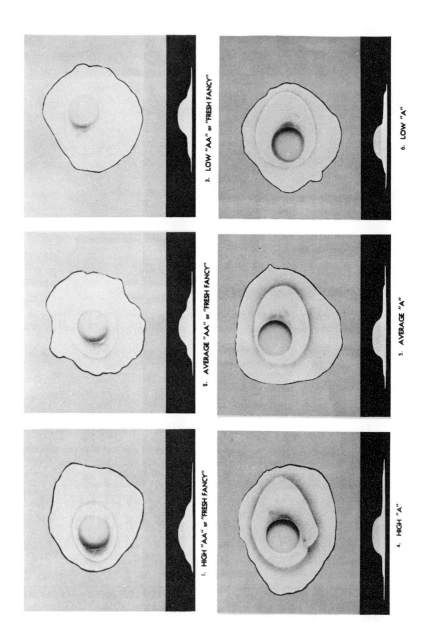

3. LOW "AA" or "FRESH FANCY"

6. LOW "A"

2. AVERAGE "AA" or "FRESH FANCY"

5. AVERAGE "A"

1. HIGH "AA" or "FRESH FANCY"

4. HIGH "A"

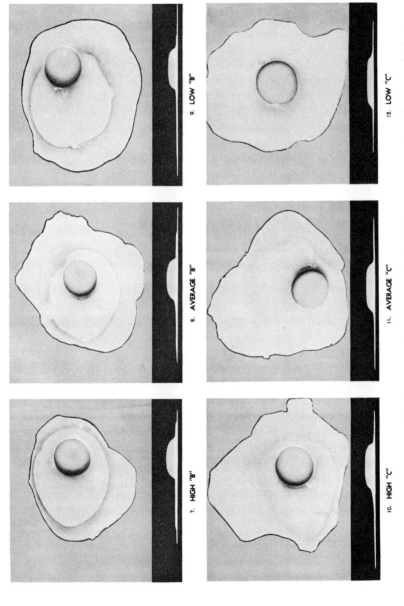

FIG. 9–14. Recommended standards for scoring the interior quality of broken-out eggs, as shown by top and side views. Courtesy USDA.

placed into storage in the spring when the flocks are in vigorous condition and the eggs are at peak quality.

Better breeding, control of flocks, feeding and care are reducing the seasonableness of eggs and stabilizing quality. Egg producers now replace their laying stock two or three times a year rather than once a year. The greatest number of eggs reach the market in April and the lowest number in January, but the high and low peaks are gradually leveling off as improved flock-control methods are used.

There are many chances for error in candling eggs. The demarcation between high quality eggs, Grades AA and A, is very hard to tell. Tolerances are therefore allowed in egg grading. These tolerances are greater for wholesale eggs than for those sent into the consumer market.

More and more objective methods are being used to judge egg quality. Eggs with blood spots on yolks or with bloody whites can now be sorted out by electronic blood spot detectors. Machines are used to sort for size. Machines are also being developed to test for soundness of shell and other factors.

The greatest step in removing human error in judging egg quality has been the introduction of a sampling method. Objective tests may be used to grade the eggs in this new method. Evaluation is by examination of representative samples taken from a lot of eggs that comes from a single flock. The sample of eggs is broken and a device called a Haugh meter measures the height of the albumen. The height of the yolk and interior egg condition are noted. Exterior qualities are evaluated. On the basis of this sampling, the lot is scored. A score of 72 or more places the egg lot from which the samples were drawn into Grade AA quality. The eggs must come from vigorous flocks fed and cared for according to prescribed standards. Eggs from flocks cannot be mixed until grading is complete.

Eggs that meet Grade AA quality may be called Fresh Fancy, Fancy Quality or Fresh Fancy Quality. They may also be labeled Grade AA quality and, in addition, the grade label may state that the eggs were "produced and marketed under the Federal-State quality control program." Eggs meeting Grade A score may be labeled Grade A with the notation that they were "produced and marketed under the Federal-State quality control program." Eggs below Grade A cannot carry the notation that the eggs are produced and marketed under this program. The label used for below Grade A must be that used for regular Grade B or C eggs. A C Grade egg would, by this new scoring system, score 30 points or below. Ten days after the eggs have been graded Grade AA or A (Fancy Quality) under this program, the eggs, if not sold, must be removed from their cartons or the grade label destroyed.

Grades

Federal consumer grades for eggs are AA, A, B and C. Equivalent federal procurement grades in wholesale purchasing are I, II, III and IV. Trade wholesale grades, closely paralleling these two standards, are Specials (Grade AA), Extras (Grade A), Standards (Grade B) and Trades (Grade C). Eggs may not receive a grade if they are dirty, have cracks or are broken, even though they meet other quality standards. The names for these ungraded eggs are respectively: Dirties, Checks and Leakers. At times the quality of these non-graded eggs may be high; thus, they may be purchased for economy reasons. Frequently, however, the quality will be found to parallel the price. A Loss egg is one that is completely inedible or one whose contents have been lost because of a broken shell.

Eggs meeting the federal standards may be stamped with the federal shield. This shield contains the letters USDA on the top and the words "graded under federal supervision" or "graded under the federal-state quality program" if the eggs are graded by the sampling method described above. The grade is also in the shield. The size of the egg may or may not be included. If not, it must be shown elsewhere prominently. The date of grading and the federal plant number in which the grading occurred may be shown. Buyers should specify that not more than 3 days shall elapse between grading and delivery and that the eggs shall be kept at 40 to 50° F until delivered.

Food facilities may purchase their eggs graded according to their own specifications and certified as meeting these specifications by a federal grader. This is called acceptance type inspection. The operation's specifications should be in the hands of the grader as well as the pur-

FIG. 9–15. Grade labels that may appear on federally inspected eggs. Note that in some instances there may be a joint federal-state grading program. The label for inspected egg products may appear as shown on the right. Courtesy USDA.

Table 9–7

Quality Factors in Federal Egg Standards

Quality Factory	AA, I or Specials (Fancy Quality)	Consumer, Procurement or Wholesale Grade		
		A, II or Extras	B, III or Standards	C, IV or Trades
Shell*	Clean, unbroken, practically normal.	Clean, unbroken, practically normal.	Clean to very slightly stained, unbroken.	Clean to moderately stained, unbroken; may be abnormal.
Air Cell	⅛ in. or less in depth; practically regular.	¼ in. or less in depth; practically regular.	⅜ in. or less in depth; may be free but not bubbly.	May be over ⅜ in. in depth; may be free or bubbly.
White	Clear, firm.	Clear, reasonably firm.	Clear; may be slightly weak.	May be weak and watery; small blood spots may be present.†
Yolk	Well centered; outline slightly defined; free from defects.	May be fairly well centered; outline well defined; practically free from defects.	May be off center; outline may be well defined; may be slightly enlarged and flattened; may show definite but not serious defects.	May be off center; outline may be plainly visible; may be enlarged and flattened; may show clearly visible germ development; may show other serious defects.

*The condition of the shell is a major factor in deciding the grade of Dirty, Check or Leaker. A Dirty should not have a broken or cracked shell. A Check may be cracked but not leaking. A Leaker has broken shell with leakage of egg contents.
†If they are small (aggregating not more than ⅛ in. in diameter).

veyor. Purveyors should be notified before bid that this inspection is a requirement and that the purveyor will pay for the service. The grader after approving the eggs will stamp the case with the square acceptance stamp. (See Figure 9–8.) The stamp will be placed so that tampering with contents is not possible. If the eggs meet federal specifications, the grader may stamp the case with a federal shield and grade. The invoice is stamped in the same manner as the cases.

Table 9–7 summarizes quality factors as established by federal standards for eggs.

Other Buying Factors

An egg lot in wholesale channels consists of two or more cases of eggs. A case is 30 dozen. Eggs are also available in the half case, or 15 dozen, at wholesale.

Table 9–8 indicates the common sizes of eggs on the market. Jumbo eggs, minimum weight 30 oz per dozen or 56 lb per case, and Peewee, minimum weight 15 oz per dozen or 28 lb per case, are available in consumer grades in addition to those eggs listed.

Specifications should state size and tolerances in sizing. Some quantity specifications state that individual cases may not contain over 10% of the eggs below the minimum weights specified. This 10% should not weigh less than the minimum specified for the next lower weight class, which means that 36 eggs in a case of large eggs may be medium size but not less. Less tolerance may be desired and specifications may read that only $3\frac{1}{3}\%$ or 12 eggs per case may fall below minimum weight. This would mean that for a case of large eggs, only one dozen could weigh less than 23 oz or, for a case of medium eggs only one dozen could weigh less than 20 oz.

Food services may at times change the size of the egg used to take advantage of favorable buys. There are limitations, however, because

Table 9–8
Market Sizes of Eggs

Size	Consumer Average Ounces per Dozen	Wholesale Minimum Pounds per Case	Allowed Range in Pounds per Case	Minimum Ounce Weight of Any Individual Dozen
Extra large	27	$50\frac{1}{2}$	50–55	26
Large	24	45	45–49	23
Medium	21	$39\frac{1}{2}$	39–44	20
Small	18	34	34–38	17

standard sizes are required for certain purposes. Most institutions must use, for instance, either large or medium eggs for breakfast eggs. They cannot change to small or peewee sizes. If the quality is the same, medium eggs are a good buy when they are at least one-eighth lower in cost than large eggs, and small eggs are a good buy if they are at least one-quarter lower in cost than large eggs.

Specifications should state allowances for quality. These include allowances for human error in grading, breakage, damage or inedibility. Consumer grades have small tolerances. Wholesale grades have greater tolerances. Many specifications allow a 2 to 5% loss for broken or inedible eggs. Tables 9–9 and 9–10 list tolerances allowed under federal standards for consumer and procurement grades of shell eggs.

Individual tolerances may be established by facilities. Some institutions specify that Grade AA eggs per case must be 80% AA, 10% or better A and the remainder B, except that 5% may be C grade, Dirties, Checks or better, and not more than 0.8% (3 eggs per case) may contain meat spots.or blood clots. The same specifications for Grade A eggs require 80% or better A, 20% B or better, except 5% may be C, Dirties, Checks or better, and 0.8% (3 eggs per case) may contain meat spots or blood clots. If a food service establishes its own tolerances, these should be consistent with good commercial practices.

Buyers should know that quality and size are not related. Small eggs may be of the highest or lowest quality and the largest eggs may be of similar varying quality. The quality of the egg also has little to do with its nutritional value. Grade C eggs are as nutritious as Grade AA. The

Table 9–9
Tolerances for Consumer Grades in Shell Eggs

Grade	80% of a Lot Average Must Be*	Permitted Tolerance†
AA	AA	15 to 20% A, not over 5% B, C or Check.
A	A or better	15 to 20% B, not over 5% C or Check.
B	B or better	10 to 20% C, not over 10% Dirty or Check.
C	C or better	Not over 20% Dirty or Check.

*Single cases in lots of two or more may not fall below 70% of the specified quality and no individual case may contain more than double the tolerance for the grade specified.

†Within tolerance permitted, an allowance will be made at receiving points or shipping destination for 1/2% Leakers in Grades AA, A and B, and 1% in C. Substitution of higher qualities for lower qualities specified under permitted tolerances is permitted.

Table 9–10
Tolerances for Wholesale or Procurement Grades in Shell Eggs

Procure- ment Grade	Wholesale Grade Equivalent	Minimum Percent of Grade or Better in Average Lot*	Maximum Tolerance Permitted in Lot Average†
I	Special	80%	15 to 20% B; not over 5% C, Check Dirty, Leaker and Loss.
II	Extras	60%	30 to 40% B; not over 10% III, Check, Dirty, Leaker and Loss.
III	Standard	40%	48.3 to 60% B; not over 11.7% C, Check, Dirty, Leaker and Loss.
IV	Trade	20%	68.5 to 80% B; not over 11.7% C, Check, Dirty, Leaker and Loss.

*Individual cases may contain not over 10% less A quality eggs than permitted for the lot, provided the average for the lot is not more than the tolerance permitted in any grade. Of 200 cases, one case in 10 is examined and may not contain over 20% less A quality eggs than is permitted in any grade.

†Within each tolerance for qualities below B, each of the grades may contain not over 3% checks and a combined total or not over 0.3% Dirties, Leakers and Loss.

color of the shell also has little to do with quality. White or brown eggs may be equally high, medium or low in quality. Boston may pay a premium for brown eggs because those are the eggs that have traditionally appeared on that market, while New York for the same reason may pay a premium for white eggs.

Storage Eggs

In trade channels eggs over 29 days old are called storage, while eggs under 29 days old are called fresh. Storage eggs may also be classified as storage or processed storage. Eggs merely moved into storage without any treatment to preserve them except by proper refrigeration and humidity control are called storage eggs. Processed storage eggs are eggs treated by oils, solvents or other fluids that seal the shell and reduce the loss of carbon dioxide and moisture without imparting color, flavor or odor to the treated eggs. The preferred treatment today is the spraying or dipping of eggs in oil.[1] Eggs may be heat treated to seal the shell but buyers should state in their specifications that such eggs are not

[1] Eggs given oil treatment immediately after laying may still have cloudy albumen after extended storage, a condition frequently noted in freshly laid eggs up to about 3 days after laying.

acceptable. These eggs may stick to the shell in breaking out and will not beat to a good foam. Heat stabilized eggs are decreasing on the markets. Proper temperature and humidity for storage eggs is 29 to 31° F and 90 to 92% relative humidity. Carbon dixode gases are sometimes introduced to assist in reducing quality losses of eggs in storage.

Eggs upon delivery should be chilled and moved immediately under refrigeration. They freeze at 27½° F. Eggs held for service may be at 45 to 55° F, but for longer periods the temperature and humidity should more nearly approach that for storage eggs. Eggs will sweat on delivery if held at too low a temperature.

Processed Eggs

About 7% of the total egg production goes into either frozen or dried eggs. About three times as much liquid is frozen as dried. Frozen or dried eggs are highly desirable for some food service use. High quality, frozen, whole eggs, carefully selected for high quality and low bacterial count, are on the market and are adaptable for use as breakfast eggs, such as scrambled eggs and French toast, and for entree dishes, such as souffles and other prepared egg dishes. Other frozen eggs lower in quality are used by bakeries. The labor saved in cracking eggs by using frozen eggs is sometimes substantial.

If top quality frozen whole eggs are purchased for breakfast or egg entree dishes, the specifications should read: "The eggs shall be from high quality, clean, edible eggs free of shells and be reasonably free from blood clots. There shall be no off-flavors or odors. No storage, check, dirty or leaker eggs shall be used. The eggs should possess low bacterial counts. The eggs should be in the natural proportions of eggs in yolks and whites."

Frozen eggs for bakery or similar uses are available as mixed whole eggs, white, sugar-yolk and just plain yolk. Sometimes bake shops use whole eggs with added yolks. Frozen eggs for food-service use are usually sold in 10-lb or 30-lb cans. A 30-lb can of whole eggs is approximately equal to 25 dozen eggs. It will usually take 45 dozen yolks or whites to be the equivalent of yolks or whites in a 30-lb can.

Store frozen eggs at 0° F or below. In large containers there is a tendency for egg solids to be heavier in the center of the frozen mass. It is wise to thaw frozen eggs under refrigeration; stir well and use.

Frozen egg whites are the albumen of the egg separated from the yolks. A pound of whites is equal to 17 to 19 large egg whites. Frozen yolks with added sugar generally contain 90 parts by weight egg yolk to 10 parts sugar. The sugar prevents the yolks from becoming rubbery from freezing. Sometimes glycerine in the amount of $2\frac{1}{2}$ to 5% of the eggs is added to eliminate this rubbery quality. The sugar is then omitted. A pound of the sugar-yolk product is the equivalent of approximately 19–20 large yolks and 1.6 oz of sugar. Yolks will be the equivalent of 21–24 large yolks per pound. Frozen whole egg in the natural proportions will contain 10 large eggs per pound. Frozen whole eggs with added yolks, sometimes called "proprietary" eggs, contain increased proportions of yolks to eggs.

Sugar, salt or other edible products may be added as stabilizers to frozen eggs. The proportions of added ingredients and type of egg should be listed on the label. This information should be noted and recipes adjusted accordingly.

Bacterial counts in eggs are lowered if the eggs are pasteurized for 3 minutes at 138° F. Homogenization improves quality. Pasteurization may harm functions of the egg in baking, if it is not done properly.

Dried eggs are used extensively in bakery production. They may also be used for cooking purposes where shell eggs or frozen eggs are difficult to obtain. Prepared bakery mixes requiring no eggs have dried eggs incorporated into them.

Dried eggs should be pasteurized at a temperature not less than 138° F for 3 minutes before drying. They should not have, after processing, more than 3 to 5% moisture. Eggs may be dried by spraying the eggs under heavy pressure through very fine apertures into chambers of circulating warm air. The dry solids fall to the bottom of the chamber. Tray-dried eggs are also available. These eggs are dried in thin film and then broken into small chips. Continuous belt drying may make a product similar to tray-dried eggs. Egg whites may be beaten to a light foam and then dried. Spray drying yields, perhaps, the best product.

Eggs may deteriorate rapidly after drying. Selection of high quality eggs for drying reduces deterioration. Development of off-colors and off-flavors has also been reduced by fermenting or using enzymatic action to eliminate the glucose in egg whites. Dried egg whites must be freed of this glucose before drying, if a stable product is to be obtained. Whole eggs and yolks retain storage stability longer when acidulated during processing. They are brought back to a natural pH after processing. Store dry eggs at 40° F or below. Pack in sealed airtight cans. Gas-packed eggs keep better than those that are air packed.

Meringue powders are available for quantity-food preparation. If the product is of good quality, they will yield good quality products and save labor.

Specify government-inspected egg products. The use of the official inspection mark indicates the egg products were prepared under continuous inspection according to strict sanitary standards. Many egg products must receive government inspection before shipment as well as inspection during processing.

Lot numbers must be placed in the federal shield stamp or upon the container. The government plant number must appear similarly. If the eggs are not processed from current production, the federal shield may not be used. Current production means that the eggs have moved through marketing channels in not over 7 days if Checks or Leakers, and not over 60 days if sound shell eggs. These eggs must have also received proper refrigeration during this time. Inspection certificates and sampling forms may be obtained for all federally inspected lots.

One pound of dried whole eggs will equal about 30 to 40 large eggs. To get 10 lb of reconstituted whole egg, use $2\frac{1}{2}$ lb of dried eggs, plus $3\frac{3}{4}$ qt of water ($7\frac{1}{2}$ lb). Egg yolks may be combined in the ratio of 5 lb yolks to 5 lb water and albumen 3 lb whites to 7 lb water, which will give in each case 10 lb of reconstituted product. These proportions are based on the percentage of solids found in the natural egg. Manufacturer's instructions on the package should be checked for exact proportions and mixing directions. One pound of dry whites is equal to 87 large fresh whites and one pound of dry yolks is equal to 47 large fresh yolks.

10 Fish and Shellfish

Wide variety and economy can be gained by featuring fish[1] on a menu. With proper preparation, fish can be a top leader. The cost per portion will usually be less than that of meat or poultry. The average consumption of fish per capita per year is 11 lb. Of this, 6 lb are fresh or frozen, 4 lb canned and 1 lb cured. Consumption of canned fish has dropped because of decreasing catches, increasing prices and competition from fresh and frozen fish. California generally leads all states in tonnage of fish caught. Massachusetts and the North Pacific area are next, in that order. Tuna, salmon, shrimp and oysters lead in value of catch.

PURCHASE FACTORS

Buyers need to know what is available and when it is available on their markets. Price is important. They also need to know what makes up quality in the various types of fish. Menu selection must be based on use and buyers should know the cooking properties of the various fish on the market. The amounts to purchase may also be challenging.

Availability

Fresh fish will be available only for short periods of time and varieties offered will be restricted to those caught in local areas. The perishability of fresh fish limits its shipment. Purchase of fish in the off-season will result in increased costs and perhaps lower quality. The peak of the fish catch is June through October, with the highest landings occurring

[1] The term *fish* used from here to Fresh Water and Sea Fish is taken to include shellfish and all marine life used as flesh food by man. Context or the word "shellfish" will indicate other use.

405

Table 10-1

A Buyer's Guide for the Purchase of Fish*

Common Name	Other Common Names	Normal Size in Pounds	Main Production Area	Season	Yield from Round Form	Fat or Lean	Common Market Forms
Barracuda		5–10	California	June	51% to fillet	L	Round, dressed, steaks, fillet
Bluefish		1–7	Mid-Atlantic	All year	52% to fillet	L	Round, drawn, fillet
Bass	Sea, striped, blackfish, black seabass, common, rockfish	2–600 depending on type	Atlantic and Pacific	Depends on type	around 40% to fillet for all types	L	All forms
Butterfish	Harvestfish	¼–1¼	Mid-Atlantic	June–Oct.	51% to fillet	F	Round, drawn, fillet
Catfish or Bullheads		1–10	Rivers, lakes	All year	19% to fillet	L	Round, dressed
Chub		2–5 oz	Great Lakes	All year	33% to fillet	F	Dressed, smoked
Cod, Atlantic		1½–10	New England	All year	31% to fillet	L	All forms
Cod, Pacific		1½–10	Pacific Coast	All year	31% to fillet	L	All forms
Croaker, Atlantic	Hardhead	½–2	South Atlantic	June–Oct.	39% dressed	L	Round, dressed, fillet
Cusk		1½–10	Atlantic	All year	58% to fillet	L	Drawn, dressed
Drum (red)	Channel bass, redfish	2–25	South Atlantic, Gulf	Winter	36% to fillet	L	Round, drawn
Drum (black)	Oyster cracker, oyster drum, sea drum	1–40	Atlantic, Gulf	Winter	38% to fillet	L	Round, drawn
Flounder (sole)	*Atlantic:*		Atlantic				Dressed, fillet
	Blackback (winter)	¾–2		Late winter	41% to fillet	L	
	Fluke (summer)	2–12		Summer	42% to fillet	L	
	Dab (seadab)	¾–2½		Apr.–May	36% to fillet	L	
	Gray	¾–4		Apr.–June	40% to fillet	L	
	Lemon	¾–4		June	41% to fillet	L	
	Southern	2–12		All year	54% to fillet	L	
	Yellowtail or dusty dab	¾–2		Aug.–Jan.	44% to fillet	L	

	Pacific: Rex, petrale, sand-dab, Dover or English sole	½ to 2	Pacific	All year	about 40% to fillet form	L	
Grouper		5–12	Gulf	All year	43% to fillet	L	All forms
Haddock		1½–7	New England	All year	48% to fillet	L	Fillet, sticks
Hake	Boston, squirrel or white hake; red or mud hake	2 to 5	New England	All year	43% to fillet	L	Fillet
Halibut		5–75	Pacific or Atlantic	Apr.–Oct.	59% to fillet	L	All forms
Herring, sea		2–4 oz	Atlantic, Pacific	Nov.–Feb.	51% to fillet	F	Round
Herring, lake		⅓–1	Great Lakes	Oct.–Dec.	72% to dressed	F	Round, dressed, smoked
Mackerel, jack		½–2½	Atlantic	Apr.–Oct.	54% to fillet	F	Round, dressed, fillet
Mackerel, Spanish		1–4	South Atlantic, Gulf	Summer		F	Round, dressed
Mackerel, king	Cero, kingfish	5–20	North Atlantic	Jan.–Apr.	53% to fillet	F	All forms
Lingcod		5–20	North Pacific	All year	38% to fillet	L	Dressed, fillet
Mullet		½–3	South Atlantic; Gulf	Sept.–Dec.	53% to fillet	L	Round, dressed, fillet
Perch, white		⅓–¾	Great Lakes	All year	36% to fillet	L	Dressed, fillet
Perch, yellow		½–¾	Great Lakes	All year	38% to fillet	L	Dressed, fillet
Perch, ocean	Rosefish	½–1¼	New England	All year	31% to fillet	L	Fillet
Pickerel		1½–3½	North Lakes	Apr.–Oct.	51% to fillet	L	Dressed, fillet
Pike, blue		½–2	Great Lakes	Sept.–Nov.	44% to fillet	L	Round, fillet
Pike, sauger		½–1½	Great Lakes	Apr.–Oct.		L	Dressed, fillet
Pike, yellow		1–3½	and	Apr.–Oct.	57% to fillet	L	Dressed, fillet
Pike, northern		1–4	Canadian	Apr.–Oct.	39% to fillet	L	Dressed, fillet
Pike, wall-eyed		1–4	Lakes	Apr.–Oct.	41% to fillet	L	Dressed, fillet
Pollock		1½–12	New England	All year	45% to fillet	L	Fillet
Pompano		½–2½	South Atlantic, Gulf	All year	52% to fillet	L	Dressed, round
Sablefish, black cod		1–15	North Pacific	Apr.–Nov.	68% to dressed	F	Dressed, steaks, smoked
Salmon, Atlantic		5–10	Atlantic	June–July	65% to fillet	F	Dressed, steaks
Salmon, chum		5–11	North Pacific	Aug.–Nov.	76% to drawn	F	Drawn, dressed, steaks, fillet
Salmon, king		5–30	North Pacific	Apr.–Aug.	73% to dressed	F	Drawn, dressed, steaks, fillet

Table 10–1 (Continued)
A Buyer's Guide for the Purchase of Fish*

Common Name	Other Common Names	Normal Size in Pounds	Main Production Area	Season	Yield from Round Form	Fat or Lean	Common Market Forms
Salmon, pink		3–6	North Pacific	July–Sept.	74% to drawn	F	Drawn, dressed
Salmon, red		5–10	North Pacific	June–Aug.	77% to drawn	F	Drawn, dressed
Salmon, silver		5–12	North Pacific	July–Oct.	76% to drawn	F	Drawn, dressed
Scup	Porgy	1/2–1 1/2	Atlantic	Mar.–June; Sept.–Dec.	48% to fillet	L	Round, dressed
Shad		1 1/2–5	Pacific, Atlantic	May–June	48% to fillet	L	Round, drawn
Skate	Rajafish	4–20	Atlantic		54% to fillet	L	Saddles, pieces
Smelt		1–2 oz	Atlantic, Pacific and Great Lakes	Feb.–June	55% to fillet; 86% to dressed	L	Round, dressed
Snapper, red		1 1/2–20	Gulf	Apr.–July	52% to fillet	L	All forms
Swordfish		50–200	New England	June–Sept.		L	Chunks, steaks
Tilefish						L	Round, drawn, dressed
Trout, lake		1 1/2 to 10	Great Lakes	May–Nov.	51% to fillet	F	Dressed
Trout, spotted	Speckled trout	1–4	South Atlantic, Gulf	Sept.–Dec.	37% to fillet	F	Dressed
Trout, gray	Weakfish	1/2–4	Mid-, South Atlantic	Aug.–Oct.	68% to dressed	L	Round, dressed, fillet
Trout, white	Sandtrout	1/2–1 1/2	Gulf	Winter	65% to dressed	L	Round, dressed, fillet
Tuna, albacore		12–25	Pacific, Atlantic	May–Nov.	67% to dressed; 73% to dressed; 58% to fillet	F	Round, steaks, chunks
Whitefish		1 1/2–6	Great Lakes	All year	47% to fillet	F	Round, dressed, fillet
Whiting		4–18	New England	May–Nov.	43% to fillet	L	Dressed, fillet
Whiting, king	Kingfish	3/4–3	Atlantic	July–Aug.	40% to fillet	L	Round, drawn
Wolffish	Sea catfish or ocean catfish	4–8	New England	Spring	34% to fillet	L	Drawn, dressed steaks, fillet

*Adapted from U.S. Department of Interior data.

Table 10–2
A Buyer's Guide for the Purchase of Shellfish

Shellfish	Other Names	Main U.S. Producing Area	Peak Production Month	Weight Information, EP Yields and Miscellaneous Information
Abalone		South Pacific	May	42% meat in shell
Clams, butter		North Pacific	All year	Shell—100 lb/sack; shucked—100–250/gal
Clams, hard*	Quahog, quahaug	North and Mid-Atlantic	All year	Bu—11 lb EP; 80 lb/sack; shucked 100–250/gal
Clams, little-neck		North and Mid-Atlantic or Pacific	All year	60 lb/bu
Clams, razor		North Pacific	Fall	80 lb/box; 16 lb EP/bu
Clams, soft*		North and Mid-Atlantic	All year	45 lb/bu; 200–700/gal shucked; 16 lb EP/bu
Clams, surf	Skimmer	North Atlantic	June	180–300/gal shucked
Conch				15 lb EP/bu
Crabs:				
Blue, hard shell		Mid-Atlantic	All year	10 to 18% meat; 5 lb EP/bu
Rock		New England		10 to 18% meat; 5 lb EP/bu
Blue, soft shell		Mid-Atlantic	May–June	used whole; 3 lb EP/doz
Dungeness		North Pacific	Apr.–June	22–26% meat
King		Alaska	June	legs only 14% meat
Lobsters		New England	May–Dec.	25% meat
Lobsters, spiny	Rock or sea crayfish, laguna lobster	Pacific	Nov.	46% tails only; most of these are imported except the Laguna caught off the coast of California and Mexico
Mussels		New England	May–Dec.	45–55 lb/bu; 10 lb EP/bu; 29% meat
Oysters:†				
Eastern		Atlantic	Fall and winter	80 lb/bu; 150–200/gal shucked (Bluepoints)
Pacific	Japanese		Nov.–Jan.	80 lb/sack; 64–240/gal shucked
Olympia	Western		Dec.–Jan.	120 lb/sack; 1600–1700/gal
Scallops:				
Bay		Atlantic	Feb.–May	500 per gal shucked; few taken in Pacific
Sea		Atlantic	Jan.–Sept.	150 per gal shucked
Sea urchins	Sea eggs			5 lb EP/bu
Shrimp:‡				
Gulf		Gulf	All year	12 to 70 per lb
Alaska pink		North Pacific	Dec.–Jan.	150–275 shelled/lb
California		Mid-Pacific	Aug.–Sept.	125–250 shelled/lb
Squid		North Pacific	June–July	5 to 6 per lb round form
Snails		Atlantic	Winter	Most imported; 20% gross weight is meat
Terrapin	Diamond-backs	Gulf	All year	21% raw muscle
Turtles:				
Sea and fresh water			All year	24% raw muscle

*Long shell or surf clams 35% yield; hard-shell clams (round shell) 17% yield drained meat average; hard-shelled clams by areas: New England 14–20%, Chesapeake 7–8%, Mid-Atlantic 10–12%, South Atlantic 6–8%, Pacific 24–28%, soft-shell yields: New England 23–33%, Mid-Atlantic 27–32%.

†Eastern oyster yield: New England and Mid-Atlantic 8–11%, Chesapeake 6–7%, South Atlantic 4–6%, Gulf 5–7%, Pacific (Japanese) 10–14%.

‡Yield from frozen headless shrimp in thawing, cooking, shelling and deveining—43% meat.

in August and the lowest in February. During low periods of fresh supplies, frozen, canned and cured stocks move onto the market. In some instances, some fresh fish may come onto the market in liberal supply during the low periods and it is wise to feature this fish at this time on the menu. Fresh-water fishing is important in local areas, but the total tonnage caught is not significant compared with the quantities of salt-water fish docked. Tables 10–1 and 10–2 give much information on the availability of fish and their marketing.

Markets

Five main fish markets exist in this country. They are located in main catch areas: Boston, New York, Gulf (New Orleans), Seattle and Chicago. There are other markets of lesser importance, such as Baltimore, Norfolk, Savannah, Gulf ports, San Francisco and Portland, Oregon, but the first five establish most trade practices. The Boston market reflects trading practices of the New England Fish Exchange. The New York market reflects practices that have grown out of the Fulton Fish and Peck Slip markets. The New York market has more variety and moves a greater volume of fish to consumers than any other market. The Gulf market reflects trade practices growing out of the shrimp ports and New Orleans. The Seattle market reflects practices adapted to the Pacific Coast, including Alaska. Chicago, an inland market, has adopted practices common to the other four from which it receives fish varieties. Because it is a large fresh-water fish market, it has also developed its own trade practices.

Much confusion exists among markets as to terminology and preparing fish for sale. Fish identities in the various markets are not always the same. Buyers should learn the common names of fish on their own markets. Most fresh fish are sold without label and, because of close similarity, substitutions are possible, some of them dishonest. Accepted practices on some markets make substitutions legitimate and buyers should learn these on their markets. On the average, sellers should be held very closely to firm specifications as to exact species, size, quality and pack. If buyers do accept substitutions, they must do it knowingly and with proper price adjustments.

Quality Standards

In 1956 the Agricultural Marketing Act was extended to include fish. Administration was placed in the Bureau of Commercial Fisheries, U.S. Fish and Wildlife Service of the Department of the Interior. Under this act quality standards are developed. To meet standards of quality, the products must come from wholesome material of good odor and taste

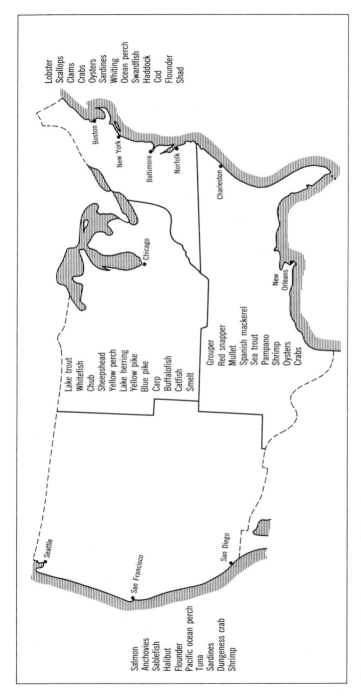

FIG. 10–1. The five primary fish markets, Boston, New York, New Orleans, Chicago and Seattle, are indicated on this map along with heaviest production of fish by species. Other markets shown are important markets and may dock larger tonnages of fish during the year than some of the primary markets.

and must be processed under sanitary conditions. Four types of inspection are offered: continuous inspection, intermittent at-plant inspection, specific lot inspection and inspection of unofficially drawn samples. These inspections are explained in Chapter 3. Certificates of inspection may be issued except for the last type of inspection. A stamp of approval for wholesomeness, which is necessary for poultry and meat shipped interstate, is not required for fish. The provisions of the Pure Food, Drug and Cosmetic Act also apply to fishery products. The U.S. Public Health Service has jurisdiction over the catch, processing and marketing of shellfish. Beds from which these products are taken must be certified for purity.

Fish will deteriorate rapidly after catching unless given proper care. Most fish live in water around 40° F, and enzymatic processes and defense mechanisms against bacteria are established for lower than normal air temperatures. When they are taken from their natural habitat, enzyme actions speed up, and flesh defenses against most bacteria are lacking.

When fish is first caught, the flesh is soft but soon stiffens and becomes firm. This firmness should remain, and fish in good condition should be firm and elastic. The flesh should spring back when pressed and should not pull easily from the bones. As a fish stales, the flesh becomes soft and flabby and an indentation remains when the flesh is pressed with the finger. The color of the flesh should be bright and clear. White-meated fish should have white and slightly translucent flesh, not pink or gray, especially around the backbone. Steaks and fillets (pronounced fĭl′ – lĕt) should have no traces of brown at the edge. The odor should be fresh and mild, not stale, sour strong or sharp with ammonia. The eyes should be bright and clear, full and bulging, not dull, wrinkled or sunken. The gills should be reddish pink, free from slime and not dull brown or gray. As a fish stales, the color of the gills fades to pink gray and then to a greenish or brownish color. The scales should adhere tightly to the skin and be bright colored, with a sheen, not dull or slimy.

Buyers should specify that lobster, crab, oysters and clams purchased in the shell be alive upon delivery. The shell and outer flesh of crustaceans turn red when cooked, which distinguishes them from uncooked or green products. Some cooked crab may turn a creamy color flecked with red spots. Some purveyors, failing to sell their crustaceans alive, may cook them after they perish and attempt to market them in cooked form.

A live lobster, crayfish or shrimp will have muscle tension. The tail will curl up under the body, rather than hang down limply. Crab will show

Table 10–3
A Buyer's Guide for Estimating Quantities of Fish

Fish	Preparation Information	Round	Drawn	Dressed	Fillet
			Estimated Pounds AP Required for 100 Portions		
Barracuda	5–6 oz steaks			31–38	
Bass, all types	5–6 oz steaks: 4–5 oz fillets		35–50	35	30
Bluefish	Half 1½ lb round fish	75		50	
Bullhead	½ 1-lb fish split			50*	
Butterfish	1 fish to the lb size		50		
Catfish	5 oz fillet	165			30
Chub	1 to 3 fish depending on size		38		
Cod	4 to 5 oz fillet	100			30
Cod	5–6 oz steak cut from 8 lb dressed fish			35–50	
Cod, scrod	Split 1¼-lb round scrod into two portions	68		50	
Cod, salt, dry	For fish cakes or creamed cod				10
Croaker	4 to 5 oz fillet	80			30
Cusk	4 to 5 oz fillet	64			30
Eels	Smoked 4 oz			25	
Flounder					
Blackback (winter)	†	76		50	30
Fluke (summer)	†	75		50	30
Dab	†	90		50	30
Gray sole	†	80		50	30
Lemon sole	†	80		50	30
Southern	†	58		50	30
Yellowtail	†	70		50	30
Pacific sole	†	82		50	30
California halibut	†	62		50	30
Grouper	5–6 oz steaks cut from 8 lb fish			35	
Haddock	5–6 oz steaks, 4–5 oz fillets	60		50	30
Hake	4–5 oz fillets	74			30
Halibut	5–6 oz steaks, 4–5 oz fillets	60		35	30
Herring, sea or lake	Round 1-lb fish per portion	100			
Herring, salted	8 oz split pieces			50	
Herring, smoked	5–6 oz				38
Mackerel	¾-lb split	100	75		
Mackerel, king	4–5 oz fillets				30
Mackerel, Spanish	3 to lb average, split	75	50		
Ling cod	4–5 oz fillets	62	50		30
Mullet	4–5 oz fillets	60			30
Perch, all types	2 fillets 2 to 2½ oz each				30
Pickerel	4–5 oz fillets				30
Pike, all types				35–50	30
Pollock	1½ to 2 lb each or 4–5 oz fillets			35–50	30
Pompano	Use ¾ to 1½ lb fish split or whole, depending on portion size desired.		75	50	30
Sablefish	5–6 oz steaks, smoked 5 oz pieces			35–50	
Salmon, baking size	Buy 5 to 12 lb dressed salmon			40	

Table 10–3 (Continued)
A Buyer's Guide for Estimating Quantities of Fish

Fish	Preparation Information	Round	Drawn	Dressed	Fillet
		Estimated Pounds AP Required for 100 Portions			
Salmon	5–6 oz steaks, 4–5 oz fillets			35–50	30
Scup (Porgy)	Purchase dressed 5 to 8 oz each or split 1-lb dressed fish.			35–50	
Shad	Steaks 5–8 oz, fillets 4–5 oz			38	30
Smelt	3 to 5 fish dressed 12 to 16 to lb			35–33	
Snapper, red	5–6 oz steaks cut from 8–9 lb fish			35–50	
Snapper, red	4–5 oz fillets				30
Shad roe	Purchase *medium* roe averaging 8 to 10 oz per pair; portion size may vary considerably, depending on type operation.				15–30
Swordfish	Steaks 5–6 oz			35	
Tilefish	5–6 oz steaks	82	60	35–50	
Whitefish	Purchase around 4 lb dressed and cut into 5–6 oz portion; fillets 4–5 oz.			50	30
Whiting	Split 1½ lb rounds or purchase ½ lb dressed fish and use 1 per portion; 4–5 oz fillets.	75		50	30
Whiting, king	4–5 oz fillets				30
Wolffish	5–6 oz steaks cut from 6 lb drawn fish; 4–5 oz fillets.	90	60		30

*Skinned.

†Small sizes may be split, center bone removed; or select fillets about 3 to the lb or cut larger fillets into 4 to 5 oz portions.

slight movement. The antennas and eyes of crustaceans may also move. A live clam or oyster will hold its shell firmly together when pressure is applied to open it. Dead mollusks usually can be detected by their open shells. Tension may remain, however, in some, even though the mollusk is dead. Sometimes live mollusks left under water can be seen to open and close their shells, and clams may extend their necks. A slight movement or jar causes the immediate withdrawal of the neck or the closing of the shell. To test the freshness of shellfish, hold close to the nose and smell. If the odor is strong, disagreeable and sharp, with a distinct odor of ammonia, the shellfish is not in good condition. A slippery, slimy condition indicates spoilage.

Upon delivery, live shellfish should be spread out, covered with moist seaweed, cloths or sacks and held at 45° F. Crustaceans may be placed in tanks while mollusks may be placed in pails of water. If fresh, live shellfish will stay alive under these conditions for approximately 5 days, and somewhat longer if placed in tanks. Live hard-shell crabs do not ship well for long distances; but the soft-shell crabs packed in excelsior or seaweed ship fairly well.

Shucked mollusks should be plump and have a clear color and sweet odor. They should be free from pieces of shell, silt and sand. The liquid should be clear and not excessive. If the mollusks appear bloated or have more than 10% liquid on them, they should be rejected. After being shucked, they can absorb considerable quantities of water, and dishonest suppliers will watersoak them to obtain higher yields. Mollusks should not be acid upon delivery, with a pH around 6.0. As they age, especially oysters, they increase in acidity, which can be detected in their flavor. Fresh-picked shrimp, crab or lobster meat, and fresh-shucked scallops, oysters or clams, should be held at 32° F but never frozen at the operation. Use should be within several days.

Turtles and terrapin belong to the shellfish group. They are used only in limited quantities. Terrapin are smaller than turtles. Frogs, eels and several other marine foods are used as specialty items in this country. In this book they are listed under shellfish because purchase criteria are much the same.

Table 10-4 gives information relative to quantities of shellfish required and Table 10-19 will give additional information of value to the buyer.

Purchase fresh fish in season. At these times the fish is in best condition and apt to be lowest in price. Select plump, full fish; fish with big heads are wasty. Order in sizes in greatest quantity on the market if they will yield proper size portions. Off sizes are apt to be more expensive. The largest size fish may not be best in quality being less flavorful and coarse in quality. Locally caught fish are apt to be better in quality, lower in price and better known and accepted by patrons than fish unknown in the area. Buyers should consult reputable dealers to learn what is on the market and the best buys available. Labor cost in preparation should be considered. Frequently final cost is less if the fish is received ready for use rather than being prepared from the shell or from round or dressed form.

Frozen fish should be solidly frozen, with no discoloration or brownish cast at the outer surface. There should be little or no odor. Wrappings of stored fish should be moisture-vapor proof. They should fit tightly around the flesh. Many large whole or dressed fish are glazed with ice and this glaze should be on the fish upon delivery. Frozen fish may lack, after cooking, the abundant flavor and moistness of fresh fish and

Table 10–4
A Buyer's Guide for Estimating Quantities of Shellfish Required

Shellfish	Portion Size or Other Preparation Information	Form in Which Purchased AP	Quantity Required for 100 Portions
Abalone	4 oz	Steaks	25 lb
Clams, hard	On the shell: little necks 450 to 650 per bu or cherry stones 300 to 325 per bu; 4 per serving.	In shell	34 doz
Clams, shucked	Cocktails, approx. 1½ oz.	Shucked	1⅓ gal
Clams, chowder	Quahaugs, 150 per bu.	In shell	1⅓ to 1⅔ bu
Crab meat*	Backfin lump from Blue crab or solid meat from Dungeness	Solid meat	or 2 gal shucked
	1½ oz per cocktail		10 lb
	2 oz for small salads		12 lb
	4 oz for large salads.		24 lb
Crab meat*	Lump or flake for creamed, creole or extender dishes, use about 1⅓ to 1½ oz.	Solid meat	8–10 lb
Crabs, soft shell	1 each about 4 to 4½″ in diameter.	Alive	100 crabs
Lobster	¾ to 1¼ lb chicken lobster	Alive	100 lobster
	or 1½–2 lb and split.	Alive	50-lobster
Lobster meat*	See crab meat.		
Oysters, blue points	Purchase 300–400 oysters per bu (approx. 75 lb per bu), 4 per serving.	In shell	34 doz
Oysters, olympia	For cocktails, 1¼ oz.	Shucked	1 gal
Oysters, fried or scalloped	Purchase *counts* 125/150 per gal or *selects* 175–200 per gal.	Shucked	2½–3 gal
Oysters, stew	Purchase *standards* 250 to 300 per gal.	Shucked	1½ gal
Scallops, sea	Medium size 175 approx. per gal for deep frying.		3½ to 4 gal
Shrimp, fried	Use Jumbo split or butterflied, about 20 per lb, using 4 to 5 per portion, or large split or round.		20 to 25 lb
Shrimp	Cocktails 1½ oz, small or Pacific.	Shelled	10 lb
Shrimp	Cocktails 5 Jumbo or Large.	Green, unshelled†	25–33 lb
Shrimp	Small salad, 2 oz shrimp, ½ c salad.	Green, unshelled†	12 lb EP, cooked
Shrimp	Large salad, 4 oz shrimp, 1 c salad.	Green, unshelled†	24 lb EP, cooked

*From 10 to 12 cans 14 oz net weight contents of crab or lobster meat are the equivalent of the quantities given here.

†Shrimp are headless AP.

there is also a flavor and quality loss in extended storage. Some types freeze better than others. Some crab meats, for instance, lose flavor and are dry and pulpy even after short freezing. Minimum drip loss is obtained by thawing fish under 40° F. Whenever possible, frozen fish should be cooked frozen, but where breading, filleting or stuffing must occur this is not possible. Frozen fish should be used immediately after thawing, never refrozen.

Frozen shellfish should be thawed under refrigeration and used immediately. Heavy losses in quality occur in refreezing; thus, it is not recommended. Cooked crab and crab meat lose quality rapidly after freezing and, as a rule, buyers should select fresh or canned crab products, rather than frozen. Shrimp, lobster, spiny lobster, shucked oysters and clams freeze better than crab. Some oysters and clams are frozen in the shell without a loss of quality.

Store frozen fish at 0° F or below. Fresh fish should be delivered chilled or packed in ice and best storage temperatures are about 31 to 32° F. Examine shipments for spoilage and damage upon receiving. A strong smell, unpleasant and acrid with ammonia, indicates lack of freshness. Many operations have separate fish storage areas or enclosed boxes for fish storage in regular storage areas.

Quantity to Purchase

The quantity of fish required to serve a given number may vary considerably, depending upon the market form of purchase. Many fish in the round or drawn form have high waste in preparation. Shellfish have very low edible portion yields. Tables 10–3 and 10–4 indicate some quantities required for serving stated numbers. Buyers should compile their own data on quantities required. Dressed fish, usually from 8 to 12 lb each, will cut out to best advantage for steaks.

Specifications for fish should state the market form. For fish, these are:

1. *Whole or round:* As the fish come from the water, but some may be scaled.
2. *Drawn:* Eviscerated and some may be scaled.
3. *Dressed or pan-dressed:* Scaled and eviscerated; usually head, tail and fins are removed. Some fish, like trout, smelt and salmon, may not have these removed. Wide differences exist in markets on what is pan-dressed or dressed fish. Buyers should ascertain what the terms mean on their market. Trout, because of their fine scales, are not scaled. Pan-dressing usually refers to dressed small fish.
4. *Steaks:* Cross sections or slices of larger sizes of dressed fish. Specifications should give portion size desired and variation in weight permitted over stated portion size.
5. *Fillets:* The flesh on either side of the backbone and over the fish bones of the thoracic cavity may be removed to make fillets. Some may have tiny

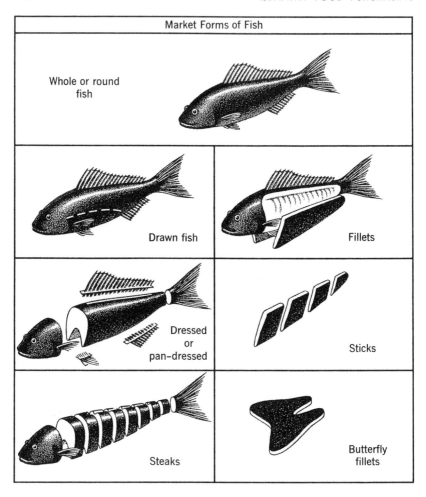

FIG. 10–2. **Market forms of fish.**

bones in them, such as fillets from mackerel or herring. Skin may or may not be removed. For some fish, breaking up in cooking is prevented when the skin is left on. A fillet cut from one side is called a *single* fillet. *Butterfly* fillets are the two sides combined.

Sticks: Fillets or steaks cut into pieces lengthwise; they are usually of uniform size.

Chunks: Pieces of drawn or dressed fish.

Market forms for shellfish will vary according to the type. Mollusks, such as oysters, clams and scallops, are sold in the shell or shucked. Shucking is the removing of the mollusk from the shell, leaving only clear meat. Mussels are usually sold in the shell only. Crustaceans, such as lobster, crayfish, shrimp or crab, are frequently sold alive, but they may also be sold cooked in the shell or as fresh solid meat (cooked meat picked from the shell and packed unfrozen in cans). Most shrimp, crayfish and spiny lobster are marketed "headless"; that is, with the head and thorax removed, leaving only the tails. Some shrimp may be sold in this form cooked, shelled and deveined, but most shrimp, lobster and crayfish are marketed raw, called "green."

Fish Cookery

To purchase fish properly buyers should learn much about cooking qualities. The flesh of fish contains only a small quantity of connective tissue and almost any type of cooking gives a tender product. Most fish are rich in flavor; sometimes flavor is such that it must be masked by piquant or flavorful sauces. The flesh of fish may be easily over-cooked, with resulting loss of flavor and moistness.

Live

Headless

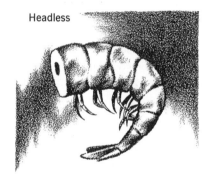

Cooked meat

Shucked

FIG. 10–3. Market forms of shellfish.

The fat content of fish may vary from $\frac{1}{2}$ to 20%. This fat content frequently dictates the best cooking method. Fat fish, such as mackerel, shad, salmon and trout, will be moist after baking, broiling and planking. Many lean fish, such as cod and haddock, will lack eating quality if prepared by dry heat methods. They are best prepared by steaming, boiling, deep frying and sautéing. A sauce is frequently added to give moistness to the flesh, or fish may be cooked in a sauce.

The high quality of protein in the flesh of fish and shellfish, their high vitamin A and D content, good iodine content if they come from the sea, and their relatively high thiamin, riboflavin and niacin content, in addition to essential minerals, make fish a desirable food in the diet.

FRESH WATER AND SEA FISH

Bass

There are a number of bass sold. Atlantic varieties may be known as *striped*, *sea*, *black*, *white* or *common* bass. Pacific bass may be called *rockfish*, *striped* bass or *sea* bass. There is a close similarity between the flesh texture and flavor of all but size and shape may be different. Bass are rich in flavor, moderately high in fat, and the flesh flakes off in moist segments after cooking. The cooked flesh is usually grayish-white, with a slightly stronger flavor than cod. It is pleasant and rich. The raw flesh freezes and stores well. Bass may be obtained in fresh or frozen form on most markets throughout the year. Very little fresh-water bass come to market.

Striped bass are the most common of all varieties. They are caught along coastal waters about 2 miles from land, usually in spawning areas. Many are caught in river beds close to the sea. Pacific striped bass, frequently called rockfish, are available fresh throughout the year. Chesapeake striped bass are also caught throughout the year, but the largest catches come in the fall, around New Jersey and Long Island. Some Chesapeake bass migrate as far north as New England during the summer.

The largest striped bass are filleted or steaked. Market sizes for the round form range from 1 to 40 lb, although some have been caught weighing 125 lb. Best sizes for a food service are 4 to 12 lb. Striped bass are olive green to blue on top and pale on the sides, turning silver on the belly. The sides are barreled out, with seven or eight longitudinal stripes showing above the pectoral fins. The body has scales. The top of the head has no scales. Common market weights of striped bass in round form on markets are given in Table 10-5.

Table 10–5

Boston Market		New York Market		Seattle Market
Jumbo	Over 15 lb	Jumbo	15 lb and up	Called rockfish and
Large	10 to 15 lb	Large	5 to 15 lb	average 4 to 5 lb
Medium	5 to 10 lb	Medium	2 to 5 lb	
Small	3 to 5 lb			

Most of the sea bass are caught on the Atlantic coast, although a similar bass is found on the Pacific markets also. Common bass are sometimes called blackfish or black sea bass. They may vary in color, according to their sea bottom habitat. Some are smoky gray while others are much darker. They are a stout-bodied fish, with a high back and flat head. The body is a paler color than the back. The mouth is usually black. The dorsal fins have a series of whitish spots or bands on them. Large numbers are caught from Cape Cod to Florida. Heavy catches are taken in May and June around New England when they spawn. They weigh ¾ to 2 lb but some may be 7½ lb. Market classifications in the New York market are: large 1¼ lb up, medium ¾ to 1 lb, small under ½ lb. White bass and black bass are also caught in Atlantic waters. The former may be as large as 50 lb while black bass may run from 50 to 600 lb.

Bluefish

The flesh of bluefish is excellent, with a distinctively sweet and savory flavor. Sizes run from 1 to 7 lb, with the smallest being found on northern markets; the average weight in Gulf markets is 4 lb, with some running as high as 10 to 20 lb. Baby blues weight ¼ to 1¼ lb. The fish is deep blue on top, with a green, silvery-tinged belly. The fins are generally of the main body tint. Pectoral fins have black blotches at the base. The fish has a moderately stout body about one fourth as deep as it is long. New York market classifications are for round or drawn bluefish: large 2½ lb up, medium 1½ to 2½ lb, small ¾ to 1½ lb and snapper under ¾ lb.

Butterfish

A number of names are given butterfish, such as harvest fish, dollar fish, shiner, sheepshead[2] and pumpkin seed. They are small fish, averaging about ½ lb each, and 6 to 8 in. long. They are colored a

[2] A different sheepshead from that caught in Gulf waters or that found on the fresh-water market in Chicago.

lead-blue on top, paling on the sides to a silvery belly. The body is very deep and flat, about twice as long as it is deep. They can be identified by their single soft dorsal fin, the almost equally long anal fin and the deep forked tail. They have no ventral fins. Identification may also be made from the short head, blunt snout and very small scales. The Boston market classifies the round form as large, mixed and small, meaning, respectively, $\frac{3}{4}$ lb or over, $\frac{1}{5}$ lb and over and under $\frac{1}{5}$ lb. The New York market classifies them by number of fish per 100 lb: jumbo—200 fish or under, large—200 to 300 fish, medium—300 to 350 fish and small—350 or over.

Cod

There are a number of cod, the name being used for a related family. Atlantic cod are haddock, pollock, hake, cusk and groundfish. The cod of the Pacific coast are a slightly different variety. Cod are plentiful both in Atlantic and Pacific waters. They average 10 to 12 lb but some may run as high as 200 lb. They are a robust fish, tapering down at the tail. There are three dorsal and two anal fins devoid of spins. The color of most of the family is dark and pearly. (See also Haddock.)

Table 10–6

Boston Market		New York Market		Seattle Market	
Cod*		Cod*		Cod*	3 lb and over
Whale	Over 25 lb	Whale	20 lb and up	Lingcod*	5 lb and over
Market	2½ to 10 lb	Large	8 lb and up		
Scrod†	1½ to 2½ lb	Market	2½ to 8 lb		
Snapper	under 1½ lb	Scrod†	1½ to 2½ lb		
Cusk*		Steak	5 lb and up		
Cusk	over 3 lb				
Scrod*	1½ to 3 lb				
Hake (red)‡	½ to 1½ lb	Hake (red)‡	½ to 2 lb		
Hake (white)‡					
Large	6 lb and over				
Small	2½ to 6 lb				
Pollock*		Pollock*			
Large	4 lb and over	Steak	4 lb and up		
Scrod†	1½ to 4 lb	Market	4 lb and up		
		Scrod†	1 to 4 lb		

*Drawn form except that for the New York Pollock it may also mean dressed.
†Term used frequently on the markets to indicate a fish weighing between 1½ and 3 lb.
‡Round form.

Cod are found on the markets as fresh, frozen and dried. Sometimes they are confused with flounder or sole and sold as that. The substitution is not legitimate for sole. The flesh is flaky and has a slighly gray, moist quality to it. The finer white, slightly drier flesh of sole or flounder is considered superior. The flesh of cod is low in fat. It can be prepared in any manner used for lean fish and for fish chowders and fish cakes. Market classifications for the cod family are given in Table 10–6.

Flounder or Sole

There is much confusion on the markets between flounder and sole. Many varieties exist and some closely resemble each other. Substitution is common. There are at least five small Atlantic varieties: winter sole, lemon sole, yellowtail or Boston flounder, gray flounder and sea dab. Two large flounders are common on the Atlantic markets, the fluke and the southern. Pacific varieties are rex, petrale, sanddab and Dover (English) sole. The latter is of high quality, resembling the fine English or Dover sole of Europe. The Seattle market calls the larger sizes Dover sole and the smaller sizes English sole.

Most flounder and sole have a common color and shape. They are gray or brownish on top and white underneath. They belong to the flatfish family, a fish that swims about normally as a minnow but later turns itself on its left side and moves by flapping along the ocean bottom. Gradually the left eye rotates to the right or upper side, and the fish becomes blind on the under side. The halibut and sablefish are also members of this family.

The fins on most flounder or sole are brownish or slaty olive in color. Some may have reddish spots on them. The caudal fin (tail fin) and margins of two long fins may be yellow. On the blind side, the caudal fin is yellow. Most of these fish are about half as broad as they are long and have an oval body. The mouth is small and the lips fleshy. Flounder and sole are found in Atlantic coastal waters from the Gulf of St. Lawrence to New Jersey and are abundant around Cape Cod. Pacific varieties are caught from California to Alaska in harbors and beach areas.

Winter sole is a high quality Atlantic fish with thick, meaty and delicately flavored white flesh. *Lemon* sole of the Atlantic approaches it in quality. The *yellowtail* or *Boston* sole is marketed in considerable quantities but is not considered as high in quality as the winter or lemon sole. The *gray* sole has an excellent flavor and may be found fresh in good supply a large part of the year. It may also be called the *fluke, craig, pole* or *witch*. The true fluke is a larger flounder. The gray sole has a brownish or russet upper side with dark transverse bars. The ventral

Table 10–7

Boston Market		New York Market		Seattle Market		Gulf Market	
Blackback		Blackback		Dover		All varieties	
Large	¾ lb up	Large	1½ lb up	Large	24″ to 30″	Large	1 to 5 lb
Small	under ¾ lb	Medium	¾ to 1½ lb	Small	10″ to 23″	Small	½ to 1 lb
		Small	under ¾ lb				
Gray	1 to 4 lb	Gray		English			
		Jumbo	4 lb and up	Large	13″ to 15″		
		Large	2 to 4 lb	Small	11″ to 13″		
		Medium	1½ to 2 lb				
Dab	1 lb and up	Dab	1 lb and up	Petrale	16″ to 18″		

fins are either the same color as the body or purplish. The pectoral fin may often be black. The gray sole is a larger sole than some of the others in this group. It may run as high as 4 lb in round form. A gray sole will usually be 2½ to 3 times as long as it is broad.

Most major markets have fresh, locally caught sole or flounder throughout the year. Market classifications are shown in Table 10–7.

Haddock

This fish is a member of the cod family, but because it is caught in such quantity, it is usually considered a separate type. It averages 3 to 7 lb, with top weight being 16 lb. It is a deep purplish color alive but turns dirty gray after death. It has black lateral lines and sooty shoulders that are called "the devil's mark." It is found along the Atlantic coast and in great quantity on the Newfoundland banks. The flesh of the fish is white and firm, with a mild, pleasing flavor. For many years haddock was marketed as a salt or smoked fish. Since the development of improved freezing methods, it is available in quantity in frozen fillet form. When haddock is slightly salted and given a light smoke, it is called "finnan haddie."

Haddock on the Boston market is marketed drawn and classified as: large—over 2½ lb, scrod—1½ to 2½ lb and snapper—under 1½ lb. Haddock on the New York market is usually drawn and classified: large —2 lb and up, scrod—1 to 2 lb and small scrod—under 1 lb.

Halibut

The halibut is a flatfish caught in the Pacific in quantity. The International Pacific Halibut Commission allows this country 65 to 70 million pounds yearly from the Pacific halibut grounds. Much smaller quantities of halibut are caught in the Atlantic. The flesh freezes well, and when fresh supplies leave the market, frozen stocks take over. The

Table 10–8

Boston Market		New York Market		Seattle Market		Chicago Market	
		Eastern Halibut					
Drawn		Dressed					
Whale	over 125 lb	Whale	over 80 lb			(Markets very few	
Large	60 to 125 lb	Large	50 to 80 lb			eastern halibut)	
Medium	12 to 60 lb	Medium	10 to 50 lb				
Chicken	7 to 12 lb	Chicken	5 to 10 lb				
Snapper	under 7 lb	Snapper	under 5 lb				
		Western Halibut					
Dressed		Dressed		Dressed		Dressed	
Whale	over 80 lb	Whale	over 80 lb	Whale	over 80 lb	Large and whale	
Large	60 to 80 lb	Large	60 to 80 lb	Large	60 to 80 lb	over 60 lb	
Medium	10 to 60 lb	Medium	10 to 60 lb	Medium	10 to 60 lb	Medium	10 to 60 lb
Chicken	5 to 10 lb	Chicken	5 to 10 lb	Chicken	5 to 10 lb	Chicken	5 to 10 lb

Pacific catch is taken from early May to mid-July. The north Atlantic has no seasons, fishing areas or regulations.

Halibut meat is white, translucent, mild in flavor and highly prized. Halibut may be purchased round, dressed, as steaks, fillets or chunks. Common market classifications are given in Table 10–8.

Federal standards for quality have been promulgated for frozen halibut steaks. A steak is defined as a piece of sliced halibut 2-oz or more in weight. These may be packed random weight or uniform weight. The uniform weight pack may also be called portion pack, and all steaks within the lot must be within a specified weight range. A slice $\frac{1}{2}$ to $1\frac{1}{4}$ in. thick is recommended. Two grades are available, Grade A and B. Factors affecting grade are dehydration or freezer burn, amount of glaze remaining, uniformity of thickness and weight, and minimum weight. Also considered are such defects as loose skin, fins, blood spots, bruises, foreign material, backbone and collar bone remaining, cartilage and poor workmanship in cutting. Texture defects may be toughness, dryness, fibrousness, or wateriness. Color defects may be discoloration of the drip liquor, light meat, dark meat or non-uniformity of color. "Honeycombing," a distinct openness of grain or slight holes in the surface, is considered a defect.

Mackerel

A number of types of mackerel are marketed. *Jack* mackerel are caught in large numbers from Cape Cod to North Maine waters in the spring and summer. The *Spanish* mackerel is also caught in the Atlantic

Table 10–9

Boston Market	New York Market	Gulf Market	Chicago Market
Mackerel	Mackerel		Mackerel
Large 2¼ lb up	Large 1 lb and up		1½ to 2½ lb
Medium 1½ to 2¼ lb	Medium ¾ to 1¼ lb		
Small 1 to 2½ lb	Tinker ½ to ¾ lb		
Tinker ½ to 1 lb	Small under ½ lb		
Tack or			
Spike under ½ lb			
Mackerel shark*	King mackerel		
25 to 200 lb	Jumbo 12 lb and up		
	Large 8 to 12 lb		
	Medium 5 to 8 lb		
	Small under 5 lb		
	Spanish mackerel	Spanish mackerel†	
	Large 1½ lb up	1 to 3 lb	
	Small under 1½ lb		

*This fish is not a true mackerel and may be called just "shark."
†Drawn.

in considerable quantities. The *Pacific* mackerel caught off the California coast is a pilchard and is usually canned as large sardines.

Mackerel are a fat fish with a rich, slightly strong flavor that is highly prized by some people. The average mackerel may be about 1 lb in weight or less, but *King* mackerel may go over 12 lb. They appear in quantity on the New York market.

Mackerel are often split and, with the backbone removed, broiled. They are also excellent pan-fried, baked, poached or steamed. For a number of years mackerel appeared on the market split and salted in brine. Boiled or steamed salt mackerel may be found on the menu as a breakfast item. The different varieties of mackerel may or may not be differentiated on a market. Some common round classifications are given in Table 10–9.

Pompano

Pompano is one of the finest eating fish. The cost per pound will usually equal that of meat or poultry. The flesh is rich and delicate in flavor. It is caught in Florida, Bermuda and Gulf waters. It weighs 1 to 1½ lb. A large part of the catch is sold fresh in local markets, but some may be refrigerated or frozen and shipped to other markets. New York and Gulf markets classify round pompano as follows: New York —large 1½ to 2½ lb, medium ¾ to 1¼ lb and small under ¾ lb; Gulf—mixed sizes ½ to 3½ lb.

Rosefish (Sea Perch)

Large quantities of this perch-type fish are caught in the New England coastal waters. The fish is shaped like a fresh-water perch and is about the same size. The texture of the flesh and flavor is also similar to that of perch. The fish is distinguished by a reddish underbelly.

Red Snapper

The flesh of this fish is much like cod or sea bass. It cooks up into large moist flakes and is considered one of the finest eating fish on the market. The flesh is rich in flavor, usually a creamy pinkish-white and has a finer texture than cod or bass. It is caught largely in Florida and Gulf waters. Some markets may substitute other fish for snapper as a local practice, but these substitutes will usually lack the quality of the true snapper. Snapper bakes, broils, poaches, steams or cooks well in sauces.

Sablefish

Unlike other flatfish, sablefish are high in fat. They are caught in substantial quantity in the North Pacific area. Another market name may be black cod. Frequently smoked, they give a richly flavored, fine product when processed in this manner. Fresh forms may be round or dressed. The Seattle and Chicago markets use the same terminology, with large being over 5 lb and small under 5 lb. The fish bakes, broils or fries well.

Salmon

This is one of our most valued and popular fish. It is generally higher in price than most fish, and, in turn, it also commands a higher price on the menu. A few Atlantic salmon are caught from Hudson Bay to Maine, but most of the salmon catch comes from the Pacific where, from Oregon to Alaska, large numbers are caught each year. Salmon spend most of their adult life in the ocean, but after maturity they enter rivers, move far inland, spawn and die. The flesh rapidly deteriorates as the fish move up river, so most catches come from the sea, bays or river inlets. Some land-locked varieties, called Kokanee or land-locked salmon or salmon trout, are caught in lakes. They are small compared with the true salmon, but the flesh is a bright salmon color, and the flavor rivals that of true salmon. They are not marketed in heavy quantity.

The Atlantic salmon is known as the Kennebec salmon and averages 5 to 10 lb, although large sizes may go as high as 60 lb. The firm,

Table 10-10

New York Market		Seattle and Chicago Markets	
Atlantic	5 lb and up	Chinook	
Chinook		Large red	12 lb and over
Large	10 lb and up	Small red	not under 26 in. and up to 12 lb
Medium	5 to 10 lb	White	26 in. and over
Chum	7 to 10 lb	Chum	5 to 11 lb
Silver		Pink	4 to 6 lb
Large	7 to 10 lb	Silver	6 to 12 lb
Medium	4 to 7 lb		

orange-colored flesh and delicate flavor make it a prized fish. Most of the catch enters the market fresh at rather high prices.

The Pacific salmon comes to market fresh, frozen, smoked (kippered) and canned. Most varieties are larger than the Atlantic salmon. The Pacific salmon varies in color from a rich orange to a pinkish white. The nutritional value of all salmon flesh is about the same, but because of redness of color some bring a higher price. The redder salmon flesh also contains slightly higher quantities of fat than the lighter colored flesh.

Red or *Sockeye* salmon averages 6½ to 12 lb. The flesh is reddest of all varieties. The body of the fish is slender and the head small. It has an excellent flavor and cooks well almost any way. *Silver* or *medium red* (also called *Coho*) salmon are about the same size as the sockeye, averaging about 9 lb. The flesh is a rich orange, slightly touched with red. The back is dark, the body silver and the belly a white silver. Some market weights may go as high as 30 lb. *Chinook* or *King* salmon is the largest of the Pacific salmon, frequently running as high as 15 to 25 lb, with 80 lb being maximum size. Its flesh is a bright salmon color. The body is deep and thick. The head is small; the back is black and the belly a white silver. Chinook salmon appears fresh on the market about the first of May. *Pink* or *humpback* salmon is the smallest of the Pacific varieties. It runs between 4 to 8 lb. The flesh is lighter in color than the Chinook, but the flavor is excellent. It is a good baking size. This salmon is frequently dressed and glazed with ice and shipped as frozen salmon. The *chum, keta* or *white* salmon is lightest in color of all salmon. It is frequently caught in rivers or bays. The size runs from 8 to 16 pounds. Chum salmon may be called *fall* salmon because the catch comes latest of the salmon catch, and it will appear on the market fresh until late November. Salmon moves in quantity through the Seattle,

Chicago and New York markets. Market classifications for dressed
salmon are given in Table 10–10.

Shad

Shad is a member of the herring family. The male is called a jack or
buck shad. Although it averages 3 lb, it may vary from $1\frac{1}{2}$ to 6 lb.
The female or the roe shad is heavier, averaging $4\frac{1}{2}$ lb and varying
from 3 to 8 lb. The female is prized for its roe or eggs, which are on the
market fresh during the late winter and spring months. Both the roe
and flesh may also be obtained in frozen form. The flesh is tender and
white, with a fine, distinctive flavor. It is popular on many menus.
Some shad is lightly smoked, and some of this smoked shad is canned.

Shad roe is considered a delicacy and is broiled, baked, dipped in
batter and deep fried or served in other ways. Roe is sold in pairs or
strips of two. One strip is about 5 to 6 in. in length, $2\frac{1}{2}$ to 3 in. wide
and approximately 1 in. thick. It is a deep orange color. The roe of
other fish, such as salmon, mackerel, whitefish, alewife, cod, herring and
mullet, may be found on the market, but none are considered to have
the quality of shad roe.

Shad is found in good abundance during peak catch seasons in
Atlantic markets. The fish is a dark blue or greenish color on the back,
white or silvery on the sides and white on the belly. There is a dusky
spot behind each gill cover, and there may be other spots near the gill
area. It has large silvery scales. Some shad are caught in the Pacific.

The New York market classifies shad: roe shad (round), 3 lb up, buck
shad (round), $1\frac{1}{2}$ lb up, skip shad (round), $\frac{3}{4}$ to 1 lb, cut (drawn) 2 lb
up. Shad roe is listed as jumbo, large, medium and small, running,
respectively, per pair, 14 oz and up, 10 to 14 oz, 8 to 10 oz and 8 oz or
under.

Smelt

Smelt are small fish caught in substantial quantities and marketed
round, headed and drawn (dressed) or as boned fillets. A fresh-water
smelt of high quality is caught in the Greak Lakes. The small silver
smelt of the Pacific coast may be called Columbia River or silver or surf
smelt. There are several sea varieties. The flesh of smelt is fine in
texture, rich in flavor and a whitish-gray translucent color. It is inexpensive and deep fries or pan-fries well. The New York, Boston, Seattle
and Chicago markets classifications for round smelt are shown in Table
10–11.

Table 10–11

Boston Market	New York Market	Seattle Market	Chicago Market
Native	New Brunswick	Eulachon	Great Lakes
Green medium	Jumbo	5 to 8 per lb	Jumbo
5½ to 7 in. or	7 in. and over	Silver	4 to 6 per lb
12 to 14 per lb	No. 1	5 to 12 per lb	No. 1
Green, small	5¾ to 7 in.		7 to 10 per lb
under 5½ in. or	Medium		Medium
15 up per lb	4½ to 5¾ in.		over 10 per lb
Sea	Small		
Large	under 4½ in.		
over 7 in. or 10 or			
less per lb			
Canadian			
Extra			
over 7 in. or 8			
to 10 per lb			
No. 1			
5½ to 7 in.			
or 12 to 14			
per lb			
Medium			
under 5½ in. or			
15 up per lb			

Swordfish

The swordfish is a large fish averaging 200 to 300 lb. It is increasing in popularity largely because the flesh freezes and holds well. The flesh resembles that of halibut. Its thick, meaty steaks are entirely free from small bones, and the flesh is soft and white, slightly grayer than halibut

Table 10–12

	Boston Market		New York Market	
Fresh			Fresh	
Large	over 100 lb		Large	110 and up
Pups	under 100 lb		Pups	110 and under
Frozen				
Dressed	over 100 lb			
Fillet or				
split	50 lb and up*			
Chunks	40 lb to 100 lb†			

*Sides or halves.
†Pieces or parts.

flesh. The flavor is rich and the texture fine. It has less oil than halibut but broils well. The Boston and New York market classifications for dressed swordfish are given in Table 10–12.

Trout

Both sea- and fresh-water trout are on the market, but sea trout appear in greater quantities. Most fresh-water trout are raised on trout farms for the market. There are a number of sea trout, and they are frequently called by names other than trout. Market classifications are given in Table 10–13.

Tuna

The quantity of canned tuna far exceeds that marketed fresh. Most tuna are caught in the Pacific, but the Atlantic dockage is also substantial. The federal government permits the following to be called tuna: Bluefin, Southern bluefin, Oriental, Albacore, Big-eyed, Yellowfin, Northern bluefin, Skipjack, Little tunny and Kawakawa. The size may vary from 10 to 1000 lb. Buyers prefer the small size tuna when using

Table 10–13

New York Market		Chicago Market		Gulf Market	
Sea trout				Sea trout	
Gray (drawn or round)				Spotted (round or drawn)	
Large	$3\frac{1}{2}$ lb and up			Large	1 to 4 lb
Large-				Medium	$\frac{3}{4}$ to 1 lb
medium	$1\frac{1}{2}$ to $3\frac{1}{2}$ lb			Small	$\frac{1}{2}$ to $\frac{3}{4}$ lb
Medium	$1\frac{1}{4}$ to $1\frac{1}{2}$ lb			White trout	$\frac{1}{2}$ to $1\frac{1}{2}$ lb
Small	$\frac{3}{4}$ to $1\frac{1}{4}$ lb				
Pin	under $\frac{1}{2}$ lb				
Spotted (drawn or round)					
Large	over $3\frac{1}{2}$ lb				
Medium	$1\frac{1}{2}$ to $3\frac{1}{2}$ lb				
Small	under $1\frac{1}{2}$ lb				
Fresh-water trout		Fresh-water trout (drawn)			
Brook trout (round)		Lake trout			
Thirds	$\frac{1}{3}$ lb	Large	8 to 10 lb		
Quarters	$\frac{1}{4}$ lb	Medium	4 to 10 lb		
		No. 1	2 to 4 lb		
		Headless	over 8 lb		
			(dressed)		
		Halfbreed			
		or Fat	all sizes		

Table 10–14

Boston Market		New York Market		Seattle Market	
Tuna	75 to 1000 lb*	Bluefin	75 to 1000 lb*	Tuna	10 to 15 lb‡
		Little	2 to 10 lb†		

*Round or dressed.
†Drawn.
‡Round or drawn.

fresh. Bonito is a related species but may not be marketed as tuna. Table 10–14 gives market classifications for fresh tuna.

Whitefish

This is one of the most popular of fresh-water fish. It is caught in the Great Lakes region and other lakes where it has been transplanted, although all are called *Lake Superior whitefish*. It is prized for its white, delicate, flaky flesh and its sweet mellow flavor. It is moderately fat and broils, bakes or pan-fries well. It is an excellent fish smoked. Because of its fine quality and limited quantity, the cost is usually high. The average weight dressed is 4 lb.

A western whitefish appears on the markets in limited quantities. It resembles the chub, which is a smaller species of whitefish caught in midwestern lakes. The New York and Chicago market listings for Superior whitefish are given in Table 10–15.

Whiting

Several varieties of whiting are caught in substantial quantities in Atlantic waters. The whiting is a small fish. The *king* whiting is known either as a *kingfish* or as a *ground mullet*. Table 10–16 gives market classifications.

Table 10–15

New York Market		Chicago Market	
Round form		Drawn form	
Jumbo	3 lb and up	Jumbo	over 4 lb
No. 1	1½ to 3 lb	Medium-large	3 to 4 lb
Medium	1 to 1½ lb	No. 1	1 to 3 lb
Dressed form	Mixed sizes		

Table 10–16

Boston Market		New York Market		Gulf Market	
Whiting		Whiting	¼ lb up	King whiting	¼ to 1 lb*
Round	½ to 4 lb	King whiting			
Dressed	½ to 4 lb	Large	over 1 lb*		
Steak	½ to 4 lb	Small	over 1 lb*		

*Round form.

MISCELLANEOUS FISH

Many other excellent fish are found on the market. These may appear on local or on the major markets during good season catches. Tables 10–17 and 10–18 summarize some market information available on miscellaneous salt- and fresh-water fish.

Table 10–17
Miscellaneous Salt-Water Fish

Boston Market		New York Market		Gulf Market	
Perch, ocean		Croaker*		Blue runner*	½ to 1 lb
(Rosefish)		Large	1½ lb up	Croaker*	¼ to 1 lb
Mixed	½ to 3 lb	Medium	¾ to 1½ lb	Grouper†	5 to 15 lb
Skate‡		Small	½ to ¾ lb	Drum‡	
Saddles	1 to 10 lb	Pins	under ½ lb	Black	
Wolffish (Ocean		Mullet*		Bulls	15 to 40 lb
Catfish)†		Large	1 lb up	Large	4 to 15 lb
----	2 to 30 lb	Medium	¾ to 1 lb	Medium	1 to 4 lb
		Small	under ¾ lb	Small	¼ to 1 lb
		Skate§		Red	
		Wings or		Bulls	15 to 40 lb
		Saddles	1 to 10 lb	Medium	3 to 15 lb
		Spot*		Rats	1½ to 3 lb
		Large	¾ lb up	Mullet*	½ to 2 lb
		Medium	½ to ¾ lb	Sheepshead†	¾ to 10 lb
		Small	under ½ lb		
		Swellfish‖			
		-----	all sizes		
		Tautog*			
		----	½ lb and up		
		Tilefish†			
		Large	7 lb up		
		Medium	4 to 7 lb		
		Kitten	under 4 lb		

*Round.   †Drawn.   ‡Round or drawn.   §Dressed.   ‖Dressed and skinned.

Table 10–18
Miscellaneous Fresh-Water Fish

New York Market		Gulf Market		Chicago Market	
Blue pike*		Buffalofish‡	3 to 20 lb	Blue pike*	$\frac{1}{2}$ lb
Jumbo	$1\frac{1}{2}$ lb up	Catfish†	1 to 40 lb	Pins	5 to 6 per lb
Regular	$\frac{1}{2}$ to $1\frac{1}{2}$ lb	Sheepshead (gaspergou)†		Buffalofish*	
Buffalofish*			1 to 5 lb	Jumbo	over 8 lb
Jumbo	over 7 lb			No. 1	4 to 8 lb
No. 1	4 to 7 lb			Medium	2 to 4 lb
Carp*				Bullheads‖	
Jumbo	7 lb and up			Jumbo	over $\frac{3}{4}$ lb
No. 1	4 to 7 lb			Large	$\frac{1}{2}$ lb
Medium	under 4 lb			Carp*	
Lake herring*				Jumbo	over 8 lb
Large	3 per lb			No. 1	4 to 8 lb
Regular	4 per lb and up			Medium	2 to 4 lb
Sauger*	$\frac{1}{2}$ to $1\frac{1}{2}$ lb			Chub†	
Sucker (mullet)*				Large	3 to 4 per lb
Mixed	1 to 3 lb			Medium	5 to 7 per lb
Yellow pike*				Small	over 7 per lb
Large	$3\frac{1}{2}$ lb and up			Lake herring†	
No. 1	$1\frac{1}{2}$ to 3 lb			Regular	4 to 7 per lb
No. 2	1 to $1\frac{1}{2}$ lb			Bluefin	3 to 4 per lb
				(Minnesota)	
				Pickerel	
				Large§	over 3 lb
				Medium*	$1\frac{1}{2}$ to 3 lb
				Sauger*	
				Lake Erie	1 lb
				Winnipeg	$\frac{1}{2}$ to $\frac{3}{4}$ lb
				Manitoba	$\frac{3}{4}$ to 1 lb
				Sheepshead*	
				Hard and soft meat:	
				Large	over 5 lb
				Medium	$1\frac{1}{2}$ to 5 lb
				Small	$\frac{3}{4}$ to $1\frac{1}{2}$ lb
				Lake Erie	1 to 5 lb
				Sucker	
				Jumbo†	4 to 6 lb
				Medium†	under 4 lb
				Mullet*	all sizes
				Yellow perch*	
				Native:	
				Jumbo	$\frac{1}{2}$ to $\frac{3}{4}$ lb
				Large	3 fish per lb
				Medium	4 fish per lb
				Small	over 4 fish per lb
				Canadian	
				Jumbo	$\frac{3}{4}$ lb
				Large	2 per lb
				Yellow pike*	
				No. 1 hard	$2\frac{1}{2}$ to $3\frac{1}{2}$ lb
				No. 2 hard	1 to $2\frac{1}{2}$ lb

*Round.   †Drawn.   ‡Round or drawn.   §Dressed.   ‖Dressed and skinned.

SHELLFISH

Abalone

Abalone is a member of the snail family found on the Pacific coast from Southern California to Alaska. California, fearing depletion of beds, prohibits export from the state and abalone in interstate commerce comes from Southern California beds in Mexico. The abalone attaches itself by suction with its strong, creamy white muscle to rocks on the ocean bottom where drivers pry it loose. This muscle is removed, cut into $\frac{1}{2}$ in. slices, pounded for tenderness and packed as steaks in 5- or 10-lb boxes. The pounding thins the steak to about $\frac{1}{4}$ in. and a 3 or 4 oz portion breaded and fried is adequate. The flesh is sweet and delicately flavored. It is likely to be tough unless given proper tenderizing treatment and rapid cooking. It is fairly high in cost.

Clams

There are many types of clams. The Atlantic coast produces the *hard* and *soft* shell and the *surf* clams. The hard-shell clams are found on the coast from Cape Cod to Texas. *Quahaugs, quahogs, littleneck* and *cherrystone* clams are not different clams but are hard-shell clams of the same variety, only different sizes. Littleneck and cherrystone sizes are frequently served raw. New Englanders call the soft-shell clam the *true* clam. It is taken from Cape Cod to the Arctic.

Pacific hard-shell clams are three distinct varieties. They are taken on ocean surfs in different areas. The *butter* and *littleneck* clams will be found in the North Pacific. The *pismo* clam is a large clam. It is usually diced for use in chowders. It is caught along the California coast. The *razor* clam is a soft-shell clam taken off the surfs around Washington. It takes its name from its shape. Market sizes are $3\frac{1}{2}$ to $4\frac{1}{2}$ in. in length of shell. It is a delicately flavored, sweet clam, popular for deep frying. Pacific clams are seldom eaten raw. They may also occasionally become contaminated with a water mite that makes the clams poisonous cooked or raw. The U.S. Public Health Service is constantly testing these products to assure their purity.

Clams are sold by the count, peck, bushel, sack or crate in the East and by the pound on the Pacific coast. Markets on the East coast grade them variously for size. Laws on the Pacific coast prevent the taking of clams under certain sizes or maturity. No size is specified for butter or littleneck clams on the Pacific coast, but regulations require that only mature clams in these varieties be taken. Butter or littleneck clams are not sized for the market but are sold mixed in 100-lb sacks or 80-lb boxes. Most markets have fresh or frozen shucked clams in gallon or No. 10 cans.

Table 10–19*
Measures and Yields of Oysters

State	Capacity of State Bushel (Cubic Inches)	Variation from U.S. Standard Bushel (Cubic Inches)	Variation from U.S. Standard Bushel (Percent)	Market Oysters Yield per State Bushel (Pounds of Meats)	Market Oysters Yield per Standard Bushel (Pounds of Meats)
Maine	2,150.4	–	–	7.01	7.01
Massachusetts	2,150.4	–	–	6.52	6.52
Rhode Island	2,150.4	–	–	7.73	7.73
Connecticut	2,150.4	–	–	7.10	7.10
New York	2,150.4	–	–	7.50	7.50
New Jersey	2,257.3	+ 106.9	+ 5.0	6.70	6.38
Delaware	2,257.3	+ 106.9	+ 5.0	6.58	6.27
Maryland	2,800.7	+ 650.3	+ 30.3	6.42	4.93
Virginia	3,003.9	+ 853.5	+ 30.7	5.88	4.50
North Carolina	2,801.9	+ 651.5	+ 30.3	5.92	4.54
South Carolina	4,071.5	+ 1,921.1	+ 89.3	5.68	3.00
Georgia	5,343.9	+ 3,193.5	+ 148.5	8.77	3.53
Florida, East Coast	3,214.1	+ 1,063.7	+ 49.4	6.56	4.39
Florida, West Coast	3,214.1	+ 1,063.7	+ 49.4	6.08	4.07
Alabama	2,826.2	+ 675.8	+ 31.4	5.61	4.27
Mississippi	2,826.2	+ 675.8	+ 31.4	5.83	4.44
Louisiana	2,148.4	– 2.0	– 0.1	4.65	4.65
Texas	2,700.0	+ 549.6	+ 25.6	6.02	4.79

Average Yields of Certain Mollusks
(Pounds of meat per U.S. standard bushel)

State	Clams Hard Public	Clams Hard Private	Ocean Quahog	Soft	Surf	Razor	Periwinkles and Cockles	Scallops Bay	Scallops Sea	Mussels, Sea	Conchs
Maine	11.00	–	–	15.00	–	–	18.00	–	6.00	15.00	–
Massachusetts	11.00	11.00	8.50	13.00	–	16.00	–	6.00	6.00	12.00	15.00
Rhode Island	12.00	–	10.00	20.00	12.00	–	–	6.20	6.00	10.00	15.00

State										
Connecticut	12.00	–	20.00	–	–	–	6.20	6.00	10.00	20.00
New York	12.00	12.00	16.00	12.00	16.00	–	6.20	6.00	10.00	15.00
New Jersey	10.00	10.00	16.00	13.00	–	–	6.50	6.00	–	15.00
Delaware	10.00	10.00	–	12.00	–	–	–	–	–	11.00
Maryland	10.00	10.00	12.00	12.00	–	–	–	–	–	20.00
Virginia	8.00	8.00	12.00	–	–	–	6.80	6.00	–	20.00
North Carolina	8.75	–	–	–	–	–	–	–	–	–
South Carolina	8.00	–	–	–	–	–	–	–	–	–
Florida, West Coast	8.00	–	–	–	–	–	5.20	–	–	–

Average Number of Crabs per Pound

State	Blue		Rock	Stone	Horseshoe
	Hard	Soft and Peelers			
	Number	Number	Number	Number	Number
Maine	–	–	3.00	–	–
New Hampshire	–	–	3.00	–	–
Massachusetts	–	–	3.00	–	–
Rhode Island	–	–	3.00	–	–
Connecticut	2.40	–	–	–	–
New York	2.40	–	–	–	–
New Jersey	1.71	3.00	–	–	0.25
Delaware	2.40	4.00	–	–	–
Maryland	2.40	4.00	–	–	–
Virginia	3.00	4.00	–	–	–
North Carolina	3.00	3.00	–	–	–
South Carolina	2.40	3.00	–	–	–
Georgia	2.00	–	–	–	–
Florida, East Coast	2.00	–	–	1.00	–
Florida, West Coast	2.00	4.00	–	1.00	–
Alabama	2.03	–	–	–	–
Mississippi	2.18	3.43	–	–	–
Louisiana	1.95	2.40	–	–	–
Texas	1.96	–	–	–	–

*Courtesy of Bureau of Commercial Fisheries, U.S. Fish and Wildlife Service of the Department of Interior.

Table 10–20

Hard-shell Clams		Soft-shell Clams	
Boston Market	New York Market	Boston Market	New York Market
In shell per bushel			
Sharp 160–200	Chowder,	Small 800–1000	Large 400
Cherrystone 325–360	large 125		Medium
Littleneck 500–640	Medium 180		or
	Cherrystone 300–325		Steamers 600–800
	Littleneck 450–650		
Shucked per gallon			
Sharp 100–125		Large 200–300	Large 200–250
		Medium 350–500	Medium 350–400
		Small 500–700	Small 600–700

Table 10–20 shows how the Boston and New York markets classify hard- and soft-shell clams per bushel or number of shucked clams per gallon.

Crab

The Atlantic and Gulf areas produce about 75% of the crabs marketed in this country. The *Blue* crab weighing ¼ to 1 lb is caught in greatest quantity. *Rock* crabs, caught in New England, will weigh ⅓ to ½ lb, depending upon the season. The flesh is slightly brown in color. This detracts somewhat from its appearance but the flavor is good. *Stone* crabs are caught in Florida waters. Only the claw meat is eaten. Considered a delicacy, they are fairly high in price. Soft-shell crabs are blue crabs caught when the crab is changing its shell. They are frequently marketed alive. They may be prepared variously but the most popular way is breaded and deep fried. *Dungeness* crabs are found on the Pacific coast from Alaska to Mexico, although Dungeness, Washington, is located on the entrance to Puget Sound where large quantities are caught. They weigh 1¾ to 3½ lb. This crab has delicate, sweet, tender meat. The claw meat is a delicate red or pink, with a more grainy texture than the body meat. Claw meat brings a higher price. *King* crabs are caught in Alaska and weigh 6 to 20 lb. They may measure 6 ft from the tip of one leg to the tip of the opposite leg. Only the legs and claws are used. The meat is sweet and delicately flavored. It is creamy white in color, but the texture is somewhat stringy and coarse. The legs and claws are cooked and shipped frozen or the meat is picked and shipped frozen. Both market types are sold by the pound. King crab meat freezes and stores better than any other crab meat. Dungeness-picked crab meat may be obtained claws only, claw and body meat or body meat only. Dungeness and King crab meat may be purchased in 1-lb or 5-lb cans, either frozen or fresh cooked. Except for local markets, Dungeness crabs in the shell are usually cooked and shipped either refrigerated or frozen. Market sizes of Dungeness crab in the shell are Ocean, 24-lb per dozen, and Puget Sound, 22-lb per dozen. Laws prohibit the sale of soft-shelled Dungeness crab. California produces some Rock crab. *Tanner* crabs are caught in Alaska waters. The western Rock crab and Tanner crab are found only in local markets.

The Gulf markets ship live Blue hard-shelled and soft-shelled crab at weights ranging, respectively, $\frac{1}{3}$ to $\frac{2}{3}$ lb and $\frac{1}{8}$ to $\frac{1}{2}$ lb. The New York market has no classification for hard-shell crabs, but sells them alive at all sizes. Boston sells mostly the rock crab. The New York market sizes for soft-shell crabs are: Jumbo $5\frac{1}{2}$ in., Large Prime $5-5\frac{1}{2}$ in., Prime $4\frac{1}{2}-5$ in., Hotel Prime 4 to $4\frac{1}{2}$ in., Large Medium $3\frac{1}{2}$ to 4 in., Medium under $3\frac{1}{2}$ in., Culls all sizes. Size in inches is measured as diameter across the back.

The federal specifications list cooked crab meat picked from the shell as lump, flake and claw. Market classifications frequently differ from this list. Most picked crab meat sold on the East coast comes from the Blue crab. The Boston market has fresh cooked flake meat in $\frac{1}{2}$-lb and 1-lb tins and broken meat in 1-lb tins. The New York market classifies cooked crab meat picked from the shell as: Jumbo Lump, all large lump white in color; Lump, small chunks from the body, white in color (may also be called "special of the back fin"); Mixed, must be over 50% lump, the remainder being flake; the flake is white and broken or is small pieces of meat from the body; Flake, all white flake meat from the body; Claw, meat picked from the claws. Claw has a brownish color and is lowest in price.

Crayfish and Spiny Lobster

Crayfish are small crustaceans resembling lobsters or shrimp in shape. They do not have two front claws. They are caught in inland streams and river inlets and average 20 to 25 per pound caught. North Carolina, Florida, Georgia and Oregon produce the main part of the catch. They are limited in supply and considered a delicacy. Some small crayfish are imported from other countries; some of these are slightly larger than jumbo shrimp. Shipment to distant markets is in frozen green form. Some may be flown fresh from Gulf markets to Chicago or New York. Some imported small spiny lobster may be sold as crayfish.

Spiny or *Rock* lobster is a large crayfish caught in the sea. Most lobster tails sold in this country are this spiny lobster with the head and thorax removed. The *Laguna* or Pacific lobster is a crayfish and has no claws. It is sold with the head on, frequently cooked in the shell. It weighs 10 oz to 2 lb. Laguna lobster have smooth shells and are yellowish green before cooking and deep red after.

Imported spiny lobster tails come from Africa, Australia and New Zealand. They have a rough shell with a color that varies from dark maroon to brown. They average 8 oz but some may weigh a pound. Some tails may be sold split. Packing for lobster tails is usually in 20-lb boxes frozen, with 20 to 28 tails in the box. The New York market has the following grades for tails from the spiny lobster: Jumbo, 16 oz and over; Large, 12 to 16 oz; Medium, 9 to 12 oz; Small, 6 to 9 oz. Some picked, cooked spiny lobster meat is sold and it is difficult to tell from true lobster meat. The meat should be a clear white color and the flavor sweet and rich.

Lobster

The *common* or *true* lobster has two large claws near the head. Most of our lobster comes from Maine, but some may be imported from Ireland. Rapid transport has made it possible to ship lobsters alive for distances up to 3000 miles. To be at their best, lobsters should be cooked alive. An uncooked lobster is a dark bluish-green or brownish-olive or blackish-brown color, which changes to a bright red on cooking. Lobsters may also be purchased in the shell green frozen, fresh cooked and cooked frozen. They weigh ¾ to 4 lb. Picked, cooked meat is available in 6-oz, 14-oz, No. 5 and No. 10 cans. Both the meat and lobster in the shell are sold by the pound.

Lobster meat is considered a delicacy and commands a good price on any menu. The claw meat is considered superior to the body meat. The meat of the male is said to be firmer and the color of the shell, after cooking, a brighter red. Some people prefer the female meat because of the roe or coral it may contain. Overcooking lobster makes it tough.

Lobsters with only one claw are called culls and frequently find their way to picked, cooked meat. The Boston market grades live lobster: Jumbo, 3 lb and over; Select, 1¼ to 3 lb; Chicken, 1 lb and Weaks, all sizes but of such low vitality they probably can live only a short time. The New York market has the following grades for live lobster: Jumbo, over 3 lb; Large, 1½ to 2½ lb; Quarter, 1¼ to 1½ lb; Chicken, ¾ to 1 lb. For most purposes the chicken lobster is desirable for one portion. Lobsters are caught all year around except for a short closed season. Heaviest supplies come to market in the summer months.

Lobsters molt by losing their shell as they outgrow it. During the first year a lobster may molt 14 to 17 times. Small lobsters frequently grow as much as 20% with each molt, although the larger ones average about a 9% increase. A 10½ in. lobster has molted 25 to 26 times and is about 5 years old. Immature lobsters are protected by law.

Mussels

The North Atlantic area produces most of the mussels marketed. They are somewhat like oysters except that they are razor shaped. The preferred size is 2½ in. or over. Mussels are sold by the bushel alive in the shell and average 45 to 55 lb per bushel. A bushel of medium sized mussels will contain 350 to 400 mussels. Fresh-water mussels are sold on some local markets.

Oysters

Oysters are fourth in value of fish caught in this country. The Atlantic areas produce the major portion of oysters from the shore and bay areas from the Maritime Provinces of Canada to Texas. Chesapeake oysters are considered the finest of all Atlantic oysters. The eastern oyster is smaller and whiter than the Pacific (Japanese) oyster. The flavor, texture and size of oysters are affected by tides, food supplies and water temperature. The best oysters are taken from cold, not warm water. Oysters must come from beds approved by the U.S. Public Health Service. Buyers should request certification by Public Health that shellfish come from acceptable beds.

Oysters from the Pacific coast may be of two varieties, the Olympia and the Japanese or Pacific oyster. The latter was transplanted by seed from Japan and is a large oyster slightly gray in color. The flavor is stronger than that of the eastern oyster, and it is not eaten raw as much as the eastern varieties. Variable water temperatures and growing conditions cause great fluctuation in the size of the Japanese oyster, which is usually larger than the eastern oyster. The Olympia oyster is also called the western oyster. It is native to Hood's Canal and the Olympia area of Puget Sound. It is small, and a gallon of shucked Olympias will number 1600 to 1700 oysters. The flavor and color are excellent. It is frequently used for cocktails. The supply is limited and declining each year. The price is high. Olympia oysters are sold in the shell by the sack. A sack full weighs around 120 lb. Pacific (Japanese) oysters in the shell are sold by the pound. When shucked, Pacific oysters are sold by the gallon.

If water containing less than 0.75% salt is used on shucked oysters, all accumulated liquid must be drained thoroughly from the oysters before they are packed. Water low in salt will be imbibed heavily by oysters during shucking. In addition, the oysters must not be in contact with

Table 10–21

Eastern Oysters				Pacific or Japanese Oysters	
Boston Market		New York Market		Seattle Market	
Live in the shell					
Large	500 per bbl	Box	150 per bu	By the sack priced by	
Medium	700–750	Medium	200	the pound; 80-lb per	
Small	900–1050	Half shell	325	sack; average 200 per	
Extra small	1050–1200	Blue point	400	sack for smaller sizes.	
Shucked per gallon					
Count	135–160	Count	160 or less	Grade A	40–64
Select	180–230	Extra select	160–210	Grade B	65–80
Standard	300–350	Select	210–300	Grade C	81–96
		Standard	300–500	Grade D	97–120
				Grade E	121–144
				Grade F	over 144

the water for more than 30 minutes. Shucked oysters, after draining 2 minutes, should have not more than 5% liquid drained off by weight.

In the East oysters are sold live in the shell by the dozen, peck, bushel or crate. Shucked oysters are sold by the gallon, either fresh or frozen. Federal standards of identity exist for processed oyster products. Table 10–21 gives commercial gradings for Eastern and Pacific oysters.

The federal standards for size are shown in Table 10–22.

Some of the Pacific markets grade oysters as small, medium and large. *Straights* on the oyster market means oysters ungraded for size.

Scallops

There are two kinds of scallops, *bay* and *sea*. Both come from a two-shelled mollusk having a scalloped edge on the shell. A wavy edge will be on the edge of bay scallops. Only the adductor muscle or "eye" that controls the shell movement is eaten. This is about 10% of the scallop, and about 1½ bushels of scallops in the shell will give 1 gal or around

Table 10–22

Eastern Oysters		Pacific or Japanese Oysters	
Extra large	160 or less per gal	Large	64 or less per gal
Large	160–210	Medium	65–96
Medium	210–300	Small	97–144
Small	300–500	Extra small	144 or over
Very small	over 500		

$8\frac{1}{2}$ to 9 lb of clear meat. Scallops are usually sold shucked, the eye muscle removed and cut into pieces. Bay scallop pieces are usually smaller than sea scallop pieces. Bay scallops are considered sweeter and superior in flavor. The texture is also more tender. The color of bay scallops is creamy white, light tan or pinkish, while the color of sea scallops is usually clear white. Most scallops on the eastern markets are taken from New England waters, the sea scallops being taken in deeper off-shore waters and the bay scallops in bays. The Pacific coast produces some bay scallops.

The Boston market lists bay scallops as 500 to 850 per gal and sea scallops at 110- to 170 per gal. The New York market classifies bay scallops as *large* if they are $\frac{3}{4}$ in. or more in diameter, *medium* if between $\frac{1}{2}$ and $\frac{3}{4}$ in. in diameter and small if they are under $\frac{1}{2}$ in. in diameter. It has no grade sizes for sea scallops.

Shrimp

Large-sized shrimp may be called prawns. Size is related to price; larger sizes bring higher prices. The Gulf coast is the source of most of our shrimp. The Pacific coast has a small shrimp that is used locally. The meat is tender, white and delicately flavored. Live shrimp are pale green or gray in color. The flesh is gray and translucent. It will turn white in cooking, with slight touches of red on the outer surface.

The heaviest production of Gulf shrimp occurs in the fall, August through December. A large, king-sized shrimp is imported from Italy, while a midget shrimp averaging 150 to 300 to the pound is imported from Iceland and Holland.

Shrimp may be marketed either fresh or frozen. Very few shrimp are sold alive except on local markets. The head and thorax are removed, leaving only the tail. They may be marketed in this manner shelled or with the shell on. They may also be cooked and marketed with the shell on or off. Green or raw shelled shrimp may also be sold breaded for frying. Government standards exist for this type of shrimp.[2] These standards allow from 47 to 50% breading in proportion to shrimp. Buyers should specify premium pack, however, allowing only a maximum of 35% breading to shrimp.

[2] The shrimp must be shelled and deveined to meet government standards. Grades are U.S. Grade A or B. There are four types under the grades:

Type I—Fantail: Split (butterfly), with tail fin and the shell segment immediately adjacent to the fin. The shrimp is split, with the tail fin free of all shell segments.

Type II—Round fantail: Round, unsplit shrimp with tailfin and the shell segment immediately adjacent to the tailfin and shrimp with tailfin free of all shell segments.

Type III—Split without tailfin or shell segments.

Type IV—Round (unsplit) shrimp without attached tail or shell segments.

Table 10–23

Chicago Market		New York Market
Extra jumbo	Less than 15 lb	No grade terms are used; buyers pur-
Jumbo	15 to 20	chase by count per pound as under 15,
Large	21 to 25	15 to 20, 21 to 25, 26 to 30, 31–35, 36–
Large-medium	26 to 30	40, 41–45, 46–50, 51–60 and over 60.
Medium	31 to 42	
Small	43 to 65	
Very small or bait	more than 66	

Gradings for shrimp with heads on at Gulf ports are: Large—under 18 per lb, Medium—18 to 35 per lb, and Small—over 35 per lb. Table 10–23 shows how the Chicago and New York markets classify headed shrimp per pound.

Miscellaneous Shellfish

Turtles may be fresh water caught or from the sea. The former are purchased live and may run from 2 to 100 lb. Sea turtles are also purchased alive or dressed in the same weight range, but usually run larger than the fresh-water turtles, on the average. Diamond-backed terrapin are a smaller variety of turtle and are usually sold alive as cows, $1\frac{1}{2}$ to 2 lb; heifers, 1 lb; and bulls, $\frac{1}{2}$ to 1 lb. Turtle or terrapin may be available on the market as chuck or clear meat.

Frogs may be purchased on the market live, from $\frac{1}{2}$ to 1 lb each. Most food facilities use only the legs and generally purchase legs only by the pair, fresh or frozen. Frog legs include the saddle or the lower part of the back. Grade sizes for legs are: extra large, 2 to 3 per lb; large, 4 to 5 per lb; medium, 6 to 8 per lb; and small, 9 to 12 per lb.

Eels may be purchased live, dressed and skinned or smoked. They are available throughout the year, although usually most plentiful in the fall. Market sizes in round form are: large 2 to 5 lb; medium 1 to 2 lb; and small, under 1 lb. Conchs and snails are available on some markets, usually live in the shell. Large snails may run around 32 to the pound. Cuttlefish (sepia) are sold in the round form, from $\frac{1}{2}$ to $\frac{3}{4}$ lb in weight. Octopus are usually sold in round form, and smaller sizes may be marketed in weights from $\frac{3}{4}$ lb up. Squid run 5 to 6 to the pound in round form.

CANNED FISH

More canned fish is consumed in this country than any other type, fresh or otherwise. Consumption is dropping per capita, however, as supplies decrease and the popularity of fresh and frozen fish increases. Wide variety is found in the canned product.

Buyers should look for neatness of pack, unbroken fish and freedom from bruises, brown blood spots, cracks, blood, entrails, scales and other defects. The color should be clear and typical for the canned fish and the liquor should be clear. Unevenly colored fish or fish bearing pink or red streaks should be rejected. The flavor and odor should be pleasant and free from rancidity or acrid taste, spoilage or other off-flavors or odors. The texture should be firm but not fibrous.

The drained weight for solid pack fish, such as dry pack lobster, crab or shrimp, should be nearly 100% of the stated net can contents. Standards of fill, as established by the federal government for oysters, state that the drained weight of the oysters shall be at least 59% of the weight of the water capacity of the can and that for dry pack shrimp this ratio shall be 60% and for wet pack shrimp 64%. Some fish packed heavily, such as sardines, tuna and salmon, will have higher drained weights.

Anchovies are a small fish caught largely in Mediterranean waters. They are filleted, given a high salt cure and canned. They may be purchased in 1-lb cans or smaller sizes. They are also sold rolled. These rolled fillets may have special fillings in the centers, such as capers, nuts or small onions. An anchovy paste is also available.

Canned clams may be purchased whole, minced or chopped. Canned clam nectar or clam broth may also be purchased. Most clams are packed for institutional use in 51-oz cans or in No. 10 cans. The liquor on the canned clams may be milky but should otherwise be clear. The clams may be creamy white or white, but not dark or gray. There should be little evidence of silt, dirt, or shells on the bottom of the can or mixed in with the clams. The meat should be tender, flavorful and free from objectionable odors.

Canned codfish may be obtained for the preparation of codfish balls and other items where codfish is used. Prepared codfish balls come canned too.

Canned crab meat from the Blue, Dungeness, King or Rock crabs is available in 5-oz, 6½-oz and 13-oz cans. The odor of the canned crab should be pleasant and sweet. There should be no trace of black caused by sulfides reacting with can linings. If desired, specifications may read that the crab shall be wrapped in paper inside the can. Paper may also be a requirement for shrimp and lobster. Can linings are being improved and it is possible that this requirement may be eliminated in the future. The color of the crab meat should be white, tinged with red on the outer surfaces, and the flavor should be sweet and mild. The texture should be typical of the variety of the crab. Specialty crab pastes are available.

Some canned herring is on the market. It is frequently sold like sar-

FIG. 10–4. A federal inspector examines Maine sardines before the can is closed and the sardines are processed. Courtesy Maine Sardine Council.

dines, packed in tomato or mustard sauces or in oil. Canned mackerel is also on the market. It is canned similarly to the manner in which herring is canned. Buyers should note defects and workmanship on these items, for they move on the market at low prices and processors may cut corners, in attempting to achieve low production costs, by neglecting to give desirable workmanship.

Canned lobster meat is available packed in containers similar in sizes packed for crab. The meat may be that of common lobster or spiny lobster. Fancy packs of crayfish are also available. Specialty lobster pastes may be obtained for use in sandwiches, hors d'oeuvres and canapes.

Canned oysters are available in No. 10 cans. Generally canned oysters are Eastern oysters. The Pacific oyster is not canned in quantity. Quality factors are similar to those given for clams above.

Fish roe is canned. It may be obtained in black or salmon-colored form. Imitation caviar may come from whitefish, shad, salmon or other fish. Only roe from the sturgeon may be labeled caviar. Sturgeon roe is also called Russian or beluga caviar.

Salmon at one time was the leading canned fish, but tuna now exceeds it in quantity packed. Salmon is usually packed in 1-lb cans, but smaller sizes may be obtained. Price is largely governed by the redness of the salmon, although the flavor and nutritional value of the lighter-colored salmon may be as good. The best salmon comes from the large body pieces. Lower-quality salmon is indicated when tail pieces, cheeks and other cuts of lesser value are found in the can.

Three types of sardines are available on our market. Imports are largely from Norway and come packed in $3\frac{1}{4}$-oz cans containing around 8 sardines. The fish is either Brisling or Silt, a small herring-type fish. Most of these imports are in oil. The second type available is the California pilchard, a large sardine that is usually packed in 15-oz net oval cans. Type of pack may be oil, mustard or tomato sauce. These sardines are coarser in texture than the small sardines and may be stronger in flavor. The Maine sardine is the third type and comprises about 70% of the total market. Most of the pack is in $3\frac{1}{4}$-oz cans in oil, but some packs are available in 12-oz cans. Most of the larger packs are in mustard or tomato sauce.

Maine sardines come from a small herring. The sizes range from 4 to 12 fish per $3\frac{1}{4}$-oz can, but the average will be found to be around 5 to 6 per can. The oil used is usually soybean oil. There are one hundred $3\frac{1}{4}$-oz cans per case.

Federal standards for grades exist for Maine sardines. In 1958 the Maine sardine industry asked the state legislature to pass a mandatory law requiring all oil-packed sardines processed in the state to be federally graded. There are four grades: Fancy, Extra Standard, Standard and Substandard. Substandard lots must be plainly marked "Substandard grade—good food—not high quality" and cannot be marketed as sardines. Factors considered in grading are defects that are largely based on workmanship, odor, taste and texture. Sardines with objectionable rancid, foreign, acrid, strong or unusual taste or odor are given zero scores and cannot be graded above substandard. Good character or texture is indicated if the sardine remains intact when lifted with a 4-tined fork ($\frac{3}{4}$ in. wide) without breaking. The sardine should not be tough or fibrous. Mushy or gritty sardines are graded down.

Canned tuna is used extensively in many food facilities. Most tuna is

FIG. 10–5. One of the finest of cured fish is smoked Lake Superior whitefish. It is rich in flavor, with a delicate white flaky meat. It is high in fat. Courtesy Smith Brothers, Port Washington, Wisc.

Table 10–24

Can Size and Type of Tuna	Drained Weight, in Ounces	Can Size and Type of Tuna	Drained Weight, in Ounces
$2^{11}/_{16}$ by $1^{9}/_{16}$ in.		$4^{1}/_{16}$ by $2^{6}/_{16}$ in.	
Solid	2.25	Solid	8.76
Chunks	1.98	Chunks	7.68
Flakes	1.98	Flakes	7.68
Grated	2.00	Grated	7.76
$3^{7}/_{16}$ by $1^{13}/_{16}$ in.		$6^{3}/_{16}$ by $4^{1}/_{2}$ in.	
Solid	4.47	Solid	43.2
Chunks	3.92	Chunks	37.9
Flakes	3.92	Flakes	37.9
Grated	3.96	Grated	38.3

caught and canned in California. Some high quality Italian *tonno*, generally packed in olive oil, is imported. To be labeled tuna, the fish must be Bluefin, Southern bluefin, Oriental, Albacore, Big-eyed, Yellowfin, Northern bluefin, Skipjack, Little tunny or Kawakawa types of tuna. Bonito may not be labeled tuna. The meat may be purchased solid or fancy pack. This pack comes from the loins of the fish and is used for cold plates and where appearance is important. Chunk style is a mixture of pieces. Around 50% of the total can contents of chunk style may pass through a $\frac{1}{2}$ in. screen. Flaked tuna is a mixture of small pieces, but the muscular structure of the flesh is retained. Grated tuna is almost granular but not pasty. Tuna may be purchased as white meat, light meat, dark meat or blended. Albacore has the lightest meat of all tuna. Drained weights recommended by the federal government for tuna are shown in Table 10–24.

CURED FISH

There are many different types of smoked, salted or otherwise cured fish. Smoked fish may be cod, halibut, trout, whitefish, chub, sablefish or others. Such salt fish as mackerel or herring, as well as cod, ling cod and others, are used. "Finnan haddie" is a popular fish served in many facilities. It is a lightly smoked and salted cod. Buyers who purchase cured-fish products in quantity should consult products available on the local markets and learn quality factors for the specific factors they purchase. They should write their own specifications to establish the quality and type of fish desired.

MARKET FISH

Recognition of fish by the buyer is frequently difficult.   Local names may be used.   The following illustrations show most of the fish marketed in this country, their names and area where caught.

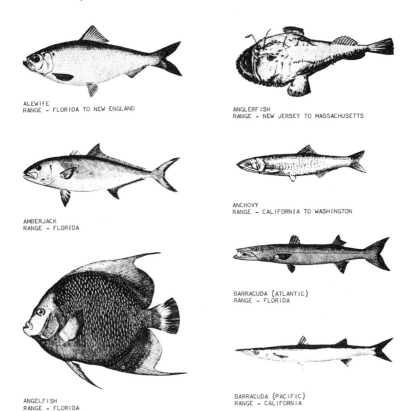

ALEWIFE
RANGE - FLORIDA TO NEW ENGLAND

ANGLERFISH
RANGE - NEW JERSEY TO MASSACHUSETTS

AMBERJACK
RANGE - FLORIDA

ANCHOVY
RANGE - CALIFORNIA TO WASHINGTON

BARRACUDA (ATLANTIC)
RANGE - FLORIDA

ANGELFISH
RANGE - FLORIDA

BARRACUDA (PACIFIC)
RANGE - CALIFORNIA

BLUEFISH
RANGE - GULF OF MEXICO TO NEW ENGLAND

BURBOT
RANGE - GREAT LAKES

BLUE RUNNER OR HARDTAIL
RANGE - GULF OF MEXICO

BUTTERFISH
RANGE - FLORIDA TO NEW ENGLAND

BONITO (ATLANTIC)
RANGE - NORTH CAROLINA TO MASSACHUSETTS

CABIO
RANGE - FLORIDA TO VIRGINIA

BOWFIN
RANGE - FRESH-WATER

CARP
RANGE - FRESH-WATER

BUFFALOFISH
RANGE - FRESH-WATER

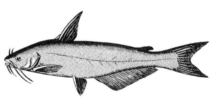

CATFISH
RANGE - FRESH-WATER

CHUB
RANGE - GREAT LAKES

CIGARFISH
RANGE - FLORIDA

COD
RANGE - VIRGINIA TO MAINE, WASHINGTON,
        AND ALASKA

CRAPPIE
RANGE - FRESH-WATER LAKES

CREVALLE
RANGE - SOUTH ATLANTIC AND GULF STATES

CROAKER
RANGE - GULF OF MEXICO TO NEW YORK

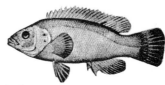

CUNNER
RANGE - NEW ENGLAND

CUSK
RANGE - NEW ENGLAND

DOLLY VARDEN TROUT
RANGE - PACIFIC

DOLPHIN
RANGE - FLORIDA TO NORTH CAROLINA

DRUM, BLACK
RANGE - TEXAS TO NORTH CAROLINA

LEMON SOLE
RANGE - NEW YORK TO MAINE

DRUM, RED
RANGE - TEXAS - MARYLAND

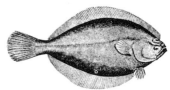

DAB
RANGE - MASSACHUSETTS TO NOVA SCOTIA

EEL, COMMON
RANGE - FLORIDA TO NEW ENGLAND AND IN
           MISSISSIPPI RIVER, LAKE ONTARIO

BLACKBACK OR WINTER FLOUNDER
RANGE - NORTH CAROLINA TO MAINE

EEL, CONGER
RANGE - FLORIDA TO NEW ENGLAND

FLUKE
RANGE - TEXAS TO MASSACHUSETTS

GRAY SOLE
RANGE - MASSACHUSETTS TO MAINE

FLYING FISH
RANGE - PACIFIC AND ATLANTIC OCEANS

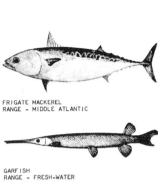

FRIGATE MACKEREL
RANGE - MIDDLE ATLANTIC

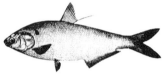

GARFISH
RANGE - FRESH-WATER

GIZZARD SHAD
RANGE - NORTH CAROLINA TO MARYLAND,
        GREAT LAKES

GOLDFISH
RANGE - LAKES AND RIVERS

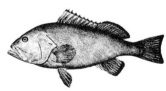

GRAYFISH
RANGE - PACIFIC

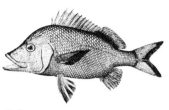

GRUNT
RANGE - FLORIDA

HADDOCK
RANGE - NEW ENGLAND STATES

HAKE, RED
RANGE - CHESAPEAKE BAY TO NEW ENGLAND

HAKE, WHITE
RANGE - CHESAPEAKE BAY TO NEW ENGLAND

HAKE (PACIFIC)
RANGE - PACIFIC

GROUPER
RANGE - TEXAS TO SOUTH CAROLINA

HALIBUT
RANGE - PACIFIC COAST - NEW ENGLAND

HARDHEAD
RANGE - CALIFORNIA

HOGCHOKER
RANGE - CHESAPEAKE BAY

HARVESTFISH OR "STARFISH"
RANGE - NORTH CAROLINA TO CHESAPEAKE BAY

HOGFISH
RANGE - FLORIDA

HERRING, LAKE
RANGE - GREAT LAKES

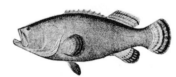

JEWFISH
RANGE - FLORIDA

HERRING, SEA
RANGE - NEW JERSEY TO NEW ENGLAND, PACIFIC
        COAST STATES AND ALASKA

HICKORY SHAD
RANGE - FLORIDA TO RHODE ISLAND

JOHN DORY
RANGE - MIDDLE ATLANTIC STATES

KING MACKEREL
RANGE - TEXAS TO NEW YORK

MACKEREL, ATLANTIC
RANGE - CHESAPEAKE BAY TO MAINE

KING WHITING
RANGE - TEXAS TO MASSACHUSETTS

MACKEREL, JACK
RANGE - CALIFORNIA

LAKE TROUT
RANGE - GREAT LAKES

MACKEREL, PACIFIC
RANGE - CALIFORNIA

MENHADEN
RANGE - GULF OF MEXICO TO NEW ENGLAND

LAMPREY
RANGE - FRESH-WATER

MOONEYE
RANGE - GREAT LAKES

LAUNCE
RANGE - NEW ENGLAND

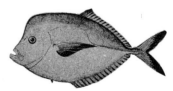

LINGCOD
RANGE - CALIFORNIA TO ALASKA

MOONFISH
RANGE - FLORIDA

MULLET
RANGE - TEXAS TO NEW JERSEY

SARDINE, PACIFIC (PILCHARD)
RANGE - CALIFORNIA TO WASHINGTON

OCEAN POUT
RANGE - NEW ENGLAND

PINFISH
RANGE - FLORIDA TO NORTH CAROLINA

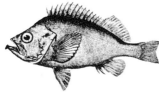

OCEAN PERCH (ROSEFISH)
RANGE - NEW ENGLAND

POLLOCK
RANGE - MIDDLE ATLANTIC AND NEW ENGLAND STATES

PADDLEFISH
RANGE - GULF OF MEXICO, MISSISSIPPI RIVER

POMPANO
RANGE - TEXAS TO NORTH CAROLINA

PIGFISH
RANGE - FLORIDA

PIKE OR PICKEREL
RANGE - FRESH-WATER

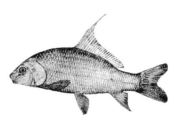

QUILLBACK
RANGE - FRESH-WATER

RATFISH
RANGE - WASHINGTON TO ALASKA

SALMON, CHINOOK OR KING
RANGE - CALIFORNIA TO ALASKA

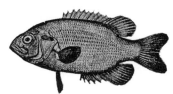

ROCK BASS
RANGE - GREAT LAKES

SALMON, CHUM OR KETA
RANGE - OREGON TO ALASKA

ROCKFISH
RANGE - CALIFORNIA TO ALASKA

SALMON, PINK
RANGE - WASHINGTON TO ALASKA

RUDDERFISH
RANGE - CALIFORNIA

SALMON, RED OR SOCKEYE
RANGE - OREGON TO ALASKA

SABLEFISH
RANGE - PACIFIC COAST STATES AND ALASKA

SALMON, SILVER OR COHO
RANGE - CALIFORNIA TO ALASKA

SAUGER
RANGE - GREAT LAKES

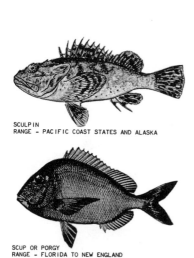

SCULPIN
RANGE - PACIFIC COAST STATES AND ALASKA

SCUP OR PORGY
RANGE - FLORIDA TO NEW ENGLAND

SEA BASS
RANGE - FLORIDA TO NEW ENGLAND

SEA CATFISH
RANGE - TEXAS TO CHESAPEAKE BAY

SEA ROBIN
RANGE - CHESAPEAKE BAY TO NEW ENGLAND

SEA TROUT OR WEAKFISH, GRAY
RANGE - FLORIDA TO MASSACHUSETTS

SEA TROUT OR WEAKFISH, SPOTTED
RANGE - MARYLAND TO TEXAS

SEA TROUT OR WEAKFISH, WHITE
RANGE - GULF OF MEXICO

SHAD
RANGE - FLORIDA TO NEW ENGLAND

SHARK
RANGE - ATLANTIC COAST, GULF, PACIFIC COAST STATES

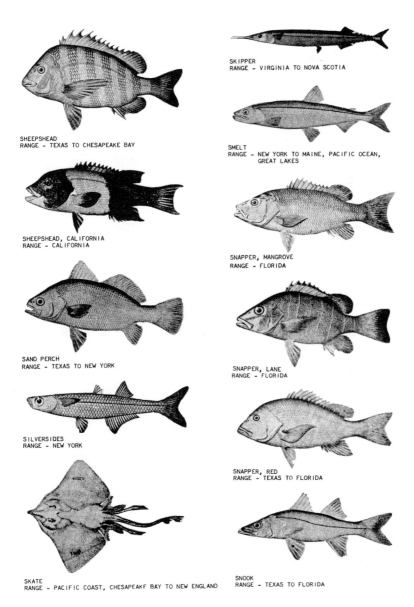

SKIPPER
RANGE - VIRGINIA TO NOVA SCOTIA

SHEEPSHEAD
RANGE - TEXAS TO CHESAPEAKE BAY

SMELT
RANGE - NEW YORK TO MAINE, PACIFIC OCEAN,
        GREAT LAKES

SHEEPSHEAD, CALIFORNIA
RANGE - CALIFORNIA

SNAPPER, MANGROVE
RANGE - FLORIDA

SAND PERCH
RANGE - TEXAS TO NEW YORK

SNAPPER, LANE
RANGE - FLORIDA

SILVERSIDES
RANGE - NEW YORK

SNAPPER, RED
RANGE - TEXAS TO FLORIDA

SKATE
RANGE - PACIFIC COAST, CHESAPEAKE BAY TO NEW ENGLAND

SNOOK
RANGE - TEXAS TO FLORIDA

SPADEFISH
RANGE - FLORIDA

SPANISH MACKEREL
RANGE - TEXAS TO VIRGINIA

SPOT
RANGE - GULF OF MEXICO TO MIDDLE ATLANTIC STATES

SQUAWFISH
RANGE - CALIFORNIA

STEELHEAD TROUT
RANGE - OREGON TO ALASKA

STRIPED BASS
RANGE - NORTH CAROLINA TO NEW ENGLAND, CALIFORNIA
         TO OREGON

STURGEON
RANGE - COASTAL AND RIVER AREAS

STURGEON, SHOVELNOSE
RANGE - FRESH-WATER

SUCKER
RANGE - FRESH-WATER

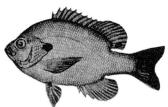

SUNFISH
RANGE - FRESH-WATER

SWELLFISH
RANGE - CHESAPEAKE BAY TO MIDDLE ATLANTIC

SWORDFISH
RANGE - NEW ENGLAND AND CALIFORNIA

TRIGGERFISH
RANGE - FLORIDA

TAUTOG
RANGE - CHESAPEAKE BAY TO NEW ENGLAND

TRIPLETAIL
RANGE - FLORIDA

TENPOUNDER
RANGE - FLORIDA

THIMBLE-EYED MACKEREL
RANGE - CHESAPEAKE BAY TO NEW ENGLAND

TUNA, ALBACORE
RANGE - PACIFIC COAST

TILEFISH
RANGE - MIDDLE ATLANTIC AND NEW ENGLAND STATES

TUNA, BLUEFIN
RANGE - CALIFORNIA, NEW JERSEY TO MAINE

TOMCOD
RANGE - PACIFIC COAST, MIDDLE ATLANTIC AND
        NEW ENGLAND STATES

TUNA, LITTLE
RANGE - MASSACHUSETTS TO TEXAS

TUNA, SKIPJACK
RANGE - CALIFORNIA

TUNA, YELLOWFIN
RANGE - PACIFIC

WHITE BASS
RANGE - GREAT LAKES

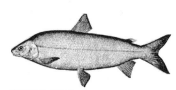

WHITEFISH, COMMON
RANGE - GREAT LAKES

WHITEFISH, MENOMINEE
RANGE - ALASKA, GREAT LAKES

WHITE PERCH
RANGE - NORTH CAROLINA TO MAINE

WHITING
RANGE - VIRGINIA TO MAINE

WOLFFISH
RANGE - MASSACHUSETTS AND MAINE

YELLOW PERCH
RANGE - GREAT LAKES, OTHER LAKES

YELLOW PIKE
RANGE - GREAT LAKES

BLUE CRAB
RANGE - TEXAS TO RHODE ISLAND

STONE CRAB
RANGE - FLORIDA

DUNGENESS CRAB
RANGE - PACIFIC COAST STATES AND ALASKA

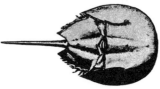

HORSESHOE CRAB
RANGE - MARYLAND TO NEW YORK

KING CRAB
RANGE - ALASKA

FRESH-WATER CRAWFISH
RANGE - RIVERS AND LAKES

ROCK CRAB
RANGE - NEW ENGLAND

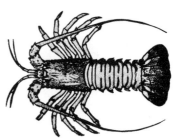

SPINY LOBSTER
RANGE - CALIFORNIA AND FLORIDA

LOBSTER, NORTHERN
RANGE - VIRGINIA TO MAINE

HARD CLAM
RANGE - FLORIDA TO MAINE

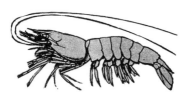

SHRIMP
RANGE - TEXAS TO NORTH CAROLINA, MAINE,
        CALIFORNIA, WASHINGTON, AND ALASKA

RAZOR CLAM, PACIFIC
RANGE - OREGON, WASHINGTON AND ALASKA

BUTTER CLAM
RANGE - PACIFIC COAST

SOFT CLAM
RANGE - MIDDLE ATLANTIC TO NEW ENGLAND,
        PACIFIC COAST STATES

LITTLE NECK CLAM
RANGE - PACIFIC COAST

CONCH
RANGE - FLORIDA TO MAINE

LIMPET
RANGE - NEW YORK AND NEW ENGLAND

FRESH-WATER MUSSEL
RANGE - FRESH-WATER STREAMS

SEA MUSSEL
RANGE - NORTH CAROLINA TO MAINE

OYSTER
RANGE - TEXAS TO MASSACHUSETTS, PACIFIC COAST

BAY SCALLOP
RANGE - FLORIDA TO MASSACHUSETTS, WASHINGTON

SEA SCALLOP
RANGE - NEW JERSEY TO MAINE

STARFISH
RANGE - ATLANTIC AND PACIFIC COAST

TERRAPIN
RANGE - TEXAS TO NEW JERSEY

GREEN TURTLE
RANGE - FLORIDA

LOGGERHEAD TURTLE
RANGE - FLORIDA TO NEW JERSEY

FROG
RANGE - FRESH-WATER, MARSHES, POND

HAWKSBILL TURTLE
RANGE - GULF OF MEXICO, AND ATLANTIC COAST
          TO NEW YORK

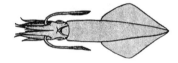

SQUID
RANGE - VIRGINIA TO MAINE, CALIFORNIA AND
          WASHINGTON

SOFT-SHELL TURTLE
RANGE - LAKES AND RIVERS

SPONGE
RANGE - FLORIDA

IRISH MOSS
RANGE - NEW ENGLAND

11 Meats

Meat is perhaps the most important food purchased by a food service. It is the center of the meal and its selection largely determines the other foods that will be served.   About one third to one half of the total food budget is spent for meat, fish and poultry, and most of this goes for meat. Approximately 160 lb of meat, excluding fish and poultry, are consumed per capita in this country.   Of this amount, 50% is beef, 40% pork (including cured pork products), 7% veal and the remainder lamb and mutton.

Precisely written specifications are necessary if satisfactory meat purchasing is to be achieved.   Good specifications are based on a sound knowledge of the factors that will meet production needs.   Recognition of meat cuts and quality is a prime requisite; grades of meat are indicators of quality and buyers need to know the factors that make up meat grades.   To purchase meat properly, a buyer should know how it is to be cooked and from that decide on grade and cut required.   Market conditions and pricing must be closely followed to know what is available.   Well-written specifications will make it possible to standardize quality, portion size and costs.

MEAT PRICING

Meat prices will follow market conditions.   Buyers should scan market reports daily for prices and factors that will influence supply and demand.   A heavy corn crop may depress corn prices to the extent that farmers may prefer to feed it to animals for market.   This may delay shipment of animals in the fall but cause heavy shipment of corn-fed animals later.   Range cattle appear on the market in greatest supply in

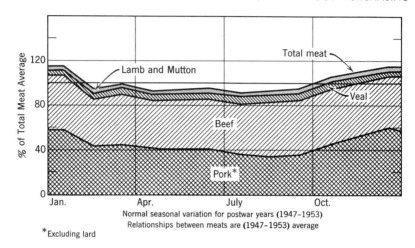

Normal seasonal variation for postwar years (1947-1953)
Relationships between meats are (1947-1953) average

*Excluding lard

FIG. 11-1.   Seasonal production of pork, beef, lamb and mutton.   Courtesy USDA.

the fall when the animals are in best condition.   Pigs born in the spring
and fall reach the market 3 to 4 months later, and prices reflect this
increased supply.   Veal and lambs reach the market in peak numbers 3
to 5 months after birth.   At certain times of the year they are scarce on
the market, and buyers pay premium prices to obtain supplies.

PHYSICAL STRUCTURE OF MEAT

To cook meat properly, one must know something about the structure
of meat.   Lean flesh is composed of muscles, which are conglomerate
bundles of fibers held together by connective tissue.   The size of the fiber
is extremely small, especially in tender cuts or cuts from young animals,
but the coarsest fibers may be distinguished by the naked eye.   The size
varies in length, depth and thickness, and this variation will affect the
grain and texture of the meat.

The quantity of connective tissue binding the fibers together will have
much to do with the tenderness and eating quality.   There are two kinds
of connective tissue, the yellow (elastin) and the white (collagen).   The
thick yellow strap that runs along the neck and back of animals is an example of elastin.   It is found throughout the muscles, especially in muscles of older animals or those muscles receiving considerable exercise.
Elastin will not cook tender but must be broken up mechanically by
pounding, cubing, grinding or other means.   The white connective
tissue, collagen, can be cooked tender.   It hydrolyzes in moist heat to

gelatin. The quantity of connective tissue in meat is governed by the age, breed, care and feed given the animal.

The quantity of fat and its condition are important factors in deciding eating quality. Fat is found on the exterior and interior of the carcass and in the flesh itself. Fat deposited between muscles or between the bundles of fibers is called *marbling*. If marbling is present, the meat is apt to be more tender, more flavorful and more moist. Much of the flavor of meat is given by fats or esters found in lean or fatty tissues of the meat. Animals fed corn, grains, peanuts or certain other types of feed absorb flavor from these feeds. Slop-fed pork has an undesirable, characteristic flavor, but corn-fed pork will be highly prized because of the nutty quality imparted by the corn oil. Extractives in meats are also responsible for flavor. Muscles that receive a great amount of exercise have a higher proportion of flavor extractives than those receiving less exercise. Shanks, neck muscles and other parts receiving exercise will give richer broths and gravies and more flavorful meat than tender cuts.

Tenderness, flavor and moistness are increased if beef is aged or ripened for a time at 36° F. Aging must be a carefully controlled process. A short time after death an animal's muscles stiffen, a condition known as *rigor mortis*. After a time enzymatic actions and increasing acidity relax the muscles, and the meat becomes soft and pliable. If the meat is cooked during rigor, it will be tough and shrink badly. This meat is called "green meat." As meat continues to hang in storage, this condition is lost, and tenderness, flavor and moistness increase. Maximum benefits of aging are obtained up to 6 weeks but most ripening occurs in the first 2 weeks. Raising the temperature will shorten the ripening process and 7 to 8 days at 45° F will age meat as much as 11 to 15 days at 34° F. Relative humidity should be 83 to 88%. The natural air movement should be 10 to 40 ft per minute. During this aging period the evaporative loss may run as high as 8% and trimming losses, because of darkening and discoloration, may run 9%. Some investigators have reported that ripened meats shrink less in cooking than unripened meats.

Pork and veal are not aged. Lamb and mutton may be aged 7 to 10 days. All meat should be held at least 3 days after body heat has been lost and preferably 7 days. Many specifications require that fresh-chilled meat shall be delivered at an internal temperature of 40° F.

MARKET REGULATION

Meat inspection was started in 1891 by the Bureau of Animal Industry of the USDA. Controls were few and did not provide for the supervision of meat after slaughter. In 1906 the Meat Inspection Act was passed and enlarged the powers of the BAI. The act applied only to meats shipped in interstate commerce. In consequence, many states passed similar laws. Supervision of processing and handling by federal authorities was required. The purpose of the meat inspection provisions was to eliminate meat diseased or otherwise unsound, unhealthy or unwholesome. Harmful dyes, preservatives, chemicals or other deleterious ingredients were forbidden. The law prevented the use of misleading names or statements on labels of processed or fresh meats and established sanitary provisions for plants, equipment and personnel. Approximately 80% of the meat consumed today is federally inspected. Approved meats bear a circle stamp reading "inspected and passed."

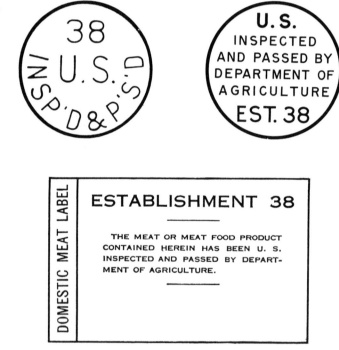

FIG. 11-2. Types of approval stamps used to indicate wholesomeness of product. The left stamp is frequently used on fresh meat, the stamp being placed on each primal (wholesale) cut. The stamp on the right frequently appears on packaged meats while the bottom stamp may be used on boxed meats. The number in the stamp is the official establishment number. These stamps should not be confused with the grade stamp shown in Figures 11-15 and 11-16. Courtesy USDA.

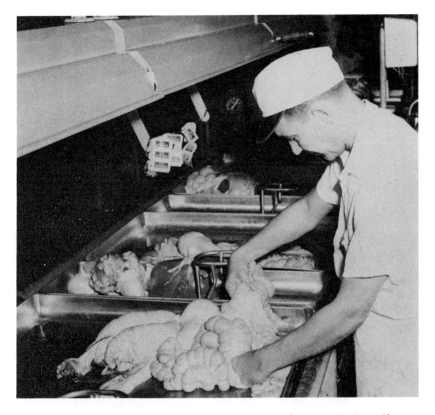

FIG. 11–3. A veterinary meat inspector gives hog viscera close examination. The carcass of the hog moves on the assembly line along with the viscera so that it can be removed if necessary. Courtesy USDA.

Each primal cut will bear the stamp, if federally approved for wholesomeness.

A plant where slaughtering or any type of meat processing takes place is called an *official establishment*. Each establishment having federal inspection is designated an individual number, and this number appears in the approval stamp.

Ante-mortem inspection is given. Once animals are placed into holding pens they may not be removed without a permit. An animal suspected of unwholesomeness is tagged "U.S. Suspect" and is given special post-mortem inspection. Animals condemned by ante-mortem inspection are tagged "U.S. Condemned" and destroyed. The meat may not be used for food, and, in some instances cannot even be used

FIG. 11–4.   A hog carcass being marked "Condemned" by a federal inspector.   Courtesy USDA.

for by-products, such as fertilizer.   The meat must be destroyed by chemicals or burning.

During slaughtering and dressing, three post-mortem inspections are held.   Head inspection is given for tuberculosis, cholera, lumpy jaw, measles and so forth.   More hog and cattle carcasses are condemned for tuberculosis than for all other diseases combined.   Viscera and other parts are next examined and, lastly, the carcass itself receives inspection. If a carcass or its viscera is condemned, tags indicate this, and the meat is destroyed under federal supervision.   At times a carcass may be suspect, and a tag reading "U.S. Retained" is placed on the carcass and viscera. Later the carcass is given special examination and is either condemned or passed.   In some instances only a part of the carcass may be condemned or the carcass may be "passed for cooking."   When a carcass is approved,

each primal (wholesale) cut is stamped with the approval stamp. State
and local stamps may also appear.

GRADING

The federal government has quality grades for dressed beef, veal, lamb
and mutton and hogs. Administration of grading is under the Meat and
Livestock Division of the USDA. The factors of conformation, finish and
quality are used to determine grade.

Conformation refers to the general build, form and shape of the carcass.
Desirable conformation is a compact, thick meat build throughout.
When viewed from the back, the carcass should be short in the hind
shanks, thick and full in the rounds, wide and thick in the loin, thick
in the rib, smooth and meaty in the shoulder and short in the neck. Best

**FIG. 11–5. Inspectors must complete reports on all animals retained or condemned.
Courtesy USDA.**

PRIME

CHOICE

GOOD

UTILITY

FIG. 11-6. Slaughter grades of lamb. These grades differ from those for dressed carcasses and are used for buying of live animals. Note blocky, full conformation of better
quality lambs compared with the thin, slender conformation of the lower grades. Cull
grade is omitted here. Courtesy USDA.

FIG. 11–7. Low grade cattle of mixed breeding. Meat yield and quality are low in such animals. Courtesy USDA.

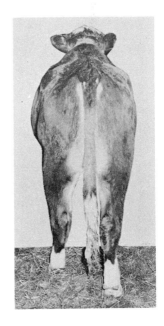

FIG. 11–8. An animal of Commercial quality that would fall in Standard grade because of its youth. Cows of similar quality would grade Commercial. Note "dished" condition on the rounds and along the back where the high-priced cuts come. Courtesy USDA.

FIG. 11–9. U.S. Prime slaughter steer. Only steers and heifers are eligible for the Prime Grade. Courtesy USDA.

Ideal and Poor Conformation on a Beef Carcass
(Side View)

Hindquarter
1. Round
2. Rump
3. Sirloin or loin end
4. Short loin
5. Flank

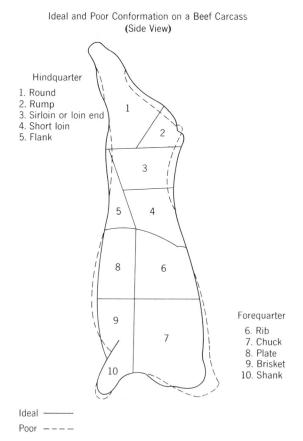

Forequarter
6. Rib
7. Chuck
8. Plate
9. Brisket
10. Shank

Ideal ———
Poor – – – –

FIG. 11–10. Dotted lines indicate poor conformation and straight lines ideal conformation. View is from side of a carcass. Courtesy National Livestock and Meat Board.

Ideal and Poor Conformation on a Beef Carcass
(Back View)

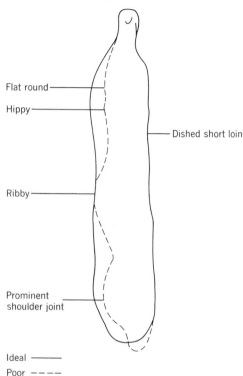

Flat round —

Hippy —

Dished short loin —

Ribby —

Prominent
shoulder joint

FIG. 11–11. Dotted lines indicate poor conformation and straight lines good conformation from the back of a carcass. Courtesy National Livestock and Meat Board.

Ideal ———
Poor — — — —

carcasses are not particularly deep in the shoulders, flank and belly but are full over the back, loins and rounds. This should not be interpreted to mean that shallow-bodied, high-flanked animals are desirable, but that excessive depth in the shoulder, brisket and flank adds little to the value and may even detract. Angular or rangy breeds will not have good conformation. A high proportion of meat to fat and bone is desirable. As a carcass decreases in conformation, the grade is lowered, and the proportion of weight of the less desirable cuts in relation to the more desirable cuts increases.

Conformation factors may vary somewhat for different types of animals. Hogs are desirable between 140 to 160 lb dressed carcass weight measuring 29 to 32 in. from the first rib to the aitch bone. The carcass should have an average thickness of 1.1 to 1.6 inch back fat. Thickness of muscling over the ham, loin, shoulders and belly is desirable. A good yielding hog of this weight should have at least 4 sq in. of loin muscle at

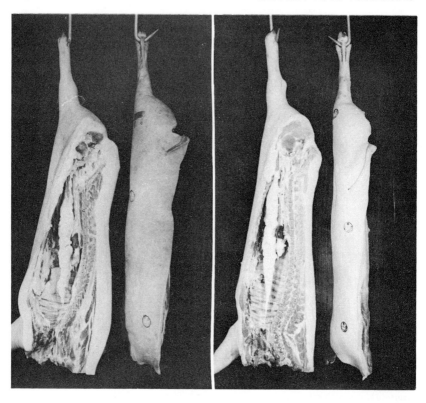

FIG. 11–12. The hog carcass on the right has come from hogs bred to give a high yield of meat cuts. The left hog will yield more lard in proportion to meat as indicated by the depth of fat back and the shortness of the cuts over the meaty areas. **Courtesy USDA.**

the 10th rib. Young animals have different desirable qualities than older animals of the same kind.

Finish, the second factor in determining grade, refers to the thickness and distribution of the fat inside and outside the carcass and in the flesh itself. The quality, color and texture of the fat are also important. Good care and feed result in good finish. Grain-fed steers and heifers will have a creamy white fat, while grass-fed animals will have a yellowish fat. The color of beef fat will also vary according to the breed and age of the animal. Green grass and legumes contain a considerable quantity of carotene, a yellow fat-soluble substance. This carotene will color beef fat yellow. Jersey and Guernsey and some other milk breeds store larger amounts of carotene than the rest of the breeds. Individual cattle also differ in their ability to store carotene. As the animal ages, the fat usually contains more carotene.

Ideal finish on animals is a smooth, well-distributed amount of white to creamy fat over the entire carcass. Excess fat indicates an animal heavily fed for too short or too long a time. Poorly bred stock respond less satisfactorily than better bred animals in taking finish.

In the interior, the finish should be smooth and even, not rippled, thick and heavy. The interior finish should be thinner than the exterior. Excessive or blotchy fat reduces grade. Marbling of the flesh appears in animals having good finish. Good quality of marbling is sought.

The best veal will have a thin, smooth covering of fat over the rump, loin, back, top of the shoulders and over the inner walls of the breast, thoracic cavity and abdomen. Veal will have little marbling in its flesh. As veal grows older, into the calf stage, the amount of finish increases.

The type, quality and distribution of fat on lambs and mutton are closely associated with their quality. Fat is one of the most important factors, therefore, in establishing grade in these animals. Lambs will have less fat than mutton but more than veal.

The finish on top quality hogs should not be excessive, although the grading in this factor differs for fat-type or lean-type hogs. The fat should be firm and white. It will not be brittle, as in cattle and sheep. Soft, oily, grayish fat is indicative of poor quality and characteristic of slop-fed hogs. Excessively soft fat on hogs indicates a "soft" hog and one that fails to firm up even at low temperatures. Soft hogs are difficult to cut up. Soft hogs may be developed by slop feeding or by feeding excessively oily meals.

Quality is the third factor affecting the grade. It refers to the color and appearance of the flesh, the amount of marbling, the smoothness, fineness and evenness of grain. Good quality is indicated by a bright, clear, typical color. The meat should be moist but not sticky. The flesh should be firm but still pliable. It should have a silky appearance. The bones should indicate youth. Good feathering or finish of fat in the interior and good deposits of fat on the flank usually indicate good quality. Graders also look at the *break* or *pop* to ascertain quality. This is the fat protrusion through the chine bone (the split spine or backbone). The more fat protrusion evident, up to a point, the more likely the animal is to be higher in quality.

Age is related to quality. Young animals tend to be of higher quality than animals past their prime. One of the best means of ascertaining age is to note the condition of the chine. In young animals of either sex, the ends on the spine projecting outward from the main bone are called "buttons." These are white cartilages on the end of the fingers or bone structures that project upward. As the animal ages, the buttons disappear and are replaced with hard bone. At about $3\frac{1}{2}$ years the

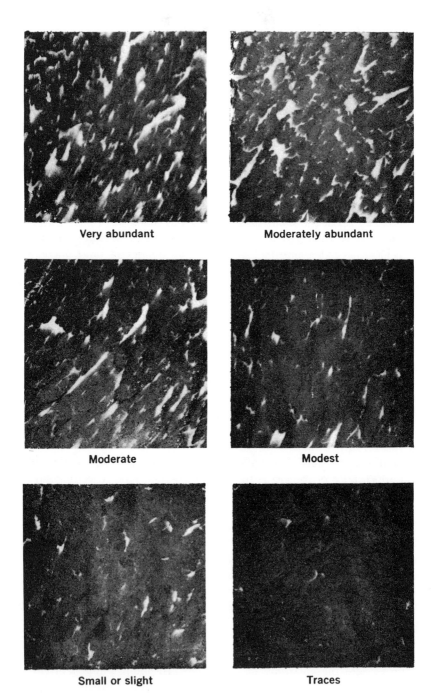

Very abundant   Moderately abundant

Moderate   Modest

Small or slight   Traces

FIG. 11–13. Marbling, an indicator of quality, may vary in the muscles. Excessive marbling will give a fatty tasting meat.

480

FIG. 11–14. A rough drawing indicating a
spool joint found on a yearling or older mutton
(left) and the break joint (right) with its 8 points
found on a young lamb.

buttons are no longer evident. The chine bone of young animals will
also be distinctly red, indicating blood development in the growing
animal. As the animal matures, the bones become harder, whiter and
flintier. The marrow or interior of the bone is less red.

In young animals the three tail joints in the rump show pronounced
joints that are also deep red. Maturity is indicated by the solidifying,
hardening and whitening of these bones. In older animals these three
joints will be completely joined. The aitch bone of young animals will
be bent at an angle of about 120°, with a noticeable knob on the flank
end. The bone straightens with age and the knob disappears. This
happens more rapidly in females than in males. Young animals of
either sex have oval ribs. As the animal ages, the ribs flatten.

The break at the fetlock of sheep is used to indicate the age of those
animals. In lambs less than a year old, the feet break at what is called
the *break joint* instead of at the fetlock spool. The break joint is a broad,
moist, pink surface with eight toothlike projections. A yearling will
show a break joint, but this will be harder, whiter and rougher in character than that of younger sheep. Sheep over a year old will have the
fetlock break at the spool or the joint (spool joint) at the lower end of
the femur bone. Attempts to imitate the break joint can be easily detected since the break is jagged, hard, dry and white.

Other Factors Influencing Grade

Weight is usually correlated with grade. Since it is a factor related to
conformation, this is understandable. Excessive weight may be cause for
down-grading. Beef carcasses run from 300 to 1000 lb. The heavier
animals frequently find their way into the higher grades, while the lighter
animals move into the lower grades. A veal carcass less than 50 lb will
be discriminated against in grading. The most desirable weight in veal
is between 80 and 150 lb. Extra heavy veal may go as high as 350 lb and
this may be called baby beef. Weight is a factor in establishing grade
in sheep, especially for lambs and yearlings.

Prices paid will also vary for animals of different weight, even though
they may grade the same. This is especially true for hogs, steers and
heifers but not so true for bulls and cows.

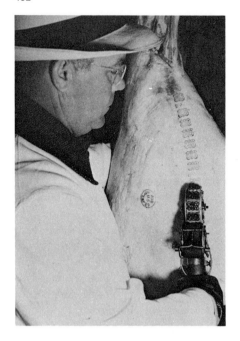

FIG. 11–15. A federal grader stamps the grade name on a beef carcass. This leaves a ribbon-like imprint. The round mark to the left of the grade stamp is the stamp of approval indicating wholesomeness. The grader's initials follow every 6th grade stamp. Courtesy USDA.

Sex differences in lamb, veal and calves make little difference in grade. However, sex does make a difference in cattle, for only steers and heifers are eligible for prime grade. About 85% of the steers and heifers on the market are in the Choice, Good and Standard grades. The highest that cows can grade is Good. Bulls and stags are graded under different standards and may grade from Choice down. There is no prime grade and very few will grade Choice. Barrows and gilts (hogs) are not differentiated in grading. Sows are graded according to a different set of standards, although the grade nomenclature used for sows is the same as for barrows and gilts. While a sow may grade U.S. No. 1, it would not have the same quality characteristics as a U.S. No. 1 barrow or gilt. Wethers, ewes and rams will seldom be graded above Good.

There are age limitations in grading. A beef older than 36 months cannot qualify for Prime, over 42 months cannot qualify for Choice, and over 48 months cannot qualify for Good. The grade of Standard was introduced to differentiate between young and older animals that graded Commercial but because of age, differed in quality. Steers and heifers with Commercial characteristics will be graded Standard, while cows having the same characteristics will grade Commercial. With cattle, age is not a factor below Commercial. Age is a factor in grading lambs, yearlings, wethers, ewes and rams and, to some extent, in grading hogs.

Table 11-1
Federal Grades for Meats

Class or Kind	Grades
Beef (steer, heifer, cow)*	Prime, Choice, Good, Standard†, Commercial, Utility, Cutter, Canner
(bull and stag)	Choice, Good, Commercial, Utility, Cutter, Canner
Calf and veal	Prime, Choice, Good, Standard, Utility, Cull
Lamb and yearling mutton	Prime, Choice, Good, Utility, Cull
Mutton	Choice, Good, Utility, Cull
Pork carcasses (barrows and gilts)‡	U.S. No. 1, U.S. No. 2, U.S. No. 3, Medium, Cull

*Cows are not eligible for the Prime grade.

†The Standard grade was primarily established to allow higher classification of young animals that fell into commercial grade and to differentiate them from older animals of commercial grade.

‡Sows are graded by the same grades, but the criteria used for establishing grade in sows differ from those used for barrows and gilts.

Defects and blemishes on the carcass will also lower the grade. Bruises on pork hams or bellies are especially significant in lowering grade.

The fact that grade is composed of a combination of factors means that many variations may occur. For instance, finish and quality on a carcass may be quite high, but because of a failure to come up to the same grade level in conformation, the animal will be dropped lower in grade than its finish or quality indicate. The various grading factors are oftentimes weighted and evaluated, one against the other, in establishing grade. An animal may have good fat coverage but fail to have it properly distributed. This may drop the carcass in grade.

FIG. 11-16. The stamp to the left is a federal grade stamp used to indicate prime grade on meats. The stamp to the right indicates that the item meets the specifications of the purchaser. It is used with acceptance type meat purchasing. (See Figures 11-57 and 11-58.) Courtesy USDA.

Table 11-2
Important Grading Characteristics for Beef

Grade	Carcass Conformation	Fat	Marbling	Flesh Color	Feather Bones
Prime	Thick fleshed, blocky.	Firm, waxy, uniform over outside.	Pronounced intermingling fat and lean.	Uniform and bright red to dark red.	Soft red, ending in white cartilage or "buttons."
Choice	Heavy to moderate.	Firm, less waxy, slightly thin to moderately thick.	Moderately abundant.	Light red to slightly dark red.	Soft and red, tinged with white.
Good	Moderately thick fleshed.	Slightly soft and somewhat oily.	Modest amount.	Light red to slightly dark red.	Soft and red, tinged with white.
Standard	Slightly blocky to moderate.	Soft and oily.	Slight to modest amount.	Light red to slightly dark red.	Soft, tending to white and flinty.
Commercial	Rangy, angular, thin fleshed.	Very thin fat covering, oily.	Practically none.	Light red to very dark red.	Red in young animals, hard and white in mature.
Utility	Rangy and irregular.	Very sparse.	None.	Dark red.	Hard and white.

The grades for beef are also divided into top and bottom of the grade, although the grade stamp does not indicate this. Buyers should always state in specifications for beef whether top or bottom grade is desired. The grades established by the federal government give minimum standards permitted within a grade, and meat that just meets the standard is at the bottom of the grade.

Federal grade stamps are rolled onto a carcass in edible blue ink. The grade appears in a line on the outer side of the rump and across the loin and rib to the neck. Initials "U.S." appear before the grade, and "USDA" appears above the grade in the shield. The initials of the grader may also be on the stamp at certain intervals. The grade shield should not be confused with the round stamp of approval indicating wholesomeness of product, shown in Figure 11-2. While federal inspection for wholesomeness is mandatory for meat shipped in interstate commerce, grading is not.

Table 11-2 summarizes some of the most important characteristics for six grades of beef purchased by institutions.

PACKER'S BRANDS

Very frequently packers sell meat under their own brands. In doing this the packer attempts to certify quality within his own classifications. Brands enable packers to offer, sometimes, a finer demarcation between qualities than is possible when federal grades are used. A buyer should realize, however, that no standards exist to which he can refer in ascertaining the quality of a brand as is possible in federal grading.

CUTTING

Meat may be purchased in the form of carcasses, sides, quarters, wholesale (primal) cuts and fabricated cuts. Cutting practices vary according to the type of animal, regional practices or use to be made of the meat.

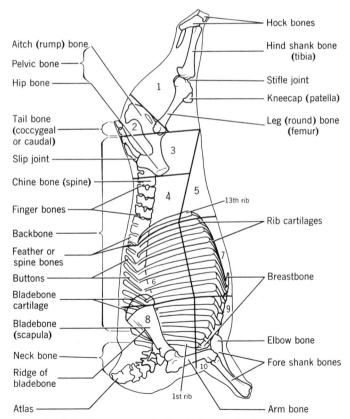

FIG. 11–17. The skeletal structure of beef with the wholesale cuts numbered as shown in Figure 11–19.

Standard Beef Cuts

Chicago   New York

# 1 Round	24%
# 2 Loin end	9%
# 3 Short loin	8%
# 4 Flank	4%
(Suet)	4%
Hindquarter Total	49%
# 5 Rib (7 ribs)	9%
# 6 Chuck (8 ribs)	26%
# 7 Plate	12%
# 8 Shank	4%

# 1 Round (with flank 'A')	24%
# 2 Top sirloin (or butt)	6%
# 3 Short hip	6%
(N.Y. full hip '21, '3)	
# 4 Short loin (incl. suet)	12%
Hindquarter Total	48%
# 5 Rib (8 ribs)	10%
# 6 Plate	10%
# 7 Short chuck (4 ribs)	16%
(N.Y. full chuck ('7 '8 '9)	
# 8 Brisket	8%
# 9 Shoulder	8%

Forequarter Total	51%
Side of beef Total	100%
12 Ribs on forequarter	

Forequarter Total	52%
Side of beef Total	100%
12 Ribs on forequarter	

FIG. 11–18.   Courtesy of Armour and Co.

Standard Beef Cuts

Philadelphia | Boston

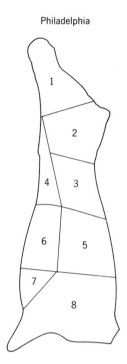 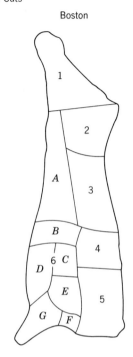

# 1 Round	18%
# 2 Rump	12%
# 3 Loin (incl. suet)	12%
# 4 Flank	4%
Hindquarter Total	46%
# 5 Rib (8 ribs)	10%
# 6 Plate	10%
# 7 Butt	4%
# 8 Chuck (5 ribs)	30%
Forequarter Total	54%
Side of beef Total	100%
13 Ribs on forequarter	

# 1 Round (with flank 'A')	23%
# 2 Rump	11%
# 3 Loin (3 ribs)	15%
Cod fat	2%
Hindquarter Total	51%
# 4 Rib (5 ribs)	6%
# 5 Chuck (5 ribs)	18%
# 6 Rattle, includes	25%
Navel— B	
Middle rib—C	
Brisket— D	
Shoulder— E	
Sticker— F	
Shin— G	
Forequarter Total	49%
Side of beef Total	100%
10 Ribs on forequarter	

FIG. 11–18 (Continued).

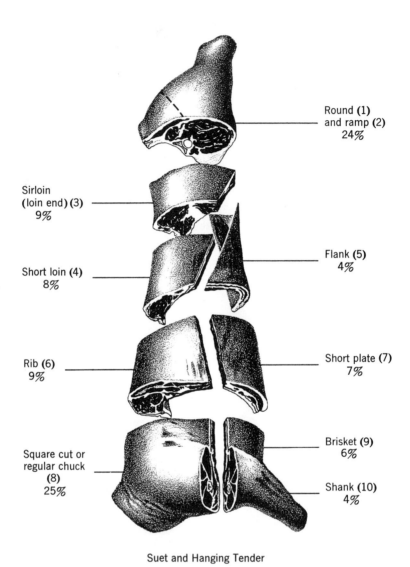

Round (1)
and ramp (2)
24%

Sirloin
(loin end) (3)
9%

Flank (5)
4%

Short loin (4)
8%

Rib (6)
9%

Short plate (7)
7%

Square cut or
regular chuck
(8)
25%

Brisket (9)
6%

Shank (10)
4%

Suet and Hanging Tender

FIG. 11–19. Wholesale cuts from a side of beef. Rump may be specified as separated from the round. The shank (10) is frequently separated from the brisket (9). Percent of wholesale cut as a part of side is also given.

BEEF CHART

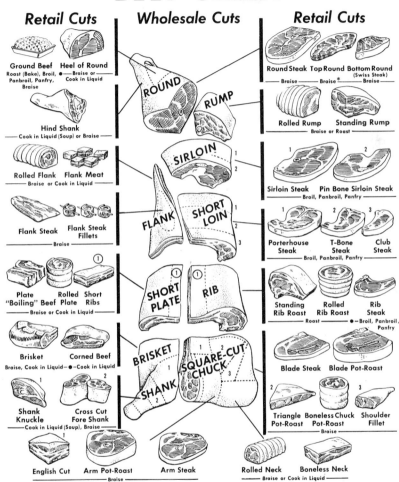

Retail Cuts

Ground Beef   Heel of Round
Roast (Bake), Broil, ●──Braise or──
Panbroil, Panfry,   Cook in Liquid
Braise

Hind Shank
── Cook in Liquid (Soup) or Braise ──

Rolled Flank   Flank Meat
── Braise or Cook in Liquid ──

**Flank Steak   Flank Steak
Fillets**
────── Braise ──────

**Plate   Rolled   Short
"Boiling" Beef Plate   Ribs**
── Braise or Cook in Liquid ──

Brisket   Corned Beef
Braise, Cook in Liquid─●─Cook in Liquid

**Shank   Cross Cut
Knuckle   Fore Shank**
──Cook in Liquid (Soup), Braise──

English Cut   Arm Pot-Roast
───────── Braise ─────────

Wholesale Cuts

ROUND

RUMP

SIRLOIN

FLANK   SHORT LOIN

SHORT PLATE   RIB

BRISKET   SQUARE-CUT CHUCK

SHANK

Arm Steak

Retail Cuts

Round Steak Top Round Bottom Round
(Swiss Steak)
── Braise ── ── Braise * ── ── Braise ──

Rolled Rump   Standing Rump
── Braise or Roast ──

Sirloin Steak   Pin Bone Sirloin Steak
── Broil, Panbroil, Panfry ──

**Porterhouse   T-Bone   Club
Steak   Steak   Steak**
── Broil, Panbroil, Panfry ──

**Standing   Rolled   Rib
Rib Roast   Rib Roast   Steak**
── Roast ──   ●─Broil, Panbroil,
Panfry

Blade Steak   Blade Pot-Roast

**Triangle Boneless Chuck Shoulder
Pot-Roast   Pot-Roast   Fillet**
────── Braise ──────

Rolled Neck   Boneless Neck
── Braise or Cook in Liquid ──

*Prime and choice grades may be
broiled. panbroiled or panfried

Beef

More and more beef is being purchased fabricated although some operations still purchase in larger cuts. The standard method for dividing a side is to divide it into fore and hind quarters by cutting between the 12th and 13th rib. This is called the Chicago cut. Other methods of division are shown in Figure 11–18. The Chicago cut is becoming more and more universal; the cutting method given in this text is based on it. When division of a side is made by the Chicago cut, the hind and forequarters are approximately equal in weight.

Carcasses should be purchased with the skirt removed along with the tendinous portion. The lean tissue will be exposed by this trim. In addition, the hanging tender, thymus gland, mediastinal tissue, heart fat, excess fat in the lower thorax or brisket and short plate should be removed. The kidney and kidney knob, plus the bloody tissue, should be removed. There should be only two tail (caudal) vertebrae remaining. This trim should apply also to wholesale or other smaller cuts.

In breaking down the hind quarter, the flank is first removed. This cut is made by cutting from the cod fat to a point about 10 in. from the tip of the chine bone on the 13th rib. The flank steak may be removed from the cod or udder and other fat. (See Figures 11–20 and 11–21a & 21b.) The serous membrane should be stripped off before pulling out the flank steak. Only minute flakes of fat should adhere to the steak. Next, a full loin may be removed by cutting down in a straight line from a point on the backbone where the last (5th) sacral vertebra and the first tail (caudal) vertebra join. Continue to a point immediately in front of the femur bone where the socket ball is exposed. (See Figures 11–22, 11–23 and 11–24.) Continue in the same straight line to the flank area on the round. In making this cut, leave the tip or rear innermost corner of the 5th sacral vertebra attached to the first tail bone. It is usually recommended on full loins under 50 lb that the distance from the chine bone to the end of the flank on the loin be 9 in. and loins over 50 lb, 10 in. Trim of fat should be $\frac{1}{2}$ to 1 in. The full loin contains the short loin and the loin end (sirloin). These two are separated by cutting between the 5th and 6th lumbar vertebrae, through to a point flush against the hipbone, taking no cartilage. (Line ab in Figure 11–22.)

On the round, the rump is removed by cutting in a straight line immediately behind and parallel with the long axis of the exposed surface of the aitch bone, leaving no part of this bone in the round. The rump is separated at the round bone immediately behind the ball joint. The shank is removed by cutting through the muscular end of the gambrel cord to the shank bone (tibia), following the bone to the stifle joint, thus

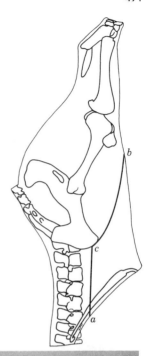

FIG. 11–20. Cut to remove flank is made from cod
fat located at "b" to end of pelvic bone at "c". The
cut then follows through the 13th rib at "a". This
distance from the top of the chine bone is about 10"
on this cut from "c" to "a". Courtesy National Livestock and Meat Board.

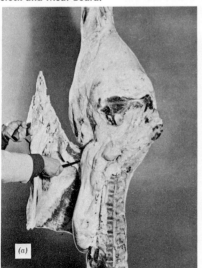

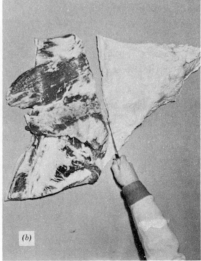

FIG. 11–21. (a) Many times beef in the quarter may be best cut up from the hook. This
illustration shows the first cut usually made in breaking down a hindquarter. The flank
is separated from the round and loin area. (See Figure 11–20.) (b) The flank may be
stripped from the fatty tissue as shown here. Courtesy National Livestock and Meat
Board.

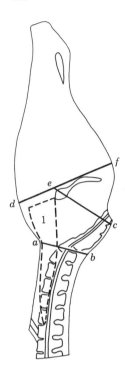

FIG. 11–22. The round and loin are frequently cut as shown. The short loin ends at line "ab" while the loin end or sirloin is found between lines "ab" and "dec." The rump forms the triangle made by lines "fce." The tenderloin is indicated by the dotted line and the rear part behind line "ab" marked "l" is the butt tender.

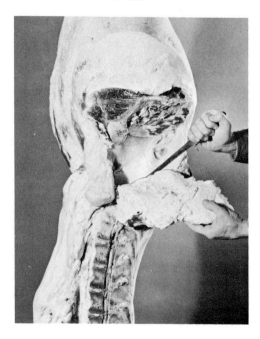

FIG. 11–23. Before the loin in the lower portion of this illustration is removed from the round, kidney fat, cod fat and other tissue are removed. The hip bone is shown protruding from the round.

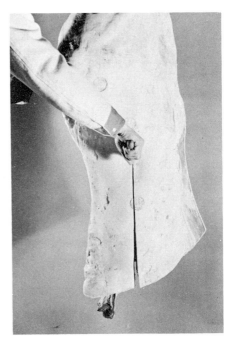

FIG. 11–24. Cutting this short into
the loin gives a full loin with steaks
which have a small tail or flank on
them.   Courtesy National Livestock
and Meat Board.

severing the shank meat and bone from the round.   The knee cap,
popliteal lymph gland and surrounding fat should be removed from the
round. See Figures 11–25, 11–26 and 11–27.

The round may be cut up into the knuckle, top (inside) round and
bottom (outside) round. The knuckle is removed, as shown in Figure
11–27.   The knuckle should not contain the knuckle bone when delivered. Next, start at the muscular end of the gambrel cord and continue along between natural seams to the inside edge of the "eye" muscle
on the face of the round.   Make a second cut from the lower edge of the
gambrel cord to the upper end of the round bone at the stifle joint. A
cut through the natural seam removes the top (inside) round. The outside or bottom round is removed with the heel attached, if the shank is
on.   The heel is next removed.   Figure 11–31 shows some of the cuts obtained from the rump and round.

The forequarter may be cut up a number of ways.   To eliminate
handling and heavy lifting, many meat cutters divide the chuck, brisket
and shank from the rib and plate by cutting between the 5th and 6th
ribs, cutting close to the 5th rib.   This separates the forequarter into two

FIG. 11–25. Separating the rump from the round. Courtesy National Livestock and Meat Board.

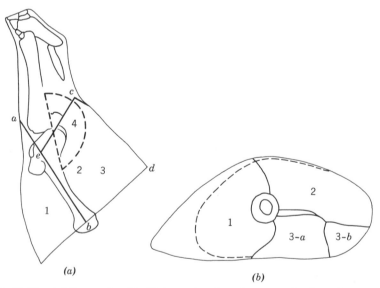

(a)   *(b)*

FIG. 11–26. (*a*) Remove knuckle (1) by cutting through meat to leg bone from (*a*) to (*b*) on both sides of round. Remove inside (top) round (2) by starting along line (*e-c*) and following seams from (*c*) to (*d*) and (*e*) to (*b*). Take off outside (bottom) round (3) by cutting through seam around heel (4). Remove heel (4) by cutting around shank and leg bones. (*b*) 1. Knuckle (tip). 2. Inside (top) round. 3*a* and 3*b*. Outside (bottom) round.

parts.   In the fore half there will be the cross-cut or New York chuck and in the rib or rear half a cut called the wing.   The latter contains the full rib and plate.   The shank may be removed by separating it from the brisket and chuck by following the dividing or natural seam and leaving the entire "lip" (web muscle) on the brisket.   The brisket can be removed by cutting along a line that removes the portion below the clod between the 2nd and 5th rib, including the top of the 2nd rib and ends

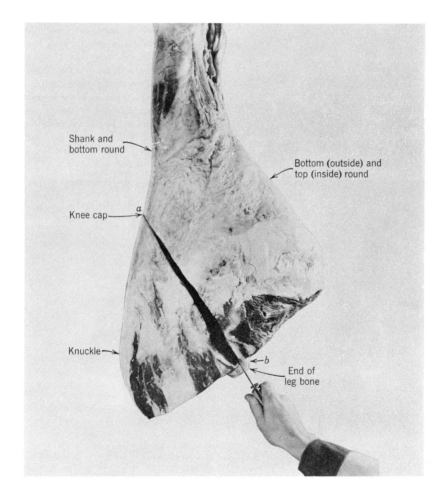

FIG. 11-27.   Cutting from the knee cap at *a* to the end of the leg bone (femur) *b* removes the knuckle leaving the bottom and top round with the shank.   Courtesy National Livestock and Meat Board.

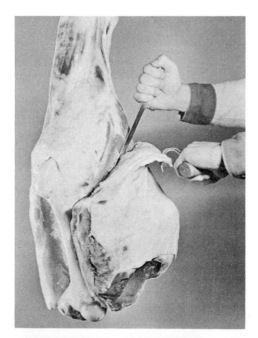

FIG. 11–28. The top or inside round is removed after the knuckle is removed. Note that the knuckle bone has been removed with the knuckle. Specifications should state that this bone must not be in the knuckle when delivered. The shank meat is below this inside or top round shown being removed. Courtesy National Livestock and Meat Board.

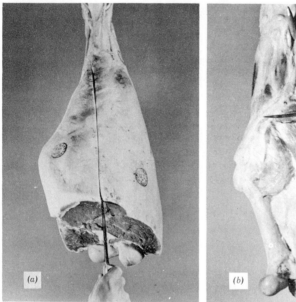

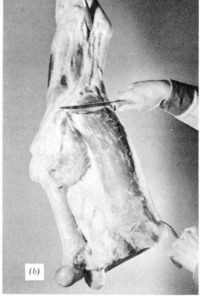

FIG. 11–29. (a) The bottom round or outside round may be divided as shown here along the natural seams. (b) Next, the final piece of the round, the bottom or outside round, is removed leaving the shank meat and bones of the round. Courtesy National Livestock and Meat Board.

496

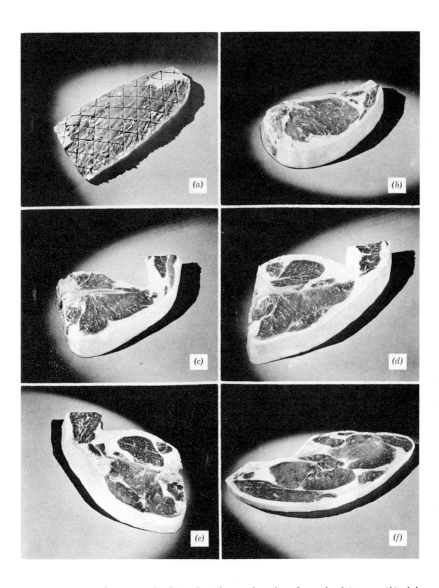

FIG. 11–30. Beef cuts: (a) flank steak. The steaks taken from the loin are: (b) club, (c) T-bone, (d) porterhouse, (e) pin-bone sirloin and (f) sirloin. The last two come from the loin end. Courtesy National Livestock and Meat Board.

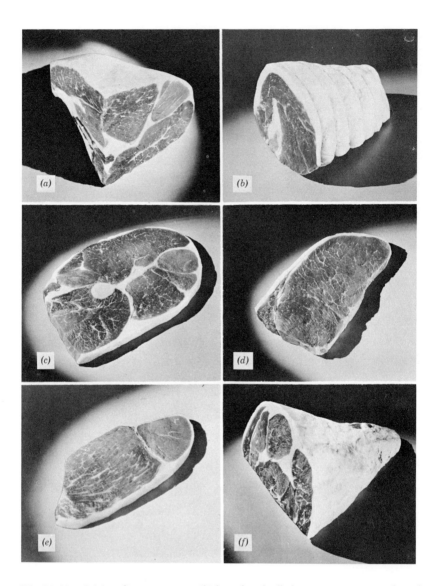

FIG. 11–31. (a) Standing rump roast, (b) boned and rolled rump roast, (c) round steak including top and bottom round and knuckle, (d) top (inside) round steak, (e) bottom (outside) round steak and (f) heel of round.

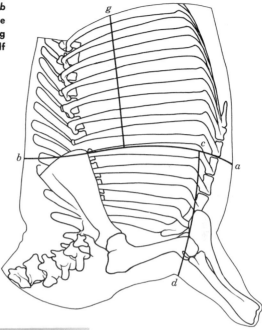

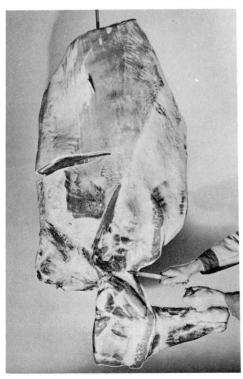

FIG. 11–33. The first cut usually made on the forequarter is that which separates the shank, as shown. Courtesy National Livestock and Meat Board.

FIG. 11-34. (a) The triangular cut shown here removes the clod. This muscle sets over the shoulder blade or scapula. Note that the wing has been partially separated from the cross-cut or New York chuck by cutting between the 5th and 6th ribs. (b) The clod lifts off easily from the scapula blade.

of the 3rd and 5th ribs. The clod, a large, heavy muscle located over the top of the bladebone (scapula) in back of the ridge, and the chuck tender in front of the ridge are easily removed. Cut along the ridge of the blade bone, starting where the arm bone joins the blade bone and continue to the top edge of the chuck. Next, cut from the extreme corner of the brisket end of the 5th rib, following the first natural seam above the ribs to a point midway between the exposed end of the arm bone and the end of the clod. The clod may then be pulled from the scapula and the chuck tender similarly removed.

The wing contains the rib and the plate. The plate may be removed by cutting in a parallel line 9 in. from the chine,[1] leaving a full rib. If a full rib is cut in a straight line from 4 in. below the extreme outer tip of the rib eye muscle on the 12th rib to 8 in. from the extreme outer tip of the rib eye muscle on the 6th rib and the chine bone, feather bones, blade bone and cartilage are removed, an oven-prepared rib is obtained. Short ribs may be taken from the rib section immediately below the prime rib and the top of the plate. The lower plate section below this

[1]On full ribs over 25 lb, this distance is 10 in.

area should not be used to make short ribs.   The short ribs should be cut into $2\frac{1}{2}$ to $3\frac{1}{2}$ in. strips.   Figure 36 shows some common cuts obtained from the forequarter.

Ground beef may come from trimmings normally produced in boning, including meat from shanks, flanks, skirts and hanging tenders, but not from heads, gullets, tongues, hearts, glands or added fat, such as suet, cod and heart fat.   This meat, if cut into approximately $\frac{1}{2}$ in. cubes, makes chili beef.   The prepared beef must be thoroughly blended if it is to be ground and no mixing must occur after grinding.   Grinding may be first through a 1 in. plate and next through a $\frac{3}{16}$ or $\frac{1}{8}$ in. plate.   The term "ground beef, special" means that the meat should come from 100% of the carcass in natural proportion of not less than 50% primal cuts, such as square-cut chucks, ribs, loins, with tenderloins and rounds excluded if desired, and 50% or less may come from trimmed flanks, briskets, navels or shanks.   These percentages should be based on bone-in weights.

Low-grade cattle are cut on the block differently than cattle to be sold in primal cuts.   The very low-grade cattle may be boned out and utilized for cured beef, canned meats or sausage.   Some of the better cuts may be retained, and boneless loins (8 to 14 lb), tenderloins (2 to

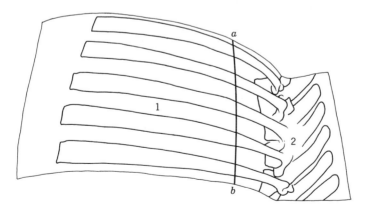

FIG. 11–35.   Here a 5-rib wing is cut from the forequarter and the rib and plate are divided along line "ab."

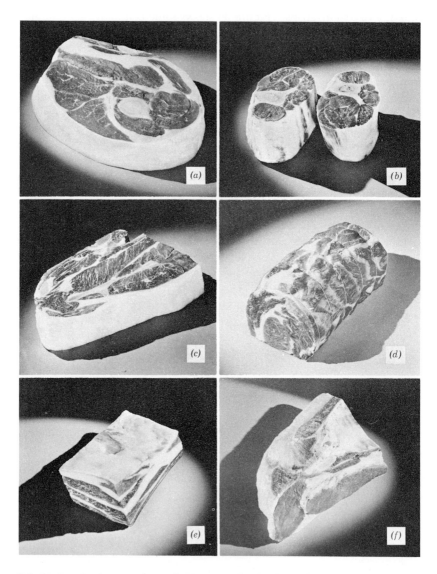

FIG. 11–36. Beef cuts: (a) arm-bone roast, (b) shank, (c) blade roast, (d) inside boneless chuck, (e) English cut (chuck), (f) brisket (bone-in), (g) corned brisket, (h) rib steak, (i) standing rib roast, (j) rolled rib roast, (k) short ribs, and (l) plate.

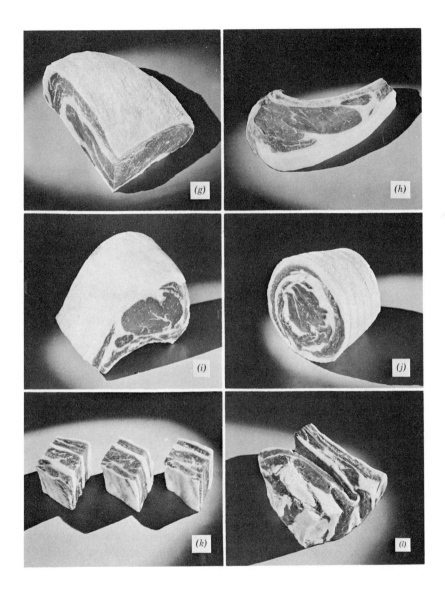

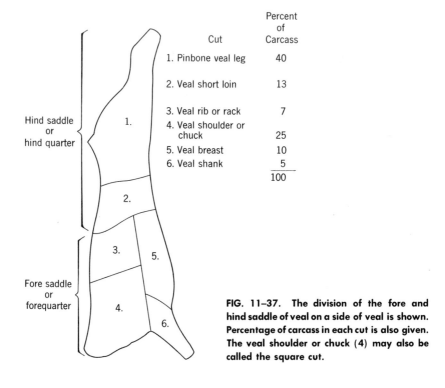

Cut	Percent of Carcass
1. Pinbone veal leg	40
2. Veal short loin	13
3. Veal rib or rack	7
4. Veal shoulder or chuck	25
5. Veal breast	10
6. Veal shank	5
	100

Hind saddle or hind quarter

Fore saddle or forequarter

FIG. 11–37. The division of the fore and hind saddle of veal on a side of veal is shown. Percentage of carcass in each cut is also given. The veal shoulder or chuck (4) may also be called the square cut.

8 lb), spencer rolls or regular rib-eyes (4 to 12 lb), shoulder clods (6 to 15 lb) and other of the better cuts may be purchased chilled or frozen at economy prices. Some steaks and other cuts from these cattle may be treated with tenderizers or cubed to make them more tender.

Veal

Veal may be cut into fore and hind saddles by cutting between the 12th and 13th ribs. This leaves the hind saddle with two unsplit hind legs and loins, and the forequarter containing double ribs, breasts, shoulder and shanks. Veal may also be split into sides and sold. The leg of veal contains the rump. Frequently the rump is removed and steaks cut from the round. These steaks may be boneless and be called veal cutlets. A center-cut roast from the leg results when the shank and rump are removed. The heel of the round is used for stew or ground meat. Sirloin steaks or roast may come from the loin end and

chops from the remainder of the loin.   If a portion of the kidney remains in a loin chop, the chop is called a kidney chop.   The rib may
make a rib roast or rib chops, and a blade roast, arm roast, or blade
or arm steaks may be obtained from the shoulder.   The shoulder may
also be boned and used for a rolled roast.   The shank and other trimmings and the breast may be cut up for diced or ground meat.   Sometimes the breast is boned and used as a roast filled with stuffing.   Riblets
may be cut from the breast.   For a number of veal cuts, see Figure
11–39.

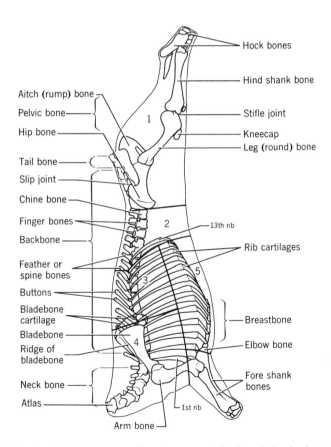

FIG. 11–38.   The skeletal structure of veal appears with the wholesale divisions made
in Figure 11–37.   Note that division of hind and fore saddles is between 12th and
13th ribs.   Courtesy National Livestock and Meat Board.

VEAL CHART

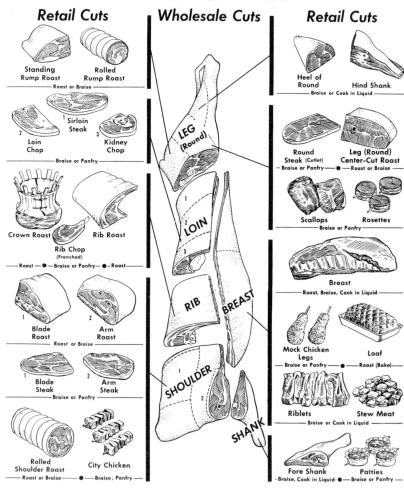

Retail Cuts

Standing Rump Roast   Rolled Rump Roast
——— Roast or Braise ———

Sirloin Steak
1
2 Loin Chop   3 Kidney Chop
——— Braise or Panfry ———

Crown Roast   Rib Roast
Rib Chop (Frenched)
— Roast — ● — Braise or Panfry — ● — Roast —

1 Blade Roast   2 Arm Roast
——— Roast or Braise ———

1 Blade Steak   2 Arm Steak
——— Braise or Panfry ———

Rolled Shoulder Roast   City Chicken
— Roast or Braise — ● — Braise, Panfry —

Wholesale Cuts

LEG (Round)

1
2 LOIN
3

RIB   BREAST

1
SHOULDER
2

SHANK

Retail Cuts

Heel of Round   Hind Shank
——— Braise or Cook in Liquid ———

Round Steak (Cutlet)   Leg (Round) Center-Cut Roast
— Braise or Panfry — ● — Roast or Braise —

Scallops   Rosettes
——— Braise or Panfry ———

Breast
——— Roast, Braise, Cook in Liquid ———

Mock Chicken Legs   Loaf
— Braise or Panfry — ● — Roast (Bake) —

Riblets   Stew Meat
——— Braise or Cook in Liquid ———

Fore Shank   Patties
- Braise, Cook in Liquid · ● — Braise or Panfry —

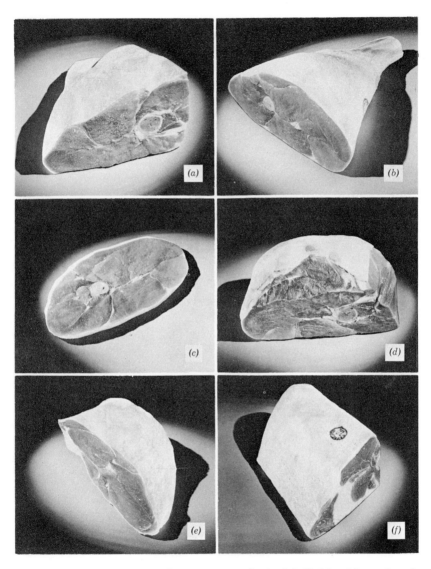

FIG. 11–39. Veal cuts: (a) standing rump roast, (b) shank half of leg, (c) round steak (d) center-cut round roast, (e) sirloin roast, (f) loin.

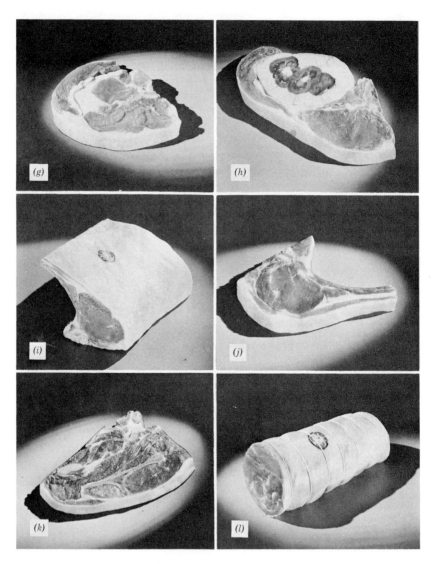

FIG. 11–39 (Continued). Veal cuts: (g) loin chop, (h) kidney chop, (i) rib roast, (j) rib chop, (k) blade or shoulder steak, (l) rolled shoulder roast. Courtesy National Livestock and Meat Board.

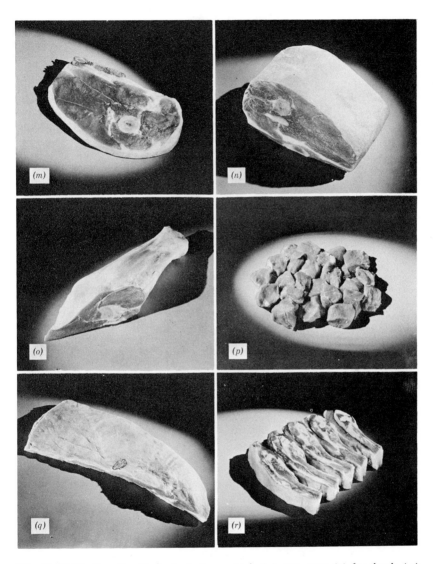

FIG. 11–39 (Continued). Veal cuts: (m) arm steak, (n) arm roast, (o) foreshank, (p) stew meat, (q) breast, and (r) riblets from breast.   Courtesy National Livestock and Meat Board.

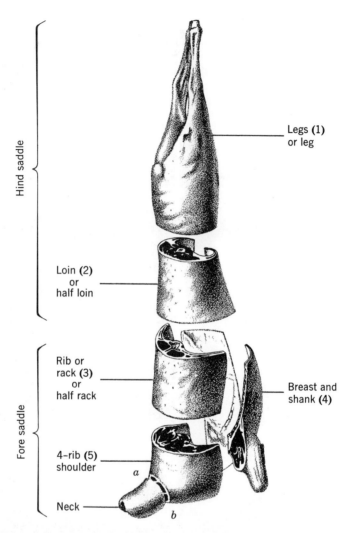

Hind saddle

Legs (1)
or leg

Loin (2)
or
half loin

Fore saddle

Rib or
rack (3)
or
half rack

Breast and
shank (4)

4-rib (5)
shoulder

a

Neck

b

FIG. 11-40. The main wholesale cuts on lamb or mutton are shown. The neck may be separated from the shoulder (5) and the cut is usually along line *ab* as shown. Only $3\frac{1}{2}$ ribs are left on the shoulder (5) leaving $8\frac{1}{2}$ ribs in the rack or rib section (3). If division of the fore and hind saddle is after the 13th rib (the most usual manner of cutting), instead of the 12th and 13th ribs, the rack or rib (3) will have $9\frac{1}{2}$ ribs. Courtesy National Livestock and Meat Board.

Lamb and Mutton

Only about one third of the lamb and mutton on the market is sold in carcass form. Most is sold in wholesale or fabricated cuts. The carcass is usually divided into fore and hind saddles. A long saddle is the hind quarter containing the rib section. Shoulders called "standard" contain $3\frac{1}{2}$ ribs and the standard rib from this type cut contains $8\frac{1}{2}$ ribs, but some local areas may add an additional rib by leaving the 13th rib on the rib end instead of cutting between the 12th and 13th rib.

Buyers may find that heavy lambs (65 lb) are sometimes lower in price on the market than lighter lambs (45 lb). Frequently, in institutions, grilled, broiled or sauted lamb items move more rapidly than stews or

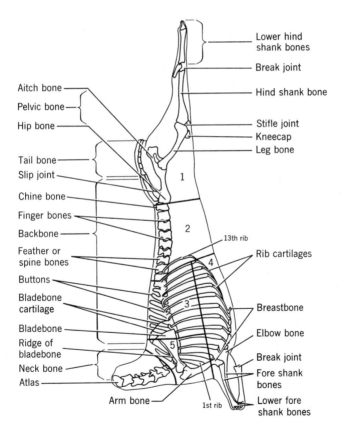

FIG. 11–41. The skeletal structure of the lamb or mutton is shown with the hind and fore saddle divisions as indicated in Figure 11–40. Courtesy National Livestock and Meat Board.

LAMB CHART

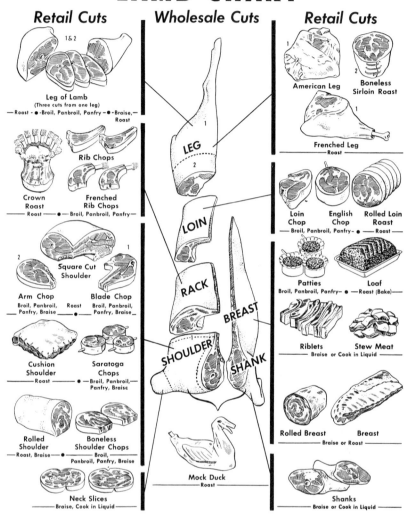

Retail Cuts

1 & 2

Leg of Lamb
(Three cuts from one leg)
— Roast - ● -Broil, Panbroil, Panfry - ● -Braise,—
Roast

Rib Chops

Crown Roast
—— Roast ——
Frenched Rib Chops
● Broil, Panbroil, Panfry—

Square Cut Shoulder

2   **1**

Arm Chop
Broil, Panbroil, Panfry, Braise
Blade Chop
Roast   Broil, Panbroil, Panfry, Braise
●

Cushion Shoulder
—— Roast ——
Saratoga Chops
● —Broil, Panbroil, Panfry, Braise

Rolled Shoulder
— Roast, Braise — ●
Boneless Shoulder Chops
— Broil, Panbroil, Panfry, Braise

Neck Slices
—— Braise, Cook in Liquid ——

Wholesale Cuts

LEG
1
2

LOIN

RACK

BREAST

SHOULDER
1
2
SHANK

Mock Duck
— Roast —

Retail Cuts

1   **2**

American Leg
Boneless Sirloin Roast

1

Frenched Leg
— Roast —

Loin Chop   **English Chop**   **Rolled Loin Roast**
— Broil, Panbroil, Panfry - ●   — Roast —

Patties
Broil, Panbroil, Panfry— ●
Loaf
—Roast (Bake)—

Riblets   **Stew Meat**
—— Braise or Cook in Liquid ——

Rolled Breast   **Breast**
—— Braise or Roast ——

Shanks
—— Braise or Cook in Liquid ——

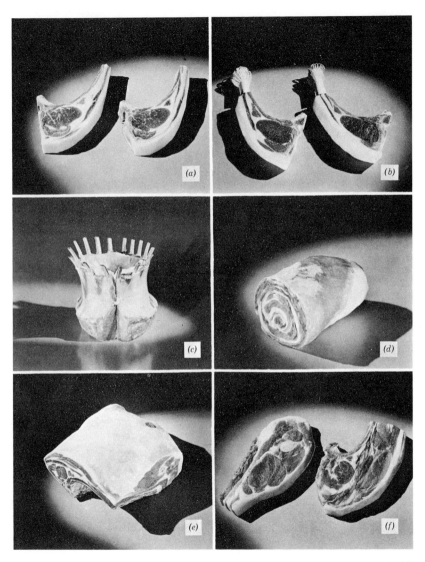

FIG. 11–42. Lamb cuts: (a) rib chop, (b) Frenched rib chop, (c) crown roast, (d) rolled breast, (e) square cut shoulder, (f) shoulder chops.

FIG. 11–42 (Continued). Lamb cuts: (g) cushion shoulder, (h) neck slices, (i) loin chops, (j) English loin chops, (k) sirloin chops, and (l) French leg. Courtesy National Livestock and Meat Board.

roasts. Division of these heavy lambs into portion cuts for this type of cookery is therefore desirable.

In cutting up a heavy lamb, the shoulder portion is removed by cutting between the 5th and 6th ribs. (See Figure 11–43a.) The kidney knobs, hanging tender and melt are removed. A cut is then made behind the 13th rib to separate the hotel rack and breasts (sometimes called the bracelet.) Next, saw about 2½ in. from the rib eye muscle to remove the breast. (See Figure 11–43c.) The loin is separated from the unsplit legs immediately in front of the hip bones. The legs may then be split with a hand saw or power saw. Next, remove the shanks from the briskets and neck by cutting about ½ in. above the elbow joint. The shoulder may then be cut as shown in Figures 11–43d and e,) to obtain ¾ to 1 in. thick arm or blade chops. The blade chops are usually split by removing the chine bone and feather bones. The remaining portion of the shoulder can be boned and then made into saratoga chops by cutting through the natural dividing seam to separate the inside piece, which is rolled, fastened with skewers and cut into saratoga chops. (See Figures 11–43f and g.) The outside pieces may be boned and used for ground meat (patties), stew meat or lambettes. It is also possible to bone and roll the shoulder, as shown in Figure 11–43h.

The shank bone should be cut off from the shank about 1 in. above the knee. These shanks may be used for braising. Lambettes are made from neck, brisket or almost any lean, boneless cut of lamb by running them through a mechanical tenderizer several times until lean and fat are mixed evenly. (See Figures 11–43i and 43j.) Trimmings and neck, shank, brisket, breast and boneless meat may be ground and made into lamb patties.

After removal of the diaphram, the meaty part of the breast may be separated at the natural dividing line to give lean, meaty ribs for barbecued ribs. It is usual to remove the backbone from the rib and loin chops. (See Figure 43k.) If desired, the meat and fat may be removed from the rib chops about 1½ in. from the ends of the rib bones to make French chops.

It is frequently desirable to remove about three 1 in.-thick loin chops from the sirloin section. The bone structure at this point makes this part difficult to carve for a roast. Cutting these at an angle will give a chop sufficiently large for one per portion. The shank of the leg should be cut off at a point 1 in. above the knee. In preparing the leg for roasting, the tail bone and aitch bone should be removed (Figure 11–43l). The stifle joint can be removed from the shank, and the shank braised with the foreshanks. Instead of using the leg as a roast, leg steaks may be taken from it.

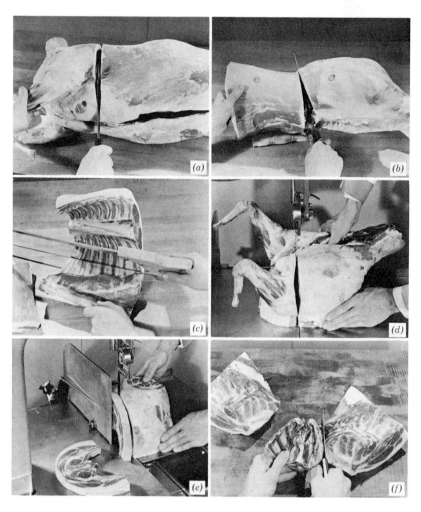

FIG. 11–43. Method of cutting heavy lamb giving a larger yield of sauteing or broiling items.

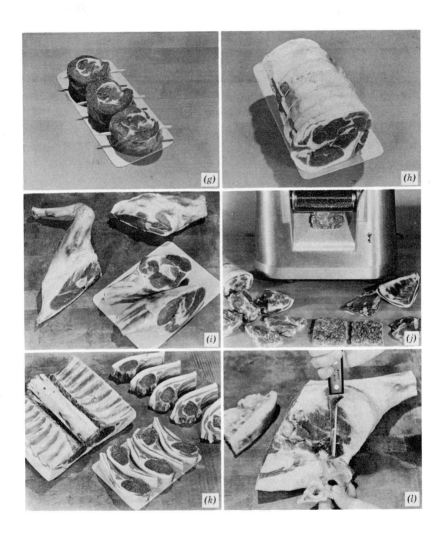

Pork

Only about 30% of the pork carcass reaches the market fresh; most is cured. Loins, fresh hams and spareribs are the most common forms of fresh pork on the market. There is some demand for fresh shoulders and side pork. Most hams are cured and smoked. The method of cutting pork may vary with different local areas. The most common division is shown in Figures 11–44 and 11–45.

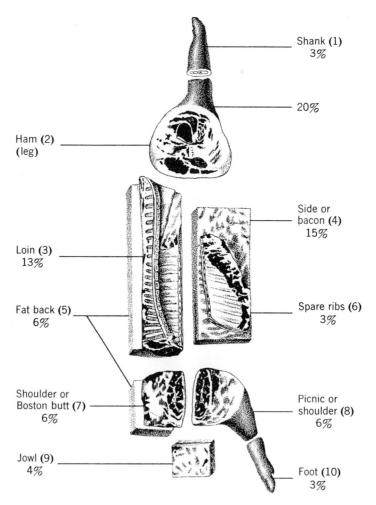

Shank (1)
3%

20%

Ham (2)
(leg)

Side or
bacon (4)
15%

Loin (3)
13%

Spare ribs (6)
3%

Fat back (5)
6%

Shoulder or
Boston butt (7)
6%

Picnic or
shoulder (8)
6%

Jowl (9)
4%

Foot (10)
3%

FIG. 11–44. The usual wholesale cuts of a pork side are shown. The fat back (5) is frequently removed in one piece before removal of the loin (3) and the Boston butt (7). The cut as a percent of side is also given.

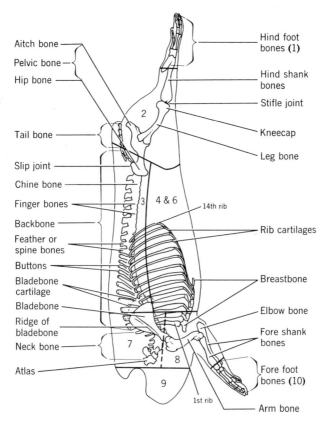

Aitch bone

Pelvic bone

Hip bone

2

Tail bone

Slip joint

Chine bone

Finger bones

3 4 & 6 14th rib

Backbone

Feather or
spine bones

Buttons

Bladebone
cartilage

Bladebone

Ridge of
bladebone

Neck bone

7

Atlas

8

9

1st rib

Hind foot
bones (1)

Hind shank
bones

Stifle joint

Kneecap

Leg bone

Rib cartilages

Breastbone

Elbow bone

Fore shank
bones

Fore foot
bones (10)

Arm bone

FIG. 11–45. The skeletal structure of pork is shown. The numbers on the cuts correspond with those shown in Figure 11–44. Note that this pork has 14 ribs while cattle and sheep have 13. The number of ribs on pork may also vary according to breed. Courtesy National Livestock and Meat Board.

Many chefs like to remove the 7-rib blade roast from the end of the loin, next removing the blade bone, as shown in Figures 11–47a and b. The meat on this blade bone can be used for chop suey meat. Next, the sirloin section is removed. The backbone is loosened and removed by sawing across the base of the ribs of the center cut at a slight angle so that the blade does not cut into the eye of the loin. (See Figure 11–47c.) This backbone may be used for boiling with kraut or for flavoring other foods, such as boiled beans. The backribs are frequently used for spareribs. A boneless section is left for pork chops. If desired, butterfly chops may be made.

PORK CHART

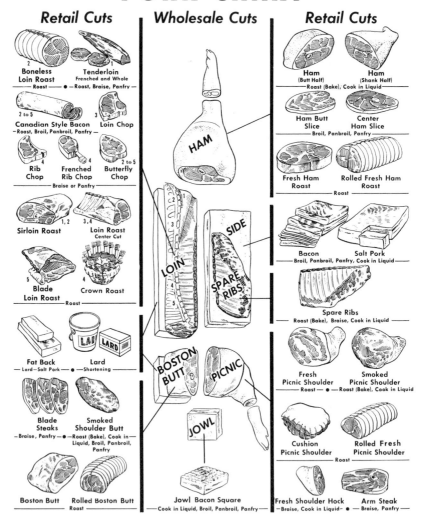

Retail Cuts

2
Boneless
Loin Roast
— Roast —

Tenderloin
Frenched and Whole
● — Roast, Braise, Panfry —
1

2 to 5
Canadian Style Bacon
— Roast, Broil, Panbroil, Panfry —

3
Loin Chop

Rib
Chop
4

Frenched
Rib Chop
4

Butterfly
Chop
2 to 5
— Braise or Panfry —

Sirloin Roast
1, 2

Loin Roast
Center Cut
3, 4

Blade
Loin Roast
5
— Roast —

Crown Roast
4

Fat Back
— Lard — Salt Pork ●

Lard
— Shortening —

Blade
Steaks
— Braise, Panfry —

Smoked
Shoulder Butt
● — Roast (Bake), Cook in
Liquid, Broil, Panbroil,
Panfry

Boston Butt
— Roast —

Rolled Boston Butt

Wholesale Cuts

HAM

LOIN

SIDE

SPARE RIBS

BOSTON BUTT

PICNIC

JOWL

Retail Cuts

Ham
(Butt Half)

Ham
(Shank Half)
— Roast (Bake), Cook in Liquid —

Ham Butt
Slice

Center
Ham Slice
— Broil, Panbroil, Panfry —

Fresh Ham
Roast

Rolled Fresh Ham
Roast
— Roast —

Bacon

Salt Pork
— Broil, Panbroil, Panfry, Cook in Liquid —

Spare Ribs
— Roast (Bake), Braise, Cook in Liquid —

Fresh
Picnic Shoulder
— Roast — ●

Smoked
Picnic Shoulder
— Roast (Bake), Cook in Liquid —

Cushion
Picnic Shoulder

Rolled Fresh
Picnic Shoulder
— Roast —

Fresh Shoulder Hock
— Braise, Cook in Liquid — ●

Arm Steak
— Braise, Panfry —

Jowl Bacon Square
— Cook in Liquid, Broil, Panbroil, Panfry —

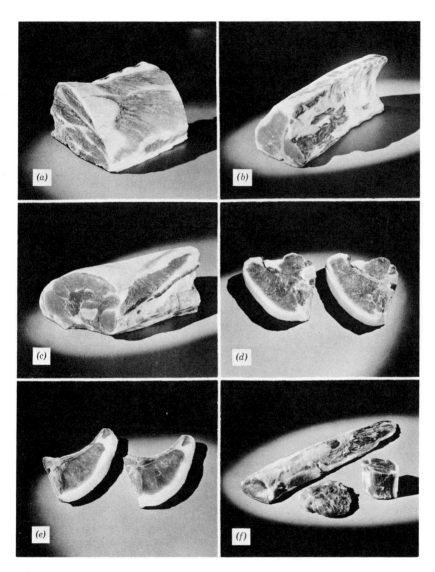

FIG. 11–46. Pork cuts: (a) blade or shoulder end of loin, (b) center cut of loin, (c) sirloin end of loin, (d) loin chop, (e) rib chop, (f) pork tenderloin.

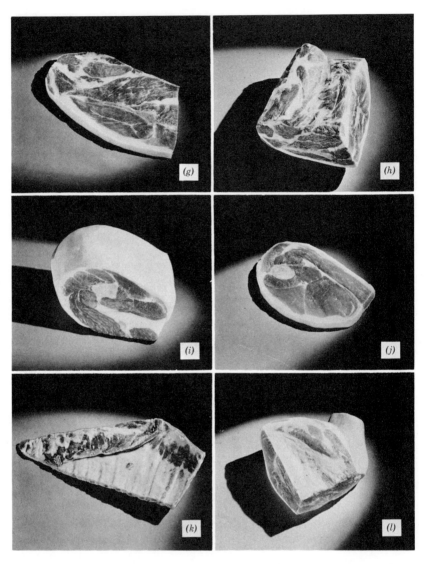

FIG. 11–46 (Continued). Pork cuts: (g) shoulder or blade steak, (h) Boston butt of shoulder, (i) arm roast, (j) arm steak, (k) spareribs, (l) picnic (shank) shoulder.

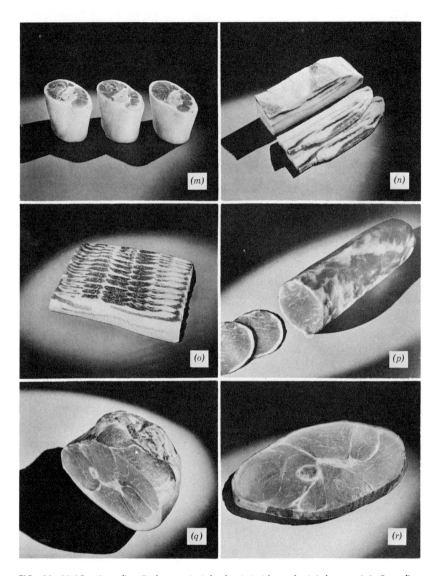

FIG. 11–46 (Continued).   Pork cuts: (m) hocks, (n) side pork, (o) bacon, (p) Canadian bacon (cured and smoked eye of meat in pork loin), (q) butt end of smoked ham, (r) center-cut ham steak.

FIG. 11–46 (Continued). Pork cuts: (s) smoked boned shoulder-butt (Boston butt), and (t) jowl bacon.

The sirloin end may be cut up by first removing the boneless, triangular-shaped sirloin meat. This may be cut into steaks or made into porklets by passing through a tenderizer; or the shoulder and loin ends of the pork loin may be removed and the chine bone removed allowing chops to be cut from the loin bone-in.

MARKET SIZES OF ANIMALS

Beef is most often marketed in carcasses 400 to 900 lb dressed weight. Many buyers for food services claim that the best portion sizes and yields are obtained from 750-lb carcasses. Very little difference is found between steer and heifer beef. Heifers may be slightly lighter in weight but because of smaller bone size may give higher yields or as satisfactory yields as steers.

Veal and calf are usually classified in dressed weights as follows:

	Veal	Calf
Light	60 to 100 lb	125 to 175 lb
Medium	100 to 140 lb	175 to 215 lb
Heavy	140 to 175 lb	215 to 260 lb

Federal standards make the following distinction between veal and calf carcasses.[2] "Differentiation between veal and calf carcasses is made primarily on the basis of the color of the lean, although factors such as

[2] USDA, Agricultural Marketing Service, SRA No. 114; issued September, 1928, and reprinted with amendments, December, 1955.

texture of lean, character of fat, size and color of the rib bones and carcass weight are also considered. Typical veal carcasses have a grayish pink color of lean that is very smooth and velvety in texture. They also have a slightly soft, pliable character of fat and narrow, very red rib bones and weigh less than 100 pounds. By contrast, typical calf carcasses have a distinctly reddish color of lean, a harder, flakier type of fat and somewhat wider rib bones with less pronounced evidences of red color and weigh more than 150 lbs."

Trade practices may classify veal according to whether it is *milk fed* or a *grasser*. A milk-fed veal has not been weaned, while a grasser has been weaned or partially weaned. Both groups, milk feds and grassers, may also be divided into "early" or "late" season animals. Trade classifications in dressed weights for milk-fed veal and grassers are as follows:

	Milk Fed	Grassers
Light	up to 70 lb	up to 110 lb
Medium	80 to 110 lb	110 to 165 lb
Heavy	110 lb and up	165 lb and up

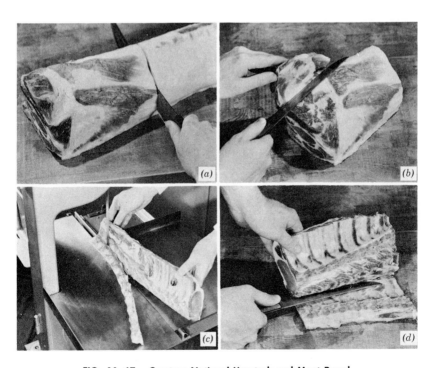

FIG. 11–47. Courtesy National Livestock and Meat Board.

Table 11–3
Average Weights for Carcasses, Wholesale and Fabricated
Cuts for Forequarters of Beef

Item No.*	Product†	Range 1	Range 2	Range 3	Range 4
		Pounds	*Pounds*	*Pounds*	*Pounds*
100	Carcass	400–600	600–800	800–900	900–up
101	Side	200–300	300–400	400–450	450– "
102	Forequarter	104–156	156–208	208–234	234– "
103	Rib, full	18–27	26–36	36–41	41– "
104	Rib, oven-prepared	16–24	24–32	32–36	36– "
105	Rib, oven-prepared (Bnls.)‡	12–19	19–25	25–28	28– "
106	Roast ready rib	13–19	19–25	25–29	29– "
107	Roast ready rib, (Bnls.)	9–13	13–18	18–20	20– "
108	Spencer roll	12–18	18–24	24–27	27– "
109	Regular roll	6–9	9–12	12–13	13– "
110	Square-cut chuck	49–74	74–98	98–110	110– "
111	Shoulder clod	8–12	12–16	16–18	18– "
112	Square-cut chuck, bnls. (Clod in)	30–46	46–61	61–68	68– "
113	Square-cut chuck, bnls. (Clod out)	22–34	34–45	45–50	50– "
114	Foreshank	8–12	12–16	16–18	18– "
115	Brisket	12–18	18–24	24–27	27– "
116	Brisket, bnls. (Deckle on)	8–12	12–16	16–18	18– "
117	Brisket, bnls. (Deckle off)	7–10	10–13	13–15	15– "
118	Short plate	11–17	17–23	23–29	29– "
119	Full plate bnls.	19–29	29–39	39–47	47– "
120	Short ribs, trimmed	4–6	6–8	8–9	9– "
121	Corner piece	4–6	6–8	8–9	9– "
122	Armbone chuck	57–86	86–114	114–128	128– "
123	Armbone chuck bnls. (Clod in)	34–53	53–70	70–78	78– "
124	Cross-cut chuck	69–104	104–138	138–155	155– "
125	Cross-cut chuck, bnls. (Clod in)	51–83	83–110	110–124	124– "
126	Cross-cut chuck (Diced)		Amount as Specified		
127	Diced chili beef		Amount as Specified		
128	Cross-cut chuck (Ground)		Amount as Specified		
129	Triangle	85–128	128–170	170–192	192– "
130	Triangle, bnls. (Clod in)	63–95	95–126	126–145	145– "
131	Beef bones		Amount as Specified		
132	Diced beef		Amount as Specified		
133	Ground beef (Regular)		Amount as Specified		
134	Ground beef (Special)		Amount as Specified		

*Note: Item number above, and in Tables 11–4 through 11–8, refers to those of the USDA Agricultural Marketing Service, Livestock Division's "Institutional Meat Purchase Specifications," from which these tables are taken.

†For description of cuts, see Cutting, pp. 485–503, and Identification of Meat Cuts, pp. 529–541.

‡"Bnls" is federal meat division's abbreviation for "boneless."

Table 11–4
Average Weights for Carcasses, Wholesale and Fabricated Cuts for Hindquarters of Beef

Item No.	Product	Range 1	Range 2	Range 3	Range 4
		Pounds	*Pounds*	*Pounds*	*Pounds*
100	Carcass	400–600	600–800	800–900	900–up
155	Hindquarter	90–144	144–192	192–216	216– "
156	Hindquarter, trimmed	79–123	123–164	164–184	184– "
157	Round (Rump and shank on)	48–72	72–96	96–108	108– "
158	Round, (Rump and shank on) bnls	39–58	58–78	78–87	87– "
159	Round, (Rump on-shank off) bnls.	35–51	51–69	69–77	77– "
160	Round (Rump and shank off)	29–41	41–56	56–62	62– "
161	Round (Rump and shank off) bnls.	26–40	40–53	53–59	59– "
162	Knuckle	6–9	9–12	12–13	13– "
163	Inside	12–19	19–25	25–28	28– "
164	Outside	8–12	12–16	16–18	18– "
165	Round (Gooseneck) bnls.	14–22	22–30	30–33	33– "
166	Round (New York style)	38–57	57–76	76–86	86– "
167	Loin, full-trimmed	34–51	51–68	68–76	76– "
168	Short loin (Pin-bone cut)	16–24	24–32	32–36	36– "
169	Short loin (Diamond bone cut)	19–29	29–38	38–43	43– "
170	Strip loin, bone-in (Regular)	12–18	18–24	24–27	27– "
171	Strip loin, bnls. (Regular)	10–16	16–21	21–24	24– "
172	Strip loin, bone-in (Intermediate)	11–16	16–21	21–23	23– "
173	Strip loin, bnls. (Intermediate)	9–14	14–19	19–21	21– "
174	Strip loin, bone-in (Short cut)	10–15	15–20	20–22	22– "
175	Strip loin, bnls. (Short cut)	8–13	13–18	18–20	20– "
176	Sirloin (Loin end)	17–25	25–34	34–38	38– "
177	Sirloin butt, bnls.	11–17	17–22	22–24	24– "
178	Top sirloin butt, bnls.	7–11	11–15	15–17	17– "
179	Botton sirloin butt, bnls.	4–6	6–8	8–9	9– "
180	Full hip	26–39	39–52	52–58	58– "
181	Short hip	17–25	25–34	34–38	34– "
182	Full tenderloin, regular	4–6	6–8	8–9	9– "
183	Full tenderloin, special	3–5	5–7	7–8	8– "
184	Sirloin (Butt) tenderloin	1½–2½	2½–3½	3½–4	4– "
185	Short (Tip) tenderloin	2½–3½	3½–4½	4½–5	5– "
186	Flank steak	1–2	2–3	3–3½	3½– "

Table 11–5
Average Weights for Carcasses, Wholesale and Fabricated Cuts for Veal and Calf

Item No.	Product*	Range 1		Range 2		Range 3	
		Veal	Calf	Veal	Calf	Veal	Calf
		Pounds	*Pounds*	*Pounds*	*Pounds*	*Pounds*	*Pounds*
300	Carcass	60–100	125–175	101–140	176–225	141–175	226–275
301	Carcass, fabricated	57–95	119–165	96–133	166–214	134–165	215–261
302	Carcass, boneless	46–77	96–135	78–108	136–173	109–134	174–212
303	Side	30–50	63–88	51–70	88–113	71–88	113–138
304	Foresaddle	31–51	64–89	53–71	90–115	72–89	115–140
305	Hotel rack, regular (Double)	6–10	12–17	10–13	17–21·	13–17	21–26
306	Hotel rack, trimmed (Double)	5–8	9–13	8–11	13–17	11–13	17–21
307	Chucks and plates (Double)	26–43	54–75	43–61	76–97	61–75	97–118
308	Chucks, regular (Double)	25–42	52–73	42–58	73–93	59–73	94–114
309	Square-cut chucks (Double)	14–24	29–42	24–33	42–53	33–42	54–65
310	Shoulder clod	2–3½	4–6	3½–4½	6–7½	4½–6	7½–9
311	Square-cut chuck, bnls. (Clod out)	10–19	23–33	19–26	33–41	26–33	32–51
312	Foreshank	1–2	2½–3½	2–3	3½–4½	3–3½	4½–5½
313	Shank and clod	3–6	7–10	6–8	10–12	8–10	12–15
314	Breast	3½–6	7–9½	6–7½	9½–12	7½–9½	12½–15
330	Hindsaddle	29–49	61–86	49–69	86–110	69–86	111–135
331	Loin, regular (Double)	5–9	11–16	9–13	16–19	13–16	20–25
332	Loin, trimmed (Double)	4–7	9–12	7–10	13–16	10–12	16–19
333	Leg, (Double)	24–40	50–70	40–56	70–90	56–70	90–110
334	Leg, oven-prepared, bnls. (Single)	9–15	18–26	15–21	26–33	21–26	33–40
335	Leg, shank off, bnls. (Single)	7–11	13–19	11–15	19–24	15–19	24–29
336	Leg, rump and shank off (Single)	4–8	9–13	8–10	13–17	10–13	17–20
337	Leg, rump and shank off, bnls. (Single)	3½–7	7–12	7–9	12–15	9–12	15–18
338	Back, regular	11–19	22–30	19–26	33–42	26–31	42–51
339	Back, trimmed	9–15	18–25	15–20	26–33	20–25	33–40
340	Hindsaddle, long-cut, regular	35–38	73–102	58–81	100–131	82–100	131–160
341	Hindsaddle, long-cut, trimmed	33–55	69–96	56–77	97–124	78–96	124–151

*When single fores, hotel racks, chucks and plates, square-cut chucks, hinds, loins, backs, legs and so forth, are specified, their respective weight shall be one half of that prescribed for double (i.e. in pairs) cuts.

Lamb may be marketed in dressed weights between 30 to 41 lb, 42 to 53 lb, 54 to 65 lb, and 66 to 75 lb. Mutton will be found in the following range: 55 to 75 lb, 76 to 95 lb, 96 to 115 lb, and 116 to 130 lb. Trade practices in some instances classify, in dressed weights, genuine lamb between 30 to 35 lb, spring lamb 40 to 50 lb, yearling mutton 50 to 60 lb, and mutton 60 lb up.

The average weight classifications for dressed hogs are 120 to 164 lb and 165 to 209 lb. Market sizes for hogs may be quoted from 120 to

300 lb and sows from 300 to 550 lb. Tables 11-3 through 11-8 show average weights of carcass and wholesale cuts. These are excellent as references in writing specifications for meats. The portion size will be closely related to the size of the animal from which the cut is taken, and buyers must specify the size of the animal in order to achieve a satisfactory portion size.

IDENTIFICATION OF MEAT CUTS

Age of an animal is indicated in a cut by the size, by the interior redness of the bone, its shape or flatness, its flintiness and whiteness, the nature of the fat, its depth and thickness, and the color and texture of

Table 11–6
Average Weights for Carcasses, Wholesale and Fabricated Cuts for Lamb and Mutton

Item No.	Product*	Range 1		Range 2		Range 3		Range 4	
		Lamb	Mutton	Lamb	Mutton	Lamb	Mutton	Lamb	Mutton
		Pounds	Pounds	Pounds	Pounds	Pounds	Pounds	Pounds	Pounds
200	Carcass	30–41	55–75	42–53	76–95	54–65	96–115	66–75	116–130
201	Carcass, fabricated								
202	Foresaddle	15–21	28–38	21–27	38–48	27–33	48–58	33–38	58–65
203	Hotel rack, regular (Double)	5–6	8–11	6–8	11–14	8–10	14–17	10–12	17–65
204	Hotel rack, trimmed (Double)	33–5	6–8	5–6	8–10	6–7	11–13	7–8	13–14
205	Chucks and plates (Double)	12–16	22–30	17–21	30–38	22–26	38–46	26–30	46–52
206	Chucks (Double)	11–14	19–26	15–19	27–33	19–23	34–40	23–27	41–46
207	Shoulders (Double)	8–10	14–19	11–13	19–24	14–16	24–29	17–19	29–33
208	Shoulders (Bonded, rolled, tied)	3–4	6–8	4–6	8–10	6–7	10–12	7–8	12–26
209	Breast and shank	4–6	8–11	6–7	11–13	8–9	13–16	10–11	16–18
230	Hindsaddle	15–21	28–38	21–27	38–48	27–33	48–58	33–38	58–65
231	Loin, regular (Double)	5–6	8–11	7–8	11–14	8–10	14–17	10–11	17–20
232	Loin, trimmed (Double)	3–4	6–8	4–5	8–10	5–7	10–12	7–8	12–15
233	Legs (Double)	11–14	19–26	15–19	27–33	19–23	34–40	23–27	41–46
234	Leg, oven-prepared	4–6	8–10	6–8	11–13	8–9	14–16	9–11	16–18
235	Back, regular	9–12	17–23	13–16	23–29	16–20	29–35	20–23	35–39
236	Back, trimmed	6–8	11–15	8–11	15–19	11–13	19–23	13–15	23–26
237	Hindsaddle, long-cut, regular	20–27	36–49	27–34	49–62	35–42	62–75	44–49	75–85
238	Hindsaddle, long-cut, trimmed	17–23	30–41	23–29	42–52	30–36	53–63	36–41	64–72

*When single fores, chucks, shoulders, hotel racks, hinds, loins, legs, backs and so forth, are specified, their respective weights must be one half of that prescribed for double (i.e. in pairs) cuts.

Table 11–7

Average Weights for Carcasses, Wholesale and Fabricated Cuts for Fresh Pork

Item No.	Product	Pounds									
		120–164	165–209	4–6	6–8	8–10	10–12	12–14	14–16	16–18	18–20
400	Carcass	X	X								
401	Ham, regular						X	X	X	X	X
402	Ham, skinned							X	X	X	X
403	Shoulder, regular					X	X	X	X	X	
404	Shoulder, skinned					X	X	X	X	X	
405	Shoulder, picnic			X	X	X	X				
406	Boston butt			X	X	X					
407	Shoulder butt (Bnls)										
408	Belly					X	X	X	X		
409	Loin, regular					X	X	X	X	X	
410	Loin, bladeless					X	X	X	X		
411	Loin, center-cut				X	X	X	X			
412	Loin, (Partially bnls.)				X	X	X	X			
413	Loin, (Completely bnls.)			X	X	X	X				
414	Canadian back			X	X	X					
415	Tenderloin, trimmed*	¼ to ½; ½ to ¾; ¾ to 1 lb									
416	Spareribs	3 lb or less; 3 to 5; 5 lb or more									
417	Hocks, shoulder	½ to 1; 1 to 1½; 1½ to 2½ lb									
418	Pork Trimmings (90% Lean)	Amount as specified									
419	Pork trimmings (80% Lean)	Amount as specified									
420	Feet (Front)	¾ to 1½ lb									
421	Neck bones	¾ to 1; 1½ to 2 lb									

*If the weight range is not specified, commercially packaged tenderloins of mixed weights ranging from ¼ to 1 lb will be acceptable.

the flesh. Old females will have barrel-shaped sides from carrying young.

The kind of animal from which the cut is taken may be indicated by the color of the flesh, the type of fat, the size of the cut, the bone and the muscle. Beef is red in color, varying from a light, cherry red to a dark, almost ruby red. Baby beef is light red. As the animal ages, the flesh grows darker. Unsexed males have light meat. Veal is a light, grayish pink and may even have a tan pink cast. The color of pork flesh is a grayish pink on young animals, changing to a delicate rose in older pork. Lamb is usually a light to dark pink, like baby beef, but mutton will be light to dark red, much like older beef.

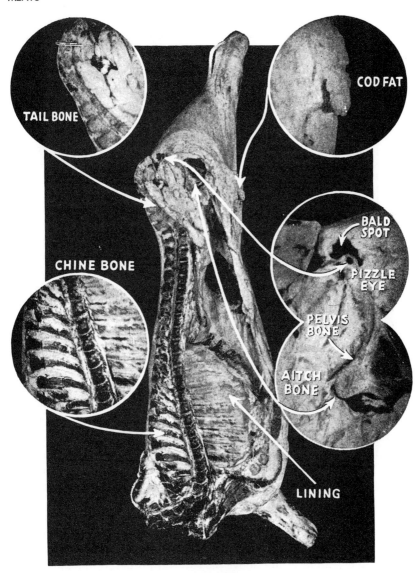

STEER

FIG. 11–48. Age and sex may be distinguished by certain factors on a carcass. The distinct tail joints and the white buttons on the red chine bone are indications of youth. The male will have a straighter pelvis bone than the female. The pizzle eye where the penis is attached with a small bald spot is used to identify sex. Cod fat will be evident on the steer. Indications of age, plus a more noticeable bald spot, pizzle eye and no cod fat plus heaviness of build are indications of a bull. Courtesy Swift and Co.

Table 11–8
Average Weights for Wholesale and Fabricated Cuts for Frozen Pork

Item No.	Product	Pounds 4–6	6–8	8–10	10–12	12–14	14–16	16–18	18–20	20–25
401-F	Ham, regular				X	X	X	X	X	
402-F	Ham, skinned				X	X	X	X	X	X
403-F	Shoulder, regular			X	X	X	X	X		
404-F	Shoulder, skinned			X	X	X	X	X		
405-F	Shoulder, picnic	X	X	X	X					
406-F	Boston butt	X	X	X	X					
407-F	Shoulder butt (bnls.)	X								
408-F	Bellies			X	X	X	X			
409-F	Loin, regular			X	X	X	X	X	X	
410-F	Loin, bladeless			X	X	X	X	X		
411-F	Loin, center-cut		X	X	X	X				
412-F	Loin, (Partially bnls.)		X	X	X	X				
413-F	Loin, (Completely bnls.)	X	X	X	X					
414-F	Canadian back	X	X	X						
415-F	Tenderloin, trimmed*	¼ to ½; ½ to ¾; ¾ to 1 lb								
416-F	Spareribs	3 lb or less; 3 to 5; 5 lb or more								
417-F	Hocks (Shoulder)	½ to 1; 1 to 1½; 1½ to 2½ lb								
420-F	Feet (Front)	¾ to 1½ lb								
421-F	Neck bones	¾ to 1; 1½ to 2 lb								

*If the weight range is not specified, commercially packaged tenderloins of mixed weights ranging from ¼ to 1 lb will be acceptable.

The fat of pork is soft and oily. Veal will have little fat. What little there is on good quality veal will be white and brittle. The color and quality of fat on beef have been described. Mutton has the most brittle fat of all. Pork can easily be distinguished from other meat types when the skin of pork is left on some cuts, such as the leg and shoulder.

Sex in some animals may be distinguished when the cut is wholesale size or larger. It is difficult to tell, however, after an animal is cut up. When the pizzle is removed from stags, steers and bulls, a small gristly spot remains just above the aitch bone. This spot looks like a small eye. Males will also have a bald spot where no fat appears between the end of the aitch bone and the covering of the rump. Females have a continuous strip of lean meat just above the exposed portion of the aitch bone. This strip extends practically from the flank to the rump. When the pizzle is removed from the male, the fat above it drops down and divides this lean strip near the middle of the aitch bone. After the testicles are removed from the male, cod fat develops in the scrotum. This is pronounced and dresses out rough and lumpy. It is easily distinguished from the smooth bag of the heifer. The milk bag is cut away in cows. The pelvic cavity of a heifer is relatively small, and the aitch bone is

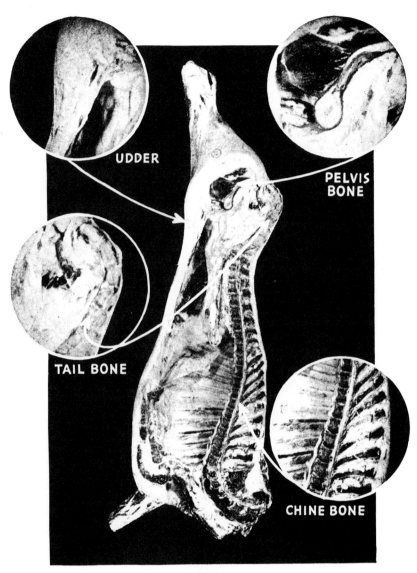

HEIFER

FIG. 11–49. A heifer will show a red chine bone with white buttons, a distinct tail bone, a small udder, and a distinctly curved pelvis bone. Courtesy Swift and Co.

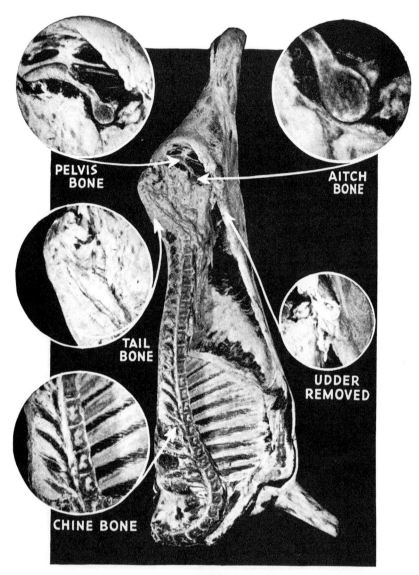

COW

FIG. 11–50. The cow shows age by its white flinty bones. The tail bone will be solid and not distinct as in younger animals. The chine will be white with no buttons. The pelvis bone will be straighter than that on a heifer. The udder will be removed. Courtesy Swift and Co.

curved with a round knob on the rump end. A cow's ribs will be rounded and barreled out, and the aitch bone will be almost straight, with a smaller knob at the rump end. Steers will show a small neck, and the pizzle eye will only be a small patch compared with the large neck of a bull and the larger pizzle eye. The steer's flesh and bones will usually show signs of youth. The meat of a bull will be dark red, almost purple. It will lack marbling and the body will lack finish. Generally, the bones of a bull are hard and flinty. A stag stands midway between a steer and bull in characteristics that identify sex.

The cut may be identified by its shape, size, color, fat, skin, bone and muscle. Of these, bone and muscle are perhaps the most important. Size of the bone may indicate the age and the type of animal. The shape of the bone will indicate the cut. Practice in bone identification will assist a buyer in learning to identify cuts of meat. Some of the most important bones in the skeleton of meat animals are:

1. *Vertebrae or spine bones*
   Cervical   7 neck bones
   Thoracic   13 attached to rib bones
   Lumbar   6 in abdominal cavity
   Sacral   5 in loin end or hip portion
   Coccygeal 3 in rump or tail area (also called caudal bones)
2. *Bones of forequarter*
   Shoulder blade or scapula
   Arm bone or humerus
   Shank bones or radius and ulna
   Ribs—in the Chicago cut, five are in the chuck, seven in the ribs, and one in the hindquarter. Seven are attached to the sternum or the breast bone.
   Chine bone—the spine bone sawed in two.
3. *Pelvis or aitch bone area*
   Forehalf or part parallel to sacral vertebrae is called the hip bone or pin bone. Sirloin steaks from this area with bone-in may be called wedge bone or round bone sirloin steaks. The latter bone should not be confused with the round bone (femur) in the hind leg.
   Rear half parallel to coccygeal vertebrae is called the rump bone. The socket joint to which the round bone of the hind leg (femur) is attached is about midway in the aitch bone.
4. *Hind leg area*
   Round bone or femur attached to pelvis.
   Knuckle is the kneecap bone; specifications should call for removal of this bone when bottom round is ordered.
   Tibia and fibula are bones in the hind leg attached to lower end of the femur.

Some of the important muscles to learn to identify are:

1. The eye of the meat or rib-eye (longissimus dorsi), the long back muscle that

runs from the neck to the rump. This is the largest muscle of the body and from it come the highest price cuts.

2. The tenderloin (psoas major), the muscle that lies beneath the lumbar vertebrae on the inside of the animal. It is the small muscle in the T-bone or porterhouse steak. The large muscle in these steaks is the longissimus dorsi.

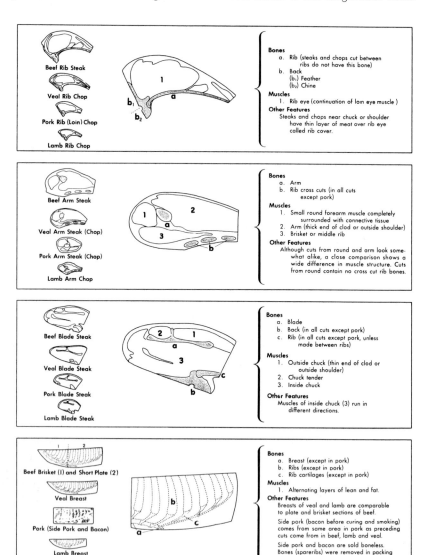

FIG. 11–51. Main muscle and bone shapes found in the forequarter. Courtesy National Livestock and Meat Board.

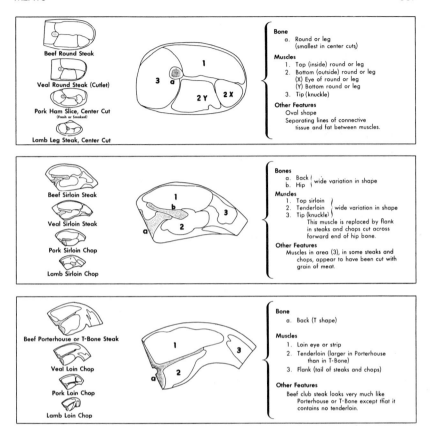

FIG. 11–52. Main muscles and bone shapes found in the hindquarter. Courtesy National Livestock and Meat Board.

3. The intercostal muscles are found between the ribs.

4. The diaphragm is called the skirt, butcher's steak or hanging tender.

5. The clod is the largest muscle in the chuck. It lies over the scapula and is triangular in shape.

6. The inside and outside (top and bottom) round are the rear muscles on the hind leg. The knuckle, or what is sometimes called the sirloin tip, is on the forepart of the leg.

Figures 11–51 and 11–52 show typical bone shapes and muscles in the various cuts. The material previously covered in cutting will also be of assistance in learning to indentify meats.

There are many variations in the cuts of meat that buyers may specify. For the most part the trade understands what these are and buyers should receive what they expect. If difficulty arises, it may be necessary to write into specifications exact definitions. The terms below usually indicate specific cuts, some of which are not according to the Chicago method of cutting; these terms, for the most part, agree with federal cuts named in Tables 11-3 to 11-8.

Standard or pin-bone short loin: Forepart of short loin.
Diamond-bone short loin: Pin-bone short loin cut through the 1st and 2nd sacral

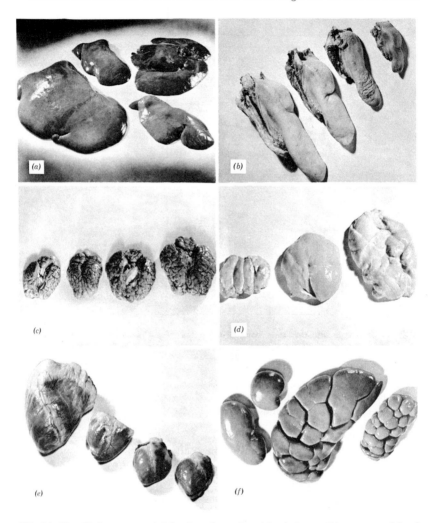

FIG. 11–53. Variety meats: (a) beef, pork, veal and lamb livers, (b) tongues of beef, veal, pork and lamb, (c) brains of lamb, pork, veal and beef, (d) sweetbreads of lamb, veal and beef, (e) hearts of beef, veal, pork and lamb, and (f) kidneys of lamb, pork, beef and veal.

vertebrae, past the illium or pelvic bone to a point just behind its flare into the hip bone.

Full tenderloin: All the tenderloin in short loin and loin end.

Short-tip tender: Tenderloin removed from the pin-bone or diamond-bone short loin.

Butt tender: Large part of tenderloin taken from the loin end; also called Filet Mignon as a steak.

Loin strip, bone-in or feather bone strip loin: Remove tenderloin from the short loin; this is also called the shell loin.

Boneless strip: Feather bones are scalped out of bone-in loin strip; steaks from this cut are frequently called New York cut or strip steaks.

Rough loin: Full loin with flank on.

Intermediate strip loin, bone-in: Regular strip loin, except that the flank edge is cut off in a straight line starting at a point on the rib end 4 in. from the extreme outer tip of the loin eye muscle and continuing in a straight line the full length of the strip loin to a point on the butt end 3 in. from the extreme outer tip of the loin muscle.

Short-cut strip loin, bone-in: Regular strip loin with flank removed 3 in. and 2 in. from the loin eye muscle respectively from the rib and butt ends. The boning of these two cuts should be done by scalping.

Sirloin butt: From loin end by removing the tenderloin butt or butt tender and all bones and cartilage removed.

Top Sirloin butt: Obtained by separating the sirloin butt through the natural muscle seam (blue tissue) and continuing through the meat toward the bottom of the sirloin.

Square-cut sirloin butt: Trimmed top sirloin butt. (See Fig. 11–62.)

Sirloin tip: Bottom of sirloin and part of knuckle.

Full hip: Knuckle and loin end are left in one piece.

Short hip: Bottom sirloin removed from full hip.

Full-cut round: Shank and rump on round.

Gooseneck round: Inside (top) round, knuckle, shank and all bones removed from full-cut round.

New York round: Full-cut round with shank and rump on but knuckle removed.

Long round: Loin end, rump and shank on.

Deckle: Fibrous portion in front of the brisket; should be specified off on brisket specifications.

Kosher chuck: Everything before the 6th rib, including chuck, brisket and foreshank.

Square-cut chuck: Shank and brisket removed from cross-cut or New York chuck.

Arm bone or arm chuck: Square-cut chuck with foreshank on.

Triangle:[3] Neck, chuck, plate brisket and foreshank.

Oven-ready rib: Cut from a point on the wing from the 12th rib measuring 3 in. from the extreme outer edge of the rib eye straight across, keeping this distance from the rib eye all the way; the chine bone, feather bones, and backstrap are removed. Exterior fat is lifted intact from over the first lean muscle

[3]In some areas the chuck, short plate and brisket are called the "rattle," the "L," the "triangle," or the "knockout."

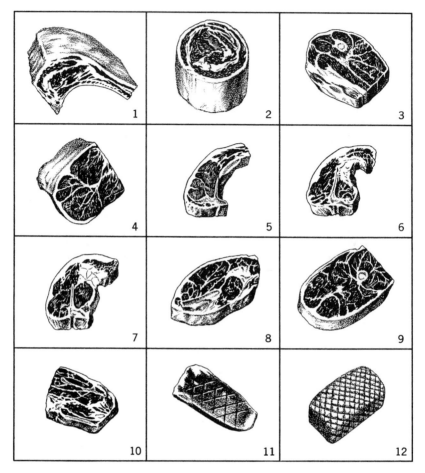

FIG. 11–54. Identify the cut; for practice, locate cuts 1 through 11, 14, 15 and 16 on Figure 11–55.

and peeled back from over the region between the 6th and 10th ribs, leaving the exterior fat covering naturally along the 11th rib and feather bone side. All the lean muscle lying above the level of the blade bone and related cartilage, and small muscle lying below and firmly attached to the blade bone, are removed. The rib is tied so as to be ready for roasting.

Spencer roll: Rib eye removed from a full rib by cutting not more than 2 in. from the extreme outer tip of the rib eye muscle on the loin end, to a point not more than 1 in. from the extreme outer tip of the rib eye on the chuck end.

The student is reminded that practice in identification is the only way that cuts can be learned. Figure 11–54 indicates how pictures showing

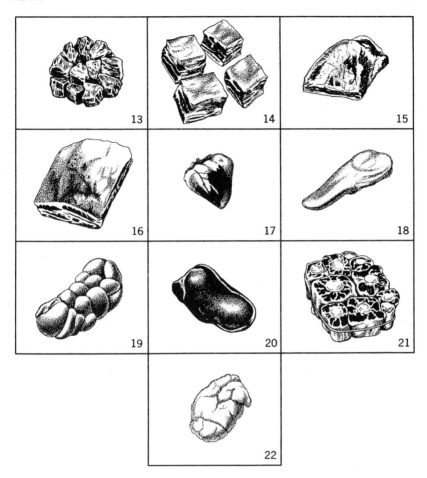

FIG. 11-54 (Continued)

the various cuts can be taken from brochures and other publications and keyed to a legend to give practice in identification. These cuts can then be located on a carcass drawn as shown in Figure 11-55. By using this method buyers may gain practice in naming the wholesale cuts on carcasses. Figure 11-56 may be used also to gain practice in cut identification.

QUANTITIES REQUIRED

The quantity of meat required for a portion may vary according to the type of operation, the patron, type of meal, or the yield factors in

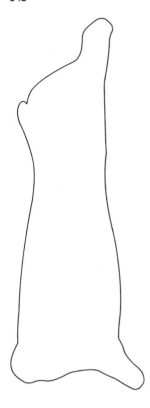

FIG. 11–55. 1, Prime rib; 2, rolled rib; 3, chuck roast;
4, pot roast; 5, rib or club steak; 6, T-bone steak;
7, porterhouse steak; 8, sirloin steak; 9, round steak;
10, shoulder steak; 11, flank steak; 12, ground meat;
13, stew meat; 14, short ribs; 15, brisket; 16, plate;
17, heart; 18, tongue; 19, kidney; 20, liver; 21, ox-
tail; 22, brains.

cutting, preparing and cooking. Some meats may have a lot of waste,
heavy trim and portioning loss. High temperatures in cooking will result in heavy shrinkage. Poor cutting or portioning techniques may
cause excessive losses. Tables 11-9 and 11-10 give approximate quantities of meat to purchase for quantity food preparation and some buying
information of value to institutional buyers.

SPECIFICATIONS

A specification for meat should state the type, cut, style of cutting,
grade, trim, depth of fat permitted, maximum and minimum weights,
size of animal from which the cut is to come, state of refrigeration
(chilled or frozen), delivery directions and general conditions. Reference to the specific cut desired by item number in the Institutional Meat
Purchase Specifications of the USDA will eliminate much detail. (See
Tables 11-3 through 11-8 for these numbers.) A check list is provided

Table 11–9*

A Guide to Number of Pounds of Beef to Buy for Roasting to Serve 100†

Cut	Style	Weight of Cooked Serving	Approximate Amount to Purchase‡
		Ounces	*Pounds*
Rib	Seven-rib standing	2.5	44
		3.0	50
		4.0	67
		5.0	88
		6.0	100
		8.0	134
Round	Rump and shank off	2.1	39
		3.0	55
		4.0	74
		5.0	91
		6.0	110
Sirloin butt	Boneless	2.1	26
		3.0	32
		4.0	50
		5.0	63
		6.0	75
Ground beef	Meat loaf (all meat)	2.1	24
		3.0	35
		4.0	46
		5.0	58
		6.0	69
Ground beef	Meat loaf (with cereal filler)	2.6	18
		3.0	21
		4.0	28
		5.0	35
		6.0	42

*Courtesy National Livestock and Meat Board.
†University of Texas, 1942.
‡If the roasting temperature is increased above 300° F. the number of pounds of meat purchased to provide any certain weight of cooked servings will necessarily have to be increased.

A Guide to Number of Pounds of Lamb to Buy for Roasting to Serve 100

Leg	Bone-in	2.2	34
		3.0	46
		4.0	62
Shoulder	Bone-in	2.7	29
		3.0	32
		4.0	42
Shoulder	Boneless	2.7	27
		3.0	30
		4.0	40

543

Table 11–9 (Continued)
A Guide to Number of Pounds of Pork to Buy for Roasting to Serve 100

Cut	Style	Weight of Cooked Serving	Approximate Amount to Purchase
		Ounces	*Pounds*
Loin	Bone-in	2.5	37
		3.0	44
		4.0	59
		5.0	74
Loin	Boneless	2.0	31
		3.0	47
		4.0	62
		5.0	78
Shoulder	Cushion	2.8	38
		3.0	41
		4.0	54
		5.0	68
Fresh ham (leg)	Bone-in	2.5	38
		3.0	46
		4.0	61
		5.0	76
Smoked or pickled ham	Bone-in	1.9	35
		2.0	37
		3.0	55
Canadian style bacon		2.7	21
		3.0	23

A Guide to Number of Pounds of Veal to Buy for Roasting to Serve 100

Cut	Style	Weight of Cooked Serving	Approximate Amount to Purchase
Leg	Bone-in	2.7	34
		3.0	38
		4.0	50
Shoulder	Cushion	2.4	22
		3.0	28
		4.0	37
Shoulder	Rolled	2.6	27
		3.0	31
		4.0	41
Round	Rump and shank off	2.0	27
		3.0	41
		4.0	54

Table 11–9 (Continued)
A Guide to Number of Pounds of Beef Steak to Buy to Serve 100

Cut	Style	Weight of Cooked Serving	Approximate Amount to Purchase
		Ounces	*Pounds*
Round	Cubed steak	3.0	26
		4.0	36
		5.0	45
		6.0	54
Round	Steak (Swiss)	3.6	31
		4.0	35
		5.0	44
		6.0	52
Loin	Steak	3.8	33
		4.0	35
		5.0	42
		6.0	53
Flank	Steak	2.7	24
		3.0	26
		4.0	35
		5.0	43
		6.0	61

A Guide to Number of Pounds of Beef to Buy for Braising and for Simmering to Serve 100

Cut	Style	Weight of Cooked Serving	Approximate Amount to Purchase
Sirloin butts	Boneless	1.9	13
		2.0	14
		3.0	20
		4.0	27
		5.0	34
		6.0	40
Chuck	Boneless	2.4	25
		3.0	30
		4.0	41
		5.0	51
		6.0	61
Plate or short ribs		4.6	38
		5.0	42
		6.0	50
		7.0	58
		8.0	66
Brisket	Corned	2.1	25
		3.0	29
		4.0	40
		5.0	50
		6.0	60

Table 11–9 (Continued)
A Guide to Number of Pounds of Lamb to Buy for Chops and Riblets to Serve 100

Cut	Style	Weight of Cooked Serving	Approximate Amount to Purchase
		Ounces	*Pounds*
Loin or rib	Chops	2.8	36
		3.0	38
		4.0	51
Breast	Riblets	3.2	30
		4.0	38

A Guide to Number of Pounds of Pork Chops, Pork Cutlets, Pork Sausage, and Bacon to Buy to Serve 100

Loin	Pork chops	4.0	40
		5.0	50
Pork Cutlets		2.4	13
		3.0	16
		4.0	22
		5.0	27
Sausage	Bulk	1.3	15
		2.0	23
		3.0	34
Bacon	Sliced	0.5	9
		1.0	18
		1.5	27

A Guide to Number of Pounds of Veal to Buy for Steaks, Chops and Cutlets to Serve 100

Tenderloin	Steaks	2.6	24
		3.0	30
		4.0	37
Loin	T-bone chops or steaks	4.1	38
		5.0	46
		6.0	56
Rib	Chops	4.9	40
		5.0	41
		6.0	48
Round	Cutlets	2.6	24
		3.0	30
		4.0	37

Table 11–10*
A Guide to the Buying and Use of Variety Meats

Kinds	Characteristics†	Buying Guide		Preparation
		Average Weight	Servings	
Liver (beef, veal, pork, lamb)	Veal, lamb, pork livers more tender than beef. Calf and lamb livers milder in flavor than pork and beef.	1 beef—10 lb 1 veal—$2\frac{1}{2}$ lb 1 pork—3 lb 1 lamb—1 lb	$\frac{3}{4}$ to 1 lb for four	Braise, fry or broil.
Kidney (beef, veal, pork, lamb)	Veal, lamb and pork kidneys more tender, of milder flavor than beef. Veal and lamb kidneys sometimes cut with chops.	1 beef—1 lb 1 veal—$\frac{3}{4}$ lb 1 pork—$\frac{1}{4}$ lb 1 lamb—$\frac{1}{8}$ lb	4 to 6 3 to 4 1 to 2 $\frac{1}{2}$ to 1	Stew, braise, broil or grind for loaves or patties.
Heart (beef, veal, pork, lamb)	Beef heart is least tender but all hearts must be made tender by proper cooking.	1 beef—4 lb 1 veal—$\frac{1}{2}$ lb 1 pork—$\frac{1}{2}$ lb 1 lamb—$\frac{1}{4}$ lb	12 to 16 2 to 3 2 to 3 1	Braise, stuff and braise, stew or grind for loaves or patties.
Tongue (beef, veal, pork, lamb)	May be purchased fresh, pickled, corned, or smoked. Make tender by proper cooking. Pork and lamb usually purchased ready to serve.	1 beef—$3\frac{3}{4}$ lb 1 veal—$1\frac{1}{2}$ lb 1 pork—$\frac{3}{4}$ lb 1 lamb—$\frac{1}{2}$ lb	12 to 16 3 to 6 2 to 4 2 to 3	Simmer in seasoned water until tender. Remove skin; serve as desired.
Tripe (beef)	First and second stomachs of beef. Plain and honeycomb, latter preferred. Purchased fresh, pickled or corned. Make tender by proper cooking.	Plain—7 lb Honeycomb—$1\frac{1}{2}$ lb	$\frac{3}{4}$ to 1 lb for four	Precook in water to make tender. Then broil, fry or braise.
Sweetbreads (beef, veal, lamb)	Divided into two parts: Heart and throat sweetbreads. Tender and delicate in flavor.	$\frac{1}{8}$ lb	$\frac{3}{4}$ to 1 lb for four	Precook in water to help keep and make firm; broil, fry, braise or cream.
Brains (beef, veal, pork, lamb)	Very tender and delicate in flavor.	$\frac{3}{8}$ lb	$\frac{3}{4}$ to 1 lb for four	Precook in water to help keep and make firm. Then scramble, fry or cream.

*Courtesy National Livestock and Meat Board.

†All variety meats are practically boneless and have high percentage of edible meat.

at the end of this section to assist the buyer in setting up specifications. Assistance in establishing specifications may be obtained from the USDA.

Meats should be inspected for wholesomeness and should bear the federal approval stamp. They should be federally graded or bear a reliable packer's brand. The USDA offers an acceptance type inspection service whereby food services may write their own specifications to suit their production need. Government inspectors will inspect to ascertain if the products meet specification provisions. If the acceptance service is used, purveyors bear the cost. Copies of the specifications should be given to the purveyors and to the inspectors. Certification that the meat meets the specifications is indicated by a shield-bearing stamp containing the words "USDA Accepted as Specified." The inspector's initials are also inside. See Figures 11–16, 11–57 and 11–58.

Acceptance service protects the buyer in that many meats require inspection during their cutting. Hamburger must be made from wholesome meat, and if it is to come from certain cuts, a check must be made to see that these are used. The quantity of fat to meat must be checked;

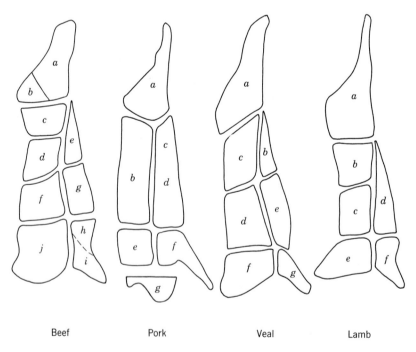

Beef   Pork   Veal   Lamb

FIG. 11–56. Name the wholesale cut on the beef, pork, veal and lamb carcasses shown here. Cuts are identified on facing page.

FIG. 11-57. A federal meat grader examining a boneless strip loin to see if it meets with a buyer's specifications in acceptance buying for distance of end of meat on flank end to eye. Courtesy USDA.

ground meat is sometimes specified as having 18 to 25% fat allowed by analysis but analysis is difficult to obtain. Experienced inspectors can sight meat to be ground and make fairly accurate estimates of final fat content of the ground product. Frequently, in fabricated cuts, the grade stamp is removed from the carcass. Acceptance inspection during processing assures buyers that the meats came from the grade specified.

Additional items may need clarification in an operation's specifications. In addition to the size of the animal or the weight range of the cut, buyers may wish to specify that the items shall come from a specified size cut, such as "pork chops shall be cut from 10 to 12 lb pork loins." Variations of ¼ oz on small chops or ½ oz on steaks over or under the specified weight only should be permitted. Buyers may wish to indicate special cutting, such as "top rounds shall be squared and trimmed so that no additional trim is required," or "top sirloin shall be squared and trimmed on both ends making it a square cut," or "the chuck roll shall be removed from the chuck by cutting on a line approxi-

Identification of Cuts in Figure

Lamb:	*Veal:*	*Pork:*	*Beef:*
(a) Leg	(a) Leg	(a) Ham (leg)	(a) Round
(b) Loin	(b) Flank	(b) Loin	(b) Rump
(c) Rack	(c) Loin	(c) Side (bacon or belly)	(c) Sirloin (loin end)
(d) Breast	(d) Rib	(d) Spareribs	(d) Short loin
(e) Shoulder	(e) Breast	(e) Boston butt	(e) Flank
(f) Shank	(f) Shoulder	(f) Picnic	(f) Rib
	(g) Shank	(g) Jowl	(g) Short plate
			(h) Brisket
			(i) Shank
			(j) Square-cut chuck

FIG. 11-58. A federal meat grader placing stamp of acceptance on a boneless strip loin. Note that three stamps are involved here: the round stamp of approval for wholesomeness appearing on the fore right, the grade stamp running along the top of the strip on the left and the acceptance stamp appearing in the center. Courtesy USDA.

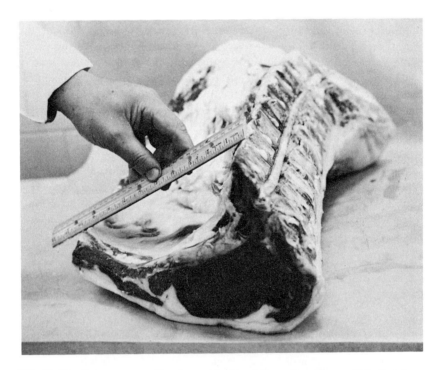

FIG. 11-59. Buyers may specify a heavy trim for a loin as shown here. Note that from the second vertebra the distance is 10 in. and that the cut is straight and parallel to the chine. Note also that the fat trim meets a specification that "fat depth shall not be over ½ in. at any point."

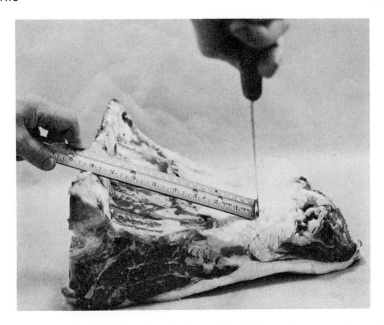

FIG. 11–60. The butcher here is cutting a bone-in featherbone strip to meet the specification which states "the width shall not measure more than 8 in. as measured from the start of the second vertebra to the edge of the flank." Note that the tail of the flank is removed in making this short a cut. This may not always be desirable.

mately parallel to the spinal cord and through the forward point of the chuck roll where the heavy muscles gradually fade out and join the thinner chuck wing," or "the full tenderloin shall be trimmed free of all ragged and thin edges; tenderloins with scores exceeding $\frac{1}{4}$ in. in depth will not be accepted." At times the area from which the cut is to come will be specified. Instances might be "chops shall be center cut only," or "ham slices from the butt or shank will not be accepted." For beef rib steaks the specifications might read: "Steaks shall be cut from ribs 8 to 12 only," or sirloin steaks "shall be cut from the center cut of the top butt only." Cutting practices vary to such an extent that specifications must give detailed cutting methods to obtain cuts desired.

Frequently exact measurements are given to establish what is desired. Buyers and sellers should work out measurements that give a suitable product. The statement of the exact length of a chop, steak or other portion will assure a more satisfactory product. For instance, specifications might state that a boneless strip "may have the flank 1 to $2\frac{1}{2}$ in. from the eye of the meat, the *longissimus dorsi* muscle." Buyers should

FIG. 11–61. Cut shown here is made to meet the requirement that "the meat edge on the chine end to the flank end of the strip shall not measure over 8 in." On a light animal as shown in this picture, this gives a very short steak which is almost all meat. This may not always be desirable.

be aware that when meat is cut very closely to the eye of the meat, the price rises. Sometimes a specification will state that the maximum length of a lamb chop shall not measure more than 2 to $2\frac{1}{2}$ times the width of the eye of the meat. It is preferred, however, to state the exact number of inches the flank end of a chop or steak shall be from the eye of the meat. The thickness of chops, steaks, liver slices or other portions should be specified.

More and more specifications are stating the per cent yield desired from the primal cut. For instance, it might be stated that the yield from a loin of pork "shall be 40% center-cut pork chops." Table 11-11 lists some percentages which might be used to write this information into a specification.

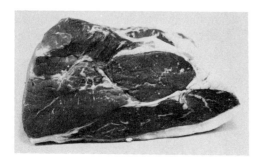

FIG. 11–62. A sirloin butt well trimmed on both sides makes a square cut sirloin as shown. The cut is also called a blocked sirloin. Note trim of fat to meet specifications stating "maximum depth of fat shall be $\frac{1}{2}$ in."

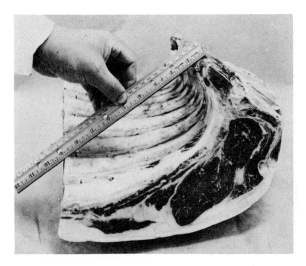

FIG. 11–63. The rib shown here from a moderately light animal meets the specification that "the distance from the chine bone to the rib end shall not be over 9 in." Note fat trim.

FIG. 11–64. The term in a specification that an oven-ready rib "shall be $5\frac{1}{2}$ x 8 in." means that the rib shall not measure more than $5\frac{1}{2}$ in. from the chine bone to the end of the rib at the loin end and not more than 8 in. measured on the shoulder end from the chine bone to the end of the rib. This rib is taken from a light animal and is slightly under these measurements.

Table 11–11
Some Standard Yields from Primal to Fabricated Cuts

Tenderloin steaks, 54% from whole tenderloin.

Boneless strip steaks, 48% from bone-in strip.

Strip sirloin club steaks, 63% from bone-in strip.

Sirloin top butt steaks, 33% from full bone-in strip.

Boneless rib steaks, 29% from standing rib.

Boneless sirloin top butt steaks, 30% from full boneless butt.

T-bone steaks, 41% from pinbone short-loin.

Pork loin cutlets, 10% from loin.

Pork tenderloin steaks, 76% from whole pork tenderloin.

Center cut pork chops, bone in, 38% from light, lean $^{12}/_{16}$ lb loins.

Center cut pork chops, boneless, 28% from light, lean $^{12}/_{16}$ lb loins.

Semi-center cut pork chops, bone in, 68% from light, lean $^{8}/_{10}$ lb loins.

Center cut ham steaks, bone in, 26% from hams.

Center cut ham steaks, boneless, 76% from boned hams.

Ham steaks, end cut, 33% from ham butt and shank ends.

Fresh ham, 76% from bone-in hams.

Pork loin, 57% from bone-in loin.

Beef chuck eye, 14% from bone-in chuck.

Beef top round, 28% from straight round.

Beef shoulder clod, 18% from bone-in chuck.

Lamb leg, bone-in, 71% from straight leg.

Lamb leg, boneless, 65% from straight leg.

Lamb shoulder, boneless, 67% from bone-in shoulder.

Veal leg, bone-in, 75% from bone-in leg.

Veal leg, boneless, 68% from straight leg.

Veal shoulder, boneless, 60% from bone-in shoulder.

The quantity of bone allowed and the way it ought to be removed should also be specified. Frequently the words "boneless" or "boned and tied" are all that are required. In certain instances greater definition may be necessary. For instance, on a chuck rolled roast, the specifications might state: "Ribs and vertebrae shall be detached from the chuck by scalping, thereby producing a smooth surface on the roll with no evidence of scores." A leg of lamb or veal might be required to be made boneless as follows: "The round bone shall be removed by the chisel method so as to leave the boneless leg in a compact piece." At times only a portion of the bone is to be removed and the amount should be stated. For instance, for a leg of lamb the specifications might read: "The shank bone shall be removed below the break joint and the tail piece shall be removed even with the rump." Specifications for chops frequently state that the chine bone shall be removed.

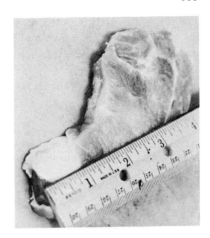

FIG. 11–65. A pork chop meets the specification that the "tail shall be 1 in. from
the eye of the meat."

The depth of fat permitted may also have to be stated.   Frequently an
allowance of $\frac{1}{4}$ to $\frac{1}{2}$ in. is made on chops or small cuts.   Steaks and
roasts sometimes may have $\frac{1}{2}$ in. as a maximum.   Buyers should adjust
specifications so that no additional trim of fat is required after they
receive it.

Frequent cutting tests should be made to ascertain the best method of
purchase for meats.   Market factors change and unless buyers are constantly alert to make checks, they may find they are not obtaining economy in their meat buying.   To make a yield test:

1. Weigh the original cut or piece and compute its total cost.
2. Cut into desired portions in ready-to-cook form.
3. Weigh these portions, trim, waste, etc. computing total weight of
each separately.

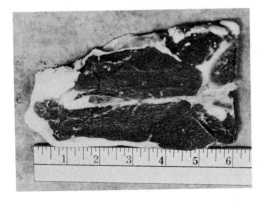

FIG. 11–66. This chop from a
baby beef meets the specification
that "the chop shall not measure
more than $6\frac{1}{2}$ in. from the point
where the flank is removed to
the chine bone as measured
across the outside surface." (In
specifications for lamb or mutton
chops the measurement is usually 1 in. shorter for mutton and
$1\frac{1}{2}$ in. shorter for lamb loin
chops.)

4. Give a valuation to the trim, suet, bones, etc. and deduct this from the total cost. The number of pounds of ready-to-cook meat divided into the remainder will give the cost per pound.

A Check List for Meat Purchase Specifications

Specifications for meats should usually include some or all of the following provisions:

1. Inspection for wholesomeness and bear federal stamp of approval.

2. USDA grade or reliable dealer's brand. Inspection of the cutting of the product may be required in the plant in addition to grading.

3. Acceptance stamp may be specified. It is usually acceptable to have cuts less than wholesale cut size packaged in boxes and the box stamped over pressure sensitive filament tape or metal table. Cost of inspection is to be borne by purveyor.

4. Certifications of inspection may be requested with an original and two copies. It is usual for one copy to accompany the meat. In most instances, certificates should not be issued over 48 hours before shipment.

5. Specify the exact cut or meat required. If federal specifications for institutions are used, buyers only need give item number.

6. Packaging should be free of flavor or odors, clean and sanitary and suited to the item. Carcass or wholesale cuts may be wrapped in crinkled brown paper, stockinettes, grease and moisture resistant paper or other approved wrap. Smaller cuts are usually packed in boxes, plastic and so forth. Buyers frequently specify that fabricated, boneless cuts or portion control cuts must be packaged separately and closely packed in suitable grease and moisture resistant paper or suitable wrappers and placed in boxes. It is common to specify that boxes shall not be over 25-lb in weight. Cured products such as frankfurters, sausage links, sliced bacon and other similar items may be packaged in smaller lots. Frozen meats may require special packaging. Packages should be strapped as specified if shipment is to be for some distance.

7. Frozen meat should be hard frozen upon delivery. Chilled meat should not be over 40° F on exterior or interior.

8. Weight range should be listed either for the carcass, side, quarter or saddle or the wholesale cut or the portion or fabricated cut. The weight range permitted may be within ounces or pounds over or under a stated size or within a specified range. Buyers should be alert to see that purveyors do not meet specified weights by making cuts long or short to meet requirements.

9. The depth of fat permitted will vary according to the type of animal, age, grade and cut. Fat can be quickly measured by an aluminum insert that bends when it meets resistance to solid flesh. Fat trim must be smoothly removed. The fat should follow the contour of the underlying muscle surface. Table 11–12 gives commonly accepted standards for depth of fat permitted on beef carcasses.

Depth of cod fat or udder fat should be specified as not over $\frac{1}{2}$ in.

For wholesale or fabricated cuts of beef specify that the average thickness of fat may be from $\frac{1}{2}$ to 1 in. and the thickest portion of fat at any one point from $\frac{3}{4}$ to $1\frac{1}{4}$ in. Seam fat may be removed or cut away to a certain specified size. In some cases removal of any or all of the seam fat would destroy the unity of the portion.

Table 11–12
Maximum Permitted Fat Thickness on Sides and Quarters of Beef

U.S. Grade	Maximum Fat at Thinnest Point Over Rib Eye, in Inches
Prime	$\frac{7}{8}$
Choice	$\frac{5}{8}$
Good	$\frac{3}{8}$
Standard	$\frac{1}{4}$
Commercial	$\frac{5}{8}$
Utility	$\frac{1}{4}$
Cutter or canner	$\frac{1}{8}$

The depth of fat permitted on mutton and lamb is usually specified as not over $\frac{1}{2}$ in. on the interior of the carcasses; in addition, kidney knobs and practically all kidney and lumbar fat must be removed except for minute flakes adhering to the lean meat. Exterior fat depth may be somewhat thicker than $\frac{1}{4}$ in. or $\frac{1}{2}$ in. For fabricated cuts maximum permitted fat depth is usually $\frac{1}{2}$ in.

Fat depth is usually not a problem in veal except perhaps in the kidney area. It may be specified as being not greater than $\frac{1}{2}$ in. on any exterior or interior portion on calves.

The depth of fat permitted for pork is usually stated for wholesale cuts only although in some cases depth of fat permitted in the interior or sides of pork may be stated. Table 11–13 summarizes the usually permitted depth of fat allowed according to the wholesale cuts of pork.

10. Sex of the animal may be stated. Buyers frequently state that steers only, heifers only, heifers or steers or cows are acceptable. Heiferettes (cows having only one calf) are not acceptable in lieu of heifers and must be considered cows. Bull or stag meat should not be acceptable unless specifically stated.

11. Type of trim should be specified. Wasty or undesirable portions may be specified as removed such as the kidney knob and lumbar fat on loin chops or the kidney may be specified as remaining with only a trim of fat taken in the area. Major tendons and gracilis membranes should be specified as removed. Bloody or rough meat should be removed. Trimming should be neat and free from all ragged and thin edges with no scoring or depth of cut permitted over $\frac{1}{4}$ in. to $\frac{1}{2}$ in. depending upon item.

12. The type of cutting should be specified. Usually meat is cut according to the Chicago method of cutting but in certain areas this may vary. Unless otherwise specified, wholesale or some fabricated cuts of lamb, mutton, veal and calves will be double and not single; that is, the cut comes from an unsplit carcass and two sides rather than one side of the carcass will be used to make the cut.

13. The thickness of the portion cut should be listed.

14. Where boneless cuts are made from the fore quarter or fore saddle of beef, veal and calf and occasionally from lamb and mutton, either for the pur-

Table 11–13

Permitted Depth of Fat on Various Sizes of Wholesale Pork Cuts

Type Cut	Weight Range of Cut	Permitted Range in Fat Depth
	Pounds	*Inches*
Hams	10 to 12	1 to $1\frac{1}{2}$
	12 to 14	$1\frac{1}{4}$ to $1\frac{3}{4}$
	14 to 16	$1\frac{1}{2}$ to 2
	16 to 18	$1\frac{3}{4}$ to $2\frac{1}{4}$
	18 to 20	$2\frac{1}{4}$ to $2\frac{1}{2}$
Shoulders	8 to 10	$1\frac{1}{2}$ to 2
	10 to 12	$1\frac{3}{4}$ to $2\frac{1}{4}$
	12 to 14	2 to $2\frac{1}{2}$
	14 to 16	$2\frac{1}{4}$ to $2\frac{3}{4}$
	16 to 18	$2\frac{1}{2}$ to 3
Shoulder picnics	4 to 6	$\frac{3}{4}$ to $1\frac{1}{4}$
	6 to 8	$\frac{7}{8}$ to $1\frac{3}{8}$
	8 to 10	1 to $1\frac{1}{2}$
	10 to 12	$1\frac{1}{4}$ to $1\frac{3}{4}$

pose of pieces, dicing or grinding the bones, bone slivers and cartilages plus the following should be removed:

a. The backstrap and all neck ligaments.

b. The prescapular lymph gland, located in the shoulder.

c. The exposed large arteries and veins in the neck.

d. Discolored meat and blood.

e. The white membrane (periosteum) remaining on the clod, chuck and rib after removal of the shoulder blade (scapula).

f. The serous membrane (peritoneum) over the inside of the abdominal section of the navel.

g. The strip of heavy connective tissue along the lower edge of the navel and of the brisket.

h. The tendon ends of the shank to a point at which the cross-section of the shank is at least 75% muscle.

i. The fibrous tissue (deckle) on the bone surface of the brisket.

j. All connective tissue and serous membranes from both sides of the skirt or diaphragm.

When boneless cuts for the same purpose are made from the hindquarter or hindsaddles of these animals the bones, bone slivers and cartilages plus the following must be removed:

a. The backstrap in the loin section.

b. The white tissue on the gracilis muscle on the inside round.

c. The white, fibrous sheet on the boned surface of the sirloin butt and rump.

d. The heavy connective tissue on the edge of the outside round adjacent to the knuckle.

e. The popliteal and preformal lymph glands.

f. The fibrous tissue over the outside of the knuckle and the white tissue (periosteum) remaining on the knuckle where removed from the round bone (femur).

g. The kneecap (patella) and surrounding heavy connective tissue.

h. The serous membrane (peritoneum) over the inside of the flank.

i. The heavy sheet of connective tissue (abdominal tunic) between the muscles of the flank.

j. The strip of heavy connective tissue along the lower edge of the flank.

k. The tendon ends of the shank to a point at which the cross-section is at least 75% muscle.

l. All mammary tissue, udders, codfat, pizzle ends, kidneys and kidney knobs.

m. Blood or discolored meat.

n. Blood vessels and heavy external and internal connective tissue in the hanging tenders.

In addition, the quantity of fat remaining may be stated. Frequently the total trimable fat is listed as not being over 10% for veal and calf and for diced beef but may be as high as 25% in some instances. Specifications for this type meat, if mixed, should state that the cuts should exist in the proportion they are obtained from the carcass and that meat originating from skirts, flanks, navels or briskets should be carefully blended with the meat derived from such cuts as the rounds, ribs, chucks and loins so the finished product will have an even distribution of fat and lean. Dicing should be made into chunks $\frac{1}{2}$ to 1 in. and may be done either by hand or machine. Grinding should be first through a coarse plate with approximately 1 in. holes and then through either $\frac{3}{16}$ or $\frac{1}{8}$ in. holes as specified.

15. In all cases where a cut is made from another cut, trim previously specified for the latter shall be understood to apply to the former unless the specifications specifically state that this trim does not apply.

16. All meat products should be derived from sound, well-dressed carcasses or wholesale market cuts from such carcasses. All meat shall be handled in accordance with good commercial practices. Cuts which have been excessively trimmed or cut long to meet specified weights or are substandard because of any reason should not be accepted. The meat should be free from objectionable odors, blood clots, scores, mutilations (other than slight), discoloration, ragged edges, superficial appendages, blemishes, deterioration, damage, mishandling, bruises, evidence of freezing or defrosting (unless frozen), freezer burn, rancidity or other detrimental factor and be in excellent condition at time of delivery. Pork must be cut from packer-style carcasses and must not be salted, cured, cooked or treated in any preservation method but should be from fresh, sound, well-dressed split chilled carcasses.

17. Aging of the meat should be specified, if desired.

18. The general specifications should also include the method of shipment and delivery, billing, payment, number of copies of bills to be mailed, etc. Every facility will have its own specific requirements to suit its needs and these must be included.

RECEIVING

Unless a check is made to see that the proper quantity and quality of meat are received, the best purchasing procedures in the world up to that point may go for naught. Meats may fail to come up to listed weights. Trim may not be that specified. Depth of cut may be too heavy or insufficient. The quality may differ from that ordered. Heavy, wasty cuts may be received, cuts that will give a low yield. Facilities frequently allow janitors, clerks, storeroom men or others to receive meats. These individuals are seldom competent to judge quality and to interpret specifications. Receiving and inspecting should be handled by a person who knows meats. Inspection at delivery should cover:

1. Inspection for quality, noting finish and marbling, color, texture, moistness and other quality factors. Check with the specifications to see if the delivery meets all provisions. Report immediately any discrepancies and mark them on the delivery slip.

2. Weigh and check to see that the quantity delivered is correct. A slight variation may be significant. Frequently shipping tickets fail to give weights and the checker will receive only so many boxes or containers and a total weight. When this is the case the checker should note on the bill of lading the weights received. This should be marked on both the copy given to the delivery agent and the copy retained. Shippers may refuse to wait for weighing. If the vendor and purchaser agree that the vendor will accept the purchaser's later verified weights, this may be permitted. Some operations ask that no weights be listed on bills so receivers must weight and mark down weights received.

3. Store at proper temperature either in refrigerators or in low temperature freezers as required. Temperature for meats under refrigeration should be from 33 to 36°F. Low temperatures should be –10°F. At temperatures lower than 33°F meats darken. Meats can absorb odors from vegetables, fruits and other aromatic products. Fluctuating temperatures for frozen meats cause crystal growth and destruction of quality in the product.

MISCELLANEOUS MEATS

Cured products should be standard, well-trimmed items cut according to the best commercial practices. Curing salts should be a well-blended mixture of salt, sugar or other sweetening agent. Sodium nitrate or sodium nitrite and potassium salts permitted by federal regulations in

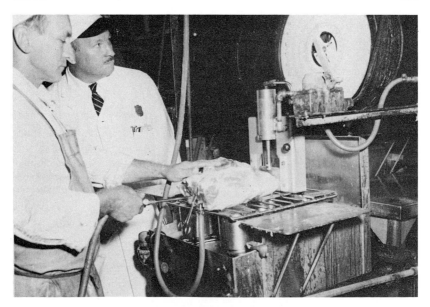

FIG. 11–67. A federal inspector supervising the pumping of a ham for curing. Regulations require that the cured smoke product can only come up to the original green weight and not more. Courtesy USDA.

any desired combination may be used to give a pleasantly flavored product. Cure may be with or without water and with or without pumping (spray or vascular) unless dry cure is specified. Final curing gain and yield in weight must conform with Federal Meat Inspection Regulations, which state that cured products may only come up to original weights. The curing should impart the typical characteristics (well-cured texture, cohesiveness, sliceability, flavor, aroma, soundness and appearance, including bright, stable color) to the finished product.

Smoking should be done in dense natural smoke from burning hardwood or sawdust or both in a conventional smoke house or smoking may be accomplished by any accepted conventional method. Smoking should be done in accordance with the Federal Meat Inspection Regulations and meet such temperature and time requirements as to impart a well-penetrated and fairly uniform deep smoke color. The products should have characteristic flavor, aroma, texture, firmness and appearance associated with well-smoked products of good quality. Smoked products shall be firm, dry and good condition and appearance. Encrusted surfaces of salt, extraneous matter and smoke-house residue should be removed. Color should be natural. Stockinettes, strings and

FIG. 11–68. A federal meat inspector inspecting the grinding of
meat for sausage.   Courtesy
USDA.

other similar hanging devices should be removed and excluded prior to
wrapping and packaging.

Hams, Canadian bacons, picnics and Boston butts should conform to
specifications previously indicated under cutting. Jowls should run from
2½ to 4 lb each and should be standard cut jowls. If boneless hams or
other products are specified, boning should be according to the best
commercial practices. Bacon may be specified as slab with rind on or
off or sliced (skinless). Number of slices per pound should be specified
and 18 per pound from bacons in the slab weighing 8 to 10 lb are recommended for most food services. Bacon cut from slabs 10 to 12 or 12
to 14 lb cannot be successfully cut into slices 18 to the pound because
these will be almost too thin for cooking. Width of bacon should be
specified as not exceeding 8 to 10 in. Specify bacon well streaked with
lean and packaged in approximately the same order as cut. Exclude
bacon ends. Specify Canadian bacons between 5 and 9 lb. Cured fat
backs may range from 12 to 14 lb. Cured clear bellies may range from
20 to 25 lb, while sweet-pickled, trimmed bellies should range between
16 and 20 lb.

Beef tongues should be sound, well trimmed, selected and handled
according to best commercial practices. They may be fresh, cured or
smoked.

Dried beef should be sliced and packed in 10-lb cartons. Specify that
the dried beef shall come from inside rounds or knuckles. Some specifications permit two thirds from this source and one third from outside
rounds. Curing should be thorough but not excessive. Slicing should
be from well-trimmed pieces free of extraneous matter. Slicing should
be at approximate right angles to major muscle fibers. Unsliced pieces
or slices showing string or hanger marks should be excluded.

Liver may be beef, calf (veal) or pork. It should be sound, strictly fresh and prepared and handled according to good commercial practices. It should be trimmed free of all external attachments, ragged edges and superficial parts including the large blood vessels and ducts lying along the liver, which should be trimmed evenly with the surface. The gall bladder should be removed. Coarse or netted livers should be rejected. Beef livers may range from 8 to 14 lb while calf livers may range from $1\frac{1}{2}$ to $4\frac{1}{2}$ lb. Pork livers may be 4 lb or less. Liver may be purchased fresh chilled or frozen. Thickness of slice is usually stated at $\frac{5}{16}$'s in.

Beef hearts should be thick, firm and trimmed free of fat. The gristly part on top and the heart cap should be removed. The hearts should be bright in appearance, and the color of the fat may range from creamy white to slightly yellow. They should be free of blood clots. They may be ordered chilled or frozen.

Corned beef should be from briskets, plates or rounds as specified. The cut surface of the cured beef should be bright and fairly uniform on the lean flesh portion. The color may range from a slight two-toned shade, grayish to light pink to medium red. Fat covering should range from slightly thin to a maximum thickness of $\frac{3}{4}$ in. on the surface of all cuts except briskets, which should not exceed $\frac{1}{2}$ in. in thickness at any area. The fat should be at least fairly firm and brittle, somewhat waxy and not oily. Weights should be subject to verification upon delivery. The corned beef may be packed 50 lb or 100 lb in barrels net drained weight. Buyers may specify delivery drained or in pickle brine. Specify briskets with the deckle off and in the weight range between 6 to 12 lb.

Sausage is a term applied to finely divided meat or meat products to which various condiments and seasonings have been added. Sausage is usually stuffed into casings but this is not a factor of identity, for there are some bulk sausage products. Natural casings, such as intestines of sheep, hogs and cattle, may be used. Many sausage products are now processed in plastic casings and, in some instances, manufacturing processes now require no casings.

Only meats inspected and passed by the federal government should be used, and the stamp of wholesomeness should be on all products or packages. High grade sausage should contain good clear meat and few trimmings. Lamb and mutton are usually not allowed in sausage products because of their heavy flavor. All sausage products require some fat for flavor, moisture and softness but excessive fat should be avoided. Moisture may be added in the amount of 10% for cooked or smoked sausage and not over 3% in fresh, uncooked or unsmoked sausage. Extenders used may be cereal, bean flour or dry milk. Specifications should

FIG. 11–69. Filling pork casings with sausage mixture. Courtesy USDA.

state the amount of extender allowed, if any.[1] In addition to the quality of the meat and the processing method, seasoning is very important. High quality spices only should be used, and these should be sterilized to prevent bacterial contamination of the meat. Sausage products may be fresh, smoked and cooked or dry (summer) types.

Fresh sausage is prepared from fresh meat, principally from fresh pork trimmings. Fresh sausage will not keep well and must be kept under refrigeration. It must be cooked also before it is eaten. Pork sausage made from pork only is the chief fresh sausage meat used. It may be obtained either in bulk or links; some brown-and-serve are available. Besides quality in the pork from which it is made, the grind, seasonings and ratio of fat to meat will be important. Specify 80% lean pork, ground first through 1 in. plate and then through a $\frac{3}{16}$ in. or $\frac{1}{4}$ in. plate. Total fat should be less than 40%.

Smoked and cooked sausages may be frankfurter or wiener style, Vienna, Bologna, liver, blood, Berliner, headcheese, souse and others. They are usually given a cure that consists of cooking and smoking. All sausages must be processed to an interior temperature of 137° F. Good frankfurters or wieners are made of a ratio of around 60 lb of beef to 40 lb of pork. Vienna sausages differ from frankfurters in that they are smaller. The sausage is about 20 in. long and is frequently marketed canned and cut into about 2 to 2½ in. lengths. Some all beef frankfurters and Vienna sausages are also made. Bologna sausage is a mixture similar to frankfurters except that the meat may not be chopped so finely. It is a large sausage, about 3 to 4 in. in diameter. Frankfurters,

[1]Federal standards allow up to 2%.

wieners, Vienna and Bologna sausages receive a light smoke. The best liver sausage is made in the proportion of 150 lb of trimmed fresh hog livers, 110 lb fresh pork jowls and 40 lb fresh pork trimmings. The materials are chopped and stuffed into hog intestines, cooked one or two hours at 155° F and then smoked 4 to 6 hours at 80 to 90° F. Headcheese is made from parts of the pork head. It is cooked and made into a jellied loaf. It may or may not have caraway and pimiento in it. Souse is the same as headcheese, with vinegar added. Berliner sausage is a luncheon meat made of large pieces of dry-cured lean pork and finely chopped beef. For cheaper products cheek meat and similar items may be used. Berliner is large like Bologna but is not smoked.

Dry or summer sausage represents a wide variety of types. Most of these originated in Europe where each community had its own particular style. Many of these sausages can now be made domestically with little difference in product. Domestic salami made with many loops and longitudinal strands of cord looks much like true Genoa salami. Milano salami with its circular twins can be duplicated. The domestically made hot salamis of south Italy are commonly seen.

The meats for dry sausage types are prepared very similarly to the meats for other sausages. The quality of meat and spices used are important factors in establishing quality. Practically all meats used in dry sausage are spread in trucks or upon benches for 48 to 72 hours to condition and dry. After this they are ground, seasoned and placed into casings. This drying and grinding process is called "rocking." Smoking

FIG. 11–70. Hanging up sticks of sausage for smoking. Courtesy USDA.

and drying are important steps in the processing. Smoking is done at
temperatures between 70 and 80° C, and the time is usually between 24
and 48 hours, depending upon the size of the sausage and the desired
degree of smoke. Italian types are not smoked, while Scandinavian,
German and Austrian types are given a heavy smoke. Drying occurs in
a "green sausage" hanging room where it is held at temperatures of 60
to 70° F and dried. In drying, care must be taken to see that molds do
not develop and that curing occurs without putrefaction.

There are many sausages in the dried sausage class. Cervelat is
chopped fine, seasoned without garlic and stuffed into hog intestines.
Salami is chopped coarsely, flavored with garlic and stuffed into beef
intestines. Salamis are frequently corded, while Cervelats, Farmer and
Holsteiner (two popular German dried sausages) are not. Thuringer is
a semi-dried sausage made from beef and some pork and a small amount
of ham. It is smoked. German salami differs from Italian in that it is
about 50% beef and 50% pork and smoked, while the Italian salami is
made from coarsely chopped pork, has more garlic in it and is not
smoked but only air dried. Miscellaneous Italian sausages or dried
cured meat are Pepperoni, Frisses and Mortadellas. Pepperoni is a
thinner sausage than salami and has whole black pepper in it. Morta-
della is made from selected lean pork with a little beef added. The
meat is finely chopped. Small cubes of fat are added. It is delicately
seasoned with spices and garlic stuffed into hog bladders and corded in
basket shape. It is not smoked but may be produced as a semi-dry or
dry sausage. Capicolli are cured, pork boneless butts, lightly smoked
and dried. Some prosciutti hams may be dried.

CANNED MEAT

The quantity of canned meat used by a food facility may vary. If
fresh meat supplies are difficult to obtain, large amounts of canned
meats may be purchased. Almost every operation, however, purchases
some meat in this form. Canning of meat to preserve it is a much more
difficult procedure than canning fruits and vegetables. The solid mass
of meat in the can and its resistance against heat penetration make it
difficult to sterilize. Some meat products, such as canned hams, must
be kept under refrigeration to keep them satisfactorily. Storage of other
smaller items is adequate at 40 to 70° F; but above 70° F thermophilic
bacteria may cause deterioration. Canned meats should not be kept
over one year. Freezing meat in cans causes a deterioration of quality,
but the meat is edible providing freezing does not swell the can until it
breaks and the meats become contaminated. Canning procedures for

meat are much like those described for fruits and vegetables except for cooking times. Lacquered cans are used to prevent the meat from reacting with the can linings.

Canned meat shipped interstate must be government inspected and approved for wholesomeness, and the round stamp indicating this approval must be on each can. Equipment, workmen and plants, as well as the product itself, must meet standards of sanitation. The poorer grades of meat and excess market quantities are usually processed. Under ruling of the federal government various chemical ingredients are forbidden for use as preservative agents. Some of the forbidden ingredients are sodium benzoate (except under special conditions), borax, boracic acid, sodium sulfite, salicylic acid and formalin.

Slab bacon may be obtained in 14-lb rectangular cans. Three to four pieces are used in making the weight. Sliced bacon is usually sliced $5/32$ in. thick. The bacon is wrapped in oiled or parchment paper. Under vacuum seal very little oxidation occurs, but there is a gradual deterioration of the bacon fat, and the product should not be kept over 6 months. Sliced bacon is usually sold in cans holding 5, $5\frac{1}{2}$, $7\frac{1}{2}$, and 16 lb net weight. Canadian-style bacon is also canned.

Boned chicken or turkey is canned. Usually the cans are 46 oz or smaller. The Food and Drug Administration limits the amount of added broth to 10% by weight of the finished product.

Corned beef is beef preserved with salt and nitrates. Some sweetening agent and spices may be added. Flanks, plates, chucks, briskets and trimmings are usually corned but some round may be. After the meat is cured (corned), it is trimmed, placed into cans and cooked. Three to 4% of meat jelly is added. It may be sold in 12 oz, 1 lb, $1\frac{1}{2}$ lb, 5 lb or 6-lb cans. Cornbeef hash is made by combining ground corned beef with 40 to 50% chopped onions and potatoes. Salt and pepper are added. It is canned in No. 10 cans or in No. 2 cans.

Roast beef is beef cut into strips or pieces $1\frac{1}{2}$ to 2 in. wide. Most of the fat is trimmed. The meat is roasted and then placed into the cans, usually with a gravy but occasionally with the broth. It may be purchased in 12 oz, $1\frac{1}{2}$ lb and 6-lb cans. Various types of stews and other products are made from beef and canned. These may be beef and vegetables, beef in gravy, meat balls, meat loaf and so forth.

Canned luncheon meat is purchased by many facilities. It may be all pork or a mixture of beef and pork. It is finely chopped, seasoned, pressed into loaves and cooked in the cans. Pork sausage meat and pork sausage links are canned. The former is in loaf form. Vienna sausage containing 40 to 70% beef and 30 to 60% pork or frankfurters with similar meat percentages are canned.

Chili con carne is a mixture of beans and meat that contains around 50% beef, 25% beans and the remainder vegetables and moisture.

Many meat and poultry products are canned with cereal products, such as macaroni, spaghetti and noodles. The FDA states that 25% meat based on uncooked weight of the meat shall be in these type products if meat is claimed as an ingredient.

Cooked hams are available canned. The shape may be made to fit the natural shape of the ham or it may be square or round. The hams should be kept under refrigeration in storage. The weight of full hams varies from 6 to 16 lb. An 8 to 10-lb canned ham is usually best for institutional use.

12 Alcoholic Beverages

The purchase of alcoholic beverages for a food service operation is a specialized task. A wide knowledge of wines, beers and distilled spirits is required. Not only are there many items to be purchased but many brands of each are available for selection also. Which brand to select may be a problem. Quality factors are difficult to evaluate and require special training to detect. Customers are likely to have wide preferences, and buyers must be able to meet these while keeping the number of beverages down to a satisfactory number. In some ways, however, purchase is simplified. Every bar must have standard "call" items. Dining areas must also stock standard items. In beverages there are standard lines and buyers may purchase these, which simplifies their purchasing task. Brand purchase is usual, for there are few if any grade standards. In some instances buyers may limit purchases to a relatively few sellers, for dealer franchises are limited and consolidated to a few in each area. Off-brands and products with limited demand should be avoided unless there is a well-thought out merchandising plan for their sale. There are few bargains in alcoholic beverages.

Alcoholic beverages are wine, beer and distilled spirits. Distilled spirits include alcohol, whiskey, brandy, rum, vodka, gin, cordials and liqueurs. These may only be produced in plants registered and operated under federal control. Wines and beers must also be produced in bonded or controlled units.

The federal government does not establish formulas or methods for the manufacture of alcoholic beverages, but rather it outlines general conditions under which the producer may operate. In a few cases limits are placed on how the product may be manufactured. Standards of identity, labeling and advertising have been established for alcoholic beverages moving in interstate commerce. Most of the states producing alcoholic beverages have laws regulating the industry. These provide for standards of identity, purity of product and so forth. Some of these state laws are more stringent than those of the federal government. Buyers should become well acquainted with their state and local regulations and follow them in their buying. Monopoly states are those in which the states themselves engage in the purchase and sale of alcoholic beverages, usually through their own state-owned and -operated stores. Some states have "local option," a provision whereby counties or other municipal communities may prohibit the sale of alcoholic beverages. Only one state, Mississippi, is "dry"; that is, no alcoholic beverages whatsoever may be sold within the state's borders.

DISTILLED SPIRITS

Quality in distilled spirits is determined largely by three factors: the product from which made, the manufacturing process and the aging. Cost is usually related to the cost of these three factors. Advertising, however, may be a significant factor in the cost of some items.

When carbohydrate products, such as starch or sugar, are utilized by yeast in its growth process, the carbohydrate is changed into carbon dioxide and ethyl alcohol. Since the ethyl alcohol has a lower boiling point (140° F) than water (212° F), it may be easily separated by distillation. In some distillations, flavor esters are also boiled off with the alcohol. These esters give the various distilled liquors their distinctive flavors.

Whiskey is perhaps the most widely used distilled alcoholic product in this country. It is made from selected grain, which is finely ground into a meal and then cooked into a mash or pastelike product. Malt is added. This assists in the changing of the starches into sugars during fermentation so the sugars are available as food for yeast. Special yeasts are used. Fermentation of the mash is allowed to proceed for 72 to 96 hours under carefully controlled conditions. When complete, the mash is heated and the potable spirits distilled from the mash. These alcoholic vapors are caught, cooled and condensed and drawn off as new whiskey. The alcoholic content is then reduced to that desired.

The strength of distilled spirits is indicated by its "proof." The proof is twice that of the percentage of alcohol in the beverage. Thus, a whiskey of 86 proof is 43% alcohol and one 100 proof is 50% alcohol. Whiskeys may not be higher than 110 proof or lower than 80 proof. The desired proof having been made, the whiskey is stored in charred oak barrels in a rackhouse for aging. After aging, the barrels of whiskey are

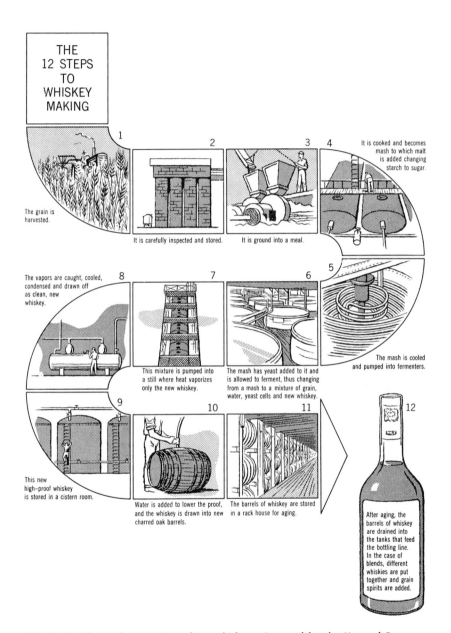

THE
12 STEPS
TO
WHISKEY
MAKING

1

The grain is harvested.

2

It is carefully inspected and stored.

3

It is ground into a meal.

4

It is cooked and becomes mash to which malt is added changing starch to sugar.

5

The mash is cooled and pumped into fermenters.

6

The mash has yeast added to it and is allowed to ferment, thus changing from a mash to a mixture of grain, water, yeast cells and new whiskey.

7

This mixture is pumped into a still where heat vaporizes only the new whiskey.

8

The vapors are caught, cooled, condensed and drawn off as clean, new whiskey.

9

This new high-proof whiskey is stored in a cistern room.

10

Water is added to lower the proof, and the whiskey is drawn into new charred oak barrels.

11

The barrels of whiskey are stored in a rack house for aging.

12

After aging, the barrels of whiskey are drained into the tanks that feed the bottling line. In the case of blends, different whiskies are put together and grain spirits are added.

FIG. 12–1. The twelve steps in making whiskey. Prepared by the Licensed Beverage Industries, Inc., New York.

drained into tanks that feed the bottling line. The reddish-brown color of whiskey is derived from the charring of the oak cask.

Bonded whiskey must be that stored at least 4 years in wooden barrels. It must be 100 proof, and the product of a single distillery during a single season. It may bear the bottled-in-bond label and be sealed with the federal government's green strip stamp. Reddish-pink stamps are used for distilled spirits not bottled in bond. Bottling must be done under the supervision of the federal government. Bottled-in-bond is not necessarily a guarantee of quality but refers to the regulatory procedures under which the whiskey is bottled and taxed. No spirits may be withdrawn from a government bonded warehouse without governmental permission. The owner of the warehouse goods may enter only in the presence of a federal official. The Bureau of Internal Revenue controls the keys and keeps all records of entries and withdrawals of spirits.

A straight whiskey is all whiskey. It is placed in charred oak barrels at not more than 110 proof and not less than 80 proof at distilling. Aging is for not less than 24 months. A blended whiskey contains not less than 20% 100-proof straight whiskey. The remaining 80% may be made up of whiskey or neutral spirits not under 80 proof. Before being placed on the market for sale, a blend is aged a short time, a period known as a "marrying" period.

Neutral spirits are spirits distilled from approved materials. The distillate comes off at around 190 proof. Neutral spirits lack distinctive taste, color and odor and are used for making gin, vodka, cordials and liqueurs or for blending with whiskey. If the neutral spirits are distilled from a fermented mash of grain, they may be called "grain" neutral spirits.

Bourbon is a whiskey distilled from a fermented mash containing not less than 51% corn. The balance of the mash may be any other grain. It is generally rye and barley malt. Corn whiskey must be distilled from a mash containing at least 80% corn. It need not be stored in charred wooden containers but may be stored in plain wooden ones. Rye whiskey must be distilled from a mash containing at least 51% rye grain.

Canadian whisky (note English and Canadian spelling of whiskey) is a distinctive product of Canada in which corn and rye are the principal grains used in the mash. It contains no distilled spirits less than 2 years old. Canadian distillers may blend their whisky either before or after the aging period. Most Canadian whisky exported to this country consists of blends. No limitations with respect to proof or distillation are placed on this product by the Canadian government.

Irish whisky is a distinctive product of Eire and Northern Ireland made from malted barley, plus other grains. It may occasionally be a

blend, being blended with other grain spirits. It is made much in the
manner of Scotch whisky except that the barley malt is not impregnated
with the smoke of burning peat as is done with Scotch whisky and therefore does not have the smoky flavor. Some Irish and other whiskies
may be called "pot" whiskies. This indicates that a single batch of
mash is distilled until the desired quantity of potable spirits is extracted.
The mash is then discarded, and another fresh batch of mash is placed
in the still and the spirits extracted. Other types of whisky are distilled
by a continuous process, a method whereby new mash is constantly introduced while old mash is withdrawn.

Scotch whisky is a distinctive product of Scotland. The base of its
mash is smoked barley for the heavy-bodied types and smoked corn for
the lighter-bodied ones. It is distilled by the pot method and aged for
at least 3 years in uncharred oak barrels or used sherry casks. Most
Scotch whisky is a blend of malt and grain whiskies. No Scotch may
enter this country under 4 years old unless so labeled. Most Scotch is
allowed to remain in the cask for 5 years or more before bottling.

Sour mash whiskies are produced by using part of the previous day's
mash instead of water to start and assist the fermentation of a new batch
of mash. This is much the same principle as that used for sour-dough
hotcakes, sour-dough hard rolls or rye bread where an old "starter" is
used.

Rum is distilled from the fermented juice of molasses or other cane
products or by-products. The distillate must not be more than 190
proof or less than 80 proof. There are two types: New England rum
and rum. New England rum is a straight rum of full-bodied type, distilled at less than 160 proof. Rum is generally a blend of rums. All
rums must show the name of the geographical area where they are made.
There are three main areas: (1) light-bodied or "dry" rums, which come
from Cuba, Puerto Rico, Haiti and the Dominican Republic, (2) full-
bodied or "rich" rums from Jamaica, Barbados, Trinidad, Virgin Islands, Demerara, Martinique and New England and (3) the Batavia
Arak or aromatic rum from Java.

Gin is made from a base of neutral spirits. These spirits are flavored
during processing, primarily with juniper berries. It is not aged. Flavor
is gained during distillation. In this process, the distillate is run through
a "gin head" containing trays of herbs and other flavoring ingredients,
such as juniper, cassia bark, coriander seed, orange peel, cardamon and
angelica. These flavor the vapors. The vapors are then condensed.
The other method of flavoring is called compounding. Neutral spirits
are stirred with added flavoring materials. They are then strained out
and the spirits bottled. Some call this latter type "bathtub" gin and

it is not commonly found on the market today. Dry gin or London gin are synonymous. The terms mean a gin lacking sweetness and having none of the grain taste or odor left from the mash from which distilled. Holland gin is also variously called schnapps, Geneva or Schieden gin. It is made in Holland from a low-proof, malt spirit base to which juniper and other seasonings have been added. The result is a more heavy body than that found in the dry gins produced in this country and England. Holland gins also bear the taste and odor of the mash from which they are distilled. Old Tom gin is a sweetened gin. Simple sirup is usually the sweetening agent. Sloe gin is a cordial deriving its flavor from the sloeberry.

Vodka is made from neutral spirits distilled at or above 190 proof, reduced to not more than 110 proof and not less than 80 proof. After such reduction the product is filtered through or treated with charcoal to be without distinctive character, aroma or taste. Most vodka is made from grains and not potatoes.

Rectification is a term used to indicate the blending of distilled spirits. A blend is a straight whiskey rectified or blended with neutral spirits. Neutral spirits, with the aid of flavoring essences and other materials, are rectified into cordials or liqueurs.

Distilled spirits flavored with fruits, aromatic herbs, flowers, juices or other flavoring materials containing at least $2\frac{1}{2}\%$ sugar by weight are called cordials or liqueurs. Many of the formulas are trade secrets and some products, such as Benedictine, Cointreau and Chartreuse, have been made for centuries by monastic orders. Whenever imitation flavorings are used in cordials or liqueurs, bottle labels must indicate this.

Brandy is distilled from a mash of fruit or from fruit juices. It cannot be less than 80 proof. Raw materials may be grapes, raisins, peaches or other fruits. To be labeled brandy, the raw material must be from grapes only. If other fruits are used, the label must indicate the fruit used, such as "apple" brandy, "blackberry" brandy or "peach" brandy. Cognac is a brandy distilled from grapes grown in the Charente area of France. The brandy takes its name from the city of Cognac in the area. Armagnac is brandy made from grapes grown in the Department of Gers southeast of Bordeaux, France. Napoleon-type brandies must be aged a specified number of years.

A statement of age on brandy bottle labels is not required in this country unless the brandy is under 2 years old. Brandies are usually aged in oak barrels from 3 to 8 years. Some American brandies may be bottled-in-bond. These must be straight brandies, 4 years of age or more, bottled at 100 proof.

Quality in distilled products may be indicated by body. This covers

Table 12-1
Federal Taxes on Alcoholic Beverages

Item	Tax Base*	Current Tax Rates
Artificially carbonated wine	Wine gallon	$2.40
Beer	Barrel	9.00
Champagne	Wine gallon	3.40
Distilled spirits	Tax gallon	10.50
Rectified products:		
Distilled spirits	Proof gallon	†.30
Wine cordials and liqueurs	Wine gallon	†1.92
Still wines:		
Not more than 14% alcohol	Wine gallon	0.17
More than 14% and not exceeding 21% alcohol	Wine gallon	0.67
More than 21% and not exceeding 24% alcohol	Wine gallon	2.25
More than 24% alcohol	Same as distilled spirits	

Table from *What You Should Know About the Alcohol and Tobacco Tax Division*, Publication No. 425 (11–58), Internal Revenue Service, U.S. Treasury Department.

*Gallon: A gallon or wine gallon is a U.S. gallon of liquid measure equivalent to the volume of 231 cubic inches. A proof gallon is the alcoholic equivalent of a U.S. gallon at 60° F., containing 50 percent of ethyl alcohol by volume. A tax gallon for spirits of 100 proof or over is equivalent to the proof gallon. For spirits of less than 100 proof, the tax gallon is equivalent to the wine gallon.

Barrel: As applied to beer, a barrel represents 31 wine gallons.

Proof: Proof is the ethyl alcohol content of a liquid at 60° F., stated as twice the percent of ethyl alcohol by volume.

(A British or Canadian proof gallon is an Imperial gallon of 277.4 cubic inches containing 57.1% of ethyl alcohol by volume.)

†This tax is in addition to the basic distilled spirits and wine tax.

the flavor and aroma of the product. A "heavy" bodied spirit is one full of flavor and aroma, while a "light" bodied one has less of these characteristics. "Character" in a distilled spirit refers to the sensory qualities that distinguish it from similar products. Color and clarity are other factors. Pleasing flavor and aroma, and a lack of rawness or harshness of flavor, are sought. The product should lack aftertaste. True flavor quality for the product is another factor indicating quality. Proof should be a factor weighed in purchase.

Table 12-1 summarizes taxes placed on alcoholic beverages by the federal government. Thirty-three states also have excise taxes.

WINE

Wine is the product of partial or complete fermentation of the juice of fruits or berries. Fermented applejuice is called cider. Even though made at a bonded wine cellar it may be sold as cider and not as wine. Cider is not subject to tax and does not come under the federal internal revenue law or permit requirements.

Quality in wine is affected by (1) the selection, planting, cultivation and harvesting of the grapes or fruit used, (2) the control of the fermentation process, (3) the care, watchfulness and sanitation taken in the processing, (4) the proper control in aging and (5) blending. Cost is also reflected by these factors. In addition, cost may be increased because of the scarcity or liberal supply of the grape or fruit used. To be called "wine," the product must be made from grapes. If made from peaches, berries or other fruit, the name of the fruit must appear before the term "wine." Only good grapes can make good wine but bad wine may come from good grapes.

Cool valleys and hillside vineyards produce the best grapes for dry or table wines. Warmer valleys and regions near desert areas have bountiful sunshine for the sweet wine grapes.

Only special grapes are suited for making certain wines. Foreign wines may usually be selected with confidence on the basis of the name of the wine. American wines, however, should be selected from the type of grape from which the wine is made rather than the type of wine. A Burgundy wine made in this country may be made from a number of types of grapes, but if the buyer selects a Pino Noir wine, a wine made from the famous Pino Noir (black) grape used to make fine Burgundies, the wine is apt to be more that of a typical Burgundy. Buyers should also be alerted to the fact that wines may be made from raisins or dried fruits. If this is the case, the label must state the source. Grapes may also differ in their suitability for wine making. Grapes may be grown for the purpose of raisins, brandy, jelly, juice, table use or wine. On the other hand, some grapes may well serve multiple purposes. The muscat makes excellent wine, as well as raisins; it is also a good table grape. The Concord grape makes only a portlike, sweet wine but is widely used for jellies and table use. Grapes with unusually strong varietal flavors, such as the Muscat and the native American groups grown in the Midwest and East, give wines a distinctive flavor. Less flavorful varieties give wines of more delicate flavors.

Grapes, or their juice or their wines may be blended to give desired flavor in a wine. Blending is especially prevalent in the American wine industry. Blending makes it possible to achieve a more consistent qual-

Zinfandel (black), for
Claret and Port

White (Johannisberger)
Riesling (greenish-yellow),
popular for Rhine Wine

Pinot Blanc (yellowish-green),
noted for Chablis types

Palomino (straw-colored),
famous Sherry grape

Pinot Noir (black), noted
Burgundy grape

Semillon (greenish-yellow),
famous Sauterne grape

Cabernet Sauvignon (jet black)
makes red dinner wine

Muscat of Alexandria
(golden) makes Muscatel

Grenache (reddish-black),
popular Rosé wine grape

FIG. 12–2. Nine of the main grape varieties used for wine making in California. All are European-type grapes, but the Zinfandel was originated in California from European stock.

ity each year. Some grapes are more acid than others; some give body to a wine; grapes are selected for these or other properties in blending. Some wines like Sauternes are traditionally made from a blend of at least three distinctive varieties of grapes. Many old wines are blended with a small amount of young wine to impart a freshness or fruitiness of flavor. Young wines may be blended soon after fermentation and then left to "marry" by aging. Wines of varying ages may be blended to produce a desired type of wine. Sherries are made by the solera system, a process in which many wines of different ages are blended at established times. Blending in this country can only be done under the supervision of the federal government. Filtering and bottling may be done in what are called tax-paid wine bottling houses.

There are two different classes of wine grapes, the European grape, the *Vitis vinifera*, and the American grape, chiefly the *Vitis labrusca* species. California is especially suited to the growing of the European grape, but the vine must grow on the roots of the American type grape to be resistant against an American root disease. California wines closely resemble those of Europe, while wines from American grapes have a distinctive flavor all of their own that some wine tasters describe as "foxy," "wild" or "grapey." This flavor is sought in several wines because it is pleasing to some clientele. Others, however, prefer the less fruity flavor of wines made from European grapes.

The degree of ripeness in the grape is important to its quality. Some grapes are allowed to develop a very high sugar content before they are picked. Others are picked just at the point of ripening. Selection and ripeness at time of picking will have much to do with the quality of the wine produced. As grapes mature they gain in sweetness and lose acidity. Dessert wines are made from grapes high in sugar and low in acidity. Table wines are made from grapes having less sugar and slightly more tartness. Dinner wines are made from grapes having about 22% sugar and dessert wines from grapes having about 24% sugar.

At the vinery the grapes are washed and crushed; the stems are removed and the grapes are placed in fermentation vats. The crushed grapes and juice are called "must." Care is taken not to crush the seeds to avoid bitterness. The skin may color the wine. A white wine, a semi-red wine called Rosé and a red wine may all be made from the same grape; the color of the wine depends upon the length of time that the skin of the grape is allowed to come in contact with the must. Skins also contribute some of the tannins or astringent qualities to the wine. Red wines will generally have a stronger flavor and a bit more astringency than those wines fermented with less contact with the skins.

After proper fermentation has occurred, the wine is run off into casks for aging. Wine that is not pressed from the pulp but is run off (called free run) is considered superior to wine pressed from the pulp. The grape pulp or residue is called "pomace." It is used for distilling into brandies, to make tartrates, ethyl alcohol, wine vinegar or other products.

Dry or table wines are fermented until fermentation stops naturally because of the lack of sugar. This is at about 12 to 14% alcohol. Fermentation may also be stopped by adding a small quantity of sulfur dioxide (used for many sweet American wines) or by pasteurization. Careful control of the temperature during fermentation must be maintained to prevent the development of undesirable aldehydes and acids. Wine vinegar may result if the temperature is kept too high. Raising the alcohol content of the wine above 14% stops fermentation. This is the method commonly used to stop fermentation in dessert or appetizer wines. A small quantity of pure grape brandy, usually of fairly high proof, is added to these wines when they have fermented to around 12 to 14% alcohol content. Dinner wines are commonly fermented to around 10 to 14% alcohol content. Sweet wines, or those arrested in fermentation by the addition of brandy, are around 16 to 20% alcohol content. California sets the minimum alcoholic content of sweet wines at 19½%. Federal government standards allow a 1½% variation over or under the stated alcoholic strength on the label for table wines and a 1% variation for sweet and appetizer wines. Muscatel, a sweet wine, has fermentation stopped early. It contains 10 to 15% natural grape sugar. Port contains around 9 to 14% natural grape sugar, while sherry may contain 12% to none. Ordinary dry sherries contain about 2½% sugar.

After fermentation the wine goes into storage casks to begin an aging process. Aging may take only a few weeks or may take years. Bottling largely stops aging. In aging the wine clarifies and increases in brilliance and clarity. Some oxidation occurs as the wine breathes through the wooden casks. This contributes to flavor development. Flavors and compounds also blend or "marry." This gives smoothness and flavor. The development of glycerine also contributes to smoothness. Some chemical changes occur. These may develop flavor and bouquet substances or aromatic esters not found in the grapes or new wine. Improvement in aging can only occur up to a certain point. After that the wine deteriorates. Age does not, therefore, completely indicate the quality of a wine. Some wines are best young while others are only at their best after long aging. Many inexpensive European table wines are aged for about a year. They are consumed soon after this because their quality will last only for a short period of time. Others belonging to vintage years, having especially high quality, may hold this quality over many years in the bottle.

The temperature during aging must be carefully controlled. Table wines and some others are best aged in cellars or rooms at controlled temperatures around 55° F. Sherry may be cooked or aged in the sun at about 100 to 140° F.

Aging of wines usually begins in large tanks holding 5000 to 100,000 gal each. Tanks may be wood, usually oak or redwood; other wines may be aged in concrete vats lined with a special coating of non-permeable, inert material. As the wine ages, it is drawn off into smaller wooden containers. Oval-shaped casks may be used to concentrate the lees or wine sediment in a small space at the bottom. Young wines have the most settlings. Old wines deposit settlings more slowly. Old wines after bottling may show settling by forming a film or crust called "chemise" on the bottle. This is usually considered a good trait and a distinct mark of age. Bottles containing sediment should be handled carefully to avoid disturbing the lees. The wine should be poured care-

FIG. 12–3. Wine aging in 1000-gallon oak oval casks. Courtesy Wine Institute of America.

FIG. 12–4. Wine storage in large concrete tanks. Courtesy Wine Institute of America.

fully from the bottle, leaving the lees in the bottom. Most wines are bottled in "push-up" type bottles. This allows the lees to collect in the depression around the raised portion. Some settlings may be the result of wine spoilage, and when accompanied by an unpleasant taste and aroma denotes a defective wine. Cloudiness in wine may be caused by movement in shipment or storage in excessively hot or cold areas. If left to stand for several weeks, such wine will usually clear.

Wine in aging is run off from one cask to the other to decant it from its settlings. This is called racking. Contact with air will encourage acetic acid or vinegar formation; thus, casks must be kept filled with additional wine, for the level shrinks in aging.

Wines may be filtered or clarified before bottling. This is a process sometimes called "finishing." The processes used may be that of running the wine through filters, chilling it to cause sedimentary material to precipitate out or using a gel-like product that will gradually settle down through the wine, carrying sedimentary material with it. Filtering is most favored.

Wine is bottled when aging has progressed to a desired point. Overaging may give an excessively woody flavor, cause it to lose character and become over-oxidized. Some aging or maturing may occur in the

FIG. 12–5. This worker in a California winery wears a wire mask when "riddling" bottles of Champagne, because in the process a bottle sometimes explodes, hurling fragments of glass. The riddling process consists of slightly turning and shaking each bottle every day for 6 months. **Courtesy Wine Institute of America.**

bottle. A few bottled wines may improve in the bottle as much as cask aging improves others. There are not many wines that will do this, however. Wine in bottles may be stored in bins neck down, and the wines may be turned frequently to encourage this aging. Sparkling wines must be treated in this manner to enable the sediment from secondary fermentation in the bottle to collect in the neck where it can be frozen and removed as a plug. Fresh wine is added to make up for the wine lost in the removal of the plug.

There are four main classes of wines: (1) appetizer wines, (2) red and white dinner or table wines, (3) red and white sweet dessert wines and (4) sparkling wines. There are many different types of wines in each class. Within these classes sixteen distinct wine types have common usage but varieties within these sixteen may number in the hundreds. Confusion occurs in wine identification because the same wine may be called by several different names. Table 12–2 summarizes common type names of wines used in this country. Italicized names after a wine indicate a foreign wine or foreign wine type closely similar to that particular wine.

Wines may be named according to their geographic origin or according to the type of grape from which they are made. Names of American wines are not used as precisely as are the foreign names for wines. The name of the foreign wine is frequently defined by law or trade association control, which restricts the use of a name to only a very specific wine. Names such as Burgundy, Rhine and Sauterne are taken from well-defined grape producing districts in Europe. A distinct type of wine is produced from the grapes from this area. The climate and soil give special qualities to the grapes of the district, distinguishing these wines from others. These wines are known the world over, and wines that resemble them closely may be named after them although they only resemble the true wine.

Table 12–2
A Common Classification of American Wine Types

Appetizer Wines

Sherry (dry to sweet) (*Sherry, Sack, Maderia, Marsala*)
Vermouth (dry to sweet) (*Vermouth*)

Red Dinner Wines

Burgundy	Claret (dry)	Rosé or Grenache (pink, dry
Barbera (*Barbera*)	Cabernet (*Red Bordeaux*)	to sweet) (*Tavel*)
Charbono	Grignolino (*Grignolino*)	Vino Rosso (semi-sweet)
Gamay (*Beaujolais*)	Zinfandel	Chianti (dry) (*Chianti*)
Pinot Noir (*Burgundy*)		
Red Pinot	Others: Concord (sweet)	

White Dinner Wines

Chablis (dry)	Rhine Wine (dry)	Sauterne (dry to sweet)
Chardonnay (*White Burgundy*)	Riesling (*Rhine*)	Sauvignon Blanc (*Graves*)
Folle Blanche	Sylvaner (*Rhine* or *Alsace*)	(dry to sweet)
Pino Blanc (*White Burgundy*)	Traminer (*Alsace*)	Semillon (dry to sweet)
White Pinot (*Loire*)		(*Graves*)
(White Pinot may also be		Haut or Chateau Sauterne
labeled Chenin or Pineau)		(sweet) (*Barsacs, Chateau*
		Y'Chem)

Others: White Chianti (dry); Muscat (dry to sweet), Catawba (dry to semi-sweet), Delaware (dry) Elvira or Eastern Riesling (not a true Riesling)

Sweet Dessert Wines

Port (red, white, tawny)	Muscatel (red, gold or black)	Tokay
(*Port*)	Muscat *Frontignon*	Angelica

Sparkling Wines

Champagne (gold or pink) Sparkling Burgundy (semi-sweet to sweet)
  (brut or extra dry, sec or semi-dry and
  doux or sweet)
  Others: Sparkling Muscat (sweet), Sparkling Rosé (dry to semi-sweet)

Some wine names have arisen from usage. Sherry comes from the English pronunciation of "Jerez," the city located in the center of the sherry producing region of Spain. Claret is not a place name but was derived from the name "vin clairette" applied by the British to the light red wines of the Bordeaux district and later to any light red dinner wine.

In this country a California wine must be made from all California-grown grapes. Eastern wines may contain up to 25% grapes not grown in the area. Since grapes or wines in California may be blended together and since these may come from various areas, California does not produce the distinct wines that foreign countries do, where the wine must be made only from grapes produced in a specified district if it is to bear a generic name.

Varietal names are also used to name wines. The principal grape used gives the name. Muscatel, Zinfandel, Cabernet Sauvignon or Grenache are made, respectively, from the golden Muscat grape of Alexandria, the Zinfandel grape developed in this country, the famous European jet black Cabernet Sauvignon grape, or the reddish-black Grenache grape popular for making Rosé wines. Zinfandel and Cabernet Sauvignon are really claret wines. Standards of identity in this country require that to bear a varietal name, an American wine must derive at least 51% of its volume from the grape whose name is used and must have the flavor and aroma of that grape. Many varietal wines are made all from the grape which gives the wine its name.

The terms "dry" or "sweet" may be confusing. Dry is used to indicate a wine having little or no natural grape sugar in it. Dry wines are not over 14% alcohol content usually but there are exceptions. Dry Vermouth or sherry may be 20% alcohol. Dry should not be used to indicate a sour or astringent quality. Dry wines may also be called table, dinner, light or natural wines. These wines are from 10 to 14% alcohol and are generally used to accompany a meal. Dessert and appetizer wines usually contain 20% alcohol. Because many of them are sweet they may be misnamed sweet wines as a group. Some may not be sweet, such as dry vermouth or sherry.

Some wines may be labeled with the state or district name as well as the wine type. The label that indicates California Sherry, Cucamonga Sherry, Fresno Sherry or New York State Sherry gives information as to the place of origin as well as the type of wine. Some generic wine names cannot be used in this country because the name refers to a distinct wine. Chateau Y'Chem is a sweet sauterne known the world over as perhaps the finest of sauternes. It is produced in a small vineyard in France. This term cannot be used in this country to indicate a sweet sauterne.

Table 12–3 gives an extensive wine list of foreign wines.

Table 12–3
Selections from the Armanetti International Wine Room

Chateau Bottled Bordeaux (Red)

Chateau	Region	Vintage	Chateau	Region	Vintage
Ausone	St. Emilion	1929	La Mission Haut		
Ausone	St. Emilion	1955	Brion	Graves	1952
Ausone	St. Emilion	1957	La Mission Haut		
Batailley	Pauillac	1945	Brion	Graves	1955
Batailley	Pauillac	1947	Lascombes	Margaux	1955
Batailley	Pauillac	1955	Latour	Pauillac	1920
Batailley	Pauillac	1957	Latour	Pauillac	1934
Beau Rivage	Macau	1955	Latour	Pauillac	1948
Beau Site	St. Estephe	1957	Latour	Pauillac	1952
Belair	St. Emilion	1955	Latour	Pauillac	1953
Belgrave	St. Laurent	1953	Latour	Pauillac	1955
Bergat	St. Emilion	1953	Latour	Pauillac	1957
Bergat	St. Emilion	1957	Leoville Las Cases	St. Julien	1949
Beychevelle	St. Julien	1955	Leoville Las Cases	St. Julien	1952
Brane Cantenac	Cantenac	1953	Leoville Las Cases	St. Julien	1955
Calon Segur	St. Estephe	1945	Leoville Las Cases	St. Julien	1957
Calon Segur	St. Estephe	1953	Leoville Poyferre	St. Julien	1955
Calon Segur	St. Estephe	1955	Leoville Poyferre	St. Julien	1957
Canon	St. Emilion	1952	Lynch Bages	Pauillac	1947
Cantenac Brown	Cantenac	1955	Lynch Bages	Pauillac	1955
Cheval Blanc	St. Emilion	1928	L'Angelus	St. Emilion	1953
Cheval Blanc	St. Emilion	1955	L'Angelus	St. Emilion	1955
Cheval Blanc	St. Emilion	1957	Margaux	Margaux	1928
Cos D'Estournel	St. Estephe	1921	Margaux	Margaux	1934
Cos D'Estournel	St. Estephe	1952	Margaux	Margaux	1952
Cos D'Estournel	St. Estephe	1953	Margaux	Margaux	1953
Cos D'Estournel	St. Estephe	1957	Margaux	Margaux	1955
Ducru Beaucaillou	St. Julien	1949	Margaux	Margaux	1957
Ducru Beaucaillou	St. Julien	1953	Monpeleu	Pauillac	1955
Ducru Beaucaillou	St. Julien	1955	Montrose	St. Estephe	1949
Durfort	Margaux	1926	Montrose	St. Estephe	1952
Gruaud Larose	St. Julien	1937	Montrose	St. Estephe	1953
Gruaud Larose	St. Julien	1952	Mouton Rothschild	Pauillac	1928
Haut Batailley	Pauillac	1953	Mouton Rothschild	Pauillac	1934
Haut Brion	Graves	1921	Mouton Rothschild	Pauillac	1952
Haut Brion	Graves	1952	Mouton Rothschild	Pauillac	1953
Haut Brion	Graves	1953	Mouton Rothschild	Pauillac	1955
Haut Brion	Graves	1955	Mouton Rothschild	Pauillac	1957
Haut Brion	Graves	1957	Nenin	Pomerol	1955
Lafite Rothschild	Pauillac	1924	Palmer	Cantenac	1924
Lafite Rothschild	Pauillac	1950	Palmer	Cantenac	1953
Lafite Rothschild	Pauillac	1952	Pape Clement	Graves	1955
Lafite Rothschild	Pauillac	1955	Pavie	St. Emilion	1952
Lafite Rothschild	Pauillac	1957	Pavie	St. Emilion	1955

Table 12–3 (Continued)
Selections from the Armanetti International Wine Room

Chateau Bottled Bordeaux (Red)

Chateau	Region	Vintage	Chateau	Region	Vintage
Petrus	Pomerol	1953	Talbot	St. Julien	1937
Petrus	Pomerol	1955	Talbot	St. Julien	1952
Pichon Longueville			Trotanoy	Pomerol	1955
Baron	Pauillac	1953	Trottevieille	St. Emilion	1947
Pichon Longueville			Trottevieille	St. Emilion	1949
Baron	Pauillac	1955	Trottevieille	St. Emilion	1953
Pichon Longueville			Trottevieille	St. Emilion	1955
Lalande	Pauillac	1955	Trottevieille	St. Emilion	1957
Pontet Canet	Pauillac	1952	Vieux Chateau		
Prieure Lichine	Cantenac	1955	Certan	Pomerol	1953
Rauzan Gassis	Margaux	1955			

Chateau Bordeaux (White)

Chateau	Region	Vintage	Chateau	Region	Vintage
Carbonnieux	Graves	1949	Latour Blanche	Saut.	1950
Carbonnieux	Graves	1952	Latour Blanche	Saut.	1955
Carbonnieux	Graves	1955	Rieussec	Saut.	1955
Climens	Saut.	1950	Suduiraut	Saut.	1945
Climens	Saut.	1952	Suduiraut	Saut.	1949
Climens	Saut.	1955	Suduiraut	Saut.	1950
Coutet	Barsac	1950	Yquem	Saut.	1949
Coutet	Barsac	1953	Yquem	Saut.	1950
Filhot	Saut.	1949	Yquem	Saut.	1953
Haut Brion Blanc	Graves	1955	Yquem	Saut.	1955
Lafaurie-Peyraguey	Saut.	1929			

Estate Bottled Burgundy (Red)

Estate	Domain	Region	Vintage
Beaune Greves	Moillard	Beaune	1955
Bonnes Mares	Hudelot	Chombolle	1953
Bonnes Mares	Adrien	Chombolle	1955
Bonnes Mares	Clair Dau	Chombolle	1957
Boucherottes	Jadot	Beaune	1955
Bressandes	Jadot	Beaune	1955
Chambertin	Trapet	Gevrey	1955
Chambertin	Damoy	Gevrey	1955
Chambertin	Remy	Gevrey	1957
Chambertin	J. Prieur	Gevrey	1953
Chass. Montrachet "Boudriottes"	Ramonet	Chassagne	1955
Ch. Corton Grancey	L. Latour	Corton	1955
Clos de Beze	Damoy	Gevrey	1955
Clos de la Roche	Remy	Morey	1955
Clos de Tart	Mommesin	Morey	1955
Clos du Chapitre	Gelin	Fixin	1957
Clos des Epeneaux	Armand	Pommard	1957
Clos de Vougeot	Morin	Vougeot	1947

Table 12–3 (Continued)
Selections from the Armanetti International Wine Room

Estate Bottled Burgundy (Red)

Estate	Domain	Region	Vintage
Clos de Vougeot	Morin	Vougeot	1949
Clos de Vougeot	Grivelet	Vougeot	1953
Clos de Vougeot	Guyot	Vougeot	1953
Clos de Vougeot	Morin	Vougeot	1955
Clos des Lambrays	Casson	Morey	1953
Clos Des Mouches	Coron	Beaune	1955
Clos Des Ursules	Jadot	Beaune	1955
Clos de la Feguine	J. Prieur	Beaune	1955
Clos Du Roi	Coron	Beaune	1957
Corton Pougets	Jadot	Corton	1957
Echezeaux	Rom. Conti	Flagey	1957
Echezeaux	Moillard	Flagey	1955
Gevry Chambertin "Les Combottes"	Jadot	Gevrey	1955
Grands Echezeaux	Mongeard	Flagey	1957
Grands Echezeaux	Gauroux	Flagey	1953
Grands Echezeaux	Rom. Conti	Flagey	1957
Grands Echezeaux	Rom. Conti	Flagey	1956
La Romanee	LeRoy	Vosne	1952
La Romanee	LeRoy	Vosne	1955
La Romanee St. Vivant	Marey-Monge	Vosne	1953
La Tache	Rom. Conti	Vosne	1953
La Tache	Rom. Conti	Vosne	1954
La Tache	Rom. Conti	Vosne	1955
La Tache	Rom. Conti	Vosne	1956
La Tache	Rom. Conti	Vosne	1957
Latricieres Chambertin	Lichine	Gevrey	1955
Les Caillerets	Boillot	Volnay	1949
Les Caillerets	Boillot	Volnay	1953
Les Epenots	L. Latour	Pommard	1957
Mazis Chambertin	Gelin	Gevrey	1955
Musigny	Vogue	Chambolle	1953
Musigny	Jadot	Chambolle	1953
Musigny	J. Prieur	Chambolle	1955
Nuits St. George "Les Richemones"	Moillard	Nuits	1955
Pernand Vergalese "Clos de la Croix de Pierre"	Jadot	Aloxe	1957
Richebourg	Morin	Vosne	1937
Richebourg	Morin	Vosne	1949
Richebourg	Noirot	Vosne	1953
Richebourg	Rom. Conti	Vosne	1953
Richebourg	Rom. Conti	Vosne	1954
Richebourg	Rom. Conti	Vosne	1955
Richebourg	Rom. Conti	Vosne	1957
Richebourg	Trapet	Vosne	1957
Romanee Conti	Rom. Conti	Vosne	1955

Table 12-3 (Continued)
Selections from the Armanetti International Wine Room

Estate Bottled Burgundy (Red)

Estate	Domain	Region	Vintage
Romanee Conti	Rom. Conti	Vosne	1956
Romanee Conti	Rom. Conti	Vosne	1957
Santenay Gravieres	Lavoreille	Santenay	1957
Vosne Romanee "Malconsorts"	Moillard	Vosne	1955

Estate Bottled Beaujolais

Estate	Prop.	Vintage
Brouilly	Depagneux	1959
Fleurie	Depagneux	1959
Beaujolais Jadot	Jadot	1957
Morgon	Depagneux	1959
Moulin a Vent	Bounerue	1959
Beaujolais Villages	Depagneux	1959
Chateau du Moulin a Vent	Blond-Damoy	1955
Chateau du Moulin a Vent	Blond-Damoy	1959
Clos des Chapitres	Dom-Clos des Chapitres	1955
Cotes du Brouilly	Chanrion	1955
Fleurie	Depagneux	1957
Moulin a Vent	Jadot	1957

Estate Bottled White Burgundy

Estate	Domain	Region	Vintage
Batard Montrachet	Fl. Larose	Puligny	1957
Batard Montrachet	Fl. Larose	Puligny	1958
Beaujolais Blanc	Jadot	Beaujolais	1957
Chablis "Blanchotts"	Pic	Chablis	1958
Chablis "Les Clos"	Simon	Chablis	1958
Chablis "Preuses"	Dom. Maladiere	Chablis	1958
Chass. Mont. "Rouchottes"	Romonet-Prudhon	Chassagne	1958
Chateau Fuisse	M. Vincent	Pouilly	1957
Chateau Fuisse	M. Vincent	Pouilly	1958
Chevalier Montrachet	Lacroix	Puligny	1953
Chevalier Montrachet	Jadot	Puligny	1958
Clos Blanc Vougeot	Guyot	Vougeot	1955
Corton Charlemagne	Jadot	Corton	1955
Corton Charlemagne	Jadot	Corton	1958
Meursault Charmes	L. Latour	Meursault	1957
Meursault Charmes	Matrot	Meursault	1955
Meursault Genevrieres	Jadot	Meursault	1957
Montrachet	Lafon	Puligny	1957
Puligny Montrachet	Jadot	Puligny	1957

Table 12–3 (Continued)
Selections from the Armanetti International Wine Room

White Burgundy (Half Bottles)

Estate	Domain	Region	Vintage
Batard Montrachett	Coffinet	Puligny	1953
Chablis "Les Clos"	Simon	Chablis	1958
Corton Charlemagne	Jadot	Corton	1958
Chevalier Montrachet	Jadot	Puligny	1958
Pul Mont. "Clos les Pucelles"	Jadot	Puligny	1955

White Burgundy (Magnums)

Estate	Domain	Region	Vintage
Chevalier Montrachet	L. Jadot	Puligny	1958
Corton Charlemagne	L. Jadot	Corton	1955
Corton Charlemagne	L. Jadot	Corton	1958
Pouilly Fuisse	L. Jadot	Pouilly	1958

Chateau Bordeaux (Half Bottles)

Chateau	Region	Vintage
Batailley	Pauillac	1955
Cos D'Estournel	St. Estephe	1953
Ducru Beaucaillou	St. Julien	1955
Haut Brion	Graves	1957
Lafite	Pauillac	1955
Lafite	Pauillac	1957
Lascombes	Margaux	1955
Latour	Pauillac	1952
Latour	Pauillac	1957
Lynch Bages	Pauillac	1955
Margaux	Margaux	1955
Margaux	Margaux	1957
Mouton	Pauillac	1955
Mouton	Pauillac	1957
Nenin	Pomerol	1955
Petrus	Pomerol	1955
Pichon Long. Baron	Pauillac	1955
Rauzan Gassis	Margaux	1955
Trottevieille	St. Emilion	1955

Chateau Bordeaux (Magnums)

Chateau	Region	Vintage
Batailley	Pauillac	1953
Batailley	Pauillac	1955
Brane Cantenac	Cantenac	1953
Calon Segur	St. Estephe	1955

Table 12–3 (Continued)
Selections from the Armanetti International Wine Room

Chateau Bordeaux (Magnums)

Chateau	Region	Vintage
Cos D'Estournel	St. Estephe	1953
Gruaud Larose	St. Julien	1949
Montrose	St. Estephe	1953
Pichon Longueville Baron	Pauillac	1952
Talbot	St. Julien	1949
Trottevieille	St. Emilion	1953
Trottevieille	St. Emilion	1955

Burgundy (Red) (Half Bottles)

Estate	Domain	Region	Vintage
Beaujolais Jadot	L. Jadot	Beaujolais	1957
Bonnes Mares	Hudelot	Chombolle	1953
Boucherottes	Jadot	Beaune	1955
Clos de Tart	Mommesin	Morey	1955
Clos de Vougeot	Morin	Vougeot	1949
Clos de Vougeot	Morin	Vougeot	1955
Corton Grancey	L. Latour	Corton	1955
Chambertin	J. Prieur	Gevrey	1953
Echezeaux	Moillard	Flagey	1955
Grand Echezeaux	Gouroux	Flagey	1953
"Les Malconsorts"	Moillard	Vosne	1955
Musigny	J. Prieur	Chombolle	1955
Nuits "Le St. George"	Bruck	Nuits	1955

Burgundy and Rhone (Magnums)

Estate	Domain	Region	Vintage
Beaujolais Jadot	L. Jadot	Beaujolais	1957
Chateauneuf du Pape "La Croze"	Rochette	Rhone	1952
Clos Vougeot	Morin	Vougeot	1949
Clos Vougeot	Morin	Vougeot	1955
Corton Pougets	L. Jadot	Corton	1955

Loire and Alsace Wines

Estate	Domain	Vintage
Blanc Fume de Pouilly	Romion	1958
Gewurztraminer	Willman	1953
Muscadet "Chateau les Montys"	Sudry	1959
Rose d'Anjou	—	1959
Sancerre "Clos de la Pousse"	Crochet	1958
Sparkling Vouvray	Marc Bredif	1955
Vouvray Nature	Marc Bredif	1955

Table 12–3 (Continued)
Selections from the Armanetti International Wine Room

Rhone Wines—Estate Bottled

Estate	Domain	Vintage
Chateau D'Aqueria Tavel Rose	Oliver	1957
Chateauneuf du Pape "Chartreuse"	Imbert	1949
Chateauneuf du Pape "La Bernadine"	Chapoutier	1953
Chateauneuf du Pape "La Croze"	Rochette	1953
Chapotier Tavel Rose	Chapoutier	1953
Cote Rotie "Brune et Blonde"	Chapoutier	1949
Cotes du Rhone Rose	Courancomme	1957
Hermitage Blanc "Chante Alouette"	Chapoutier	1953
Hermitage "La Chapelle" (Red)	Jaboulet	1952
Hermitage "La Chapelle" (White)	Jaboulet	1955
Chateauneuf du Pape "Chartreuse"	Imbert	1953

German Wines (Original Abfullung) Rheingau

Vineyard	Vintage
Eltviller Rheinberg General (Von Simmern)	1959
Hallgartener Deutelsberg Beerenauslese Cabinet (Von Loewenstein)	1959
Hallgartener Hendelberg Spatlese Cabinet (Von Loewenstein)	1959
Hallgartener Hendelberg Auslese Cabinet (Von Loewenstein)	1959
Hallgartener Shoenhell Auslese Cabinet (Von Loewenstein)	1959
Hattenheimer Nussbrunnen Cabinet (Von Simmern)	1957
Kiedricher Sandgrub Auslese (Dr. Weil)	1959
Kiedricher Wasser Rose Feine Spatlese (Dr. Weil)	1959
Marcobrunner Spatlese Cabinet (Von Simmern)	1959
Rauenthaler Herberg Spatlese Cabinet (Von Simmern)	1959
Rauenthaler Nonnenberg Trockenbeerenauslese	1953
Rauenthaler Rothberg Spatlese Cabinet (Von Simmern)	1959
Rudesheimer Berg Rottland Cabinet (State Domain)	1955
Schloss Eltz Spatlese (Graf Eltz)	1953
Schloss Vollrads Yellow Seal (Graf Matuschka)	1959
Steinberger Cabinet (State Domain)	1959

Palatinate

Vineyard	Vintage
Diedesheimer Leinhohle Beerenauslese (Wolf-Erben)	1957
Forster Pechstein Spatlese (Wolf-Erben)	1959
Forster Kirchenstuck Auslese (Dr. B. Wolf)	1953
Ruppertsberger Nussbien Auslese (Wolf-Erben)	1959
Wachenheimer Bachel (Dr. B. Wolf)	1957
Wachenheimer Boelig Trockenbeerenauslese	1957
Wachenheimer Gerumpel Auslese Cabinet (Dr. B. Wolf)	1953

Table 12–3 (Continued)
Selections from the Armanetti International Wine Room

Mosel

Vineyard	Vintage
Bernkasteler Badstube Spatlese (Bergweiler-Prum)	1957
Bernkasteler Doktor Auslese (Wwe Dr. Thanisch)	1958
Bernkasteler Doktor Spatlese (Wwe. Dr. Thanisch)	1958
Bernkasteler Pfalzgraben Spatlese (Thanisch)	1957
Brauneberger Juffer-Sonnenuhr Spatlese (F. Hagg)	1955
Eitelsbacher Karthauser Hofberger Auslese (H. W. Rauthenstrauch)	1953
Graacher Himmelreich Auslese (J. J. Prum)	1958
Graacher Himmelreich (J. J. Prum)	1955
Graacher Himmelreich Spatlese (Thanisch)	1957
Graacher Domprobst Spatlese (Thanisch)	1957
Wehlener Sonnenuhr Auslese (J. J. Prum)	1958
Wehlener Sonnenuhr Spatlese (J. J. Prum)	1958
Zeltinger Schlossberg Naturrein (F. Wilhelm Gymnasium)	1955

Much wine is shipped in barrels, railroad tank cars or tank trucks to distant bottling areas. This saves shipping costs and avoids precipitation of sediment that sometimes occurs in shipping. The method of distribution may vary from state to state. In some states purchase may be made only from state-controlled sources. Some states prohibit the sale of wines from bulk sales while other states may permit a restaurant to purchase in bulk and sell in bottles for table use. Some European wines may be purchased in barrels and bottled in this country. Buyers should learn the local regulations and purchase according to them. Table 12–4 indicates sizes of wine containers in which wine is sold.

Dining areas will usually serve wine in fifth's ($\frac{1}{5}$ of a wine gallon), tenth's ($\frac{1}{10}$ of a wine gallon), splits (around 6 to 8 oz) or by the glass. The amount in a glass will vary but dinner or table wine should be served in a glass large enought to easily contain a standard portion of 4 oz. Extra large bottles such as Magnum (52 oz), Double Magnum or Jeroboam (104 oz), Tappit-hen (128 oz), Rehoboam (156 oz), Methusaleh (208 oz) Salmanazar (312 oz), Balthazar (416 oz) and Nebuchadnezzar (520 oz) may be used for special occasions.

Operations should usually store their wines in two locations, one for floor stock where it may be obtained for quick service and one for main storage. Both areas should be cool, around 55° F. A storage area 5 ft high by 7 ft long has been found sufficient to store about a $1000 stock consisting of 38 cases of 17 different wines. Shelves are usually 18 in. deep. Most wines are stored on their sides and bins should be constructed to suit the bottle size carried. Quick location of the wine required should be provided. Main or reserve storage areas should provide storage for sweet wines standing upright and bin storage for table wines which must rest on their sides. Case storage should be provided so cases may, if necessary, be set on their sides. Good inventory control and locked storage should be provided. The Wine Advisory Board, 717 Market Street, San Francisco 3, will assist buyers in setting up standards for stock and stock rooms.

Judging wine quality is a process of evaluating specific taste factors. These factors may vary with different wines. A wine taster seeks a balanced wine or a wine which has flavor, aroma, color, clarity and other factors properly balanced for the type of wine. The wine should be pleasing in flavor. The acidity may vary according to the type of wine and acidity should not be confused with sour or astringent qualities or off-fermentation results but the tartness that arises from natural fruit

Table 12–4
Sizes of Wine Containers

Tank cars (1 to 6 compartments)	6,000 to 10,000 gal
Puncheon	84 to 160 gal
Pipe	117 to 140 gal
Butt	100 to 140 gal
Barrel (average)	50 gal
Half-barrel (average)	25 gal
Kegs	15, 10, 5, 3, 2 and 1 gal
Demijohns	4.9, 3 and 2 gal
Gallon jug	128 fluid oz
Half-gallon jug or bottle	64 fluid oz
Magnum	52 fluid oz
Quart	32 fluid oz
Vermouth bottle	30 fluid oz
Chianti bottle	30 fluid oz
Four-fifths quart ("fifth")	25.6 fluid oz
Three-fourths quart	24 fluid oz
Champagne bottle	24 to 26 fluid oz
Champagne half-bottle	12 to 13 fluid oz
Pint	16 fluid oz
Four-fifths pint (half-bottle or "tenth")	12.8 fluid oz
Three-fourths pint (half-bottle)	12 fluid oz
Dinner wine splits	6 and 6.4 fluid oz
Chianti split	8 fluid oz
Champagne splits	6.2 and 8 fluid oz
Miniatures	2, 3 and 4 fluid oz

Wine ... CROWNING TOUCH TO YOUR DINING PLEASURE

Food and wine are the perfect marriage — even a sandwich takes on special magic when wine accompanies it. Here are the wine-and-food combinations we believe you'll enjoy. But there are no rules. Try any wine, and see how much pleasure it adds to your favorite dish!

APPETIZER WINES

BEFORE YOUR MEAL: *As a cocktail, or with appetizers or soup*

Order No.			Glass
1	Sherry, Brand Name	(Calif.)	$.00
2	Dry Sherry, Brand Name	(Calif.)	.00
3	Dry Sherry, Brand Name	(Spain)	.00
4	Vermouth-on-the-Rocks, Brand Name	(Calif.)	.00

RED DINNER WINES

WITH HEARTY DISHES: *Such as steak, roast beef, chops or Italian dishes*

Order No.			½ Bottle for 2	Bottle for 4
10	Burgundy, Brand Name	(Calif.)	$.00	$0.00
11	Pinot Noir (Burgundy), Brand Name	(Calif.)	.00	0.00
12	Claret, Brand Name	(Calif.)	.00	0.00
13	Cabernet (Claret), Brand Name	(Calif.)	.00	0.00
14	Zinfandel, Brand Name	(Calif.)	.00	0.00
15	Chianti, Brand Name	(Calif.)	.00	0.00

WHITE DINNER WINES

WITH LIGHTER DISHES: *Such as fish, chicken, sweetbreads or omelets*

Order No.			½ Bottle for 2	Bottle for 4
20	Chablis, Brand Name	(Calif.)	$.00	$0.00
21	Pinot Blanc (Chablis), Brand Name	(Calif.)	.00	0.00
22	Riesling, Brand Name	(Calif.)	.00	0.00
23	Sylvaner, Brand Name	(Calif.)	.00	0.00
24	Sauterne, Brand Name	(Calif.)	.00	0.00
25	Semillon (Sauterne), Brand Name	(Calif.)	.00	0.00

ROSÉ (Pink) WINES

WITH ALL FOODS: *Luncheon or Dinner*

Order No.			½ Bottle for 2	Bottle for 4
30	Rosé, Brand Name	(Calif.)	$.00	$0.00
31	Rosé, Brand Name	(Calif.)	.00	0.00
32	Vin Rosé, Brand Name	(Calif.)	.00	0.00

SPARKLING WINES

PERFECT ANYTIME: *To make any meal a festive occasion*

Order No.			½ Bottle for 2	Bottle for 4
40	Champagne Brut (Dry), Brand Name	(Calif.)	$0.00	$0.00
41	Champagne Sec (Medium), Brand Name	(Calif.)	0.00	0.00
42	Champagne, Brand Name	(France)	0.00	0.00
43	Pink Champagne, Brand Name	(Calif.)	0.00	0.00
44	Sparkling Burgundy, Brand Name	(Calif.)	0.00	0.00

DESSERT WINES

AFTER DINNER: *With cheese or coffee*

Order No.			Glass
50	Port, Brand Name	(Calif.)	$.00
51	Muscatel, Brand Name	(Calif.)	.00

FIG. 12–6. The format for a wine list recommended by the Wine Advisory Board for use to assist those who do not know wine selection. Courtesy Wine Institute of America.

acids. True color may be almost water-like, amber, gold, red, rose or other depending upon the color of the wine. Some ports may have a tawny or brownish tinge instead of a bright ruby red color. This color may result from aging and finishing (filtering or clarifying) which is an indication of quality. If caused by a failure of grapes to have sufficient coloring qualities, it is looked upon as a defect. Usually grapes lacking coloring qualities also lack flavor qualities. Clarity is sought but may not always be an indication of wine quality. Usually wines should have brilliance and clarity to indicate good processing methods were used to bring out the true color of the grape. Body refers to the consistency or thickness of the wine. Some wines should have a heavy body with good substance, such as Burgundies, while others should have a thinner, more watery quality, such as the lighter Bordeauxs. Smoothness of flavor should be evident, and some smoothness should be derived from the development of glycerine in fermentation. Good aroma or fragrance should be evident. Bouquet is the part of fragrance originating from fermentation and aging. Aldehydes may be a part of bouquet. Esters developed in the aging process may also be a significant part of bouquet. Astringency or the bitter quality of the wine may arise because of the quantity of tannin and other substances absorbed from skins and seeds. Some astringency is desired in wines such as clarets, burgundies and chiantis but in others a lesser quantity is desirable. Some wines like vermouth may be made purposely astringent by using herbs to increase that quality. Sweetness or dryness should be suited to the type of wine. Dryness should not be confused with tartness or acidity. Dryness comes from the lack of natural grape sugars. Balling or Brix degree readings may be obtained to indicate the degree of sweetness.

Good wine should not have a corky flavor, a flavor which arises because of flavoring substances absorbed from the cork, nor any other off-flavor developed after bottling. Yeasty, overfermented wines can be readily detected. Excess of vinegar or aldehydes give rise to unpleasant taste reactions. A wine should be tasted by placing a small amount in the mouth, and obtaining the aroma as it wafts up through the nostrils. It is not necessary to swallow the wine in tasting. Tasters look for flat wines lacking in aroma, wines sometimes called "insipid." Sharp flavors are not sought but some young wines may have fresher and somewhat sharper flavors than old wines. This may be desirable depending upon the wine. Sherries and some wines that have been aged and blended should have a mellow, soft, ripe, well-matured flavor. These softer flavors are usually more predominant in the sweet wines too. The nutty or what is called *rancio* flavor of sherry is highly prized but would be objectionable in other wines.

BEERS

Beer is a beverage containing $\frac{1}{2}\%$ or more of alcohol, brewed from malt or from any substitute, such as grain, grain products, sugars or sirups. The federal government classifies under beer: beer, ale, porter and stout and in this text beer is used at times as a generic term meaning all these. Ale, porter and stout are sometimes called the ale group. Saké, a Japanese beer or wine, is classed as a beer for tax purposes. Beers may only be made in breweries under the control of the federal government. Beers have been long known to man. Recent improvements in processing, however, have improved the quality of the product, and consumption has risen because of this. It is also a moderate beverage from the standpoint of alcoholic content.

At least 90% of the beer sold in this country is the lager type. Lager beer is produced by a fermentation carried out at low temperatures. The yeast at the end of the fermentation period slowly settles to the bottom. Lager beer for this reason is sometimes called "bottom fermented." This is in contrast to some beers and ale which are "top fermented" or fermented at a higher temperature. When fermentation ceases with top fermented products, the yeasts float on the top. Another characteristic of lager beer is that it is aged or matured in rather cold storage for a number of months. Lager beer was developed in Germany while ale and ale-type products were developed by the British.

Ale is more tart and paler than lager beer and has a more pronounced hop flavor. Porter and stout are ales. Porter is more sweet and less hoppy than ale. It is also brewed from a darker malt. Stout is sweeter than porter. It is also stronger, darker in color and heavier in flavor than the others in the ale group. The flavor is heavy with malt.

A good quality barley is used to make beers. This is sprouted or germinated and in sprouting many of the starches are converted to a sugar called maltose. The sprouted grain is next roasted much like coffee is roasted and the amount of roasting will determine the eventual color and body quality of the brew. After roasting, the malt may be finely ground with a cereal product such as corn grits (hominy) or brewer's rice. The malt grain or mixture of malt and cereal is then cooked to gelatinize the starch grains. The slightly thickened liquid is then filtered from the grain residue. This residue is used for stock feed. The liquid is called *wort;* it is a sweetish mixture not characteristic of the end product. This wort is next percolated over hops adding a desired bitterness. After cooling somewhat, a yeast is then added. The yeast grows at the expense of the carbohydrates in the wort, producing carbon dioxide and alcohol.

When fermentation is complete, the yeast is removed and the liquid drawn off. Lager beer is stored in closed tanks to age. It is then filtered and bottled, canned or kegged. If it is bottled or canned, it is pasteurized and carbonated. Most keg beer is not carbonated but is delivered to the retail outlet where it is carbonized as it is sold. Some of these products may, however, be "krausened." This is a process in which young, active beer is added to an aged product to give it carbonation.

Beers may differ in flavor and quality because of the type of barley and other products used, the amount of roasting given the barley and the length of time the hops are percolated. Processing method used is another critical factor. The type of water used is important. Many firms carefully process the water used for their products. Use of a single cell yeast culture or a combination of yeast cultures will make a difference in the final product. The temperature used during aging is influential. Cereal adjuncts such as corn or rice will develop a specific flavor in beer while beer or ale made from all malt will have an entirely different flavor. Sometimes sugars may be added instead of a starch adjunct. Package beer, that is, bottled or canned beer, may differ from the draught beer brewed at the same brewery. Draught beer may not be pasteurized while packaged beer is. Draught beer is commonly made with corn as the cereal adjunct. Most packaged beer is brewed with rice as the cereal adjunct.

Buyers should purchase only that quantity of beer required to meet no more than a 2 week period of sale. Beer and ale should not remain in a cooler more than 2 weeks. Draught beer is perishable and should be consumed soon after purchase. It should also be held under refrigeration. The dispensing system should be sanitized carefully each day. Beer and ale should be served at 42 to 44° F in clean glasses.

A barrel of beer is 31 gal. About 460 8-oz glasses are obtained after spillage in dispensing from a barrel. Spillage is calculated at 10%. The quantity of beer in a barrel obtained in dispensing is the equivalent of about 25 cases of 12-oz bottles.

Bibliography

American Can Company, *Canned Food Manual*, printed by Davis, Delaney and Harris, New York, 1943.

American Dry Milk Institute, *The Grading of Dry Whole Milk and Sanitary and Quality Standards*, Bulletin 913, Chicago, 1947.

American Hospital Association, *Manual of Specifications for Canned Fruit and Vegetables*, Chicago, 1947.

American Spice Trade Association, *Spices, What They Are and Where They Come From*, New York, 1956.

"American Wines," *Holiday Magazine*, pp. 109–114, August, 1958.

Amerine, M. A., and M. A. Joslyn, *Table Wines: The Technology of Their Production in California*, University of California Press, 1951.

Armour and Company, *Buying Beef*, Chicago.

Beckman, Theodore N., Harold H. Maynard, and William R. Davidson, *Principles of Marketing*, 6th ed., Ronald Press Company, New York, 1957.

Benjamin, Earl W., James M. Gwin, Fred L. Faber and William D. Termohlen, *Marketing Poultry Products*, 5th ed., John Wiley and Sons, New York, 1960.

Bynum, Lindley, *California Wines: How to Enjoy Them*, Homer H. Boelter Lithography, Los Angeles, 1955.

Canada Dept. of Agriculture, *Buy by Grade*, Ottawa, 1960, Cat. No. A 73–1048.

Cereal Institute, *Buying, Care and Serving of Breakfast Cereals*, edited by Jennie Rowntree, Chicago, 1958.

Eckey, E. W., *Vegetable Fats and Oils*, Reinhold Publishing Corp., New York, 1954.

Frooman, A. A., *Five Steps to Effective Institutional Food Buying*, A. A. Frooman and Associates, Chicago, 1948.

General Mills, *The Story of Cereal Grains*, Minneapolis, 1944.

Grossman, H. J., *Grossman's Guide to Wines, Spirits and Beers*, Charles Scribner's Sons, New York, 1955.

Hauguard, Hans, "Why Buy Poultry on an Eviscerated Weight and Grade?" *Poultry Processing and Marketing*, 62:8, August, 1956.

Hill, R. G., *A Fruit and Vegetable Buying Guide*, Home and Garden Bulletin, No. 41, U.S. Department of Agriculture, U.S. Government Printing Office, Washington, D.C., April, 1955.

Household Finance Corporation, *Better Buymanship, No. 3., Fresh Fruits and Vegetables*, Chicago, 1941.

Herrick, Arthur D., *Food Regulation and Compliance*, Revere Publishing Company, New York, 1944.

Institute of Shortening and Edible Oils, *The Chemistry of Food Fats and Oils*, Washington, D.C., August, 1957.

Johndrew, O. F., Jr., W. E. Hauver, Jr., and L. Kilpatrick, *Poultry Grading Manual*, U.S. Department of Agriculture Handbook No. 31, U.S. Government Printing Office, Washington, D.C.

Kraft Foods Company, *The World of Cheese*, Chicago, April, 1954.

Licensed Beverage Industries, *The ABC's of Alcoholic Beverages*, 155 E. 44th St., New York.

Lowe, Belle, *Experimental Foods*, 7th ed., John Wiley and Sons, New York, 1955.

Melville, John, *Guide to California Wines*, Doubleday and Co., New York, 1955.

National Dairy Council, *A Newer Knowledge of Cheese*, Chicago, revised 1954.

National Livestock and Meat Board, *Meat Manual*, 4th ed., Chicago, 1950.

National Livestock and Meat Board, *Ten Lessons on Meat Cookery*, 7th ed., Chicago, 1950.

Personal communication from Mr. Dwight E. Avis, Director, Alcohol and Tobacco Tax Division, U.S. Treasury Department, Internal Revenue Service, Washington, D.C., dated June 15, 1960.

Reid, Margaret G., *Consumers and the Market*, 3rd ed., F. S. Crofts and Company, New York, 1948.

Rivers, Frank, *The Hotel Butcher, Garde Manger and Carver*, Hotel Monthly Press, Chicago, 1935.

Seagram-Distillers Company, *An American Tradition*, 375 Park Ave., New York.

Sammis, J. J., *Cheese Making*, 10th ed., The Cheesemaker Book Company, Madison, Wisc., 1942.

Sanders, G. B., *Cheese Varieties and Descriptions*, Agricultural Handbook No. 54 U.S. Department of Agriculture, U.S. Government Printing Office, Washington, D.C., 1953.

Stewart, Jean L., *Foods: Production, Marketing, and Consumption*, Prentice-Hall, New York, 1938.

Swift and Company, *Boning and Cutting Veal for Profit, Facts You Should Know About Beef, How to Buy Meat, Cuts of Meat and How You Can Identify Them*, Chicago.

Tea Bureau, 22 Regent St., London, S.W. 1, *Tea and Tea Blending*, Hazel, Watson and Viney, Ltd., London and Aylesbury, 1951.

Ukers, William H., *The Romance of Coffee*, The Tea and Coffee Trade Journal Company, New York, 1948.

United Fresh Fruit and Vegetable Association, *Fruit and Vegetable Pointers*, 777 14th St., N.W., Washington, D.C.

Uribe, C. Andres, *Brown Gold—the Amazing Story of Coffee*, Random House, New York, 1954.

U.S. Department of Defense, *Cutting and Preparing Lamb—TM 10–408* and *Cutting and Preparing Beef—TM 10–407*, U.S. Government Printing Office, Washington, D.C., July, 1957.

U.S. Department of Agriculture, Agricultural Marketing Service, U.S. Government Printing Office, Washington, D.C.:
Egg Buying Guide for Consumers, Home and Garden Bulletin No. 26, May, 1954.
Government Inspection of Processed Fruits and Vegetables, Miscellaneous Publication No. 98, 1946.
Grading and Inspection of Eggs and Egg Products, Bulletin No. 159, revised January, 1959.
How to Buy Eggs, Leaflet No. 442, 1958.
Institutional Meat Purchase Specifications, General Requirements, Series 100, 200, 300, 400, and 400 F, 1959.

Marketing Farm Poultry, Farmers' Bulletin No. 2030, revised August, 1955.

Official United States Standards for Grades of Meat:
    Carcass Beef, June 1956.
    Lamb, Yearling Mutton and Mutton Carcasses, February, 1957.
    Pork Carcasses, Barrow and Gilt, July, 1955.
    Veal and Calf Carcasses, September, 1956.

Outline of Suggested Specifications for Purchasing Processed Fruits and Vegetables, Miscellaneous Publication No. 565, 1945.

Potatoes for Consumer Education, AIB No. 178, 1957.

Poultry Grading and Inspection, Agricultural Information Bulletin, No. 173, 1959.

Poultry Grading Manual, revised May, 1959.

Questions and Answers on Government Inspection of Processed Fruits and Vegetables, Miscellaneous Publication No. 598, 1946.

Regulations Governing the Grading and Inspection of Egg Products, effective March 29, 1955.

Regulations Governing the Grading and Inspection of Poultry and Edible Products Thereof, and the United States Classes, Standards and Grades with Respect Thereto, effective July 1, 1960.

Regulations Governing the Inspection of Poultry and Poultry Products, effective January 1, 1959 (Mandatory Program).

Regulations Governing the Inspection and Certification of Fresh Fruits, Vegetables and Other Products, SRA–AMS 93, revised January 4, 1957 and Supplement 1, issued June, 1957.

Regulations Governing the Meat Inspection of the USDA, December, 1957.

Rules and Regulations of the Department of Agriculture Governing the Grading and Certification of Meats, Prepared Meats and Meat Products, February, 1957.

Standardization and Inspection of Fresh Fruits and Vegetables, Miscellaneous Publication 604, 1946.

Standards for Fresh Fruits and Vegetables, Fresh Fruit and Vegetable Division, dated variously.

Standards, Inspections, Marketing Practices, Title 7—Agriculture (Meat Products), August, 1956.

The Inspection Stamp as a Guide to Wholesome Meat, Agricultural Information Bulletin No. 92, 1956.

U.S. Grades for Beef, 1957.

U.S. Standards for Cheese and Dairy Products, Dairy Division, dated variously.

U.S. Standards for Grades in Comb and Extract Honey, August, 1933 and April, 1951.

U.S. Standards for Grades in Maple Sirup, February, 1940.

U.S. Standards for Grades in Olive Oil, March, 1948.

U.S. Standards for Grades in Olives and Pickles, dated variously.

U.S. Standards for Grades in Peanut Butter, September, 1942.

U.S. Standards for Grades in Processed Fruits and Vegetables, Processed Fruit and Vegetable Division, dated variously.

U.S. Standards for Grades in Refiners and Sugar Cane Sirup, January, 1952 and April, 1951.

U.S. Standards for Grades in Rough Rice, August, 1959.

U.S. Standards for Grades in Shelled and Unshelled Nuts, dated variously.

U.S. Department of Health, Education and Welfare, Food and Drug Administration, U.S. Government Printing Office, Washington, D.C.:

Food and Drug Administration—What It Is and Does, FDA Leaflet No. 1, 1958.

Definitions and Standards under the Federal Food, Drug and Cosmetic Act, No. 2, Parts 14, 15, 16, 17, 18, 19, 25, 27, 29, 42, 45, 51, 53, various dates.

General Regulations for the Enforcement of the Federal Food, Drug and Cosmetic Act, Title 21, Part 1, revised June 1958.

Read the Label, FDA Publication No. 3, 1958.

Requirements of the United States Food, Drug and Cosmetic Act, FDA Publication No. 2, revised September, 1958.

What Consumers should Know about Food Standards, October, 1958.

U.S. Department of Interior, Fish and Wildlife Service, U.S. Government Printing Office, Washington, D.C.:

Distributing and Marketing of Frozen Fishery Products, Leaflet 431, 1956.

Fishery Statistics of the U.S., 1957, Statistical Digest No. 41, 1957.

Fresh and Frozen Fish Buying Manual, Circular No. 20, 1954.

Regulations Governing Processed Fishery Products, July, 1958.

U.S. Standards for Grades of Fish, various dates.

U.S. Department of the Navy, *Meat Handbook*, Navsanda Publication No. 55, U.S. Government Printing Office, Washington, D.C., 1945.

U.S. Treasury Department, Internal Revenue Bureau, *What You Should Know about the Alcohol and Tobacco Tax Division*, Publication No. 425 (11–58), U.S. Government Printing Office, Washington, D.C., 1959.

Van Slyke, L. L., and W. V. Price, *Cheese: A Treatise on the Manufacture of American Cheddar Cheese and Some Other Varieties*, revised ed., New York, Orange Judd, 1949.

West, Bessie Brooks and Levelle Wood, *Food Service in Institutions*, 3rd ed., John Wiley and Sons, New York, 1955.

Wheat Flour Institute, *From Wheat to Flour*, Chicago, 1958.

Wine Advisory Board, 717 Market St., San Francisco:

The Wine Growing Industry, Handbook No. 1, 1957.

Wine Growing and Wine Types, Handbook No. 2, 1957.

The Sale of Wine in Stores, Handbook No. 3, 1957.

The Sale of Wine in Restaurants, Hotels and Clubs, Handbook No. 4, 1957.

Wilson, Stephen, *Food and Drug Regulation*, American Council on Public Affairs, Washington, D.C., 1942.

Williams, Harold M., "Buying Poultry on an Eviscerated Graded Basis," *American Egg and Poultry Review*, 18:2, February, 1956.

Winter, A. R., and E. M. Funk, *Poultry Science and Practice*, J. B. Lippincott Co., Philadelphia, 1941.

Wood, Adeline, *Quantity Buying Guides*, revised ed., vols. 1 and 2, Ahrens Publishing Company, New York, 1957.

Appendix

Grade terms for Canadian foods differ from those of the United States but the basic factors deciding grade are closely similar. The following summarizes Canadian grades for many food products and some of the grade factors contributing to those grades:

Beef

For meats Canada has a round, brown Canada Approved stamp, which, like our round, purple stamp, Inspected and Passed, indicates wholesomeness of product. All beef for interprovincial, foreign or import trade must be inspected and approved. Grades in beef are indicated by ribbon brands as follows:

Red Brand (Canadian Choice): High quality, high proportion of meat to bone, good covering of fat and the lean is well marbled.

Blue Brand (Canada Good): Good quality, slightly lower proportion of meat to bone and less fat and marbling than the higher grade.

Brown Brand (Canada Standard): Lower proportion of fat to lean meat than Blue Brand.

Canada Commercial: Lower proportion of meat to bone than Canada Standard and the proportion of fat may vary.

In Canada most of the Choice and Good grades, Red and Blue brands, respectively, and some of the Standard (Brown brand) are branded.

Butter

All creamery butter sold in Canada is graded with the grade mark shown on the main panel of the wrapper and the carton in which the butter is sold. Market weights must be ¼ lb, ½ lb, 1 lb or multiples of one pound. Grades are:

Canada First Grade: Excellent flavor, well made, smooth, waxy texture, uniform in color.
Canada Second Grade: Slightly imperfect in flavor; may be defective in texture or uneven in color.
Canada Third Grade: Inferior to Second Grade in flavor, texture or color.
Below Canada Third Grade: Lowest quality.

Cheese

Institutional buyers should use wholesale grades. Purchase Canada First Grade in curing desired: mild, medium or old. Only Cheddar cheese over 20 lb in weight shipped interprovincially or exported must be graded, but the Canada Department of Agriculture continually checks cheese composition on all markets.

Eggs

Canadian grades for eggs are:

Canada Grade A1: Clean, normal in shape, sound shell and of highest interior quality.
Canada Grade A: Fairly well-rounded yolk, surrounded by thick albumen; practically clean, practically normal in shape, sound shell, which may show rough areas and be slightly ridged.

Sizes for these grades are:

	Extra Large	Large	Medium	Small	Peewee
Per Dozen	27 oz	24 oz	21 oz	18 oz	less than 18 oz
Minimum Weight per Egg	2¼ oz	2 oz	1¾ oz	1½ oz	less than 1½ oz

Two other grades of eggs are available. Canada Grade B egg should be reasonably clean, slightly abnormal in shape, sound of shell but it may show rough areas and definite ridges. The yolk is moderately oblong, slightly flattened and enlarged, surrounded by albumen which is less firm than in Canada A. Canada Grace C must not have a broken shell but may be dirty or stained. The shell surface and shape may be irregular; the yolk is oblong, enlarged or flattened, surrounded by weak watery albumen.

Grades A1 and A are used for breakfast eggs. Grade B eggs are used for baking or other cooking purposes while most Grade C eggs find their way into commercial frozen egg products.

Fresh Fruits and Vegetables

Most fruits and vegetables shipped in interprovince trade must meet grading, packaging, marking and inspection regulations of the Canada

Department of Agriculture.   Separate provincial grading is required in
the various provinces.   These resemble the federal regulations.   Grades
must be marked on all closed packages of fruits and vegetables and open
packages of apples, celery, cantaloupes and tomatoes.   Packages or containers used for fresh fruits and vegetables must meet standardized dimensions.

Canadian Grades for fresh fruits are:

Apples: Canada Extra Fancy, Canada Fancy, Canada Commercial or "C".
Apricots: Canada No. 1, Canada No. 2, and Canada No. 3.
Grapes: Canada No. 1, and Canada No. 2.   When the latter are packed in
baskets or hampers the grade may be marked Canada Domestic.
Peaches, Fresh Prunes, Cherries and Plums: Canada Select, Canada No. 1, and
Canada No. 2 and, like grapes, when packed in baskets or hampers may be
called Canada Domestic instead of Canada No. 2.
Pears: Same as Apples when packed in boxes but when packed in baskets,
etc., the grades are Canada No. 1, Canada Domestic and Canada No. 3.

Canadian grades for vegetables are, generally speaking, Canada No. 1
and Canada No. 2.   An additional grade is provided for onions, Canada
No. 2.   There is only one grade for Canadian waxed or unwaxed table
turnips, Canada No. 1.   Potatoes have additional grades.   There are
Canada Fancy (not largely sold), Canada No. 1, Canada No. 1 Large
and Canada No. 2.   Round varieties of Canada No. 1 must be $2\frac{1}{4}$ in.
minimum diameter and long shaped varieties 2 in. minimum diameter.
Canada No. 1 Large must not be less than $3\frac{1}{4}$ in. in diameter; Canada
No. 2 must not be less than $1\frac{3}{4}$ in. in diameter.

Quality factors listed for United States grades may be consulted for
the most part for Canadian fruits and vegetables, although in some cases
these may differ slightly.

Honey

All honey shipped interprovincially must be graded.   Ontario, Mani-
toba, Saskatchewan, Alberta and British Columbia have provincial grading identical with the federal grades.   Color classes are: white, golden,
amber and dark; grades are No. 1, No. 2, No. 3 and Sub-Standard.
Color does not affect grade.   Some honey on the market may be pasteurized.

Maple Sirup

Only the Province of Quebec requires grading of maple sirup.   The
grades are Canada Fancy, very light amber color, delicate flavor; Canada Light, light amber color, strong flavor; Canada Medium, dark
amber color, stronger flavor; Canada Dark, dark color and may have

trace of fermentation.   All containers must be marketed with net weight.
Maple sirup must weight at least 13 lb 2 oz per gal.

Milk, dry

Dry milk powders may be purchased graded.   Institutional buyers
should specify Canada First Grade.

Processed Fruits and Vegetables

Most plants processing fruits and vegetables in Canada are under reg-
istration with the Canada Department of Agriculture.   All products,
canned, frozen or dehydrated in these plants must be graded according
to quality and the label must state the grade.   Imports must comply
with Canadian grading regulations but do not have to carry the word
Canada on the label.

Canned Fruits and Vegetables

The grade must be shown on the label with the net weight of contents
in fluid ounces. [1]   Fruit in sirup or sweetened fruit juice must show percent of sugar used and those packed without sugar must have on the
label "Without Sugar" or "Unsweetened."   Grades are:

Canada Fancy: Nearly perfect as possible; packed from sound, clean fruits or
vegetables at best maturity; free from blemishes; of good color and uniform in
size; clear liquid.
Canada Choice: May have slight size variation, color and maturity but must
come from sound, clean fruits or vegetables fairly free from blemishes; liquid
fairly clear.
Canada Standard: From products of good quality but that are not necessarily
of the uniform size required in higher grades.
Sub-Standard: A low quality product packed from clean, sound fruits and
vegetables that need not be uniform in maturity, color or size.

Sizes may be specified for peas or beans.   Sizes are Nos. 1 to 6.   If
peas and beans are not graded for size, the label must state: "Ungraded
as to Size," "Assorted Sizes," or "Mixed Sizes."

No water may be added to any fruit and vegetable juice and be labeled
a juice.   Grades for juices are Canada Fancy and Canada Choice.

Grades for frozen fruits and vegetables are:

Canada Fancy: Highest grade with qualities similar to those for canned Fancy
except that the product is frozen.
Canada Choice: Not as perfect in appearance as Fancy quality but of good
flavor, color, size and maturity.

Dehydrated fruits and vegetables have the following grades:

[1] Permitted can sizes in fluid ounces are: 10, 15, 20, 28, 48 and 105.

Apples: Canada Fancy, Canada Choice and Canada Standard.
Blueberries and Vegetables: Canada Fancy and Canada Choice.

Labels for jams or jellies must indicate as an ingredient pectin or corn sirup, if used. Fluid ounces must be marked on glass, tin or wax paper containers. Standard container sizes are:

Fluid Ounce	Net Weight
2½ oz	3 oz
6 oz	8 oz
9 oz	12 oz
12 oz	1 lb
24 oz	2 lb
48 oz	4 lb

If a label carries the word "pure," the contents shall be sugar and a specified amount of the fruit named. Only a very small amount of acid or pectin may be added to make up any deficiency of natural acid or pectin in some fruits. When the label reads "jam with added pectin" the product may contain sugar, a specified amount of the fruit named and a considerable amount of pectin. If coloring or permitted preservative are added, the label must so indicate. If a jam is made with apple pulp or juice added, the label must read "apple and . . . jam." In this type jam containing apple, pectin, glucose, corn sirup, coloring and permitted preservative may be added but must be declared on the label. If a jelly is made with added pectin, it must contain not less than 32% of the named fruit juice; pectin, coloring and a permitted preservative may be added but must be on the label.

Poultry

Graded poultry only may be sold in many communities. Buyers should ascertain local regulations. The grade mark will appear on the breast as a metal tag or on a transparent lithographed bag. Different colors are used to indicate grade. Conformation, fleshing, fat and dressing are considered as factors in determining a grade. The Canada Approved stamp for wholesomeness appears only on poultry slaughtered and eviscerated in federally inspected plants. Inspection for wholesomeness is compulsory only when poultry moves interprovincially or is imported or exported.

Grades for chickens, capons, turkeys, ducks and geese are:

Canada Grade Special (Purple Brand): Shall be of highest quality. The bird shall be normally formed, very well-fleshed; fat should show generally over the breast, thighs and back; young turkeys weighing 8 lb or less and eviscerated shall have breast, thighs and back reasonably well covered with fat; turkeys weighing more than 8 lb, eviscerated, and other poultry shall have the breast, thighs and back well covered with fat; relatively free from discoloration, tears and pinfeathers.

Canada Grade A (Red Brand): Shall have normally formed conformation and be well fleshed; may have a slightly curved keel bone; the fat on chickens should show over breast and thighs; young turkeys weighing 8 lb or less, eviscerated, shall have the breast and thighs reasonably well covered with fat and moderate covering of fat over the back; other poultry shall be reasonably well covered with fat. A few small tears, minor discoloration and a small number of pinfeathers are allowed.

Canada Grade B (Blue Brand): Shall be normally formed but may have a slightly crooked keel bone. The bird may not be as well fleshed and as well covered with fat as Canada Grade A birds. Moderate-sized tears, relatively minor discoloration and pinfeathers that do not seriously detract from the bird's appearance are allowed.

Canada Grade Utility (Blue Brand): The bird must be Grade B but one or more of the parts of the bird may be missing.

Canada Grade C (Yellow Brand): The bird shall be fairly well fleshed; it may have large tears, pinfeathers and prominent discoloration.

Canadian buyers should obtain from their Department of Agriculture definitions of grades for other products at wholesale grade levels. If these are not available, the United States factors establishing grade may be used as models for writing specifications.

Index